GEOGRAPHICAL ESSAYS

BY

WILLIAM MORRIS DAVIS

EDITED BY

DOUGLAS WILSON JOHNSON

DOVER PUBLICATIONS, INC.

This Dover Edition
was first published in 1954
and is an unabridged republication
of the 1909 edition

EDITOR'S NOTE

An endeavor has been made in this volume to meet the growing demand for an edition of Professor Davis's most important geographical essays. Since it was not possible to include within the limits of a single volume all essays which students of geography desire to see reprinted, the editor was asked to select a limited number, and to prepare them for publication. He can hardly expect that his choice will meet with unanimous approval, but he believes it will appear that the selections herewith presented are fairly representative of the author's contributions to the science of geography.

For sake of uniformity in style, method of treatment, etc., minor modifications have been made in many of the essays, so that they do not always conform exactly to the text as originally published. A large number of the illustrations have been redrawn, while a few have necessarily been omitted. In special cases portions of the text have been materially revised to bring them into accord with recent discoveries, or to eliminate matter inappropriate for publication under the present circumstances. Such alterations as have been made have received the author's approval. The original form of any essay may be found by consulting the citations given in the Table of Contents.

The essays admit of a natural classification into two main groups: those concerned chiefly with the teaching of geography, included in Part One, Educational Essays; and those dealing with the principles of the science of geography, more especially that branch of the science known as physiography, included in

Part Two, Physiographic Essays. Under each part the essays are grouped according to subject-matter rather than in the order of their publication. A more recent essay precedes an older essay on the same general subject, whenever it appears desirable that the older essay should be read with a full knowledge of the author's latest opinions.

For the reproduction of the essays in the present form, the publishers are indebted to the several publications in whose pages the essays originally appeared, and by whose courtesy they are reprinted here.

DOUGLAS WILSON JOHNSON

HARVARD UNIVERSITY

CONTENTS

PART ONE — EDUCATIONAL ESSAYS

PAGE

I. AN INDUCTIVE STUDY OF THE CONTENT OF GEOGRAPHY . . 3
Presidential address at the second meeting of the Association of
American Geographers, December, 1905. *Bulletin American
Geographical Society* (1906), XXXVIII, 67–84.

II. THE PROGRESS OF GEOGRAPHY IN THE SCHOOLS 23
*First Year Book National Society for the Scientific Study of Educa-
tion* (1902), Part II, 7–49.

III. THE PHYSICAL GEOGRAPHY OF THE LANDS 70
Popular Science Monthly (1900), LVII, 157–170.

IV. THE TEACHING OF GEOGRAPHY 87
Educational Review (1892), III, 417–426; IV, 6–15.

V. THE EXTENSION OF PHYSICAL GEOGRAPHY IN ELEMENTARY
TEACHING 105
An address delivered before the Middlesex (Massachusetts)
Teachers Club, in Boston, October 8, 1892. *School and Col-
lege* (1892), I, 599–608.

VI. GEOGRAPHY IN GRAMMAR AND PRIMARY SCHOOLS 115
School Review (1893), I, 327–339.

VII. PHYSICAL GEOGRAPHY IN THE HIGH SCHOOL 129
School Review (1900), VIII, 388–404.

VIII. THE NEED OF GEOGRAPHY IN THE UNIVERSITY 146
Educational Review (1895), X, 22–41.

IX. PHYSICAL GEOGRAPHY AS A UNIVERSITY STUDY 165
(Last four pages omitted in the reprint.) *Journal of Geology* (1894),
II, 66–100.

X. METHODS AND MODELS IN GEOGRAPHICAL TEACHING . . . 193
A lecture delivered before the Scientific Association of Johns Hopkins University on February 13, 1889. *The American Naturalist*
(1889), XXIII, 566–583.

XI. PRACTICAL EXERCISES IN PHYSICAL GEOGRAPHY 210
Compiled from two essays on same subject, one published in the
*Proceedings Fifth Annual Conference New York State Science
Teachers Association* (1900), the other published in *National
Geographic Magazine* (1900), XI, 62–78.

XII. FIELD WORK IN PHYSICAL GEOGRAPHY 236
(First four pages omitted in reprint.) *Journal of Geography* (1902),
I, 17–24, 62–69.

PART TWO — PHYSIOGRAPHIC ESSAYS

PAGE

XIII. THE GEOGRAPHICAL CYCLE 249
Geographical Journal (1899), XIV, 481–504.

XIV. COMPLICATIONS OF THE GEOGRAPHICAL CYCLE 279
Eighth International Geographic Congress, 150–163.

XV. THE GEOGRAPHICAL CYCLE IN AN ARID CLIMATE 296
Journal of Geology (1905), XIII, 381–407.

XVI. PLAINS OF MARINE AND SUB-AËRIAL DENUDATION . . . 323
Bulletin Geological Society of America (1896), VII, 377–398.

XVII. THE PENEPLAIN 350
Originally written in reply to a paper by Professor R. S. Tarr on the same subject. Reprinted with numerous minor changes. *American Geologist* (1899), XXIII, 207–239.

XVIII. BASE-LEVEL, GRADE, AND PENEPLAIN 381
Journal of Geology (1902), X, 77–111.

XIX. THE RIVERS AND VALLEYS OF PENNSYLVANIA 413
National Geographic Magazine (1889), I, 183–253.

XX. THE RIVERS OF NORTHERN NEW JERSEY WITH NOTES ON THE CLASSIFICATION OF RIVERS IN GENERAL . . . 485
National Geographic Magazine (1890), II, 81–110.

XXI. RIVER TERRACES IN NEW ENGLAND 514
Bulletin Museum of Comparative Zoölogy (1902), XXXVIII, 281–346.

XXII. THE SEINE, THE MEUSE, AND THE MOSELLE 587
National Geographic Magazine (1896), VII, 189–202, 228–238.

XXIII. THE SCULPTURE OF MOUNTAINS BY GLACIERS 617
Presented in abstract before Sections C and E of the British Association at Cape Town, August 17, 1905. *Scottish Geographical Magazine* (1906), XXII, 76–89.

XXIV. GLACIAL EROSION IN FRANCE, SWITZERLAND, AND NORWAY 635
Proceedings Boston Society Natural History (1900), XXIX, 273–322.

XXV. THE OUTLINE OF CAPE COD 690
Proceedings American Academy of Arts and Sciences (1896), XXXI, 303–332.

XXVI. THE MOUNTAIN RANGES OF THE GREAT BASIN 725
Bulletin Museum of Comparative Zoölogy (1903), XLII, 129–177.

INDEX 773

GEOGRAPHICAL ESSAYS

PART ONE

EDUCATIONAL ESSAYS

I

AN INDUCTIVE STUDY OF THE CONTENT OF GEOGRAPHY

The Need of Comparing Opinions. One of the objects to which geographers may well direct their attention is the nature of the whole subject of geography, under whose broad shelter individual studies are carried on. If we work only in view of our chosen field within the whole area of geography, we lose something of breadth, although we may gain much in depth. Our work will become more serviceable to others if it is presented in such a manner that its relations to the whole subject are made clear. Not only so; we may often benefit ourselves by systematically setting forth the place of our individual studies in geography as a whole, for we may be thereby led to discover that the systematic sequence of parts is interrupted here and there by gaps, which can be filled by well-directed effort.

But it is manifest that, if we should attempt to make exposition of our ideas concerning the relation of our own studies to the whole subject, we must have previously gained a tolerably definite idea of the nature of the whole. Very likely we each have some such conception. If so, it would be profitable to institute a collection and a comparison of opinions, though it can hardly be doubted that they would show much diversity.

Examples of Geographical Statements. As a contribution towards such a collection of opinions, I propose to consider the nature or content of geography in this essay; but instead of presenting an abstract definition of the subject, the problem will be regarded from the other side. There will first be presented

3

a number of sample statements that are presumed to be geographical because they are taken from geographical works; these statements will then be analyzed in order to discover their essential nature; finally, an attempt will be made to discover the nature of the whole subject of geography on the basis of the statements thus analyzed; that is, to discover the content of geography on the basis of an inductive study. The statements to be presented are taken from a variety of sources — text-books, treatises, and journals; they are often condensed from the original.

Here, for example, is a first set of items or statements: There are three native states in the Himalaya which are independent of British rule. The rivers of southern Gascony flow in radiating courses. There are more than three hundred asteroids. The average man has about eighty-seven cubic inches of brain. The mean depth of the ocean is about two miles. A new map of France on a scale of 1:50,000 is in course of publication. Protozoa are the simplest forms of animals, consisting of a single cell. The magnetic poles do not coincide with the poles of rotation. Celtic is spoken in Wales, the Highlands of Scotland, and western Ireland. Cotton is produced in the southern United States. The fall of rivers is usually greatest in their upper courses. The Grand Duchy of Prussia became a kingdom in 1701. Cryptogams are flowerless plants. The Hindu Kush, the highest mountains of Persia, trend to the northeast. Australia has many marsupials, of which the kangaroo is the largest. Amundsen has successfully made the Northwest Passage.

If all these statements are truly of geographical quality, it follows that all similar statements would be of geographical quality also. We should then have, in a complete geography, accounts of all states, in the Himalaya or elsewhere, dependent or independent, of British or of other rule; descriptions of the course of rivers in all parts of the world; additional facts about other bodies in the heavens besides the asteroids; accounts of man's other organs than his brain; details as well as averages of ocean depths; descriptions of multicellular as well as of unicellular animals, and of flowering as well as of flowerless plants; reports on old as well as on new maps of France and of all other countries, whatever their scale; items concerning terrestrial magnetism as well as concerning the position of the magnetic poles; reports of all sorts of voyages; accounts of all changes of duchies to kingdoms and of kingdoms to duchies, and of other political changes as well; mention of the animals of other lands than Australia, and of the products of other countries than our southern states; announcements of voyages in all parts of the world in all centuries.

The Complexity of Geography. The first impression about so varied a collection of statements would be that the subject under which they are all properly included must be a sort of omnium-gatherum, without any well-defined unity of substance. Such, indeed, geography has been thought to be by some critics. A closer examination of our materials must be made in order to see if we really have to do with a heterogeneous collection of incoherent facts, without continuity of thought or unity of discipline. It may be that some of the items above cited do not justly belong under geography, and that an enchainment not apparent at first may be found to bring the remaining items and their proper fellows into some systematic association.

On reviewing the statements given above it appears that some are concerned with matters remote from the earth and commonly associated with astronomy; that some are concerned with matters of a personal or technical nature; that a third group of statements contains accounts of inorganic features of the earth, and a fourth group contains accounts of organic inhabitants of the earth. Let us examine these several classes to see how far they may be justly considered geographical.

Excepting as an astronomical statement is found to be related to terrestrial matters in such a way as to throw light on them, it should not be considered directly or indirectly geographical, in spite of the mention of such a matter in a geographical text-book; for by common consent geography has to do primarily with the earth. Hence the mere statement of the number of asteroids should be excluded from our consideration. It may, however, be advisable to retain in elementary text-books certain statements concerning planets in so far as they serve to emphasize the globular form of the earth by showing that there are other bodies like it, and such mention of the sun and moon as is needed for the understanding of insolation in relation to climate and of gravitation in relation to tides; also such account of the stars as shall serve in the proof of the rotation of the earth and in the determination of the attitude of its axis. Nevertheless, all these items seem to be only indirectly associated with our subject; they do not aid us to discover the real nature of geography.

Technical and personal items may naturally be associated with geography if the things and events with which they are concerned are of a geographical quality, as maps and explorations certainly are. The announcement of the publication of a new map or of the completion of a remarkable voyage is therefore a piece of appropriate geographical news. Accounts of old maps, of old voyages, and of old ideas are very illuminating in showing how the geography of to-day has been developed, but they belong more with history than with geography when presented in order of time.

Non-Geographical Statements. Many of the statements under the two remaining classes — which concern inorganic and organic matters on the earth — are properly geographical if we judge by the repeated occurrence of such statements in many geographical works. Yet we cannot believe that all statements about inorganic and organic matters on the earth belong under geography. It is easy to instance a number of such statements from geographical sources which can hardly be regarded as having any clear association with geography. Consider, for example, the following set of items, all taken from geographical text-books:

The gastrula stage occurs just before maturity in the sponge. All substances transmit electrical energy. Crystallization is explained by supposing that the cohesive force of molecules is not exerted equally on all sides. After 1810, several independent republics were formed in South America. The Rosaceæ have regular flowers.

However interesting and useful these items of information may be, they can hardly be regarded as geographical, even under the very broadest interpretation of our subject. They have probably been added to the text-books from which they are quoted in the belief that they are worth knowing, and that the pupils in our schools will have little chance of learning them if they are not brought in under the popular subject of geography. I question the advisability of such a method of promoting popular education; but that is another story. Our problem is to distinguish these and many similar statements from a large variety of other statements concerning the inorganic and organic terrestrial matters, so as to know which are properly of geographical quality and which are not.

Statements involving Relations. The best solution that I have been able to find for this problem comes from a consideration of such statements as are included in the following third set of extracts, which, like the other two, have been taken from geographical sources:

The people of the Dalmatian coast are largely engaged as fishermen on the Adriatic; here the Austrian navy obtains its best seamen. A number of gulfs and mountain ranges naturally divide the people of Europe into groups or nations. Some parts of Bengal are so favored with rivers that almost every cottage has a navigable stream at its door, and the Bengalese farmer keeps his boat, just as the English farmer keeps his gig. Northern Uganda is drier, rain often fails, grass is short, and dry-country animals, such as zebras and ostriches, abound. The level land near lake Titicaca is of small extent, and is occupied by alkaline marshes subject to overflow; for this reason the Indians cultivate the slopes in preference, converting them into narrow terraced garden beds. The periodic or monsoon winds that blow alternately now in one direction and now in the opposite along certain coasts, as between India and East Africa, have long been favorable to navigation and trade. In northwest France the farm-houses on the chalk uplands are gathered into compact villages around one or more deep wells, because the ground water there is deep below the surface and difficult to obtain; but in the valleys the houses are scattered, because each family can easily procure its own water supply with little trouble.

Geography a Study of Relations. These statements differ from some of those of the two earlier groups of citations in that they each contain at least two kinds of elements, one of which stands in a more or less distinctly causal relation to the other. The statements vary in that some of the relations suggested are relatively simple, while others are more complex, and in that some statements are rather empirical, while others are more fully explanatory; but they are all alike in that they involve a relation of cause and effect, usually between some element of inorganic control and some element of organic response. As such, these statements are examples of the most generally treated material that I can find; and hence I am disposed to say that any statement is of geographical quality if it contains a reasonable relation between some inorganic element of the earth on which we live, acting as a control, and some element of the existence or growth or behavior or distribution of the earth's organic inhabitants, serving as a response; more briefly, some relation between an element of inorganic control and one of organic response. The geographical quality of such a relation is all the more marked if the statement is presented in an explanatory form. There is, indeed, in this idea of a causal or explanatory relationship the most definite, if not the only, unifying principle that I can find in geography. All the more reason, then, that the principle should be recognized and acted upon by those who have the fuller development of geographical science at heart.

Geography as the Study of Location or of Distribution. There still exists in some quarters a tendency to limit geography by definition to the study of location, leaving the study of all the things that are located to other subjects. There is so little support for this narrow view of the subject to be found in modern geographical books that it need not be further considered. Another and more widely accepted definition treats geography as the science of distribution. This is particularly a British view of the subject, and at least one British geographer urges that the distributed things should not be regarded as belonging to geography at all; but his writings are broader than his definition. While location and distribution must always be important elements of geography, all geographical books give much attention to the nature of the things that are distributed, and all recent books give much weight to the relations in which the distributed things occur; hence relationship seems to me the primary principle of the two, and distribution takes a secondary rank. The thing must be known before its distribution can be serviceably studied. The division of the peoples of Europe into groups or nations in consequence of the division of Europe by gulfs and mountain ranges is a geographical relation, in which the unlikeness of the things distributed takes precedence of their distribution.

Indeed, if geography were only the science of distribution, — that is, the regional aspect of other subjects, — it would be hardly worth while to maintain the study of geography apart from that of the subject whose regional aspect it considers. Moreover, if geography is defined simply as the science of distribution, then the distribution of anything is a fit subject for geographical study. Under such a definition the distribution of hypersthene andesite, or of books of poetry, would be part of our responsibility; but there is nowhere any indication that geographers feel responsible for the distribution of such things. Again, if distribution is given first rank, the regional or spacial occurrence of all sorts of things is thereby given so great an importance that an insufficient place is left for systematic considerations; yet most books first present things of a kind together — that is, they present the subject systematically — before they take up the distributional or regional treatment of different kinds of things. Moreover, distributional treatment is too apt to take up one kind of thing at a time, and follow it wherever it is found, thus failing to give account of the natural occurrence of many kinds of things in their actual association which regional geography demands.

As a matter of fact, nearly every example that is presented in this essay as an example of a geographical relation might, if desired, be presented as an example of distribution, and nearly all statements of distribution may be turned around so that they shall enter into or constitute relations; hence the total content of geography would be much the same under either principle. The relations that could not be presented under the head of distribution are those which are the same everywhere; but it seems to me rather arbitrary to include relations that vary from place to place, and to exclude relations that are world-wide in their uniform occurrence. For example, the composition of the atmosphere or of the ocean, always accepted as an appropriate matter for mention in elementary texts, deserves no place in geography, treated as the science of distribution, until the minute variations of composition from place to place are considered.

In any case, location and distribution are fundamental elements of geography, and maps of the lands and charts of the oceans are essential in its every chapter. In view of the importance of these elements, some are disposed to attach an undue value to surveying as a part of geography. But surveying properly belongs in geography about where writing belongs in literature, and if it is given higher rank the student may, by misfortune, turn his chief attention to the art of mapping instead of to a study of the things that are mapped.

Regional Geography. It has been well maintained by certain German geographers that geography is concerned with the "material filling of space"; that is, geography has to deal with regions or districts, as occupied by all the kinds of things that there occur together. This, however, is only the regional aspect of geography, and before it can be treated, the geographer must have a good acquaintance with the different kinds of things that occur in various regions, that is, with systematic geography. It is with this second aspect of the subject that we are here chiefly concerned.

Physiography and Ontography. If the principle of explanatory relationship be adopted as a general guide to the content of geography, it follows that neither the inorganic nor the organic elements which enter into geographical relations are by themselves of a completely geographical quality; they gain that quality only when two or more of them are coupled in a relation of cause and effect, at least one element in the chain of causation being inorganic and one organic. When they are considered separately, but as if in preparation for an understanding of the causal relations in which they will later be presented in the study of geography proper, they may be considered as sub-geographical; and then the inorganic elements may be called physico-geographic, or physiographic, and the organic elements may be called ontographic. Common usage recognizes the first of these divisions, but not the second, as we shall see later. It is well to emphasize the clause "as if in preparation for an understanding of the causal relations in which they will later be presented in the study of geography proper"; for many items which, under this proviso, are of physiographic or of ontographic quality, may under another proviso belong in other departments of knowledge.

Physiographic Matters. This may be made plainer by citing particular cases in which a number of different topics, familiar from their occurrence in books on geography, will be seen to fall under other subjects when they enter into non-geographical relations. For example, the size and rotation of the earth, and the general movements of the tides, are undoubtedly physiographic elements, yet both may be treated appropriately under astronomy when they are considered in their relations to other planets. Sea water, when regarded as a liquid compound which holds various salts in solution, may be studied properly by the chemist with regard to its composition; nevertheless, sea water as the medium in which organic forms live is an indispensable subject for physiographic inquiry. The horizontal strata of plateaus are a fit topic for geological investigation, as regards their origin and history, but they are no less a subject for physiographic investigation as affecting present form. It therefore seems impossible to determine, merely by a consideration of the thing studied, whether it belongs to physiography or not.

A given object may belong under several different sciences, and may be treated in text-books on different subjects; it is the relation into which the object enters that determines its place.

There are, however, certain inorganic topics, commonly found in geographical books, which seldom, if ever, enter into relations with organic topics, and which would, therefore, under the strict application of the principle of relationships, be ruled out of physiography, and thus out of geography also. Such are cirrus clouds and halos, the crevasses and blue veins of glaciers, and the polar flattening of the earth. Nevertheless, most or all of these topics will probably hold their places in books on physiography, because they serve to complete the picture of the whole earth as the home of life. In any case, little is gained by a very strict or over-logical application of a useful principle of classification in a problem such as we are considering.

Ontographic Matters. The determination of the science under which a thing belongs by means of the relations into which the thing enters is an even more important guide in ontography than in physiography. For example, one may read in a certain text-book of geography that all forms of life consume food. In so far as the assimilation of food, and the organs by which it is accomplished, are concerned, the consumption of food belongs under physiology; but the consumption of food is an ontographic matter in so far as it brings an organism into contact with the rest of the world and thus causes it to enter into geographical relations. Commercial geography is largely concerned with relations that grow out of this element of ontography. Water is essential in organic processes of many kinds. This is, again, a physiological matter if it is examined with reference to the processes of circulation, but it is ontographic when it is found to lead to a relation with the sources of water supply: villages gathered around deep wells on the chalk uplands of north-western France are examples of the geographical relation thus brought about.

Plants and animals tend to diffuse themselves, or to be diffused, over the earth. This is a fundamental fact, usually associated with the study of biology; but the limits of diffusion, and in many cases the means of diffusion, are determined by physiographic controls; hence the tendency to diffusion is an ontographic matter.

The need experienced by all forms of life to secure food, already instanced, leads to many other relations than those of commercial geography. The need of food is satisfied without going in search of it if the food is contained in a moving medium that surrounds the organism; hence those organisms that live chiefly upon food contained in one or the other of the two great mobile envelopes of the earth — the atmosphere or the hydrosphere — are often rooted or fixed: the air or water currents carry the needed food to the waiting plant or animal, and this is surely too important a geographical relation to be omitted from a broad consideration of our subject. Other organisms take advantage of the currents of air or water to be passively carried about by them, taking their food when they happen to come upon it. If they are land dwellers, they are so small that they can easily be wafted about by the winds; if they are dwellers in water, they may gain greater size by assuming about the same specific gravity as that denser medium, so as to float easily in its perpetual currents. Still a third class of organisms move of their own volition, and in connection with these there are all manner of geographical relations. Some of them involve the development of wings, whereby motion can be effected in the comparatively unsustaining air, as in the case of many insects and birds, of a few mammals, and formerly of some reptiles; some involve the development of fins to produce motion in the sustaining water. These examples are as good illustrations of organic responses to inorganic controls as are the canoes and the steamships of uncivilized and of civilized man.

It follows from the preceding paragraph that the more closely our standard geographical material is examined, the more clearly it appears that its ontographic as well as its physiographic elements may fall into other sciences when they are treated in other relations, and that they become most distinctly geographical when they enter into the causal relations of the kind set forth above. The rise and fall of the tides is a physiographic matter when it is seen to determine the distribution of certain forms of life, such as barnacles, or to influence the availability of harbors for the entrance of shipping; the occurrence of coal is a physiographic matter when it is found to influence the industry of a district and the commerce between nations; the small size of spores, pollen, and germs is an ontographic matter when it is seen to be related to their transportation by the thin air; the sensitiveness of organisms to temperature changes is an ontographic matter when it is shown to affect the distribution of plants and animals over the earth. Yet all these matters may be treated with entire justice under other sciences than geography. It is, therefore, to my reading, of capital importance, in determining whether a statement is of geographical or of sub-geographical nature, to know how far it constitutes or enters into causal relations of the kinds that have here been considered.

Is Ontography a Part of Geography? It is perfectly true that many of the illustrations just given are not commonly regarded as belonging under geography, but it seems to me that their exclusion is illogical and arbitrary. They are practically all to be found in certain standard geographical works, and many more might be taken from such books as Ratzel's "Anthropogeographie" and Beddard's "Zoögeography." The general principle by which one should be guided in determining the relevancy of such matters is as follows: If a certain relation between an inorganic control and a responding organism is a geographical relation, then all similar relations are also geographical. For example, a well-known text-book makes the statement that water plants are supported by the relatively dense medium in which they grow, and hence do not need strong, woody stalks such as many land plants have. This is an excellent example of a geographical fact : it involves a relation between an organic growth and an inorganic medium. But the flight of birds, the small size of germs, the essential agreement between the specific gravity of fish and of water, the universal habit of breathing oxygen, — all involve similar relations. The first example seems to me undeniably geographical ; the others are no less so. To exclude the latter from geography while including the former would be to set very arbitrary limits to our subject.

It may, perhaps, be objected that flight and breathing are processes of too ancient origin to be considered as geographical, but inasmuch as they have been maintained to the present time by inheritance through persistent conditions of environment, they have the same right to a place under geography as is enjoyed by such examples as the prevalence of the fishing industry on the Dalmatian coast, or the custom of the French farmers on the chalk uplands of living in compact villages ; for these habits, also, are not independently originated by each man who follows them, but are continued by inheritance through persistent conditions of environment.

There are certain matters frequently encountered in text-books of physical geography which belong better, it seems to me, under the head of ontographic relations. Such are the distribution of plants and animals, and the races of man. The association of such topics with physical geography is probably the result of conceiving all the rest of the subject as contained under political geography. The contrast of physical with political conditions may serve well enough in elementary books, where the distribution and behavior of man are the chief subjects in political geography, and where plants and animals are therefore thrown in with physical geography ; but in the more advanced and general treatment of the subject such an arrangement is not satisfactory. It does, however, seem legitimate to introduce as often as desired ontographic responses in a physiographic text, in order to show at once the kind of response that certain controls call forth, and thus to impress the fact that the physiographic items are really related to ontographic items; a similar introduction of physiographic items is appropriate in chapters on ontography. This practice is followed by certain writers.

There are three definite positions and many indefinite positions that might be taken with respect to the attention that should be given by geographers to organic considerations. The narrowest position limits geography almost entirely to the inorganic features of the earth, — that is, to physical geography, or physiography. This is the view of geography held by some historians, who take unto themselves practically all the human element that is so commonly encountered in political geography. An intermediate position would include physiography and the more manifest relations into which it enters with various forms of life, and particularly with man, but would not accept responsibility as to the less manifest responses of various living things. This seems to be the position taken by many geographers, more or less consciously. The third position would treat ontography as thoroughly as physiography, and would search for all the geographical relations of physiographic controls and ontographic responses. This is certainly the broadest of the three positions, being, as many would feel, too broad, and involving too much overlapping upon other subjects. For my own part, there seems to be so manifest a necessity of gaining a responsible knowledge of ontography, at least of elementary ontography, before geography proper can be successfully treated, that ontography should come to be regarded as a part of it. The analytical and inductive methods of this paper, therefore, lead me to adopt the third position; and I believe that this position is essentially consistent with the opinion of writers who, like Ratzel and Reclus, have cultivated the most advanced or matured stage of geographical science.

The Importance of Explanatory Relations. Although various facts which may make parts of relations between inorganic controls and organic responses, or which are met with in preparation for an understanding of such relations, thereby gain a most characteristic geographical flavor, a very brief review of geographical books will suffice to show that many statements there included do not explicitly possess this flavor. In the first place, in the older books the idea of relationship had no distinct recognition. That was the time of memorized names of capes, of empty boundaries, of unexplained lists of products. Almost anything about the earth or its inhabitants was then accepted if it reached a satisfactory degree of what is called "importance." In the newer books the principle of explanatory relationship is very generally acted upon; there are, nevertheless, many relations stated so empirically that the pupil may fail to gain from them a full appreciation of the best essence of geography. Consider, for example, the following statement from a good textbook: "Some form of Celtic is spoken in Wales, the Highlands of Scotland, and western Ireland." This is nothing more than an empirical statement of a fact of distribution. Many a student might memorize such an item without gaining any clear insight into its geographical meaning. The real point is that the early inhabitants of Great Britain, being attacked by invaders from the continent on the east, survived only where pursuit was difficult, as in the rough ground of Wales, in the rough and distant ground of the Highlands, or in the distant and isolated ground of Ireland; and hence only in those localities is the early language still preserved. The fact that Celtic, as Celtic, is spoken in certain parts of Great Britain belongs to philology as well as to any other subject; the fact that Celtic is the language that was once spoken generally through Great Britain might come under history as well as under any other subject; but the fact that Celtic is still spoken in rough, distant, or isolated parts of Great Britain, because of their roughness, distance, or isolation, is a local example of an important class of relations between controls and responses, and as such it belongs distinctly under rational geography.

The Expansion of Geography. Geography has still much progress to make. There is not only much to be done in the way of exploration of little-known lands and seas, but many of the more civilized countries still merit closer study than they have yet received if we may judge by the notable incompleteness of the best handbooks and treatises. One method of carrying the subject forward consists in outdoor observation, and this method cannot be too highly recommended to those who wish to contribute to the fuller development of our subject. When we realize that we have no modern and maturely developed account of the geography of such a state as Virginia, or Ohio, or Colorado, or California, it becomes evident that abundant opportunity for exploration lies near home. But there is a second method by which geography may be promoted; that is, by thinking about what we see, and thus expanding every example of a geographical relation that we find to its farthest legitimate extension. Take, for example, the common case of a road which runs through a notch in a high ridge; such a detail of location is a response of the ontographic element, movement, to the physiographic control, gravity; hence all such responses to gravity should be searched out so that they may be systematically treated as to kind, and regionally treated as to distribution. Such matters are surely as properly of a geographical quality as are various responses to sunshine which are always found among the standard matters of our books. How many more responses to the universal and persistent force of gravity there may be, we do not yet know. Again, take such an example as that afforded by the habit of working by day and summer and resting by night and winter. These are responses to the controls of light and heat in contrast to darkness and cold, which result from the illumination and warmth of the rotating and revolving earth by an external sun. This suggests that all other responses to light and to darkness should be sought out and studied: for it leaves the limitations of our subject very vague if we make a beginning with such relations and do not carry them to an end; it makes the limitations very arbitrary if we make a beginning of such relations and stop with the first or the second or the third example, instead of pressing on to the very last.

It is an application of this same principle that makes it impossible to limit the organic side of geography to man; for the habits which man has developed in his search for food, clothing, shelter, and so on, are in very many ways closely analogous to those developed by animals in a similar search. In the same way the sensitiveness of man and animals to climatic conditions by which limits of distribution are so largely determined is paralleled by the sensitiveness of plants to similar conditions. Life is a unit; if one form of life comes under the study of geography because it responds to physiographic controls, then all forms of life come under geography.

The expansion of geography through time is likewise inevitable unless it is most arbitrarily limited to the "present day." Precisely the same principles have been embodied in the relations between physiographic and ontographic elements in the past as are embodied in them now. It is therefore most illogical to think of geography as a science that deals only with to-day. There has always been a geography, all through the geological ages; geology is the integration of all its momentary or geographical differentials. We may never know very much about the successive geographies of the past, but all the fragments that have thus far been learned assure us that it was of essentially the same order as the geography of the present. The recognition of this principle is of the greatest importance to geography, and to geology as well.

The Subdivisions of Geography. It is but natural that the different phases of human geography should have been more fully developed than the other branches of our science. Political geography, frequently overrunning civics, economics, and history, has long been familiar as an elementary subject; but with us it has seldom been carried into the higher reaches of education. Commercial geography is rapidly gaining an important place in our schools, and is meeting the danger of becoming almost as empirical as the old-time lists of products of the several states. Biogeography has several parts. Anthropogeography, as expanded by Ratzel, seems destined to become an important subject in the universities, because of the greater insight that one gains through it into history. Zoögeography and phytogeography are in my opinion, as a rule, too strictly limited to facts of distribution alone; these divisions of the subject should be expanded so as to include for animals and plants a consideration of what would correspond to the political and commercial geography of man. Paleogeography is occasionally treated, but it must always be a fragmentary subject, because it is based on fragmentary records; it will, however, be better treated by geologists in proportion as they have had geographical training.

The growth of explanatory treatment, which makes so characteristic a difference between the content of geography in books of a hundred years ago and of to-day, is chiefly due to the different amounts of general knowledge in stock then and now, and consequently to the different philosophies then and now prevailing. The subject has thus gained greatly in strength, in disciplinary value, and in living interest. At the same time geography has come to cultivate more and more — some would say, to trespass more and more upon — the fields that are also cultivated by other subjects. If the trade winds are not simply described as to region of occurrence, direction of blowing, weather conditions therein prevailing, and so on, but are also explained as parts of an extensive convectional circulation between equator and poles, modified by the deflective effect of the earth's rotation, all this explanatory matter has a strong flavor of physics. If the occurrence of plants of a certain kind in a given region is not merely asserted, but is shown to be the result of climatic conditions to which the plant responds, owing to its sensitiveness to temperature and moisture, this closely resembles certain chapters of botany, and the same may be said regarding the relation of animal distribution to zoölogy. If the boundary of a state, the location of a city, or the industry of a district is rationally explained instead of empirically stated, the explanation is of a kind likely to be found in books on history and economics. Shall we then, in view of this, relinquish explanatory treatment to other subjects and content ourselves with empirical statements? Shall we adopt the limitation to the location of things, as above suggested, and thus avoid duplication with other subjects? No. Duplication is unavoidable; and, moreover, it is reciprocal. The historian, as well as the botanist and the zoölogist, must borrow from the geographer all manner of facts regarding location, extent, distribution, climate, form, movements, products, populations, and so on; the geologist can hardly make a step into the realm of the past without having made preparatory study of the present. Overlapping and duplication are unavoidable. We must each of us try as far as possible to concentrate upon his own subject; but we must at the same time borrow and quote with the utmost freedom from any other subject that will give us aid in the consideration of our own.

Examples of Helpful Duplication. One of the most interesting fields that I have run across in geographical research is that open common where geography and philology overlap. It has often been remarked that the Arabs of the desert have many terms for sand dunes, evidently because they are familiar with the many forms that sand dunes there assume; their language has developed in a peculiar direction as an ontographic response to their peculiar physiographic environment. In the same way the people of the Alps have various terms by which to name mountain summits of different shapes; this is another ontographic response to a peculiar physiographic environment. But there are other less manifest examples of a somewhat different kind. We treasure as a fine geographical example the long preservation of ancient forms of speech in remarkable purity in Iceland, an out-of-the-way island; and, by way of contrast, we like to mention Malta, an island that is very much in the way, where the mingling of peoples has resulted in the mixture of Arabic and south-European tongues. We have already called attention to the diffusion of organic forms as a fundamental ontographic fact, and we know that variation is an ontographic consequence when diffusion leads to a physiographic environment that involves separation as a result either of distance or of isolation. As examples of this sort of geographical relation we may point either to the several species of cassowaries on the islands of Australasia, or to the several races of man on the larger divisions of the lands, — where barriers formed by the oceans are supplemented by a desert barrier in the Sahara and by a mountain barrier in the Himalaya, — or to the several nationalities in Europe, where gulfs and barriers are so important. But why not continue this line of inquiry, and instance, as another example of variation following on diffusion and separation, the differentiation of the Romance languages from Rumania to Portugal, and thus bring in the interesting story of the division of the *langue d'oc* and the *langue d'oui* by the central highlands of France? Why not include the even more extraordinary

story of the words "pecuniary" and "fee," which have come
to look so unlike on their arrival in our composite language
because of their different paths of travel from their common
source? This is of just as good geographical quality as is the
contrast between the whites and the blacks in our southern
states; they began alike somewhere long ago, and have come to
be different through long ages of separation before they are again
found together, — and separation is an important element of
physiographic control.

Not only speech but figures of speech are affected by physiographic environment. Two examples of this are found among
far-separated maritime peoples who were so impressed by the
manner in which a boat is guided by its rudder that they both
came to use a word, which primarily meant a stick and secondarily a stern oar, in a later figurative sense meaning the guidance or control of a whole people. One of these examples is
found among the Scandinavians, where the same word is used
in "the helmsman *steers* the boat" and in "the king *steers* the
people"; here the original and the figurative meanings of the
word both survive to-day. The other example began with the people of the eastern Mediterranean and is now spread through all
the Romance languages and the Romance element of English.
French still preserves the original sense of the word in *gouver-
nail*, for "rudder"; but we have lost that sense, unless perhaps in
a passage in the Bible concerning the "governor" (helmsman
or captain) of a ship, and only know the figurative sense: the
word "govern" is therefore a long-lasting response to an early
maritime environment. In contrast to these maritime examples
is one from the Arabian desert: a missionary has told me, — in
reply to the question, "What is the Arab word for 'govern,' and
what is its origin?"—"It is a word that means 'guide,' and is
derived from the word meaning 'to guide a horse.'" In all
these cases it is as legitimate to instance the effect of environment on language as to instance its effect on industry.

The Practical Value of defining the Content of a Subject. In
occasional conferences with different geographers on such questions as have been treated in this essay, I have gained the impression that they attached relatively little value to abstract

considerations, and that it sufficed them to go on with their work without inquiring particularly into the general content of the subject under which it belonged, and without attempting to develop what may perhaps be called the more philosophical view of the subject as a whole. There was a time when I shared this indifference to abstract inquiry — a time when I was, as it were, overwhelmed with the great quantity and variety of material with which I had to make myself more or less familiar, and when there seemed to be no more need than there was occasion of bringing it all under an orderly and systematic scheme. But that time is now a good many years ago, and since then I have passed out of the stage of life in which, we are assured, our original work is to be completed, and have entered well upon the later stage in which the contemplation and arrangement of work previously done is, we are told, more attractive' than the accomplishment of new work. It is, perhaps, for some such reason that I have devoted this essay to the content of geography as a whole, because I am persuaded that there is a practical value in abstract considerations such as I have presented, even for younger men, and that if a general scheme of work in accordance with some broad and philosophical view of one's chosen science is formulated by a young geographer early in his career, he will profit greatly from it ; for he will thus be led more surely and directly to detect all the facts that are pertinent to any inquiry he may enter upon. Such a scheme is always open to modification as experience increases. If the geographer undertakes field study, as I hope he may, either at home, where there is plenty of field work to do, or abroad, where there is still more to be done, it will serve him well to know as definitely as possible the essential quality of the work before him. If he wishes to become an all-round geographer and to give a thorough geographical account of the region of his field work, he will be greatly aided in keeping his eyes open to the facts before him by bearing in mind the systematic content of the science as a whole, a part of which he proposes to study in the region he has selected.

II

THE PROGRESS OF GEOGRAPHY IN THE SCHOOLS

Encouragement from Recent Progress. The most notable characteristic of the condition of geography in the schools during recent years is the marked improvement that it has experienced. The improvement accomplished, and still in progress, is most encouraging. The rate of advance is as great as is consistent with sound development. Chief among the impulses toward this march of improvement in geography, as in various other school subjects, have been the reports by committees of specialists, particularly those published by the National Educational Association. These reports have furnished many excellent suggestions, which superintendents and teachers have either adopted or discussed ; and the discussions thus excited may be considered as beneficial to the subject over which they are held as were the improvements that were immediately adopted. All this is most gratifying. Let reports, improvements, and discussions continue. Geography in the schools will thrive on them.

Direction in which Further Progress is most Needed. There remains, however, much to be done. The one thing which would be, above all others, most helpful in continuing the progress already made, is the development of a higher ideal as to the content of geography among mature students.

Geography is too generally treated as an Elementary Study. It is a singular fact that there are, particularly in this ambitious country, very few students of geography as a mature subject. Most persons of full age who are directly concerned with geography are engaged in presenting its supposed elements to immature pupils. Very few are engaged in developing geography for mature students. Very few mature students are carrying forward original research in geography of a grade at all comparable to the research now so generally accomplished in various standard mature subjects. How many original investigators in geography do you know? Ask the same question concerning physics and chemistry, geology, botany, and zoölogy, mathematics and astronomy, philology, history, and literature, and make note of the contrast that all these maturely developed subjects present to geography. All these other subjects have habitual representation in our colleges and universities. Many of them engage the attention of professional experts. Geography is seldom recognized in these higher educational reaches. Nor are there, except rarely, professional positions in which mature geographers are employed on advanced work. There are truly many topographers, many pilots, many clerks in post-offices and express companies, many officers of our consular service, all of whom have contact of one kind or another with geography; but there are very few professional geographers, deservedly so called. It is true that many persons travel far and wide over the world, and some of them write very entertaining books; but travel no more makes the traveler a geographer than it makes him a botanist or an historian. Mere facts of occurrence and location have about the same rank in geography that words have in literature, dates in history, and specific names in botany and zoölogy. A traveler's narrative is no more a geographical work because it makes mention of a hill and a harbor than it is a botanical work because it tells something about a forest and a swamp. It is chiefly among the small body of explorers that we find mature geographers; and yet not all of these brave and energetic workers attempt to develop the more scientific aspects of geography. Explorers are generally men of resolute action rather than of an analytical turn of mind, and they too often have about the same relation to mature geography that collectors of wild animals have to mature zoölogy. All of these workers, professional and amateur, contribute their sheaves of fact to the total gathering of geographical knowledge, but the facts thus gathered stand in need of discussion and coördination; the sheaves must be threshed and winnowed. The advanced workers, seriously engaged in separating the grain from the chaff and assorting the grain according to its quality, are few indeed.

Illustration from Disputed Boundaries. The boundaries between nations are frequently defined in terms of topographical forms, and one might expect that here at least a mature understanding of geography would have been developed. But there are two recent and serious disputes regarding boundaries in which the misunderstandings arise directly from the treatment of topographical features in an elementary, immature manner. The Argentine-Chilian boundary, as verbally defined in the treaty of 1881, takes no account of the possible occurrence of valleys going through the mountain range, so as to predetermine beyond chance of misunderstanding the course of the boundary in districts where the continental divide departs significantly from the crest line of the cordillera of the Andes. The terms of the treaty appear to have been based on the antiquated idea that mountain ranges must rise between river basins, and that rivers cannot pass through mountain ranges; an idea which, as Prince Krapotkin has shown, has long worked mischief in the cartography of Asia by placing ranges where none exist and by omitting them where they occur; an idea which would long ago have disappeared from geography had the subject been maturely and scientifically developed.

The Alaskan boundary, as verbally defined in the British-Russian treaty of 1825, takes no such account of the possible complexity of mountain form and irregularity of coasts as to preclude misunderstandings that might arise with respect to the summits of mountain ranges, or with respect to outer and inner shore-lines. It is true that the treaty here in discussion was made three quarters of a century ago; yet even at that time the occurrence of detached and discontinuous ranges and of irregular coasts was perfectly well known, and it would seem that the commissioners who framed the treaty might have avoided all possible ambiguity had they based their definitions on a more mature study of topographical forms. I do not propose to express here any opinion regarding the rights in either of these disputes, but only to call attention to the fact that the disputes have resulted from an inadequate comprehension and definition of topographical forms; that is, from the employment of an elementary knowledge of geography in the treatment of a problem where an advanced knowledge would have been much more appropriate.

Illustration from Immaturity of Geographical Terminology.
Any subject that is pursued from elementary teaching through
secondary and collegiate study to the highest reaches of independent investigation is always accompanied by an expanding
terminology. The terms that suffice for the beginner do not
suffice for the advanced student. It is true that the terminology
thus developed is sometimes of an embarrassing fullness. It is
sometimes unnecessarily detailed, but there can be no question
that it is on the whole of great value. It is well that the specialist should be cautious about introducing new terms; that he
should test his inventions by home use before offering them in
print to his colleagues. It is true also that of the total number
of terms invented by the specialist in this field or that, many per-
ish, and only the needed ones survive in general scientific use.
If it were possible to endow all specialists with so much wisdom
that they could foresee the needs of the next generation, and
invent only such terms as would prove of permanent value, much
of the difficulty that is inherent in the question of terminology
would disappear; but such wisdom is not granted to investigators any more than to lawmakers. All that can be expected is
that each individual shall work carefully and honestly, and that
the processes of natural selection and the survival of the fittest
shall operate in terminology as well as elsewhere. The development of new methods and the discovery of new results make the
introduction of new terms inevitable. A good name is of great
assistance in making the thing named more generally known.
A growing terminology is characteristic of all growing sciences.

In reviewing the literature of geography it is remarkable to
note that the terminology of school days is so little extended in
the productions of mature writers. Consider, for example, the
subject of mountains. Look over any school geography and
count the nouns and adjectives that are used with a technical
meaning in the chapter on this subject; chain, range, peak,
summit, ridge, pass, are among them. Now look over the best
essay that can be found in which a mountainous region is described by a mature writer for mature readers, and make another
count of the same kind. The adjectives will be found to have
" grown up "; that is, they comprise a number of more learned

words, — such as precipitous, stupendous, imposing, formidable, — yet none of these are introduced with anything like technical definitions : they are used in a general literary sense such as will be understood by the polite reader. Among the nouns there will be a moderate number of new words, most of which are taken from the local *patois* of the mountain people, or from the somewhat colloquial language of mountain climbers ; but there is nowhere any sufficient indication that these new words are taken from a systematic, consistent, and thoroughgoing terminology of mountain forms. The same is true of nearly all the other divisions of geography. Even in reports so important as those of the Mississippi River Commission, certain features of the great river and its flood plain go practically unnamed and therefore unnoticed. The small number of technical geographical terms that have been introduced by a few writers have as yet gained little general currency.

The absence of a mature terminology appropriate to mature geographical descriptions is one of the most patent signs that geography is not maturely developed.

Inattention to Mature Geography has a Bad Effect on School Geography. There can be no question that the neglect of geography as a subject for mature study has had and still has an injurious effect upon the condition of geography in the schools. Special emphasis must be given to this point, for it is not generally enough recognized. One may attend a conference of superintendents and teachers before whom geography is a subject for discussion, and hear much said about this or that aspect of the subject, about this or that device for its presentation, and yet hardly a suggestion may be made to the effect that teachers of geography should be better taught, and still less is an intimation offered that geography itself is in need of more mature development as a scientific study. It is not in our own country alone that this complacent attitude prevails : recent articles by representative foreign authors contain practically no indication that geography in the schools still suffers from lack of preparation on the part of the teacher, and from lack of advanced work on the subject in the universities. These deficiencies are less noticeable in continental schools, particularly in Germany, where it is so often the case that a secondary teacher holds the degree of doctor of philosophy; but they are certainly serious in Great Britain, where geography in the schools is a very commonplace study, in spite of the enormous importance of geography to the British empire.

Deficiency of Higher Learning in Geography. The most conspicuous evil consequence of this state of things is the want of a well-developed body of higher geographical learning, with respect to which the geography in the schools shall stand only as a beginning. It is unfair to look to teachers of the supposed elements of a subject for the development of its more advanced parts; school-teachers are fully occupied with duties of their own. The body of higher learning must be developed in geography as it has been in other subjects, namely, by the devoted work of specialists who give their best thought to the advance of their subject. Many specialists in other sciences are professors in colleges or universities, experts in governmental bureaus, or amateurs of high intellectual rank; but geography is seldom represented in this goodly company, and hence the development of mature geography is slow. Many subjects that make their beginning under the cover of geography outgrow their shelter and attain an independent maturity. Thus astronomy, geology, botany, zoölogy, history, government, and economics — extracts from whose contents are first introduced into school work along with geography — gain places for themselves in college, while geography disappears. It is as if the trunk subject had subdivided, like an elm, into many divergent branches, each of which flourishes alone. I wish the simile might be that of a sturdy pine whose trunk is not sacrificed, however many limbs it gives forth. There can be little question that, as long as geography is not represented in colleges, the future teachers of geography in the schools will be insufficiently educated in their subject.

Deficiency of Higher Learning discourages High Ideals. In the absence of a mature development of our subject, its ideals must be of a low order, and its early steps can make only uncertain progress in advancing toward an unknown goal. What would the Latin, the geometry, the physics of our schools be if those subjects had no representation in the colleges! How definitely the first steps in these subjects lead toward the great body of their higher learning! How greatly would the geography of the schools be improved if geography had as well established a place in our colleges as history has! I will not here take up the question whether geography is entitled to so universal a recognition. Some educators may think it is not, and certainly the existing distribution of appointments in our colleges would confirm that opinion; but it may be safely maintained that if a professorship of geography existed in every college where there is a professorship of history, our ideals as to the mature content of geography would be much enlarged above what they are to-day, and our conception of what constitutes the elements of the subject would be correspondingly changed. We should at least be cured of the forlorn idea that geography is only the study of the location of things.

One of the most evident results of the immature development of geography is that details rather than principles have been dwelt upon in school work. This is not so true now as it was twenty years ago, but it is still too often true. It is by no means always the fault of the teachers. It may be due in large part to the low ideals indicated in official examination papers, for if examinations are largely directed to testing a knowledge of the innumerable details of geography, then the teacher must cram the pupil, and cramming trains the memory rather than the intelligence. On the other hand, if emphasis is given, both in teaching and in examinations, to general principles and important relations, under which items are adduced simply as illustrations, then the intelligence as well as the memory is developed. Items of occurrence and location are not to be neglected, but they should be studied in their natural relations instead of as isolated facts.

This principle is now pretty generally understood. It is agreed that a cape, a river, a boundary, a city, must not be merely located and memorized, and then set aside, unused, unrelated to anything else; for with teaching of this kind the essential spirit of geography remains dormant. Yet such is the popular pressure for a knowledge of the names and places of things that many things are learned merely by place and name. It is usually held to be necessary to go briefly over a large number of items, even if there is no time to learn their relations without slighting other parts of the subject; but this supposed necessity is open to question. It should be carefully considered whether the names that are learned have been chosen with good judgment from among the countless items of geography; whether they are really chosen at all, or simply inherited from a time when geography had not reached its present development; whether their choice is made with due regard to the higher reaches of geography, and not merely in obedience to a poorly educated public sentiment as to the content of our subject; and finally, whether items should, after all, be given so much prominence as they have often had, with the result of subordinating the large principles under which the items stand only as individual examples.

Value of Principles versus Items illustrated by Geometry and Physics. A possible rearrangement of the emphasis on items and principles in geography may be illustrated by reference to the actual practice in geometry and physics. No good teacher would approve of memorizing the particular figure of a theorem in geometry, with its individual proportion of parts, its attitude on the blackboard, and its special lettering, as a means of learning the general quality of the theorem that the figure illustrates. It is the generality of the theorem that is impressed; it is the possibility of applying a general principle to any particular case that falls under it that must be emphasized in good teaching. So in physics; as much care as is necessary may be properly expended on the construction and manipulation of a piece of apparatus, but the emphasis of good teaching must be given to the principle which the apparatus is used to illustrate. I believe that it is possible to discover and establish general principles in geography likewise, and to teach individual items chiefly as illustrations of the principles under which they fall.

It must be admitted, however, that geometry and physics are not so closely analogous to geography that the best method of study in the first two is, therefore, the best in the third also. The lettering of a chalk figure on a blackboard and the construction of a piece of simple apparatus have no such importance as an actual village in a valley or as an actual island in the sea. Nevertheless, geographers may profit by taking heed of the subordination of item to principle in geometry and physics; they may, perhaps, be thus aided in perceiving the proper relation of the specific to the general in their own subject.

Examples of Excessive Detail in the Study of Counties. In illustration of excessive attention to detail, let me cite certain official examinations that have sometimes included such questions as, " Name the counties in order along the southern border of this state." Such questions have been defended because it is held to be desirable that every inhabitant of a state should know the counties into which his state is divided; but this assumption is wide open to doubt when it is seen that the counties cannot be learned except by sacrificing something else. It is by no means demonstrated that the time demanded in acquiring this knowledge has been used to the best advantage by the pupil. Very little application is made of the knowledge after it is acquired. It would be interesting to inquire of pupils thus trained whether the list of counties is gladly retained in the memory of mature years, or willingly forgotten. Surely, if forgotten, the loss does not impair the usefulness of a citizen, since the forgotten items can be easily regained when wanted. There are very few of our most intelligent friends who carry in their memories such items as the names and relative position of all the counties in their home state or in any other state, and it is certainly very rarely the case that any well-educated man or woman regards such use of memory as a measure of a cultivated intelligence. Truly, something about counties may well be taught under political geography, and still better under civics. The subdivision of the larger counties of early settlement into smaller counties, as population grows, deserves mention in history; and the unorganized "plantations" still found in the backwoods of Maine may well be cited as examples of retarded development, illustrating to-day a condition through which other states have long ago passed. But, as a matter of fact, while the division of a state into counties is a matter of practical convenience for various purposes of record and administration, the actual counties into which a state is divided are not worth memorizing in competition with the many more educative problems of geography. If counties were the whole content of geography, we might have to learn them all over the country, but they sink into insignificance in comparison with many other matters in the actual content of our subject. If a sheriff, an express agent, or a postal clerk needs to know the counties of a state (very likely not the state in which he was " raised "), he can learn them at short notice, and the rest of us can get along very well by looking up any particular county in an atlas when we want to know something about it ; and, by the way, the habit of looking up things in an atlas is worth the memorized lists of the counties in a dozen states. Indeed, in some respects the subdivision of states into counties is outgrown; notably with regard to county prisons, into which all classes of local malefactors are thrown, unclassified, greatly to the injury of many of them, and hence to the harm of the community. This may have been justifiable when means of transportation did not include railroads, but it endures to-day in the more closely settled states only as the inheritance of an earlier condition which has not yet changed into appropriate relation to its new environment.

The "tier of counties" question is probably less common now than it used to be, but it serves to illustrate very well a low ideal as to the content of geography on the part of examination boards, and the subordination of school work to an uneducated public sentiment that demands of school children a multitude of details, concerning many of which intelligent persons do not regret their ignorance, because their minds are occupied with better things. While the low ideal exists, the work of the teacher and the examiner must lead up to it. When the ideal as to the content of geography is raised, school work will rise with it to a higher grade than it now reaches, and then the counties of a state will be counted among the " honorable points of ignorance."

The Three Stages of Geographical Development. As a means of leading toward higher ideals, let me now attempt to show that geography as a mature subject is capable of a higher development than it has yet reached. In this connection it will be well to review briefly the three stages of development recognizable in the progress of our venerable subject. Until within about a hundred years the content of geography consisted of a body of uncorrelated facts concerning the earth and its inhabitants. The facts were described empirically, and as a rule very imperfectly. Their location was noted, but their correlations were overlooked; it had not, indeed, been clearly made out that correlations existed. This blindly inductive first stage was followed by a second stage, which was opened by Ritter's exposition of the relationship between the earth and its inhabitants. True, Ritter and his school did not carry the idea of relationship systematically through all parts of the subject; and such relationships as were noted had to be explained on the old doctrine of teleology — the adaptation of the earth to man — instead of on the modern principle of evolution, — the adaptation of all the earth's inhabitants to the earth. It is this principle which characterizes the third stage of progress, and along with it goes a principle of almost equal importance; namely, that all the items which enter into the relation between the earth and its inhabitants must be explained as well as described, because explanation aids so powerfully in observing and appreciating the facts of nature. It should be noted that the two great advances by which the third stage of geographical progress is set forward from the second are the contributions of others than geographers: the principle of organic evolution is owed to the biologists; the principles under which explanation is found for the features of the earth are owed chiefly to astronomers, physicists, and geologists. This indebtedness might not have been so heavily contracted if the geographers of the older school had been less content with a purely inductive treatment of their subject; if they had asked themselves not only where and what, but also how and why things are as we find them.

The Content of Modern Geography. Geography has to-day entered well upon its third stage of progress. The "causal notion" is generally admitted to be essential in the study of the relation of the earth and its inhabitants. Thus understood, geography involves the knowledge of two great classes of facts: first, all those facts of inorganic environment which enter into relationship with the earth's inhabitants; second, all those responses by which the inhabitants, from the lowest to the highest, have adjusted themselves to their environment. The first of these classes has long been studied as physical geography, although this name has been used as a cover for many irrelevant topics. In recent years there has been a tendency to compress the name into the single word "physiography."

The second of the two classes of facts has not yet reached the point of being named, but perhaps it may come to be called ontography. Ecology, to which increasing attention is given by biologists, is closely related to what I here call ontography, yet there is a distinction between the two, in that ecology is concerned largely with the individual organism, while ontography is intended to include all pertinent facts in structure, physiology, individual, and species.

Neither physiography nor ontography alone is geography proper, for geography involves the relation in which the elements of its two components stand to each other. Each of the components must be well developed before geography can be taken up as a mature study.

The relations involved in geography, as thus understood, are of the most varied nature. A relation that has been frequently quoted since Ritter first called attention to it is the one between the irregularity of continental coast lines and the stage of human development; but a continuous series may be made from this large and general relation to such trifling matters as the relation that determines the point where a common road bridges a stream. Evidently, then, it is not the dimensions of the relation that determine its geographical quality, although its dimensions may have much influence in fixing the stage at which it may be profitably introduced in school work, and the emphasis that is to be given to it there. Oceans, lofty mountain ranges, and deserts are formidable barriers that oppose the migration of plants and animals; but from these great controls over the movement of whole species and races a continuous series of examples might be made, leading down to the control that a hill slope exerts over the direction of a plow furrow.

It is not only to the inorganic parts of the earth that man is related, but to the organic parts as well. It is the scarcity of plant and animal food that limits the human population of deserts, just as it is the aridity of climate that limits the number of desert plants and animals. It is the density of forest growth under equatorial rains that has made some of the savage natives of New Guinea expert canoe men : the rivers there are more available as highways than the plant-crowded land. The relation of population and industries to the cotton, corn, and wheat crop of the United States is a standard geographical problem. Moreover, while attention was formerly given in largest part to the relation of the earth to man, and while this still seems properly enough to characterize the more elementary stages of geography, a large share of attention in its mature stages must be given to the relation of the earth to all kinds of life, and to the interrelations of all kinds of life in so far as they involve considerations of place and space. Cattle are excluded from certain parts of Africa by the tsetse-fly ; this is as good geography as is the relation of the Gaelic and English languages to the Highlands and Lowlands of Scotland. Man was once looked upon as set apart from the rest of organized beings, but this is no longer possible. The devices that he has employed and the battles that he has fought in gaining his present place resemble, more than they differ from, those by which all plants and animals have gained their places. Indeed, it is but the commonplace of comparative zoölogy to-day to see in man a great number of structures and processes that have been inherited from a time when he was not man ; and many of these structures and processes are responses to his physical environment.

A science cannot be cut off arbitrarily in the midst of a continuous series of relations that characterize it. Geography must consider the ontography of the lowest beings as well as of the highest. It should therefore be our effort, in giving to geography a mature development, to open our conception of its content as widely as possible, rather than to set narrow limits to it ; to probe all the elements of physical environment and all the manifestations of life in order to discover examples of relations that have thus far been overlooked. Only when geography is thus more fully constituted a mature subject will it be possible to make the best selection of those parts which may be considered elementary ; only through the development

of the higher reaches of the subject can the lower reaches be
best ordered. It is for this reason that these somewhat transcendental considerations deserve the attention of thoughtful
and progressive teachers.

The Unity of Geography. It is especially the factor of relationship of earth and inhabitants that characterizes geography as a
subject apart from other sciences, and that gives an essential
unity of content and discipline to all its varied parts. Objection
has been made to geography because of its composite nature; it
has been reproached with being only a patchwork of scraps from
many other subjects, without any essential quality of its own.
These assertions do not seem to me to have force: in the first
place, because other subjects as well as geography are composite
if they are judged only by the things that they treat, and by the
processes employed in their study; and, in the second place,
because geography, properly understood, has as well defined an
essence of its own as other subjects have.

It is perfectly true that the geographer, even the young geographer, must learn something of the planets in connection with
his study of the earth as a globe, something of the behavior of
gases in connection with his study of the atmosphere, something
of the history of the earth in connection with his study of land
forms, something of the structure of plants and animals in connection with the ontographical half of his subject; but it is no
less true that the astronomer must learn something of the earth
as a globe in connection with his study of the planets, the physicist must learn something of the atmosphere in connection with
his study of gases, the geologist must learn something of existing land forms in connection with his study of the past history
of the earth, the biologist must learn something of the lands and
the seas in connection with his studies of plants and animals.
One is tempted to say that all things seem to be shared by all
sciences, and that each science can be defined only in terms of
the relation in which it studies things, rather than in terms of
the things that it studies. The geographer learns what he wishes
to know about the earth as a globe, even though this chapter of
his study may be related to astronomy; about the atmosphere,
even though he may divide this part of his subject with the

physicist; about plants and animals, even if this seems to be a trespass on biology; but finally he strings all the things he has learned on the thread of the relation between earth and life. The unity of consideration thus gained warrants the inclusion of all these things under his subject of study, and it gives us a right to consider the subject of study as a science unit.

The Complexity of Geography. It should be no reproach to geography that it is concerned with a large variety of things, some of which are treated elsewhere, for the same may be said of all the other sciences. Every material thing that is studied by the geographer is also fit for study by the chemist and the physicist. The chemist may wisely inquire into the nature of the elements and compounds that are found in minerals, plants, and animals. The physicist may advisedly study the physical properties of these things and the forces by which they interact. If the chemist and the physicist study in their laboratories rather than outdoors, this is only because they are more interested in systematic than in regional physics and chemistry; in the establishment of general laws than in the record of individual occurrences. The weathering of a rock surface, the fall of a rock fragment from a cliff, are processes that come under the laws of chemistry and physics; but the chemist and the physicist do not trouble themselves especially about the innumerable repetitions of these processes in nature; they are satisfied with establishing the laws that generalize the processes, and with good reason, as I shall show further on.

It should surely be no reproach to the mature geographical investigator that he must study many kinds of things, and that he must share many subjects with other sciences, for all this is equally true of the geologist and the historian. The geologist must know much of chemistry and of physics, much of geography and of biology; but he strings all his facts on a single thread, the sequence of events in the earth's history, and thus arranged they belong to geology. The historian must know all manner of things in the realms of geography, language, and economics, and he would do well to know something of biology if he would really appreciate many of man's motives; but all the facts that he gathers are to be arranged so as to exhibit the sequence and relationship of events in human progress, and thus arranged they belong to history.

Not only do other sciences resemble geography in gathering their items from many fields of knowledge, but like geography they employ many methods in reaching their results. If geographers must follow the methods of the astronomer in order to understand the earth as a globe, of the physicist in order to appreciate climatic factors, of the geologist in order to understand land forms, of the biologist in order to apprehend the responses of living beings to their environment, they are neither peculiar nor unfortunate in this breadth of exercise. The astronomer has long had to use mathematics, yet astronomy is not mathematics, and mathematics is not astronomy. In recent years the astronomer has had to learn much of physics and chemistry, yet no one thinks of confusing these well-defined sciences on that account. Changes of color on Mars with his change of seasons suggest that the astronomer will soon have to borrow something from the biologist; so much the better if he does, and we may be sure that both astronomy and biology will thrive under the new régime. The chemist constantly employs the methods of the physicist and the mathematician; like every one else, he uses language to express his thoughts, although language is the special study of the philologist; and he must follow accurate processes of thought if he would reach good results, even though the processes of thought are the special province of the logician.

In view of these comparisons it does not seem to me that geographers need fear that their subject is so complex as to be in danger of disintegrating, provided they give heed to its integrating essence. Geography is complex, like other sciences; but, like other sciences, geography is unified by the continuity of its essential quality through all its varied parts. Possibly geography is the most complex of all sciences — some one science must stand at the head of the list in this respect, but it must therein differ only in degree, not in kind, from its fellows; and it is yet to be shown that complexity is not an attractive advantage in leading the student along many profitable lines of thought, instead of a deterring disadvantage.

The Limits of the Sciences. Although one may be at some pains to indicate the limits by which his science is reasonably bounded, it does not follow that he must hold himself too narrowly within these limits. Truly, the astronomer is chiefly concerned with the heavenly bodies, but he is welcome to come down, if he wishes, to things terrestrial, and to define the boundary of Colorado in terms of astronomical quantities; but he might as consistently consider himself responsible for the explanation of plant growth during the season when the sunshine is long and strong. The boundary of Colorado by meridians and parallels is as truly a geographical matter, as truly a response to physical environment, as is the settlement of a colony at a protected bay head, or the building of a beaver dam in the open valley of a small stream.

The geologist may, if he so desire, supplement his historical account of the formation of the lake Superior iron ores, of the telluric forces by which the ore bodies were deformed, and of the erosion by which they were laid bare, with a consideration of the modern times of discovery and exploitation, and, in order to impress his students with the richness and magnitude of the ore deposits, he may explain how they have led to the development of great business undertakings; and he is perfectly welcome thus to overrun the fields of geography, history, economics, metallurgy, and so on. The physicist may exemplify the laws of gases by explaining the heat and dryness of the chinook wind, or he may illustrate the laws of fluids in a discussion of the waves of the sea; but the winds and the waves are none the less elements of geographical environment. The historian is welcome to introduce as much geology and geography as he desires into his account of the promontories and bays of Greece; the wonder is, indeed, that he does not do so more freely than is to-day habitual; he is certainly warranted in explaining the steam engine, the Bessemer process of making steel, and the various applications of electricity as events of high importance in the progress of the last century and a half; and he is fully justified in giving some account of the principles of organic evolution, because they have so profoundly modified philosophical and religious thought in the last third of a century. Surely, all these things are as pertinent to the history of man as are the revolutions of a more military sort.

It is, however, a significant fact that astronomers do not find time to tell anything about the boundary of Colorado; they are too much occupied with their own affairs to take up geographical problems. Geological text-books have no pages to spare for the history of the development of iron-ore mining around lake Superior; they have, indeed, hardly pages enough to tell all that is desirable as to the origin of the ores. It is only in the largest volumes of history that space is found for accounts of the inventions that have revolutionized the modern world, although these inventions are quite as pertinent to the subject of history as are the tactics of a general on a battle-field. As a matter of fact, such subjects as astronomy, geology, and history are so rich in materials and so well organized in methods that they are seldom tempted to run over other fields than their own; and it is to this condition of abundant material and well-organized method that I hope to see geography advance. The geographer may, if he wishes, tell about the individual features of other planets than the earth; but there is so much to say about the earth as a globe that everything about the other planets must be excluded that does not aid the study of our own planet. He may turn back from the present to the past, and describe the results of many geological discoveries; but it is unwise to do so unless these discoveries bear immediately on present geographical conditions. He may feel tempted to explain the principles of systematic botany and zoölogy, and to enlarge upon the facts of history; but in so far as these excursions lead him into fields that are outside of geographical relationships, he had better avoid them, not because such excursions are uninteresting or unprofitable in themselves, but because they take time that can ill be spared from geographical duties. I hope to see the teacher of geography spend his time as carefully as the teacher of geometry or of chemistry does. Let him, by all means, enrich his subject by introducing all manner of pertinent illustrations; let him show an intimate acquaintance with, and a warm sympathy for, all the sciences, but let him be jealous of unwarranted infringements upon the hours allotted to his own science, and earnest in preserving its integrity. Under such a teacher no student will complain that the content of geography is so complex and its methods are so diverse that it has neither unity nor discipline.

Systematic and Regional Geography. The attention given to general principles and to specific items differs greatly in the different sciences. One reason for this is that some sciences are concerned chiefly with the abstract relations or the general properties of things, while others are more concerned with the things themselves. Another reason is that in some sciences a principle or a category of phenomena may be exemplified by a great number of instances, and here a large share of attention is given to the general principles under which the instances may be grouped; while in others the number of illustrative instances is small, and here attention is given chiefly to individual things.

Geometry and algebra are not concerned with things at all, but only with the relation of the forms and the quantities of things. Their methods are characteristically abstract, mental, deductive, and their resort to diagrams and equations is only as an aid to the memory. All their demonstrations could be performed with the eyes shut, in the dark, if memory sufficed to follow the necessary operations through the successive steps that lead to the result. Specific instances, as in diagrams and equations, are of value only as illustrations of general principles, as has already been stated. Geometry and algebra are therefore systematic and universal instead of being local or regional; they have no necessary association with any special place or time.

Physics and chemistry deal with the properties and relations of matter; they necessarily study individual specimens of matter, but this is in order to gain results of general application. They adduce specific instances as examples of general principles; but no one would think of attempting to teach the physics and chemistry of Minnesota, for example, although Minnesota is full of matter and energy; there is not enough of local quality to make the physics and chemistry of a state worth considering apart from the physics and chemistry of the world.

Zoölogy and botany are concerned with things; yet the effort of the zoölogist and botanist is to generalize, both as to the form and growth of the individual and as to the development of the race or species. Thus systematic zoölogy and systematic botany (meaning by these phrases not merely the study of classification, but also of individual growth and of racial development as far as they are generalized) attain a high importance. On the other hand, the individual and the grouping of individuals attract attention, because plants and animals are not uniformly spread over the world. Regional zoölogy and regional botany thus gain an importance that has no likeness in mathematics, physics, or chemistry.

Astronomy is largely specific, particularly so with regard to bodies like planets, of which but few examples are known; yet classification and the establishment of general principles are attempted whenever possible, as, for example, in the grouping together of stars according to their proper motion, their parallax, or their spectrum; or in the demonstration that the planets move around the sun in ellipses. The long duration and the systematic movements of most of the things studied in astronomy give the individuals a greater importance than is attained by biological individuals; for the extremely small size, the brief existence, and the unpursuable movements of many organic forms turn attention from the individual to the species.

When we come to geography, its traditional treatment is found to be very largely specific, as has been already indicated. The establishment of categories, under which related phenomena are brought together, is seen in the use of such elementary terms as " river," " coast," " harbor," " city," and so on; but the well-recognized categories are few in number compared to those established in botany and zoölogy, and many of the categories are of so general a nature that they do not suffice to indicate clearly the characteristic features of the things that are brought under them. Moreover, it is so common to give a large share of attention, as has already been pointed out, to such items as name and location that many a pupil must fail to appreciate the general relations of the examples that he studies. In a word, systematic geography is very poorly developed, while specific or regional geography is overgrown although incomplete. This is as if the botanist gave little attention to the kinds of plants that grow on the earth, and devoted most of his attention to the place of occurrence of his vaguely defined genera.

I therefore invite special attention to the need of developing, as maturely as possible, the systematic side of geography, as one of the means of most effectively improving the condition of geography in the schools.

Systematic Geography is concerned with the kinds of relationships that exist between the earth and its inhabitants. The actual relationships are countless; the different kinds of relationships are very numerous, although less numerous than the relationships themselves. The number of kinds is so great that it is highly desirable to arrange them according to some scheme of classification, so that similar kinds of relationships may be brought into near association with one another, while unlike relationships may be set farther apart. It thus becomes essential to analyze the relations into the elements that are related, and to divide these elements into as many categories as may be needful, and then to classify these categories. By no other method can confusion be avoided in a subject so large as that with which we are concerned. I therefore propose to outline here some of the chief systematic divisions of the two parts of our subject, and to point out in particular certain divisions whose systematic arrangement is not yet generally agreed upon.

Systematic Physiography. The four chief divisions of physiography are the earth as a globe, the atmosphere, the oceans, and the lands; but the content and the order of presentation of these divisions vary in different books, and a fifth division, the distribution of plants and animals, is added by some writers. This addition may be defended on various grounds in elementary study, but it is always open to the serious objection that it involves an essentially regional treatment, and that it therefore belongs with the regional study of the continents and their physical subdivisions rather than with the general study of the categories into which the physical features of the earth are divided. It remains to be determined by experiment whether it would not be more useful to limit the proposed fifth division to a systematic consideration of the physiographic factors by which the distribution of plants and animals is controlled, and to place the study of organisms, in so far as it is geographical, under ontography or under regional geography.

Further subdivision of systematic physiography varies greatly with different authors, as may be illustrated by a brief consideration of the treatment of the lands. The older writers gave, as a rule, insufficient attention to this division of the subject, but this defect is now in process of rapid correction. Yet, although the different kinds of land forms are gaining an increasing attention in the newer text-books, the plan of subdivision of this large and important heading is not yet agreed upon. I venture, therefore, to offer for consideration the following outline of a scheme for its mature treatment :

1. The general features of the lands as contrasted with those of the atmosphere, the ocean, and the ocean bottom. The weathering and washing of the land surface and the attack of the sea on the land border result in slow changes of form. Branching valley systems, draining to the sea, are the most characteristic signs of these changes. The long continuation of the destructive changes must result in the reduction of any land surface, however high and uneven at first, to a low, featureless plain, close to sea level ; and every example of land form must stand somewhere in the cycle of systematic changes which end in the plain of degradation.

2. The lands may be more specifically treated under three headings : (*a*) land forms of various structures, and in various stages of the process of sculpture ; (*b*) streams by which the sculpture is controlled, here including glaciers as a climatic variant of water streams (winds, active in desert regions, have already been treated under the atmosphere ; waves and currents, active along the land margin, have been treated under the ocean) ; (*c*) land waste on its way to the sea. These three headings are to be further subdivided as follows :

(*a*) Land forms should be subdivided first as to structure and second as to stage of development in the cycle of sculpture. The simplest structures should be considered first, and of these coastal plains may well lead the list, while mountains of greatly disordered structure come near its close. Under each of these categories young forms, that is, forms in an early stage of the cycle of sculpture, should be treated first ; then mature forms ; finally old forms. Crustal movements, occurring at any time, interrupt the previous cycle and introduce a new one.

(*b*) Although rivers and valleys have been briefly considered in the introductory account of the lands in general, and although they have been encountered repeatedly in the accounts of the different kinds of land forms, a special subdivision may be well made for their fuller consideration. Here rivers and their valleys form the leading topic, the argument by which the subject is entered ; and as such they may be presented in much greater detail than was appropriate when they were only secondary topics, as under land forms.

(*c*) The forms assumed by the waste of the land on the way to the sea merit recognition; they are fully worthy of an independent place in the scheme of treatment in relatively advanced study, although for more elementary work the topics of this subdivision may be distributed under others.

3. The consequences of special climatic conditions, dry and cold, deserve treatment apart from the consequences of normal climatic conditions; here deserts and glaciated areas may be placed. Any kind of a land form in any stage of sculpture may be now, or may have been recently, arid or glaciated; hence this chapter must follow those which discuss the sculpture of land forms in a normal climate.

4. The shore-line is best given a final chapter to itself, so that all kinds of land forms may be known when the work of the sea upon the lands is taken up. Shore-lines should be classified first according to their original outline as determined by the kind of land form on which the sea came to lie when the present relative position of land and sea was assumed; and second according to the advance in the systematic changes that are produced by the action of the sea on the original outline.

Principles of Systematic Physiography. There are several principles of importance to be observed in the treatment of systematic physiography.

The number of categories into which physiographic items are divided should be, as has already been suggested, greatly increased over the usual limit, and the categories should be treated as idealized types as far as possible. Each category should be illustrated, if possible, by a type diagram, on which the essential features are clearly presented, and from which the unessential details are carefully omitted. Then, in order to connect the ideal with the actual, good examples of the various types should be instanced, the examples being selected chiefly from the home country, but without undue neglect of the rest of the world.

The various categories of the subject must receive explanation as well as description, because of the great aid that comes to the memory through the understanding, and because of the higher order of intelligence that is developed by a rational instead of an empirical consideration of things. Explanation has long been accorded to the phenomena of the atmosphere and of the ocean; it should be applied with equal care to the forms of the land. For this purpose it is necessary to accept in a more whole-souled manner than is customary among geographers the processes of deformation and erosion by which the lands are given their observed forms. It does not suffice to stop at small illustrations, such as sand dunes and gorges; the value of uplift in producing coastal plains, of deformation in producing block mountains, and of erosion in carving the uplifted forms, must be more fully recognized. It is chiefly by the adoption of this principle that the progress of recent years has been made.

It should be observed that, with the explanatory treatment, there comes a good share of deductive consideration, hitherto not consciously recognized as a part of the mental equipment of the geographer in his study of the lands. Although inference and deduction have been abundantly exercised in explaining the winds and the tides, it seems to have been thought that deduction had no place in the treatment of land forms. It may, however, be safely affirmed that, as a matter of good practice, deduction enters largely into any serious attempt at giving systematic explanation to plains and plateaus, mountains and volcanoes, rivers, valleys, and shore-lines. This phase of physiographic study deserves careful consideration by those who wish to make the most of the newer methods.

Every category of physiographic elements should be accompanied by examples of the responses made to it by organic forms. It is not enough to take up the organic responses afterward; the habit must be formed of associating these responses with the study of the environing elements. It is too often the case that physiographic features are treated independently, as if they had no connection with the organic world, even when such connection may be easily found. Such treatment does little toward the formation of the habit of bringing the two halves of geography into their natural relations. The usual treatment of the earth as a globe under the title of mathematical geography gives good illustration of unrelated physiography. It should always be pointed out, in studying this division of the subject, that the wide distribution of organic species is an immediate consequence of the globular form of the earth; for only a globular earth can have its surface so generally level as to permit organic migration over large areas. The restraining effect of mountain ranges as barriers should suffice to show how greatly the facility of movement from place to place over most parts of the earth is dependent on the surface of the globe being not far from level, when considered as a whole. Examples of organic consequences thus related to physiographic controls are the very life of the subject.

Finally, the various categories of physiographic elements should be arranged according to a reasonable system. The elements coexist in nature, but in our study of them their consideration must be linear, one after the other. There is to-day no generally accepted order of arrangement. For example, the School of Geography of the University of Oxford offers a long vacation course for the summer of 1902, including a series of lectures on "Types of Land Forms and their Distribution," under which the following headings are announced : "Table-lands," "Young Folded Mountains," "Denudation Highlands," "Plains," and "Coastal Regions." Again, a committee of the New York State Science Teachers' Association has submitted a report in which shore-lines follow the ocean and precede the lands. Evidently discussion is needed on this problem of arrangement in order to bring about some approach to a consistent system. Hence even so subordinate a matter as that of arrangement calls for more serious consideration by mature students than it has yet received.

Regional Physiography. The physiographic description of a limited region cannot be profitably undertaken until after systematic physiography has been well developed. It is true that the whole content of physiography consists of items gathered from definite localities, and that the parts must be known before the whole ; but it is equally true that no well-ordered account of any region can be given until the facts gathered from many parts of the world have been thoroughly discussed and systematized.

The regional account of Minnesota, for example, involves the position of Minnesota on the globe, and the place of Minnesota with respect to the general system of atmospheric movements, and thus draws something from the first and second divisions of systematic physiography, as above stated. It involves the existence of the state as part of a large land mass, and thus draws something from the general features of the large land masses ; and with this goes the effect of a central continental position on climatic conditions. The further account of the state involves the description of all the different kinds of land forms within its borders ; if these items are to be presented with best effect, they must follow an order that indicates their general relations, and this draws largely from the systematic study of land forms. It may therefore be urged that the mature development of systematic physiography will do much to advance the mature understanding of regional physiography, and that a student who has carried his systematic studies as far as the condition of the science allows, will make excellent progress when he turns his attention to the study of a limited area. There are, however, very few monographs by which the truth of this contention can be supported ; there are, as yet, very few works in which the physiography of a region has been maturely studied in view of a well-developed scheme of systematic physiography.

Relation of Systematic and Regional Physiography. The older books on physical geography frequently contained chapters on the several continents, in which the attempt was made to present the actual distribution of the different kinds of physical features that had been briefly explained on earlier pages. The tendency to-day is to replace the pages formerly allowed to regional description with an extension of the pages allotted to systematic description, for the reason that no sufficient knowledge of the many kinds of things treated in physical geography can be gained if the actual distribution of the many kinds of things over the world is attempted. The increased attention thus given to systematic study is certainly an advantage, and if the idealized types of systematic study are illustrated by a good number of actual examples from many parts of the world, the student will have no ground of complaint. It is as much a mistake to attempt regional physical geography in the year that is granted to this subject in the high school as it would be to teach the flora or the fauna of various countries in the year that is allotted to botany or zoölogy. All the trend of the newer teaching in the biological sciences is in the direction of a more appreciative knowledge of typical forms, studied in view of their relations to large problems of growth, classification, and evolution. School study of the distribution of plants and animals is in danger of deteriorating to a mere study of names, and the same is true of regional physical geography. If the description of the continents is attempted in the year that is given to physiography in the high school, the time given to systematic physiography must be very insufficient, and the regional description must therefore be very defective.

There are, however, certain divisions of systematic physiography in which what seems at first to be a real or regional study is advisable ; namely, the chapters on the atmosphere and the ocean. The reason for this may be easily seen. The greater features of temperature distribution, atmospheric circulation, rainfall, and climate are really parts of a physiographic phenomenon whose dimensions are as large as the earth. Like the earth itself, the atmospheric shell as a whole must be considered if we wish to acquire an understanding of the relations of its parts. We have but one atmospheric shell with which to deal, and hence the study of its parts, such as the trade-winds, the subtropical belts, and so on, becomes specific and to that extent regional. In the study of rivers, on the other hand, there are many examples to illustrate the relations of the various parts, — basins, divides, valleys, streams, flood plains, deltas, etc., — and here the treatment necessarily becomes general, with allusion to specific examples only as a means of illustrating general principles.

The atmosphere is not, however, treated wholly by the regional method ; for like the parts of rivers which have small dimensions relative to the earth on which they occur, there are in the atmosphere also certain smaller phenomena of frequently repeated occurrence in place or time. These are always given a general instead of a regional treatment, and specific examples from particular regions are cited only as illustrations of the categories under which they fall. Land and sea breezes, mountain and valley winds, thunder-storms and tornadoes are examples of these smaller phenomena ; no text-book attempts to describe them all.

It is the same with the ocean. As a continuous and remarkably uniform sheet of water, the actual ocean may be treated as a physiographic unit. Variety in composition, temperature, and movement is limited for the most part to its surface portion; and even here the distribution of temperature and the arrangement of the larger currents are essentially symmetrical with respect to the equator, as if they were but parts of a large terrestrial phenomenon. When it comes to minor features like local currents, mention can be given to only a few typical examples, such as are afforded by the backset eddies between the Gulf Stream and the Carolina coast, by which the cuspate capes of that interesting shore-line are determined. So with the tides; the unity of this terrestrial phenomenon and its relation to the moon and sun should be pointed out and explained; but the infinite variety of tidal details along the ocean shores can be taught only by means of type examples, each of which is chosen to illustrate a class of tidal movements.

Something of regional treatment may be given to the first subdivision of the chapter on the lands, for the larger continental masses are so few that they naturally take our attention individually, as the individual planets take the attention of astronomers. On the other hand, the plan of continental structure and relief is so intricate that it is not yet well resolved even by the most advanced students; hence systematic physiography cannot dwell long on the large divisions of the lands. The continents are best studied under regional physiography.

Systematic Ontography. We may bring from the systematic study of physiography the conviction that a carefully arranged classification is worth the labor that its preparation has cost. The possession of a scheme of classification fosters the habit of referring newly found items to their proper place among their fellows. Items thus properly placed become much more valuable as elements of a well-coördinated series than when arranged empirically, as, for example, in the order of acquisition. Let us, then, take up ontography with the intention first of seeking out all manner of individual examples of responses made by organisms to their environment, and then of arranging the examples in a logical order with respect to certain general principles.

Thus arranged, similar items are soon generalized into categories, each one of which is described as a type, rationally explained in relation to the factor of physical environment that has produced it, and illustrated by specific examples. There can be little question that the subject will grow rapidly if it is thus cultivated.

It is to be noted that the classification here proposed deals with organic responses as effects, and that the physiographic causes therefore enter only secondarily. In systematic physiography it was the causes or controls that were classified, and the organic effects came in secondarily. Thus the threads of physiography and ontography run different ways; they are the warp and the woof whose close interweaving shows us the plexus of relationships that constitute the content of geography proper. On whichever series of considerations one may begin, he will be led over the whole subject if he follows the series to its end.

The chief writer on what I am here calling ontography is Ratzel, who has given an elaborate discussion of human conditions in relation to their surroundings in his " Anthropogeographie." The subject deserves an even more general and more systematic treatment than it there receives. This is not the place to set forth its many divisions, but I may be permitted to indicate briefly some of the more striking ones.

Every organic species may be considered as possessing certain structures, as carrying on certain habitual life processes, and as occupying certain habitats. Many of the structures, processes, and habitats are responses to physiographic causes; as such they enter into the content of ontography and indicate its three chief divisions. The light bones and feathers of flying birds are a response to their flight through the unsustaining air. The torpidity of many animals during winter is a response to climatic conditions. The division of a genus into several similar species on the different islands of an archipelago, as in the remarkable case of the cassowaries, is the response to the production of the islands by the partial submergence of a once continuous area. Numberless instances of these kinds might be cited.

Each of the three divisions of ontographic responses is of two kinds. The responses of one kind are brought down as inheritances from beginnings in an earlier time, maintained to-day because their physiographic controls are persistent; these are the more numerous (except, perhaps, as regards habitat). The responses of the other kind are of recent development, and are therefore the more immediate material of ontography. Those of the first kind are, however, only less directly pertinent to ontography, for they are the responses to the paleographies of geological time, and can be cut off from those of to-day only by an arbitrary separation.

The most important inherited responses are those determined by long persistent conditions of environment, such as are common to the physiographies of all ages. The habit of breathing oxygen, for example, universal among plants and animals, may be reasonably regarded as a response to the widespread occurrence of this gas, uncombined, but active in entering into combination with organic substances, whether it is dissolved in the ocean or free in the atmosphere. A great number of animals have a dorsal and a ventral portion, and an arrangement of skeleton and muscles with respect to the vertical line of gravitative force. This is evidently the result of living on an earth whose mass greatly exceeds that of the organism. Escape from responsibility to omnipresent gravity is possible only for those forms whose density equals that of the medium in which they live, as with many marine animals, or whose minuteness makes them the play of every passing breeze, as with innumerable microscopic organisms.

The difference of coloring of the ventral and dorsal surfaces is the response to the external source of the light by which the earth's surface is illuminated. The downward growth of plant roots and the upward growth of stems seem to be responses both to light and to gravity. All organs of sight, voice, and hearing appear to be responses to physical properties of environing media. The development of these organs has been slow, but, once developed, their profit has been so great that they have been persistently inherited wherever the conditions under which they were developed have endured. Sight is the means of taking notice of the bundle of strongest solar radiations directly incident upon or reflected to the organism; it is given up after being once acquired only by cavern animals living in total darkness. With the development of sight on the part of pursuers, there seems to have come the device of invisibility on the part of some of the pursued, as with those transparent marine organisms that so perfectly imitate the invisibility of the water in which they float. Hearing is the device for taking note of the air or water waves that are excited by some neighboring disturbance. Voice is rarer than hearing, and seems to be especially associated with the organs for air breathing in the higher vertebrates.

The list of responses of this kind, stated in association with their causes, would be very long before it was complete. There is to-day, unhappily, no place where the list is to be found on record. All the examples of responses given above may be connected by a continuous series of other examples with the most modern and commonplace illustrations of geographical relationships. It is only under the most arbitrary ruling that the immediate, simple, and manifest responses are considered pertinent to geography, while the remote, complex, and obscure responses are referred to some other science or neglected. The resort to talus crevices for shelter by beasts, and to caves under overhanging ledges by man; the use of mud by wasps, of twigs by birds, of wood, stone, or ice by man in building shelters; the housing of colonies of bank-swallows in sand-banks and of communities of Chinese in loess bluffs; the settlement of beavers on watercourses, of men at fords and harbor heads; the gathering of a manufacturing population about the water-power of modern Niagara, — all these are examples of the ontographical habit that organized beings have of taking advantage of their surroundings. All the content of economic or commercial geography, whose modern development is of so promising an interest, is but a manifestation of a special phase of this universal habit. It is of course desirable to select the simple, the manifest, or the "important" for exposition in elementary teaching, but the mature geographer can be satisfied with no such arbitrary bounds for his study.

The location of roads between neighboring villages on a plain, of highways over passes, of tunnels through mountains, of ship channels in harbors, offer many examples of responses to physiographic controls. The course of the paths beaten down by wild animals in the jungle, of the trails worn by cattle on their way to the rare watering places of arid regions, of the lanes followed by pillaging ants, offer equally good, although less conspicuous, examples of the same kind. The fleetness, the endurance, the venom of the animals of arid deserts have been instanced as striking examples of responses to an environment where the maintenance of life is difficult. The spirit of independence characteristic of the Swiss has been regarded by one writer as the cause of the maintenance of independent organization even in very small village communities; but it has lately been shown by Lugeon that the physiographic conditions inherent in valleys among lofty mountains are such that only small villages can be developed; and thus interpreted the spirit of independence must be regarded as the result of the ontographic subdivision of Swiss settlements into small villages. The growth and distribution of plants of different kinds, as influenced by rocky surfaces, composition of soil, depth and abundance of ground water — problems of modern ecology — are all of as strictly a geographical nature as is the distribution of human populations, and all may be treated systematically or regionally.

Ontography should be pursued even into forms of language and habits of thought. It is well known that mountaineers have a greater number of terms for peaks, ridges, and passes than are to be found among the inhabitants of plains; that dwellers in the deserts find need of giving different names to various kinds of sand dunes, while the people of a moister climate get along very well with only one. "The river of life" and "the valley of the shadow of death" are figures of a manifestly geographical origin, while "amount," "insulate," and "isolate" involve somewhat concealed geographical figures; but the origin of "rival," "derive," and "arrive" in a geographical root would be hardly noticed by any one but a philologist, yet these words certainly serve to show the importance that has long been given to the shore-line that divides land and water. In how many other ways language is ontographic, no one has yet learned. Fewkes has shown how largely the religious ceremonial of certain Indian tribes of the arid Southwest is based on climatic conditions;

thunderclouds and lightning flashes are conventionalized in religious decoration. We are perhaps prepared to ascribe the simple religions of pagan savages in greater or less degree to physiographic sources; but it seldom occurs to us that the position and the character of the heaven and the hell that are so closely bound up with the faith of many a Christian are of an equally physiographic origin. The ontographic half of geography will have abundant material when it is taken up for serious study by mature students.

The content and treatment of courses on regional ontography can be inferred from what precedes; they cannot be detailed here, for lack of space, but they would include all that is commonly understood by political and commercial (economic) geography, along with a greater emphasis on the relation of these effects to their causes than is commonly allowed.

Systematic and Regional Geography. Systematic geography is the orderly study of the relations between all the categories of physiography and ontography. Regional geography is the orderly study of all these relations that are manifested in a limited area. It would be premature to attempt now to state the order in which the categories of geography, thus understood, should be taken up. That is a matter which may well engage the attention of mature geographers for some time to come without exhausting the discussion that it deserves. My object in devoting a paragraph to the heading above is to reiterate the necessity of carrying forward mature geographical study toward the goal here indicated, as a practical means of improving the condition of geography in the schools. The elements of the subject most fit for presentation in the schools cannot be determined until the subject, as a whole, is more thoroughly discussed than it is to-day; and the presentation of the elements cannot be of the best while the teachers' knowledge of the subject is far below the capacity of their years, as is now generally the case.

Relation of Mature Geography to School Geography. In the foregoing pages I have considered the higher reaches of geographical study, because it seems to me otherwise impossible to make wise plans for the lower reaches; but in order that this paper shall not be concerned too largely with questions that may seem almost transcendental, it may close with what may be popularly called a few "practical suggestions," though, for my own part, I believe that all the suggestions here made have a practical bearing on school-teaching.

Better Preparation of Teachers. One of the most direct results that would follow from the more general pursuit of geography as a mature study would be the improvement in the preparation of teachers. This is an improvement that is, according to my experience, sadly needed. The acquaintance that I have made during a number of sessions of the Harvard summer course in geography has convinced me that teachers of geography are by no means informed up to their capacity even concerning the elementary aspects of their subject. The idea that most bays are merely drowned valleys is a surprise to many teachers; the idea that a river which exhibits the "normal" sequence of parts usually described is a mature river, and that young and old rivers must normally have a different arrangement of parts, is a novelty to them. The widespread distribution of species and the extended development of commerce have seldom been considered rationally as the responses to the opportunities for movement offered by a globular earth. The division of mankind into races has been usually treated empirically instead of as primarily a response to the continental division of the lands, and secondarily to important mountain and desert barriers. There is no lack of a conscientious desire nor of a capacity to learn; but the conclusion has been forced upon me that many of the teachers whom I have met have been intellectually half-starved in their previous study of geography; and yet the teachers to whom I refer may fairly be considered as of better than average quality, for the very reason that they have spent their summer vacations in trying to make themselves better still. It is not necessary to inquire here into the causes of their deficient training, but the remedy of the deficiency may be looked for with much confidence in the elevation of the general status of geographical study that would accompany its habitual treatment by specialists in colleges and universities. It is important to emphasize in this connection the need of a broader and higher preparation for teachers, so that they may know a good deal more than they have to teach, and thus gain the easy mind that characterizes the proficient expert. The recognition of geography by colleges and universities will, I believe, do more than anything else to realize this desirable end. The individual teachers who may read this paragraph will not be able alone to exert much pressure toward a change to a better order of things in this respect; but the organized body of teachers and superintendents that constitutes the National Educational Association can do much in this direction if they are once fully persuaded of the need of doing it.

Better Equipment of Geographical Laboratories. It is not so very long ago that physical and chemical laboratories were unknown even in the best secondary schools. The rapid development of observational and experimental teaching in these subjects makes me hope that the time may not be long distant when the best high schools will, as a matter of course, be provided with a room that may properly be called a geographical laboratory, and that this room will contain a good working collection of material for the observational study of geographical problems. Some such laboratories already exist. As strong an organization as that of the New York State Science Teachers' Association has favorably considered the appointment of a committee to prepare a report upon the proper equipment of a geographical laboratory; and a collection of materials for geographical teaching has lately been exhibited in Iowa. All this may fairly be taken as a hopeful sign of the times. When the grammar schools take up the idea of practical work in geography, the matter of laboratory equipment will become of so large commercial importance that publishers will enter the field; and the walls, racks, and tables of the schoolroom will not be so bare as they are to-day. But it is evident that the better preparation of teachers must precede the fuller equipment of laboratories, and that the teachers must first become familiar in their own training with the use of abundant laboratory materials, such as should be found in institutions of higher learning, but such as are to-day too generally wanting even there. Among the materials most needed are wall maps, not merely of climatic elements, of oceans, and of continents, but of typical features of continents also ; good pictures and maps of the actual examples by which type forms are illustrated, models of land forms, lantern slides in large variety, well-selected series of weather maps, plentiful large-scale topographical maps such as are published by our various governmental bureaus, and so on. Those who are known to have gathered together a laboratory equipment of this kind are frequently in receipt of letters from superintendents and teachers asking how the collection may be duplicated; and the letters are difficult to answer, because the collections have been brought together piecemeal. But it is a hopeful sign that dealers in lantern slides are getting out catalogues of subjects especially selected for the illustration of physical geography, and the coming decade will undoubtedly see further progress in this line. Yet here again it will only be a repetition of the experience in physics and chemistry, in botany and zoölogy, if the laboratory equipment for teaching geography in schools is largely developed in the more fully furnished laboratories of our colleges.

Replacement of Items by Generalities. The hopeful progress that school geography has made in the last twenty years is characterized largely by a diminution in the number of isolated empirical items to be committed to memory, and by a corresponding increase in the number of principles and generalizations to be intelligently studied. There is no reason for thinking that this progress has reached its limit; there is, on the other hand, much ground for believing that as the teachers, and the teachers of teachers, of geography gain a larger and broader understanding of the subject in its mature development, the replacement of the lonesome empirical item by the rational category, under which the items are grouped in good fellowship, will continue to increase beyond its present moderate measure. Items must still be presented in abundance, for young pupils need plenty of specific information; but the items should be introduced in illustration of the categories to which they belong rather than as sufficient unto themselves. In the earlier years of school study the items ought to precede the category and the generalization, for first progress must be largely inductive; but by the time that the high school is reached, and probably for a year or two sooner, deduction may be used to a significant extent; that is, the generality may be presented first, and the items may then follow as deductions from it instead of preceding as elements of its induction. Many teachers are already using the deductive method in teaching the distribution of wet and dry regions as determined by the relation of mountain ranges to the terrestrial wind system; and the success of the method there testifies to the success that may be expected in other cases where the mental processes involved are of a simple and safe order. This matter deserves more emphasis and amplification than I can give it here; suffice it to say, that geography will become more and more a scientific study in proportion to the use that is made of the fully developed scientific method, which always involves deduction along with induction in treating problems where any of the essential facts are unseen.

As geography becomes rational, the purely *memoriter* method will hold lower and lower rank in its lessons. Such a topic as state capitals, learned in old-fashioned days as a monotonous recitation, may be enlivened by an enlarged treatment in which many other facts than mere name are associated with the capital city. Many of these peripheral facts may be forgotten, but the central fact will remain more firmly fastened in the memory than if it had but one empirical attachment. So with state boundaries; the mere recitation of boundaries, apart from the geographical relations of the boundaries, is dull work; dull in the book, dull in the teacher, dulling in the pupil. Instead of having such matters learned as mere feats of unreasoning, unassociated memory, they should always be combined in a rational way with other things, so as to make for intelligence and to develop in the pupil the habit of looking for the meaning of things instead of dulling or even repressing that excellent habit. When rivers are taught only by name and place, it must be that little more is said about them in the text-book and known about them by the teacher. It is very questionable whether it is worth while to use any share of school hours in learning so slender a geographical item as the mere name of a river. It would be much better to omit altogether the account of a country that is thus treated in earlier school years, and to take it up for the first time when its general geography is treated in such a manner that mountains, climate, rivers, products, and cities are properly associated. It is well known that the best schools are making excellent progress in such lines as these; but it is not yet time to flatter ourselves that pressure toward such progress is unnecessary.

Geographical Facts must be made more Real. I recall the true story of a little girl learning her lesson in a question-and-answer geography. *Ques.* "Do the stars shine by day as well as by night?" *Ans.* "They do." The little victim was seen rocking herself to and fro, as if to give even a muscular aid to her memory, and repeating, "They do, they do, they do — they do, they do, they do." The theory of teaching has far outgrown such absurdities, but the practice has not, and we must continue to protest against them. I have in my own experience seen members of a class of teachers try to answer the question, "Why are the days longer than the nights in summer?" by recalling the words from some printed page instead of by attempting to visualize the plain facts of nature. The moral of this is that the facts of geography must be made more real than they can be by studying only the words of a book. All sorts of observational devices must be summoned to the aid of the printed page. The importance of this principle will be more fully realized when it is recalled that children can know much more than they can say; that their power of observation is far greater than that of expression; and that equality of these two powers is not always reached even in mature minds. In order, therefore, that the little that young pupils can say about geography shall be properly proportioned to their whole mental acquaintance with the subject, they should be provided with material, especially with material for observation, in much larger quantity than they are expected to recite, and in much more realistic form than mere names and definitions of unknown things.

Yet such is our servitude to conventional methods that we constantly fail to teach by things; the teaching by words is so much easier. Consider, for example, the rotation of the earth. What is simpler than to observe in an effective manner the elementary facts upon which this extraordinary conclusion is based? and yet how few school children ever learn these facts by well-directed observation before they learn the verbal statement of the conclusion printed in a text-book. There is no inherent difficulty in having the necessary observations made by school children at different hours during a two-session school day, — particularly that most significant observation, that on the second day the sun can be seen to approach from the eastern side of the sky the position that it had in the sky twenty-four hours before. Again, with latitude, in how many schools of our country are the necessary facts taught by observation before terms are introduced and definitions are memorized? Yet here induction is surely the safe and sound method. I am convinced that the vagueness of popular understanding about things of this kind comes from an over-emphasis of verbal definitions in school years, while facts easily observed are under-emphasized. It would be well to replace the names, diameters, and distances of the planets — matters of small geographical import in any case — with the observational proof that there are planets or other earths to be seen in the sky, and that young observers can easily follow them among the stars. All these errors of method would be reduced or excluded if the teacher were perfectly easy-minded on such problems; and the easy mind is best gained through practical acquaintance with observational methods such as should characterize the more mature stages of geographical study.

Geography indoors should be as largely as possible supplemented by outdoor observations by the pupils; yet I have found a great diffidence among teachers as to outdoor observation, even on their own part. They may have learned very well indeed everything that a book has to say about the origin of valleys, they may profess belief in the destructive work of the streams that flow through the valleys, yet when it comes to taking a class of children outdoors and using the examples of geographical forms such as the neighborhood affords, there is too often an undue hesitation. The teacher's lack of self-confidence would be greatly diminished if her own school work had been more liberally guided, and if her days of professional preparation had been spent in the consideration of a decidedly more mature phase of geography than that on which her skill is afterward to be exercised.

Laboratory Exercises must be Specific. With an increasing realization of geographical facts will come an increasing accuracy and definiteness of knowledge about them; and this will be a great advance, for at present geographical ideas are apt to be hazy. My recent experience with Harvard admission examinations in physiography leads me to fear that pupils in secondary schools do not look upon this division of geography as capable of clear statement, such as they know is expected in Latin and geometry. The answers to such a question as, "Describe and show by diagrams the development of a valley and its flood plain from a young to a mature stage," indicate too often a vagueness of understanding that is extremely disappointing, the more so in that it reflects imperfect methods of teaching as well as of learning. The correction of this difficulty is not to be secured by insisting on precise verbal recitations from the textbook any more than similar difficulties in geometry would be overcome by insisting on verbatim recitation of theorems. The needed reform will be found in realistic exercises in geography corresponding to blackboard demonstrations and graphic constructions in geometry. But it is essential that the realistic exercises in the geographical laboratory should be carefully planned, in order that they should be closely pertinent to and illustrative of the text, and that they should call for accurate thinking and performance on the part of the pupil. The elaboration of a series of fifty or more such exercises in physiography is greatly needed; and those who have experience in work of this kind should be encouraged to give specific account of their methods in some of our educational journals, or, better yet, to prepare laboratory manuals in which explicit directions shall be given as to outfit and process. Among the simplest and at the same time most valuable exercises of this kind for the chapters on land forms, mention may be made of the drawing of outline maps from block diagrams of typical forms. The block diagram being an oblique bird's-eye view, and the map being seen from directly overhead, there is just enough difference between the two to require intelligence in changing the diagram to the map, and yet not to demand more than elementary geographical knowledge and simple manual skill. Maps thus prepared should always be accompanied by a descriptive and explanatory text.

Laboratory exercises should not be limited to physiography; they should be devised for all divisions of geography, for the devices by which the reality of geographical items and the truth of geographical principles are to be impressed on young pupils cannot be compressed into a text-book. They are the peculiar responsibility of the teacher and the laboratory. Just as the breadth of opportunity in a university increases with the abundance of its funds, so the variety of devices by which school children are aided in their studies will increase with the liberality of a teacher's preparation. One of the most promising of all methods towards escape from enslavement to verbal texts is the cultivation of a body of higher learning and the encouragement of teachers to acquire larger and larger parts of it, however elementary their later teaching may be.

The Rational Element and the Disciplinary Value of Geography increase Together. It is very likely that one of the reasons for the general omission of geography from the list of college studies is that it does not, as ordinarily treated, afford sufficient intellectual discipline to gain a place among other subjects whose value in this respect is held to be greater. It is noticeable, however, that physical geography has a more general representation in colleges than any other branch of the subject. Hence it may be expected that other branches will gain a place as fast as they prove themselves worthy of it by showing that they may be as disciplinary and profitable as physical geography is. However this may be, there can be no question that the disciplinary side of geography deserves more emphasis than it has usually received in school-teaching. The remarks made above as to the rank of the " tier of counties " question are pertinent to this paragraph also. There is every reason to hope that, commensurate with the development of a body of higher learning in geography, there will be an increase of the disciplinary value of school geography. Let it not be forgotten that good progress in this direction is already being made. The intelligent use of weather maps, for example, is a case in point. No wide-awake teacher of physical geography to-day can be content without using a series of actual weather maps in illustration of weather types; the exercises that may be based on these maps are disciplinary in a high degree. The records shown on the maps may be given a real value by comparing them with local school records. The discussion of the map records offers admirable training in induction, generalization, and deduction. Exercises may be made of a very practical kind, training the hand in construction and the mind in expression. The knowledge thus gained leaves little room for credulity in a subject where credulity has long flourished. How different all this is from the old-fashioned empirical description of weather changes! Studies of this kind inculcate a really scientific method; they make for intelligence as against mere docility; they aid in opening a broad understanding of the processes of nature. And yet, accessible as weather maps are to-day, simple as are the methods of their practical disciplinary use, it is rarely the case that they are used to their full value, even in high schools, much less in grammar schools.

Every good thing that may be said about weather maps may be said with equal value about studies of land forms, provided the study is based on laboratory material as appropriate to the needs of this division of geography as weather maps are to the other. But while weather maps are very generally available, models of land forms are relatively rare and expensive. The most disciplinary results in this division of the subject must therefore wait until models are made and used in greater number in college teaching, until the teachers of teachers become familiar with the models during their college course, until the intending teachers of geography are made acquainted with a good variety of typical models in their own high-school and normal-school course, and until the models themselves are demanded for the future geographical laboratories in high schools and grammar schools. It is largely for the National Educational Association to say whether our great-grandchildren or our grandchildren or our children shall be the beneficiaries of such improvements as better laboratory equipment will aid in bringing about.

Certain Parts of Geography are not presented in Good Sequence. With the various improvements already noted, we may expect to see a better sequence established in the order of introduction of certain elements of geographical study. As the rational method is further developed, there will be a decrease in the number of things that are arbitrarily introduced on account of their asserted importance, even though they must be given an empirical instead of an explanatory treatment. It may be going too far to say that this class of topics will ever be as completely excluded from geography as it is from such purely deductive studies as geometry and algebra, where no one pretends to introduce a theorem or a principle before it can be logically approached by a series of preparatory steps; yet it should be noted that in subjects such as physics and chemistry, where inductive and deductive methods are combined, the sequence of topics is logical — hardly less logical than in mathematics. It is not customary to make an empirical statement concerning entropy in an elementary text-book on physics, however important the principle of entropy may be to the more advanced student. Again, a careful selection of things to be studied is noticeable in the modern books on botany and zoölogy, although this method involves the omission of all mention of many plants and animals that were formerly included in more comprehensive texts on natural history; this is because a real knowledge of a few things that may be studied observationally is held to be of greater value than a nominal knowledge of a greater variety of things.

Certain divisions of geography seem to be in need of a critical examination as to the logical sequence of their parts. There are at present too many instances in which the introduction of a topic seems to be more indicative of a desire on the part of the author of the text-book to display his knowledge than of a judicious estimate as to what is appropriate to the pupils who are to use the book. The treatment of the tides sometimes offers illustration of this difficulty. It is as if the author felt bound to make mention of certain facts or theories because of a supposed public or scientific demand for them, even though they may involve principles which the pupils who are to use the book cannot be expected to have learned. The theory of the general circulation of the atmosphere and the effect of the earth's rotation on the course of the winds afford similar instances of the attempted introduction of relatively advanced explanations into elementary texts, because of a supposed conventional or popular demand for them. A way out of the difficulty in these cases may be found by touching very lightly on the more involved parts of the explanation, and by replacing the more difficult parts with a selection from the abundant matters of fact which can be easily apprehended, and which go far toward forming a sound basis on which real explanation may be based in later years.

The flattening of the earth at the poles is given an exaggerated importance by being included in the first account of the globular form of the earth. The explanation of the seasons is often attempted before the pupil has gained any inductive basis for the capital fact of the earth's annual revolution around the sun. Latitude and longitude are as a rule introduced too early. The methods of finding latitude that are sometimes taught include data empirically provided by the teacher. Rearrangement is needed in all such cases if geography is to become largely disciplinary.

Distribution of the Divisions of Geography in Secondary Schools. General descriptive geography, which constitutes the body of the subject in the years before the high school, need not be subdivided according to the scheme of classification of the divisions of geography given above. It makes a beginning in all of the divisions. As at present conducted, good progress toward better methods is everywhere noticeable, but there is still room for a greater development of systematic, explanatory, and realistic treatment, as has been indicated on the preceding pages. Change in the order of parts is not seriously demanded; change in the proportion and emphasis of parts is going on in a wholesome manner, and largely in the direction here advocated. Among the results of these changes is a possible saving of time by the omission of unnecessary details, so as to permit the introduction of elementary systematic physiography in the last year before the high school. There are many reasons for this change, which I have elsewhere set forth at some length; but it may be here noted that the change would have the beneficial result of presenting some of the outlines of physiography to a greatly increased number of school children ; and if the subject really has the educational value that is claimed for it, this would be a national blessing.

High-school geography should be of two kinds. If the feeding lower schools do not provide a course in elementary physiography, then the high school must provide it, and by preference in an early year. If no special course on regional physiography, such as the physiography of the United States or of North America, is offered, then the systematic course should give as many specific illustrations of its categories as possible. In the necessary absence of a course on systematic ontography in secondary schools, ontographic responses should be liberally introduced in connection with their physiographic controls. If, on the other hand, the high school is served by lower schools in which a good course on elementary physiography has been given by well-trained teachers to well-trained pupils, then the high school has manifestly two courses to offer. Regional physiography of the United States may be introduced in an early year so as to precede a later course in commercial geography, in advanced systematic physiography, or (should the subject approve itself when tried in colleges) in systematic ontography.

The early regional course should be liberally broadened by including mention of features like those of the home country, but situated elsewhere in the world, and by abundant mention of organic responses to local physiographic features. It could thus be made disciplinary and educative in a high degree. The course on commercial geography is, if well founded on earlier physiographic courses and well developed in view of systematic ontography, destined to take an important place in the schools ; but it must carefully avoid the danger of introducing too much empirical detail.

The course on more advanced systematic physiography could, if placed in a late high-school year, reach a stage of relatively rigorous discipline, for the inculcation of which more serious books, as well as better-prepared teachers and better-equipped laboratories, would be needed than are to be found to-day. If these suggestions seem visionary, one need only look at the extraordinary progress made in the last fifty years of our school history to count upon the realization of all these schemes in the next fifty. It goes without saying that the courses thus instituted should be so well taught that they could be built upon by still more advanced work for those students who go to college.

Educational Value of Geography. There are two different standards by which the value of a school study may be measured. One is the so-called practical standard of use in life work ; the other is the more intellectual standard of capacity for enjoyment. There is no danger that this practical nation, with its marvelously rapid material progress, will fail to give due prominence to the practical side of school studies ; there is some danger that the intellectual side may in a measure be neglected, from the very magnitude of our material prosperity.

The practical side of geography is best taught in a well-developed course of commercial geography placed in the later years of the high school, after earlier courses on general geography in the grades, and a course on elementary physiography either in the grades or in an early high-school year, as above suggested. Here, if anywhere, is it important that the principles of systematic ontography, developed as they ought to be by collegiate and university study, should find application. If commercial geography is to gain the place it deserves, it is of vital importance that it should be rationally taught as that part of regional geography in which man, the trader, responds so marvelously to his environing conditions. We have only to regret that the keen practical intelligence by which the successful American of to-day has so greatly magnified the share taken by our country in the commercial geography of the world, finds so many analogies in the habits of the predatory species of the lower animals and in the behavior of the robber barons of feudal times. This suggests that commercial geography should be paralleled by a good course in ethics.

The intellectual profit of geography comes from the enjoyment that every active mind finds in really seeing the facts of the world about him. The great pleasure that has come to thousands of us, young and old, in recent years from the observational study of birds demonstrates the capacity, hitherto latent in that respect, of the average person for a high measure of simple, unpractical intellectual enjoyment. A corresponding pleasure is in store for those who learn, see, and appreciate the. abundant facts and relationships of geography, many of which must enter into the experience of every life. If the possibility of making a happy adjustment of one's self to his environment comes with the fuller appreciation of the order of nature, so much the better. It is evident, however, that the enjoyment of the opportunities of mature life will not have been increased for those whose school geography was merely a study of words in a book, or of names on a map, rather than of the meaningful facts of the world. Hence the intellectual no less than the practical value of geography will depend largely on the excellence with which it is taught.

III

THE PHYSICAL GEOGRAPHY OF THE LANDS

The most important principles established in physical geography during the nineteenth century are that the description of the earth's surface features must be accompanied by explanation, and that the surface features must be correlated with their inhabitants. During the establishment of these evolutionary principles, exploration at home and abroad has greatly increased the store of recorded facts; the more civilized countries have been in large part measured and mapped; the coasts of the world have been charted; the less civilized continents have been penetrated to their centers. This harvest of fact has been an indispensable stimulus to the study of physical geography; yet it cannot be doubted that the spirit which has given life to the letter of the subject is the principle of evolution, — inorganic and organic. This is especially true of the geography of the lands.

The century has seen the measurement of higher peaks in the Himalayas than had been previously measured in the Andes. The Nile has been traced to its source in the lakes of equatorial Africa, verifying the traditions of the ancients; and the Kongo has been found to cross the equator twice on its way to the sea. Facts without number have been added to the previous sum of knowledge. But, at the same time, it has been discovered that the valleys of mountain ranges are the work of erosion; that the product of valley erosion is often seen in extensive piedmont fluviatile plains; that waterfalls are retrogressively worn away until they are reduced to the smooth grade of a maturely established river; and that interior basins are slowly filling with the waste that is washed in from their borders to their floors. Here are explanatory generalizations involving, yet going far beyond, matter of direct observation. Such generalizations in geography correspond to the recognition in astronomy that planetary movements exemplify the law of gravitation; they are the Newton as against the Kepler of the subject.

The sufficient justification of the demand that has now arisen for explanation and correlation in the study of land forms is found in the repeated experience that until an explanatory description of a region can be given, one may be sure that some of its significant elements pass unnoticed; and until the controls that it exerts on living forms are studied, one may be confident that its geographical value is but half measured. A sentence from Guyot's "Earth and Man" may here be taken as a guide: "To describe, without rising to the causes, or descending to the consequences, is no more science than merely and simply to relate a fact of which one has been a witness." There could hardly be devised a more concise and searching test of good work than this quotation suggests. The causes, in so far as the physical geography of the lands is concerned, have been learned chiefly through the study of geology; yet it does not by any means follow that all geologists are possessed of such knowledge of these causes as will constitute them geographers. The consequences have been learned through the study of evolutionary biology; yet a distinct addition to the usual discipline of biology is required in order to apprehend its geographical correlations. The limited space allowed to this article will require that further consideration of the consequences be excluded, in order to give due consideration to the causes.

One of the preparatory steps in the century's advance was taken by the German geographer, Ritter, who, near the beginning of the century, advocated a new principle that may be illustrated by the change in the definition of geography from "the description of the earth and its inhabitants" to "the study of the earth in relation to its inhabitants"; but advance beyond this beginning was for a long time obstructed by certain ancient beliefs. Theological preconceptions as to the age of the earth and the associated geological doctrine of catastrophism, although attacked by the rising school of uniformitarianism, were then dominant. They gave to the geographer a ready-made earth, on which the existing processes of change were unimportant. Furthermore, the belief in the separate creation of every organic species led to the doctrine of teleology, which maintained the predetermined fitness of the earth for its inhabitants, and of its inhabitants for their life work. All this had to be outgrown before geographers could understand the slow development of land forms and the progressive adaptation of all living beings to their environments. Yet the beginning that Ritter made was of great importance, and it would have led further had it not happened that for many decades professors of geography in Europe brought chiefly a historical training to their chairs, to the almost entire neglect of physical geography. In the last thirty years there has been a reaction from this condition in Germany and France, but Italy, with many professors of geography in her universities, still for the most part follows historical methods.

In the victory of the uniformitarians over the catastrophists began the fortunate alliance of geography with geology. Instead of believing in cataclysmic upheavals and in overwhelming floods, Playfair and other exponents of the Huttonian school taught that mountains were slowly upheaved and slowly worn down. The simplicity of Playfair's argument finds excellent illustration in the often-quoted passage regarding the origin of valleys.

> Every river appears to consist of a main trunk, fed from a variety of branches, each running in a valley proportioned to its size, and all of them together forming a system of vallies, communicating with one another, and having such a nice adjustment of their declivities that none of them join the principal valley either on too high or too low a level; a circumstance which would be infinitely improbable if each of these vallies were not the work of the stream that flows in it.

Descriptions of valleys should always recognize the share that rivers have had in eroding them, or else the "nice adjustment of their declivities" may pass unnoticed.

It should be noted, however, that to this day explanation is not always allowed an undisputed place in the treatment of the lands, however fully it is accepted as appropriate to the presentation of other divisions of physical geography. But the manner in which explanation is extending over a larger and larger part of the subject gives assurance that the geographers of the coming century will insist upon a uniformly rational treatment of all divisions of their science. The active phenomena of the earth's surface first secured explanation; it has long been considered essential to explain as well as to describe such phenomena as the winds of the air and the currents of the ocean; indeed, this is now so habitual that many geographers who may object to the explanation of a peculiar kind of a valley as a trespass upon geology will nevertheless demand an explanation of rainfall and tides, although these truly geographical subjects are manifestly shared with physics and astronomy. Land forms of very elementary character, like deltas, or of rapid production, like volcanoes, have had to give some account of themselves all through the century; but it was not for many years after the announcement of Playfair's law that the erosion of valleys by the rivers that drain them came to be regarded as a subject appropriate to a geographical treatise. Only in the later years of the nineteenth century has the fuller treatment of this beautiful subject been attempted; even now much of it remains to be developed in the twentieth century.

The treatment of physical geography will be much more even, to the great advantage of its students, when explanatory description is applied to all its parts. The alluvial fans at the base of arid mountains should be accounted for as well as the dunes of deserts. The fault cliffs of broken plateau blocks and the weathered cliffs of retreating escarpments deserve to be considered as carefully as the wave-cut cliffs of coasts; the essential differences of these forms are reached most easily through their explanation. The varied sculpturing of a mountain slope may, in time, come to be as well understood as is now the erosion of a simple valley in a low plain.

One of the most notable elements of the century's progress is the increasing breadth of view gained as explanatory descriptions are extended further and further over the geographical field. At first explanation was given to various individual features, item by item; now it is recognized that an appropriate place must be provided for all kinds of land forms in a comprehensive scheme of physiographic classification. Many instances of the earlier stage might be given, beginning with examples from the works of Humboldt, the acknowledged leader of scientific explorers in the opening of the nineteenth century. His attempts, more or less completely successful, to explain the facts that he observed, as well as to correlate life with environment, may be traced all through his writings; but his "Cosmos" (1845) did not reach a careful discussion of land forms, although it entered so far into an explanatory treatment as to consider the formation of mountain ranges.

Innumerable examples of isolated facts and special explanations, unrelated to a comprehensive scheme of physiographic classification, might be taken from the reports of exploring expeditions and of geological surveys; from books of travel and from geographical and geological journals with which the nineteenth century has filled so many library shelves; but lack of space will prevent mention of all sources, save a few treatises in which the accumulated knowledge of their time is summarized. Such a work as Mrs. Somerville's "Physical Geography" (1848) gives in the early pages a brief, general consideration of land forms, and then enters at once upon the areal description of the continents; later pages present a short outline of the features of rivers, and then the rivers of the world are taken up. This is as if a text-book of botany should pass rapidly over the structure and classification of plants, and devote most of its pages to the flora of different regions. Again, Klöden's compendious geography includes a volume on "Physical Geography" (3d ed., 1873), in which much material is gathered; but the treatment is very uneven, as is natural in the absence of a good scheme of classification. Glaciers receive much attention, but valleys are rather curtly dismissed; deltas are elaborately described, but little space is given to other forms assumed by the waste of the land on the way to the sea. Ansted's "Physical Geography" (5th ed., 1871) contains an abundance of facts, but many of them are of a kind which could better be presented on a map than in verbal form. Many pages are devoted to statistical statements, from which no student can gain inspiration for further study.

A decided advance over earlier books in the way of rational or explanatory treatment is found in the works of Peschel and Reclus; it is to the former that a reaction against the historical treatment of geography in Germany is largely due, while the latter is to be credited with an enlarged attention to the detail of land forms; but the books of neither of these authors recognize the systematic evolution of land forms. The same may be said of various other treatises which approach, but do not yet reach, the ideal that seems to be in sight. One of the chief responsibilities of the geographer — the description of landscape — cannot be fully met by students who accept the principles set forth in these books as their guides; for, in spite of the increasing attention given to the lands in modern books, and in spite of the greater number of forms recognized, the combination of all forms in a well-organized whole is not yet accomplished.

It seems to have been against the empirical method of such books as Ansted's that Huxley protested in the preface to his "Physiography" (1878), urging its replacement by a more educative method. He wrote:

I do not think that a description of the earth, which commences by telling a child that it is an oblate spheroid, moving around the sun in an elliptical orbit, and ends without giving him the slightest hint towards an understanding of the ordnance map of his own country, or any suggestion as to the meaning of the phenomena offered by the brook which runs through his village, or of the gravel pit whence the roads are mended, is calculated either to interest or to instruct. . . . Physiography has very little to do with this sort of Physical Geography. My hearers were not troubled with much about latitudes and longitudes, the heights of mountains, depths of seas, or the geographical distribution of kangaroos or *Compositæ*. . . . I endeavored to give them . . . a view of the "place in nature" of a particular district of England — the basin of the Thames — and to leave upon their minds the impression that the muddy waters of our metropolitan river, the hills between which it flows, the breezes which blow over it, are not isolated phenomena, to be taken as understood because they are familiar. On the contrary, I endeavored to show that the application of the plainest and simplest processes of reasoning to any one of these phenomena suffices to show, lying behind it, a cause, which again suggests another, until, step by step, the conviction dawns upon the learner that to attain to even an elementary conception of what goes on in his own parish, he must know something about the universe; that the pebble he kicks aside would not be what it is and where it is unless a particular chapter of the earth's history, finished untold ages ago, had been exactly what it was. . . . Many highly valuable compendia of Physical Geography, for the use of scientific students of that subject, are extant; but in my judgment most of the elementary works I have seen begin at the wrong end, and too often terminate in an omnium-gatherum of scraps of all sorts of undigested and unconnected information, thereby entirely destroying the educational value of that study which Kant justly termed the "propædeutic of natural knowledge."

Here we find clear recognition of the need of introducing a consideration of causes, just as was urged by Guyot; and furthermore a recognition of the need of linking together in their natural relations all the items which constitute the content of the subject. It may, however, be contended that the attempt to combine in a single course of study the elementary principles of chemistry and physics, of geology and astronomy, along with those of physical geography is not practicable from an educational point of view; such a combination will not secure either the clear knowledge or the strong discipline that can be derived from systematic courses in two or three of these subjects, presented separately. Text-books like Hinman's "Eclectic Physical Geography" and Mill's "Realm of Nature," in both of which a broad range of other than geographical subjects is covered, do not seem to-day to be in so much favor as those books which attend more closely to the true content of our subject. Indeed, with respect to physical geography, considered from the scientific and educational point of view, a report on College Entrance Requirements, published by our National Educational Association, presents the best definition and outline of the subject that has yet appeared. It advises the omission of irrelevant matter, however interesting such matter may be in itself. The principles of physics and the succession of geological formations with their fossils, the classification and distribution of plants and animals, must be taught elsewhere; but much profit may be had from terrestrial phenomena by which the principles of physics are illustrated, and from the consequences of past geological changes in determining present geographical conditions, and especially from the physiographic controls by which the distribution of organic forms is determined.

The general scheme under which all land forms may receive explanatory description must consider chiefly the movement and erosion of the earth's crust. Deformation offers a part of the earth's crust to be worked upon. Various destructive processes of erosion work upon the offered mass, and the streams, with their transported waste, follow the depressions carved in the surface. So important is the element of erosion, and so leading is the part played by rivers in erosive work, that McGee would gather all land forms under a classification determined by their drainage systems. Others have preferred a classification based, first, on peculiarities of structure as determined by accumulation and deformation, and, secondly, on the progress of erosion; but in either scheme the erosive work of rivers is so important that a sketch of the progress of the physical geography of the lands towards a systematic classification of its items may well follow the order in which valleys have been explained, branching off, as occasion may require, from the leading theme of rivers that flow under a normal humid climate to special conditions of erosion under an arid or a frigid climate. The progress which has made the physical geography of the lands what it is to-day is more the work of geologists than of geographers; and the chief reason for this is the indifference of many geographers to the physical side of their subject, — an indifference that was undoubtedly favored by the cultivation of historical geography in continental Europe, and by the acceptance of the traveler or explorer as a full-fledged geographer in Great Britain. In the United States it is only in the latter part of the century that the physical geography of the lands has gained a scientific standing, and the advantages that it now enjoys are geographical grafts upon a geological stock.

The emancipation of geology from the doctrine of catastrophism was a necessary step before progress could be made towards an understanding of the lands. The slow movements of elevation and depression of certain coasts in historic time were of great importance in this connection. Studies of geological structures at last overcame the belief in the sudden and violent upheaval of mountain chains, which, under the able and authoritative advocacy of Élie de Beaumont, held a place even into the second half of the century. But even when it came to be understood that mountains and plateaus have been slowly upheaved, it still remained to be proved that the valleys and cañons by which they are drained were produced by erosion, and not by fractures and unequal movements of elevation.

Advance was here made on two lines. Along one, a better understanding was gained of the forms producible by deformation alone; along the other, sea currents, floods, and earthquake waves, to which the earlier observers trusted as a means of modifying the forms of uplift, were gradually replaced by the slow action of weather and water. Processes of deformation were found to act in a large way, producing massive forms without detail — broad plains and plateaus, extensive domes, simple cliffs, and rolling corrugations; and thus it was learned that the varied and detailed forms of lofty mountain ranges and dissected plateaus must be ascribed almost entirely to the processes of erosion. But it should be noted that in exceptional instances land forms initiated by deformation, so recently as to have suffered as yet only insignificant sculpture, may exhibit much irregularity. The most striking example of this kind, an example of the very highest value in the systematic study of land forms, is that afforded by the diversely tilted lava blocks of southern Oregon, as described by Russell.

Turning now to the second line of advance, it is noteworthy that so keen an observer as Lesley insisted, as late as 1856, that the peculiar topographical features of Pennsylvania, which he knew and described so well, could have been produced only by a great flood. But the principles of the uniformitarians were constantly gaining ground against these older ideas; and after the appearance in England of Scrope's studies in central France and of Greenwood's polemic little work on " Rain and Rivers " (1857), victory may be said to have been declared for the principles long before announced by Hutton and Playfair, which, since then, have obtained general acceptance and application.

Yet even the most ardent uniformitarians would, in the middle of the century, go no further than to admit that rain and rivers could roughen a region by carving valleys in it; no consideration was then given to the possibility that, with longer and longer time, the hills must be more and more consumed, the valleys must grow wider and wider open, until, however high and uneven the initial surface may have been, it must at last be reduced to a lowland of small relief. The surface of such a lowland would truncate the underground structures indifferently; but when such truncating surfaces were noticed (usually now at consider-able altitudes above sea level, as if elevated after having been planed, and therefore more or less consumed by the erosion of a new system of valleys), they were called plains of marine denudation by Ramsay (1847), or plains of marine abrasion by Richthofen (1882). To-day it is recognized that both subaërial erosion and marine abrasion are theoretically competent to pro-duce lowlands of denudation; the real question here at issue concerns the criteria by which the work of either agency can be recognized in particular instances. In the middle of the century not only every plain of denudation but every line of escarpments was held by the marinists to be the work of sea waves; and it was not till after a sharp debate that the bluffs of the chalk downs which inclose the Weald of southeastern England were accepted as the product of ordinary atmospheric weathering, instead of as the work of the sea. Whitaker's admirable essay on "Subaërial Denudation," which may be regarded as having given the victory in this discussion to the subaërialists, was considered so heterodox that it was not acceptable for publica-tion in the *Quarterly Journal* of the Geological Society of Lon-don, but had to find a place in the more modest *Geological Magazine* (1867), whose pages it now honors. So signal indeed was this victory that, in later years, the destructive work of the sea has been not infrequently underrated in the almost exclusive attention given to land sculpture by subaërial agencies. Truly, the sea does not erode valleys; it does not wear out narrow lowlands of irregular form between inclosing uplands, as was maintained by some of the most pronounced marinists in the middle of the century; but it certainly does attack continental borders in a most vigorous fashion, and many are the littoral forms that must be ascribed to its work, as may be learned from Richthofen's admirable "Führer für Forschungsreisende" (1886). As this problem cannot be further considered here, the reader may be at once referred to the most general discus-sion of the subject that has yet appeared, in an essay on "Shore-line Topography," prepared by Dr. F. P. Gulliver as a thesis in his graduate work at Harvard University (1896), and published in the *Proceedings* of the American Academy in 1899.

At about the time when the sub-aërial origin of valleys and escarpments was being established in England, the explorations and surveys of our western territories were undertaken, and a flood of physiographic light came from them. One of the earliest and most important of the many lessons of the West was that Playfair's law obtained even in the case of the Grand cañon of the Colorado, which was visited by the Ives expedition in 1858. Newberry, the geologist of the expedition, concluded that both the deep and fissure-like cañon and the broader valleys inclosed by cliff-like walls " belong to a vast system of erosion, and are wholly due to the action of water." Although he bore the possibility of fractures constantly in mind and examined the structure of the cañons with all possible care, he " everywhere found evidence of the exclusive action of water in their formation." This conclusion has, since then, been amply confirmed by Powell and Dutton, although these later observers might attribute a significant share of the recession of cliffs in arid regions to wind action. In a later decade Heim demonstrated that the valleys of the Alps were not explicable as the result of mountain deformation, and that they found explanation only through erosion. By such studies as these, of which many examples could be given, the competence of rivers to carve even the deepest valleys has been fully established; yet so difficult is it to dislodge old-fashioned belief, that Sir A. Geikie felt it necessary to devote two chapters in his admirable " Scenery of Scotland " (1887) to prove that the bens of the Highlands were not so many individual upheavals, but that the glens were so many separate valleys of erosion; and as able an observer as Prestwich, a warm advocate of the erosion of ordinary valleys by their rivers, maintained (1886), with the results of our western surveys before him, that fissures were probably responsible for the origin of the deep and narrow cañons of the Colorado plateau.

The tumultuous forms of lofty mountains, "tossed up" as they seem to be when viewed from some commanding height, are, in by far the greater number of examples yet studied, undoubtedly the result of the slow erosion of the valleys between them; but it should not be forgotten that regions of very recent disturbances — as the earth counts time — may possess strong inequalities directly due to deformation.   The tilted lava blocks of Oregon have already been mentioned.   The bold forms of the St. Elias Alps, also described by Russell, are regarded by him as chiefly produced by the tilting of huge crustal blocks on which erosion has as yet done relatively little work.   An altogether exceptional case is described by Dutton, who says that on the margin of one of the "high plateaus of Utah a huge block seems to have cracked off and rolled over, the beds opening with a V and forming a valley of grand dimensions." "Rift valleys," or trough-like depressions produced by the down-faulting of long, narrow, crustal blocks with respect to the bordering masses, are occasionally found, as in eastern Africa, where the "Great Rift valley" has been described by Gregory.   Trough-like depressions of similar origin, but much more affected by the degradation of their borders and the aggradation of their floors, are known to European geographers in the valleys of the Saône and of the middle Rhine.   But no rift valley, no depression between the tilted lava blocks, resembles the branching valleys that are produced by the erosive action of running water.

Thus far, while much attention had been given to the work of rivers, little or no attention had been given to the arrangement of their courses.   It seems to have been tacitly assumed that the courses of all streams were consequent upon the slope of the initial land surface.   The explicit recognition of this origin, indicated by the provision of a special name "consequent streams," was an important step in advance due to our western geologists.   The discovery soon followed that rivers have held their courses through mountain ridges that slowly rose across their path; the rivers, concentrating the drainage of a large headwater region upon a narrow line, cut down their channels as the land was raised.   This idea first came into prominence through Powell's report on the Colorado River of the West (1875), in which he gave the name "antecedent" to rivers of this class.   He believed that the Green river, in its passage through the Uinta mountains, was to be explained as an antecedent stream.   Much doubt has, however, been thrown upon this interpretation. Other accounts of antecedent rivers have been published, and to-day the Green is not so good a type of antecedence as the Rhine below Bingen, the Meuse in the Ardennes, or several of the Himalayan rivers in the gorges that they have cut through the youngest marginal ridges of the range.

Rapidly following the establishment of these two important classes of valleys came the recognition of the very antithesis of antecedent rivers in those streams which have grown by headward erosion along belts of weak structure, without relation to the initial trough lines. To these the term "subsequent" has been applied. It is frequently in association with streams of this class that drainage areas are rearranged by the migration of divides, and that the upper waters of one river are captured by the headward growth of another. This is accomplished by a most beautiful process of inorganic natural selection, which leads to a survival of the fittest and thus brings about a most intimate adjustment of form to structure, whereby the more resistant rock masses come to constitute the divides, and the less resistant are chosen for the excavation of valleys. Many workers have contributed to the solution of problems of this class, notably Heim, in his studies of the northern Alps (1876), and Löwl, who showed that in folded mountain structures of great age the original courses of streams might be greatly altered through the development of new lines of drainage (1882). A valuable summary of this subject is given by Philippson in his "Studien über Wasserscheiden" (1886). The extraordinary depredations committed by the waxing Severn on the waning Thames have recently been set forth by Buckman. The trimming of side branches from the slender trunk of the Meuse has been recognized in France. Many remarkable instances of stream captures have been found in the Appalachians, where the opportunity for the adjustment of streams to structures has been exceptionally good. Hayes and Campbell have, on the other hand, emphasized the importance of drainage modifications independent of the growth of subsequent streams on weak structures, but governed by a slight tilting of the region, whereby some streams are accelerated and their opponents are retarded.

It should be noted that the proof of the adjustment or rearrangement of drainage marks a victory for the uniformitarian school that is even more significant than that gained in the case of the antecedent rivers ; for in one case a growing mountain range is subdued by the concentrated discharge of a large drainage area, but in the other case the mountain slowly melts away under the attacks of the weather alone on the headwater slopes of the growing valleys.

The reason why all these studies of land carving are of importance to the geographer is that they greatly enlarge the number of type forms that he may use in descriptions, and that they recognize the natural correlations among various forms which must otherwise be set forth in successive itemized statements. The brief terminology learned in early school days, somewhat enlarged by a more mature variety of adjectives, is usually the stock of words with which the explorer tries to reproduce the features of the landscapes that he crosses, and as a result his descriptions are often unintelligible ; the region has to be explored again before it can become known to those who do not see it. The longitudinal relief of certain well-dissected coastal plains, or the half-buried ranges of certain interior aggraded basins, may be taken as examples of forms which are easily brought home and familiarized by explanation, but which commonly remain remote and unknown under empirical description.

It may be urged that in many geological discussions from which geography has taken profit, consideration is given to form-producing processes rather than to the forms produced. This was natural enough while the subject was in the hands of geologists ; but geographers should take heed that they do not preserve the geological habit. The past history of land forms and the action upon them of various processes by which existing forms have been developed, are pertinent to geography only in so far as they aid the observation and description of the forms of to-day.

Further illustration of the growing recognition of form as the chief object of the physiographic study of the lands is seen in the use of the term "geomorphology" by some American writers ; but more important than the term is the principle which underlies it. This is the acceptance of theorizing as an essential part of investigation in geography, just as in other sciences. All explanation involves theorizing. When theory is taken piecemeal and applied only to elementary problems, such as the origin of deltas, it does not excite unfavorable comment among geographers. But when the explanation of more complicated features is attempted, and when a comprehensive scheme of classification and treatment, in which theorizing is fully and frankly recognized, is evolved for all land forms, then the conservatives recoil, as if so bold a proposition would set them adrift on the dangerous sea of unrestrained imagination. They forget that the harbor of explanation can only be reached by crossing the seas of theory. They are willing to cruise, like the early navigators, the empirical explorers, only close along shore, not venturing to trust themselves out of sight of the land of existing fact; but they have not learned to embark upon the open ocean of investigation, trusting to the compass of logical deduction and the rudder of critical judgment to lead them to the desired haven of understanding of facts of the past.

One of the bolder explorers of the high seas of theory is Powell, who defined in the term "base-level" an idea that had long been more or less consciously present in the minds of geologists, and which has been since then of the greatest service to physiographers. Powell and his followers, especially Gilbert, Dutton, and McGee, have consistently carried the consequences of subaërial erosion to their legitimate end in a featureless lowland, and have recognized the controlling influence of the base-level during all the sequence of changes from the initial to the ultimate form. It is not here essential whether such a featureless lowland exists or ever has existed, but it is absolutely essential to follow the lead of deduction until all the consequences of the theory of erosion are found, and then to accept as true those theoretical deductions which successfully confront the appropriate facts of observation. Only in this way can the error of regarding geography as a purely observational natural science be corrected. Following the acceptance of the doctrine of base-levels came the method of reconstituting the original form initiated by deformation, as a means of more fully understanding the existing form; for only by beginning at the initial form can the systematic sequence of the changes wrought by destructive processes be fully traced and the existing form appreciated. This had often been done before in individual cases, but it now became a habit, an essential step in geomorphological study. Naturally enough, the terms of organic growth, such as young, mature, old, revived, and so on, came to be applied to stages in the development of inorganic forms; and thus gradually the idea of the systematic physiographic development of land forms has taken shape. This idea is to-day the most serviceable and compact summation of all the work of the century on the physical geography of the lands. It recognizes the results of deformation in providing the broader initial forms on which details are to be carved. It gives special attention to the work of destructive processes on these forms, and especially to the orderly sequence of various stages of development, recognizing that certain features are associated with youth, and others with maturity and old age. It gives due consideration to the renewed movements of deformation that may occur at any stage in the cycle of change, whereby a new sequence of change is introduced. It gives appropriate place not only to the forms produced by the ordinary erosive action of rain and rivers, but to the forms produced by ice and by wind action as well; and it coördinates the changes that are produced by the sea on the margin of the land with the changes that are produced by other agencies upon its surface. It considers not only the various forms assumed by the water of the land, such as torrents, rapids, falls, and lakes, appropriately arranged in a river system as to time and place, but also the forms assumed by the waste of the land, which, like the water, is on its way to the sea. In a word, it lengthens our own life, so that we may, in imagination, picture the life of a geographical area as clearly as we now witness the life of a quick-growing plant, and thus as readily conceive and as little confuse the orderly development of the many parts of a land form, its divides, cliffs, slopes, and water courses, as we now distinguish the cotyledons, stem, buds, leaves, flowers, and fruit of a rapidly maturing annual that produces all these forms in appropriate order and position in the brief course of a single summer.

The time is ripe for the introduction of these ideas. The spirit of evolution has been breathed by the students of the generation now mature all through their growing years, and its application to all lines of study is demanded. It is true that the acceptance of inorganic as well as of organic evolution is often implied rather than outspoken; yet evolution is favorably regarded, as is proved by the eagerness with which even school boards and school-teachers, conservatives among conservatives, hail the appearance of books in which the new spirit of geography is revealed. In the last years of the century, the school-books most widely used in this country have made great advance in the explanatory treatment of land forms. Tarr's physical geographies and Russell's monographic volumes on the "Lakes," "Glaciers," "Volcanoes," and "Rivers" of North America, all presenting land forms in an explanatory rather than an empirical manner, have been warmly welcomed in this country. Penck's " Morphologie der Erdoberfläche " (1894), although largely concerned with the historical development of the subject, presents all forms as the result of process. De Lapparent's " Leçons de géographie physique " (1886) treats land forms genetically; and a second edition of the book is called for soon after the first. " Earth Sculpture," by James Geikie (1899), and Marr's " Scientific Study of Scenery " (1900) carry modern ideas to British readers. The books of the coming century will certainly extend the habit of explanation even further than it has yet reached.

This review of the advance of the century in the study of land forms, the habitations of all the higher forms of life, might have been concerned wholly with the concrete results of exploration, as was implied in an earlier paragraph. Travels in the Far East of the Old World, or in the Far West of the New, have yielded facts enough to fill volumes. But such a view of the century has been here replaced by another, not because the first is unimportant, — for it is absolutely essential, — but because the second includes the first and goes beyond it. Not the facts alone, but the principles that the facts exemplify, demand our attention. These principles, founded upon a multitude of observations, are the greater contribution of the closing to the opening century in the study of the forms of the land.

IV

THE TEACHING OF GEOGRAPHY

The Physical Basis of Descriptive Geography

Several valuable books on methods of teaching geography
have been written in recent years, giving emphasis to various
matters of importance. One shows that the home district should
furnish the first examples on which geographical descriptions
are based, and that a knowledge of the examples should precede
a definition of the terms by which they are named. Another
calls for an extension of physical geography at the expense of
political geography. A third justly maintains the need of introducing fresh material from various sources in addition to the
brief statements of the text-book. We have among our New
England teachers successful exponents of all these principles,
and the newer text-books are to a moderate extent adjusted to
them. But there is another principle that has not, it seems to
me, received sufficient consideration. This is the importance of
the more advanced study of physical geography by all teachers
of geography in any of its branches, even by those who have
only elementary school work to carry on.

All good teaching requires that the teacher should possess a
sound knowledge of his subject, beyond the limits of his class
work. Live teaching excites questions from the scholars, and
thus leads to verbal excursions from the immediate subject in
hand. When well managed, such excursions are of great value,
because they spring from the pupil's desire, and not merely from
the teacher or the text-book. Good answers to such questions
can come only from the background of knowledge in the teacher's
mind. They cannot be supplied by pedagogical methods, or by
text-books, or by uncandid pretensions on the part of the teacher,
so soon apparent to his class. I have no sympathy whatever
with the belief sometimes encountered that methods will make

up for want of knowledge; or with the more prevalent impression that knowledge will replace method. Of the two, knowledge is undoubtedly the more important and should come first; but a proper understanding of both is the desideratum. In this paper I wish to consider one element of the knowledge that teachers of geography should acquire; namely, the kind of information required in order that the facts and principles of physical geography may be clearly presented. I choose this subject because of the increasing attention given in recent years to physical over simply descriptive and political geography, and also because the text-books and hand-books to which teachers are accustomed to refer do not seem to me to present the principles of physical geography in a satisfactory manner.

Let me illustrate by some specific examples. Take four great waterfalls. The lofty fall of the Yosemite valley leaps in a slender current over the precipitous wall of that extraordinary chasm and plunges sixteen hundred feet before its scattered mists gather again for further flow as a stream. The world-renowned Niagara descends in great volume over a limestone ledge into the gorge below. The Shoshone falls, on the river of that name in Idaho, drop from one gorge into a deeper one over a sheet of lava. The rapids known as the first cataract of the Nile roll and toss over ledges of crystalline rocks that interrupt the generally smooth course of that great river. With which of these shall we compare the falls of the Merrimac, by whose power the looms of Lowell are driven? Shall the comparison be made as to height, as to volume, or as to origin and physical conditions? The latter is the only natural ground for geographical comparison.

The Yosemite fall leaps into a deep valley which its waters had no share in making. The stream did not produce the cliff over which it falls. A little notch has been cut at the top, but the cliff as a whole was ready-made for the stream to fall over. Niagara has indeed cut more than a notch. It has cut a gorge seven miles long in the limestone capping, all the way back from the bluffs at Lewiston; but the river did not make the bluffs where the falls started. The bluffs are of much greater age than the river. Its current was turned over them long after their form was gained. They are not river-made, nor are they like in origin to the cliffs of the Yosemite. The Shoshone falls are river-made through and through. The river there began a new course on a flat lava plain. As its channel was deepened, the harder lava flows were cut through near the surface and the looser materials beneath were then worn out more quickly. The falls began where the waters dropped from one level to another. Since they first appeared, the gorge has been lengthened backward many miles, like a ditch cut at the end. The river found the country featureless, and in the little advance that has as yet been made in carrying away the lava plain and reducing it all to sea level, the water has by its own action made its falls. The rapids of the Nile are of quite another class. On either margin of the valley of the Nile may be seen the horizontal edges of bedded rocks which once stretched all across the valley from side to side. The river at first flowed over their surface, then cut its channel down through them, and at a certain depth unexpectedly encountered a buried ledge of hard crystalline rocks ; a portion of an old buried land, and probably an old hilltop, which, by reason of its height above the buried lowlands thereabouts, was first encountered by the down-cutting river. This obstacle produced the rapids ; they are not steep, because the slope of the old buried hill is gentle, as far as it is uncovered.

The falls of the Merrimac at Lowell, at Manchester, and at various other points ; the falls of the Connecticut at Turner's Falls, at Holyoke, and elsewhere, are closely related to the cataracts of the Nile. It is not true that the whole of the old country on which the ancestors of the Merrimac and the Connecticut once flowed has been buried, but the valleys of the ancient rivers have been buried even to a depth of three or four hundred feet by a filling of clay, sand, and gravel that was washed into them. These deposits covered many a rugged ledge and rocky spur on the slopes of the ancient valleys, and when the rivers at a later time turned to cleaning out the clogging of gravel and sand, they lighted unawares, like the Nile, on various buried ledges. The Merrimac thus developed its falls at Manchester, or perhaps I should say, Manchester developed at the falls ; and the same way again with Lowell, Lawrence, and many busy villages. The Connecticut likewise uncovered various buried ledges, at nearly all of which there are now manufacturing towns and cities. New England enterprise has known how to take good advantage of these river accidents. Now it is perfectly true that the water power developed in a river of a given volume, falling a certain height, is the same whether the fall originates in one way or another. The height of the falls is indeed an important matter; but in teaching about rivers, the teacher must not stop with numerical statistics. He must appreciate something also of the physical history of the rivers. These alone give basis for physical comparisons.

I make no attempt here to explain in full these different kinds of falls, nor to state the reasons for the conclusions just outlined. That would require deliberate study. My object is simply to illustrate what is meant by the physical basis of descriptive geography, and to show by immediate example what kind of information on such subjects every teacher of geography should possess in order to answer the questions from his class with enlivening fullness and to place the principles of the subject clearly before his pupils. Perhaps the teacher might not have in mind the particular examples of river development here presented; but they nevertheless illustrate the kind of knowledge that he should gain. They serve also to illustrate in a definite way what kind of geographical information a person should gain if he studies at a university with the idea of preparing himself to teach geography. The examples cited are taken directly from among many others that constitute the subjects of elementary lectures to college students. I believe that a large fund of this kind of information should be in mind before one need give much attention to methods of teaching geography.

It must be borne in mind that it is not supposed for a moment that every teacher who has learned such facts as these would forthwith teach them to his classes. They are not his weapons, but his armor. They constitute the foundation of his knowledge, on which he can build explanatory stories in his many times of need. He may, for example, be telling his class how it happens that the capital of New Jersey is located at a certain point on the Delaware, where there are rapids at the head of tide water. He may refer to the growth of Rochester in western New York at the powerful falls of the Genesee. He may wish to mention the many towns and cities of the West that have grown up at the falls and rapids of rivers; as, for example, Louisville, Minneapolis, Grand Rapids, Sauk Rapids, Rapid City, and Great Falls. He may wish to explain why water-power towns are absent in certain parts of the country, and comment on the consequent distribution of manufacturing indus-tries. In all this he will find satisfaction, and his class will find entertainment and bright instruction, if he addresses them as one who is well informed beyond the page of his text-book and who knows more than he tells.

The teacher of geography, if he would be successful, must not stop with the elementary explanations that are given in the text-books of the day. He must be sufficiently informed to expound the text of the books. If his class reads of the recession of Niagara and the consequent future draining of the level plain now drowned under lake Erie, let him emphasize the story by telling of the broad lacustrine plain of the Red river of the North, laid open by the melting away of an icy barrier over Canada that not long ago held up an extended sheet of water where there are now rich wheat fields. When his pupils read of the erosion of valleys, of which all the books now make some mention, he must tell of the cañon of the Colorado as an in-stance of a vast erosive work. But he must also point out that, however great a work the excavation of this cañon is, it is only the beginning of the mighty task that awaits the river. The cañon is only the well-marked waterway, down which must be carried all the stupendous mass of the wasting plateaus on either side. The teacher should, when illustrating the vast work of erosion, turn from a cañon, however deep, and look at the record of a much greater destructive work near at home in the plateau of New England, — the reduced remnant of a once great mountain system, now laid low. Here is completed the work that the Colorado has only just begun. If the class learn, as they should, of our Atlantic coastal plain as a portion of the sea-bottom lately raised and laid bare, and thus exposed to erosion by rain and rivers, let them learn also of old lowlands, now raised to highlands, and thus exposed to a renewed attack from the agents of erosion. This again may be illustrated at home, for our New England plateau was a lowland when it was worn down from its once mountainous height, and our existing valleys have been excavated only since the lowland was subsequently elevated to a higher position, as a gently inclined plateau, with its southern and eastern margin at the seashore, thence rising inland until it reaches an altitude of fifteen or sixteen hundred feet in the northwestern part of Massachusetts.

Although some of these statements may seem novel, yet they fall directly in line with others of simpler nature that are not only asked for from teachers, but taught to young pupils. One of the most earnest advocates of a rational and observational method of teaching geography urges that the surface of the earth should be described as that of a living organism. He teaches the washing of soil down slopes and the likeness of little deltas to great alluvial plains, even as first steps in elementary classes. Such a beginning is excellent, but we need a legitimate extension of this beginning. I have sometimes ventured to ask a teacher questions about rivers and valleys, such as those just considered; and it usually appears that they are unfamiliar matters. Sometimes they are regarded as irrelevant; as belonging to geology perhaps, but not germane to geography, — the "description of the earth's surface." It matters little under which of these confluent sciences such subjects are catalogued; but I protest emphatically against the belief that they are beyond the necessary equipment of teachers of geography. When sand dunes are described, the most elementary teaching of geography does not hesitate to explain their origin by the action of the wind. Volcanoes are seldom mentioned without some reference to their origin by eruption of lava and ashes from a deep-seated source. Few text-books nowadays omit to state that valleys are cut out by streams; but they seldom carry the same explanation to its legitimate end and mention regions where the valleys have widened so far as to consume the hills and reduce the region to a worn-out lowland, a lowland of denudation. Yet the relics of such lowlands dominate our geographical forms to-day. An old lowland of denudation now uplifted and dissected is a widespread element of the topographical features of our Atlantic slope. No just comprehension of our geography can be gained without some appreciation of it. What I lament is that while a beginning of physical explanation is made, it is not carried out systematically and seriously, either in the text-book or in the preparation of the teacher. The text-book falls short of its duty in failing to present clearly enough the real meaning of geographical forms, and in falling behind the progress of geographical science in such matters. The teacher too often halts with the text-book. Many of the principles and explanations are not too difficult for children to understand. They are readily accepted when presented deliberately and in gradual succession, with vivid and correct illustrations.

More attention to physical geography is called for by all the leading writers on the improvement of geographical teaching. Further study in this direction is therefore needed by those who are preparing to teach. More attention to the home district is demanded even in the earliest classes. Better training is therefore needed in the appreciative recognition of the meaning of the physical features of the land immediately about us; for wherever the teacher goes, his geographical laboratory is in the fields about him, and he must be prepared to solve its problems and present them properly to his classes.

While dwelling on the importance of a better understanding and teaching of physical geography, I do not wish to underrate the value of the rational teaching of political and descriptive geography. Yet it does seem that until the features of the earth's surface, the fundamental subject of geography, are well understood in their natural relations, only an artificial meaning can attach to their introduction into descriptive geography. It is excellent to read of the introduction of fresh material by teacher and pupil into the descriptions of one country or another. I plead for the same freshness and originality of illustration in teaching about the physical features of the earth, and I believe that in the coming years a much greater share of time will be allotted to this division of the subject than is now the case.

The change that lies in the future for physical geography has already overtaken the biological sciences. The brief descriptions of numerous species of plants and animals, which children once learned under the name of Natural History, are now replaced by the careful examination of a few forms, chosen to illustrate broad homologies. Physics and chemistry are also in process of liberation from text-book control, and no well-equipped school where these subjects are taught is now without its laboratory, in which simple experiments may be performed by the pupils as a means of really learning the fundamental principles of these sciences. The beginnings of a change to a laboratory method in teaching geography are seen where sand and clay models are used; but this beginning leaves nearly everything to be accomplished. This is so partly because the means of illustration are inadequate and cease in the higher classes, where they ought to be extended; and partly because the principles that should guide the preparation of illustrations of one kind and another are as a rule so little considered.

I must repeat, in order not to be misunderstood, that many subjects and illustrations, which are here referred to as essential for the preparation of the teacher, should not be known in order that they should be taught, unless in the higher classes of the grammar schools or in high schools. They should be known in order to give the teacher a reserve of strength with which to overcome the difficulties of his elementary work. Let me again take up some specific illustrations.

I have already referred to the brief mention that is made in most text-books of valleys, and sometimes of land forms in general, as the product of erosion of a once larger land mass, the waste of the older land having been carried by rivers to the sea. But where do we find the deserved mention of the forms assumed by the waste of the land on its way to the sea? The land waste encumbers the mountain sides, forming vast talus slopes. In dry climates the waste extends broadly from the base of the mountains over the lowlands in gently inclined plains. The waste often clogs rivers, choking up their valleys. Where a side stream brings an overload of waste into a main stream, it builds a delta at the junction, just as the main stream builds a delta at its mouth in standing waste. Indeed, sometimes the side stream chokes up the main river and converts it into a linear

lake, like lake Pepin, a beautiful expansion of the upper Mississippi. I have told children of this lake ; they like to hear of it,
and its meaning is not beyond their comprehension. In direct
contrast with the case of lake Pepin is that in which a fully
loaded main stream builds up its flood plain with the excess of
land waste that it brings down from its head waters. The flood
plain thus rises faster than the plains of the small side streams ;
and these, not having enough land waste with which to build up
their plains, must fill their valleys with water up to the level of
the main stream, and thus form lakes. River flood plains should
be regarded simply as the temporary resting place of the excess
of waste washed into the river by the decay of the land. Being
composed of fine materials, they are fertile regions, as in the
broad bottom lands of our great Mississippi. Yet they may be
traced back by gradual changes to the stony talus slopes of the
mountain sides, with which they are in many ways correlated. A
whole series of interesting comparisons may thus be introduced,
each one having for its object the illustration of some otherwise
barren recitation of geographical names. Just as events of human
history serve to impress the relations of geographical forms on
a child's memory, so the events in the history of the forms themselves have a great value as mnemonics. They give a sense of
reality where the text-book gives little more than words.

Teachers have sometimes asked me where they should go to
find illustrations of the kind here named. No one book contains
them. Nothing but continual searching, reading, and studying
will secure them.

What to Avoid in Teaching Geography

The subtitle given to this part of the essay expresses, as
briefly as possible, a few general considerations that I wish to
present in contrast to those discussed above. The theme there
was, in effect, What should the teacher know ? The conviction
that he should be informed far beyond the limits of his teaching
was illustrated by bringing forward a number of specific examples
of the kind of facts that I think every live teacher should have
in mind. I shall now consider the opposite side of the question,

—What is unnecessary, or unimportant, or injurious, in geographical teaching? The undesirable elements encountered, to a greater or less degree, in teaching geography are divisible into superfluities and errors. I shall consider a number of these in order.

In the first part, the chief emphasis was given to the importance of storing the teacher's mind with facts and explanations on the physical side of geography; not that other sides should be overlooked, but that I found space for illustration of only one division of the subject. It should now be repeated, as was then said, that knowledge of this kind is not to be discharged by the teacher in a flood, overwhelming the pupils before they can appreciate it, but that it should be presented only when called for, piecemeal, slowly, and chiefly in the way of illustrating or explaining subjects that are more directly pertinent to the usual routine of the study. It is perhaps not often that teachers of geography should be advised to husband their information; and yet I can believe that a well-taught beginner might overtask his class with an exuberance of illustration, making the geographical diet too rich for his pupils. An excess of precision is also to be avoided; minuteness of knowledge is not to be expected in children. Strong, broad descriptions are preferable, in which the chief elements of form, area, climate, resources, and population are linked together in a natural and effective way, and emphasized by illustration, whereby the essentials are easily remembered by pupils of ordinary ability. Over-zeal, leading to excess in quantity or precision, is characteristic of first efforts, when the facts of the subject have not taken positions proper to their relative importance. There is a want of perspective in such teaching; matters of detail are brought forward and confused with larger matters of much greater importance; but with practice this mistake disappears. It is not a mistake of the kind we are apt to suffer from; and I mention it chiefly because it might at first naturally follow from the acceptance of the advice already given, to the effect that teachers should be widely informed before beginning to teach.

In contrast with this, I may mention a mistake of quite another kind, and probably the most serious of the difficulties that now afflict geography. This comes with teachers whose preparation is insufficient. They feel their weakness. They see necessity of strengthening their teaching, but not possessing the elements of strength in themselves, they try to borrow, and then too often add difficulty instead of value to their instruction. It is for this reason that there is so much useless memorizing in the study of geography. It must be very stupid work to both teacher and pupils. A teacher well informed on the subjects introduced briefly in the text-book would feel choked if he had no opportunity of bringing in appropriate side-illustrations and explanations. A teacher not well informed has no sufficient fund of illustrations with which to refresh the tiresome facts of the page, and therefore they alone constitute the subject of his teaching. Too great stress is then necessarily laid on verbatim recitations, for there is nothing else with which to occupy the time. This is a sad difficulty, and it attends poor teaching in all subjects. I know of a case in which a teacher of history, feeling that his class was not doing work enough, required each student to memorize the names and dates of the popes, in order to give more body to the class work, — a poverty-stricken expedient. I have been told of another case in which a class in geology had to recite from Dana's "Manual of Geology," word for word, — a most shocking misuse of that excellent compendium. Is there, however, any subject in which this error is so common as in geography? It is not alone the fault of the teachers, as many text-books are evidently prepared with the idea that every word is to be learned. How, except by rote, could a scholar make intelligent report of such a paragraph as this, extracted from a well-known English text-book of physical geography:

The Danube receives a large number of tributaries, of which the most important are, on the right, the Isar, Inn, Raab, Drave, Save, Morave, and Isker. On the left are the Altmühl, Regen, Waag, Gran, Theiss, Temes, Aluta, Sereth, and Pruth. Many of these are large streams with other important tributaries. The Danube drains upwards of 300,000 square miles of country.

Pages could be filled with quotations of that kind; yet to what do they lead? If it be conceived that any one should ever wish to memorize facts so unimportant, let them be learned from the map, where they are more expressive than in a printed list. If it is important for the tributaries of all rivers to be stated outside of the maps, place them in tabular form, and utilize the space thus gained by inserting something worth remembering about one or another of the examples, — something that is not better presented in maps or tables. It is sad to think of children being perplexed with such stuff as is given in the above quotation, yet the book from which it is taken reached a fifth edition only twenty years ago.

It should be noticed that the correction of this error does not lie so much in the substitution of one text-book for another, as they are now constituted, but in the improved use of books by giving less attention to the unimportant paragraphs. This correction is in the hands of the teacher; he must, from his own knowledge, aided by wall maps and the school library, relieve the monotony of text-book teaching. If I should condense into the fewest words the intent of this part of my argument, they would be: " Avoid verbatim recitations; put something of life and nature into teaching."

Between the two extremes of superabundance and barrenness, a middle path must be selected by experience and good judgment. Facts that appear isolated must be bound together in their true relations; trivial matters must be lightly passed over; matters of importance, in which the class finds difficulty, must be kept in hand and expounded till familiar. The best results of such a method can be gained only by a judgment so good and an experience so long that nothing but the truly professional spirit of teaching, entered on as a life work, will insure the improvement that we all desire and strive for.

Lest some might misinterpret what I have just said, to mean that all memorizing of the facts of geography should be omitted, I must state explicitly that in geography, as in spelling, there seems to be no way of avoiding a large amount of memorizing, if the pupil is to have a sufficient fund of information with which to extend his own experience in later life. The labors of English spelling can be lightened by grouping words of similar derivation, as I used to learn them in my " Scholar's Companion "; but I cannot imagine any method by which the labor of learning to spell can be entirely done away with. So with geography; it is essential that every child should learn the names and positions of the larger geographical elements; but to learn them simply as recitations of words printed in a book is a fatal mistake. Several years must be included in the geographical course, during which the world has to be gone over and over, with more care and thoroughness at each repetition, before the familiarity that we all should have with it can be gained. This labor cannot be omitted, but it may be lightened by judicious illustration. Still, there is no royal road. I have no recipe by which all but the easy parts of the subject can be omitted and yet have the pupil well taught. Wide information on the part of the teacher and attentive effort on the part of the pupil are essentials to success; but the labor thus thrown on both need not be dull and stupefying.

How shall the teacher know what need not be taught? What are the unessentials in the routine work of geographical teaching? We may learn something here by asking one another a series of questions that children may have to learn at school. The small value of some of the questions is not so well indicated by our having forgotten the answers as by our not caring if we have forgotten. It is natural enough that many things learned at school should be forgotten afterward when the mind is occupied with other things. It must not be inferred that Latin and Greek should not be studied in school because they are afterward forgotten; we are sorry enough if we cannot translate from the ancient languages when we meet them in words or passages. But this is not the case with the names of the branches of the Danube. Who cares whether he can at call repeat them in order? He may know that the Inn comes in from the Alps and the Theiss from the plains of Hungary; the others may be looked for on a map if they are wanted. It is this indifference to the facts of routine geography that tells us of their small value. It is the easy recovery of them, when desired, that makes the memorizing of their names so useless. They appear clearly enough on the maps. Leave them there till wanted, and select from the many a few about which something more than a name can be given; not that name and incident both need to be learned by heart, but that the incident supplied by the teacher serves as a little barb to hold the fact in the memory. If the teacher, with all his preparation, has no incident or illustration pertinent to the facts, let them pass hardly noticed; if they are so unimportant that he knows nothing more than their name and place, as given on the map, and as any one might know them, in spite of his having given time to careful preparation on the various sides of geographical study, then omit them and turn the attention of the class to something that he can tell more about. It may be that the choice of subjects made by the teacher will not always include the most important places and subjects, but it should at least include the things he can best teach; and, as such, the things of the highest value to the class under his instruction.

The incidents, illustrations, and explanations to which I have repeatedly referred should be introduced not only to help the pupil's memory but also to increase the reality of the subjects that are studied. Take care that the names learned from the text or the map represent places and things, and not words or lines. We have all heard of the man who confessed that his chief recollection of Austria was as a red patch on the map hanging on his schoolroom wall. Last summer I heard of a similar example. A little boy was watching his aunt draw and color a map of the United States; when Ohio was reached and a blue tint given to it the boy exclaimed, "Ohio is not blue; it is green." Emphasis in his teaching had been given to the unrealities of geography.

There is now less reason than existed formerly for urging the postponement of astronomical and mathematical geography till the later years of study. Teachers generally agree that a beginning must not be made on the unseen, but on the visible facts and forms of the school district. Still, even young pupils may at an early age become familiar with the earth as a globe, with the idea of passing over its great rotundity and reaching one land after another. It is not this so much as the ideas of poles and equator, latitude and longitude, that may well be delayed till the general distribution of lands and oceans is learned. The seasons, the noon altitude of the sun, the varying length of the day and night, are subjects that can be best taught by observation. Let the members of the class be required to contribute records for a school journal, to be kept continuously for a number of years. Let them thus accumulate facts from which they may discover for themselves the dates of high and low sun, of long and short days. Do not rob them of the opportunity of discovering simple correlations, as open as these are to elementary investigation. Let them study out the phases of the moon. From the records thus obtained, ask a class if they can tell how much farther away the sun is than the moon. If the school is on tide water, let it be the duty of the members of the class in rotation to detect the time and height of high and low water, and correlate these changes with the movements of the moon and sun. Let them thus learn the important lesson that the world is wide open to their individual study, and that great reward follows the attentive use of their opportunities. The quantity of facts secured may be in the end less than those recited in a few days, parrot fashion, from an unmeaning page; but the quality of the facts learned by individual observation more than makes up for their lessened quantity.

Directly in connection with the above is the suggestion that technical terms should be delayed until the ideas that they represent have become familiar from observation or description. Leave definitions, which always represent generalizations, until the mind is familiar with the facts that call for comparison and definition. Avoid the appeal to authority as justification for any statement unless good reason goes with it. Do not often introduce personal authority in elementary teaching. Do not say, "In Ganot's treatise on physics, as edited by Professor Atkinson, the following remarks are made on this head"; or, "Mr. R. H. Scott gives the following statements from Mohn's treatise." All these names are excellent sources for quotation; but young pupils should not be troubled by the interruption of the ideas that such sentences cause. This appeal to authority tends to subordinate exactly the spirit of rational independence that should be encouraged. If the statements that are to be quoted are not self-explanatory, their explanation, but not their authors, should be given.

Avoid hobbies. Do not be too methodical, too logical. Do not try to compress the variety of nature into rigid and artificial concepts, types, and diagrams. Generalization is, of course, an important aid in expressing the recurrence of a series of similar phenomena; but when it becomes more complicated than the phenomena themselves, it is of no value. For example, "Land may rise from and above the river bed; then there will be two slopes within the two slopes which form the river basin, and, consequently, there will be two lines which bound the two slopes that rise above the river bed." It is hardly worth while to go roundabout so far in order to say that rivers may include islands between their banks! An excess of logical demonstration of elementary matters will not infrequently leave the teacher behind the class. Children do not care much for argument, but prefer acquisition, and are willing enough to accept anything within reason. Vivid description and appropriate explanations need no enforcement by a constructed and visibly logical method.

Be careful of hasty generalizations. While the smaller continents possess simple slopes from their mountain axes to the sea, the largest of the land areas contains so great an interior basin that it should not be overlooked even in the most elementary presentation of continental form. Do not jump too rapidly to conclusions. It is not safe to say, "The lack of long and broad slopes is the plain reason why Africa remains for the greater part in barbarism." Do not over-emphasize trifles. Leave to rival book agents the trivial dispute about the particular lakelet in which the Mississippi rises. The general plan of a book is a thousand times more important than its citation of the latest census reports. Grasp and teach the spirit, not the letter.

I shall add but a few paragraphs on geographical errors. Most of these are found in the divisions of geography that are concerned with explanation of phenomena; that is, in meteorology and oceanography. In these subjects the text-books are nearly always behind the times.

The subject of tides is too difficult to introduce into early teaching except in a descriptive way. The usual account of the tide opposite the moon is nearly always defective. A case may be quoted in which an author rather incredulously says, " There is a great pulsation of the entire ocean, called the tides, which is supposed to be the yielding of the water of the globe to the attraction of the moon on the side nearest the moon, and the holding back of the land from the water, on the side farthest from the moon"; and then adds naïvely in a footnote, " This explanation has never seemed quite clear to me in presenting it to children, and it seems to me possible that science has not yet fully explained the tides." If the explanation, as given, really represented the present state of scientific investigation, the footnote would be well justified. It is useless to attempt to explain the tides without at least an elementary knowledge of mechanics. They may be described and good reasons discovered for referring their rise and fall to the joint action of the moon and sun; but their explanation had better be omitted than travestied.

The winds are seldom adequately treated in the ordinary text-books. It is generally said that the air around the equator is heated and rises; then the colder air on either side rushes in to fill the vacuum thus formed. This is as if one should say a lever rises under a weight to fill the vacuum caused by the ascent of the weight. The general circulation of the atmosphere is referred to the differences of temperature between the equator and poles; and, on this basis, a tyro in physics will predict the occurrence of low pressure around the equator and high pressure about the poles; yet in the charts of atmospheric pressure often introduced into the recent books on physical geography, the pressure around the poles is found to be low and not high. Any independent pupil would be justified in rejecting a theory which was apparently so soon discountenanced by the facts.

Rain is nearly always wrongly explained. It is referred to the mixture of two masses of air, both saturated with vapor, but of unlike temperatures, — an inadequate and extremely unlikely process; or it is referred to the cooling of ascending currents of warm lower moist air by the cold of the upper regions, or by the cold of the mountains on their path; but the main cause — the spontaneous cooling by expansion of ascending currents — is either half-mentioned or altogether omitted. The easy belief in the artificial production of rainfall by explosions naturally follows from the imperfect teaching of this subject.

The influence of the earth's rotation on the course of the winds, the ocean currents, and rivers is hardly ever properly presented. There is always either the implication or the direct assertion that bodies moving east or west are not deflected from their course, and that the turning to the right or left, in one hemisphere or the other, is found only in motions along the meridian. This is all wrong. The deflective effect of the earth's rotation is independent of the direction of motion. It is as great on a motion to the east or west as to the north or south. It is least near the equator, where it is generally referred to; and greatest near the poles, where its action is seldom mentioned. The usual reference to the lagging of the trade winds, as they move toward the equator and reach latitudes of faster eastward rotation, would, if logically carried out, warrant the belief that friction with the earth's surface prevents the lagging of the winds, and that their oblique course must be accounted for independently of the earth's rotation. The reader may, if he wishes, see the disastrous consequences of this argument in Laughton's "Physical Geography of the Winds and Currents," an English work of good standing, but one in which this particular subject is topsy-turvy.

How shall the earnest teacher avoid such errors and superfluities as I have mentioned? There is only one way, and that is, to study and think untiringly. It is indeed unfortunate that a simpler prescription cannot be given to overcome the difficulty that many a teacher would gladly be rid of. Something will be done by the introduction of better and better text-books and works of reference; more will be done if school boards can be prevailed upon to give teachers sufficient leisure to consider and plan out their heavy tasks. But the burden of the work of improvement lies with the teachers themselves.

V

THE EXTENSION OF PHYSICAL GEOGRAPHY IN ELEMENTARY TEACHING

The attempt is made in the elementary teaching of geography to give the pupil some idea of the form of various land areas. The chief means of accomplishing this large task are ordinarily found in a brief chapter treating of descriptive or of physical geography, and introducing certain terms, such as plain, plateau, mountain, valley, river, bay, cape, and so on. Various land areas are afterwards described in accordance with this terminology.

It is my contention that the definitions of the terms thus introduced are not, as a rule, well founded on a clear comprehension of the essential principles of physical geography, and that in too many cases they have little to do with physical geography, being simply descriptive, and not physical at all. To make this clear I shall illustrate what seems to me the important difference between these divisions of the subject.

Descriptive geography attempts to characterize the infinitely varied forms of the land in an absolute manner, without reference to their origin, and with little consideration of their natural relations. A cañon is simply a narrow valley, not a young valley. It is represented as differing from other valleys simply in width, not in age. A valley is a depression of greater or less width between adjacent higher masses ; its origin, by deformation of the earth's crust, or by the destructive agencies of the weather, is often omitted as if irrelevant, or as if it should not be mentioned because the subject in hand is not called geology. A bay is an indentation of the coast line ; its production by the drowning of a valley is unmentioned.

Physical geography attempts to arrange the forms of the land in a natural order, dependent on their evolution under the combined action of internal constructive forces and external destructive forces. The cañon of the Colorado is then represented not simply as a deep and narrow valley; it is narrow because it is still so young that it has not yet had time to grow wider; it is deep because of its precocious development, resulting from the great height of the plateaus in which it is incised. The valley of California is taken as the type of a large valley of deformation, produced by the uplifting of mountains on either side; the valley of the Hudson, or of the Ohio, might be presented as the type of a valley of erosion, both of these being wider than the cañon of the Colorado because they are older, and less deep because the land in which they are eroded is not so high as the plateaus of Arizona. Certain irregularities of the seacoast are rationally referred to the effects of the submergence of an eroded land area; thus Delaware and Chesapeake bays, Albemarle and Pamlico sounds, are simply named "drowned valleys," a phraseology that any child may understand; rivers like the Hudson, having large volume, although fed by a small drainage area, are called "drowned rivers," because their volume is dependent on their submersion beneath sea level.

Descriptive geography, or that which ordinarily passes for the physical geography of the land, lags far behind the present state of knowledge of land sculpture. The understanding of the features of the land surface has advanced wonderfully in the last half century, even in the last quarter century; but the texts, in most cases, seem as if they were written on the basis of an earlier and much less extended knowledge. They are extremely timid regarding the destructive work of the weather. They are sadly incomplete regarding the manifold products of glacial action. They are deficient concerning the meaning of the varied forms of the seacoast. I believe that the chief reason of these various shortcomings is to be found in the want of a practical knowledge of field geology and field geography on the part of the authors of text-books. No worthy knowledge of physical geography can be gained without such a preparation. The time is past when it is admissible to describe the surface of the land independently of the structure beneath the surface and without regard to the forces that have attacked the structure, reducing it by greater or less amounts from what it was originally towards what it will be ultimately. A description of the land that is inattentive to these manifest and natural processes of evolution is in the highest degree arbitrary and antiquated.

The rational understanding of the features of the land surface can be advanced only by the introduction of some natural system of description of land forms, based on the natural processes of their evolution. I shall refer here only to the system which seems to me most satisfactory. This begins by classifying all regions according to the geological structure on which their initial form depends; it then sub-classifies them according to the degree of advance that has been made by the destructive processes of erosion in reducing the initial form to its ultimate extinction in a lowland of denudation. I shall not delay here to consider the complications that follow from the interruption of one cycle of destructive work before its completion by the introduction of a new constructive process; all this may be logically included in the fully expanded statement of the system. It will be sufficient now to illustrate its application by a few simple examples. But before doing this we must recognize carefully the different positions taken by the pupil and the teacher with regard to the subject.

The aim of the entire undertaking must be kept in mind. It is to give our school children so clear an idea of the more common forms of the land that they may appreciate them when reading or when traveling about over the country, thereby gaining a better understanding of history, past and present. For this purpose a series of selected and emphatic examples should be presented, fully illustrated by diagram or model. The variety of illustration cannot be great, but it should be sufficient to enforce an understanding of young and old forms, of elevated and depressed coast lines, of normal and accidental events in river history, and so on. Each of these examples should be enforced by the selection of some particular region which serves as its type. The prominence given to one or another division of the subject may depend largely on the opportunity afforded by the surroundings of the school. The whole world cannot be covered, but a clear understanding may be given of features which have a world-wide distribution, and whose more especial occurrence may, if desired, be made the subject of later study.

But in the selection and presentation of examples, it is essential that they should follow in a natural order, and that the teacher should be acquainted with the system of nature to which they all belong.

A parallel may be drawn with the teaching of botany. A class, at the beginning of this subject, is taught a variety of terms in giving names to the various parts of plants; preferably from the plants themselves, or, in lack of that, from good drawings. The terms thus taught are selected from a much larger number familiar to the expert botanist; taken all together, they have a rational bearing on the natural relationships by which different kinds of plants are classified, and by which their processes of growth are explained. The simpler processes of growth are considered in early teaching, and the genetic relation of various parts is thus brought to light. The essential point here is that the introductory teaching of botany should be guided by an understanding of the whole subject on the part of the teacher, and not simply by a verbal knowledge of the elements that the scholars are to learn, or by a knowledge, however extended, of the medicinal or agricultural uses of plants. Geography, on the other hand, is too often taught as if it were an entirely separate subject from geology, and not merely a subdivision of the study of the earth as a whole. It is a misfortune that we have no English word to include both geography and geology, which naturally belong together. It might then be easier to insure a general knowledge of the whole science on the part of the teacher, even if his scholars were to learn only the rudiments of one of its divisions.

The teacher of elementary botany must know something more than he is expected to teach. He must be reasonably familiar with the more difficult orders, of which little mention need be made in elementary classes, as well as with the simpler orders from which nearly all elementary illustrations are drawn. He must know something of the more obscure processes of growth concerning which a class of beginners can learn little, as well as of the more manifest processes which every child may observe. Otherwise, the teacher would not be qualified in the modern sense of qualification.

The teacher of elementary geography should, in like manner, be familiar with the general system of classification of land forms, and the fundamental principles of geology on which the classification is based, as well as with the larger natural and political divisions of the world, their physical features, inhabitants, and so on ; and the fundamental principles of geology here referred to should have been learned in the field, not in the class room ; otherwise, they are as artificial as the knowledge of botany that comes only from books. The information of the teacher must go beyond that expected of the scholar in order to make his teaching safe and sound. Teachers sometimes claim to teach more than they know ; but I have never heard this claim quoted with satisfaction by the teachers' pupils. With this explanation I may now return to my theme, and illustrate what is meant by a natural system of physical geography, indicating at the same time something of the difference of knowledge expected of teacher and scholar.

Mountains early claim a scholar's attention. They may have had abundant narrative and descriptive illustration in the earlier classes of the grammar schools. The Alps may be taken as examples of vigorous mountain forms, important alike from their height and from the frequent mention of them that the scholar will afterwards meet in history, if not in travel. Later classes come to the more physical consideration of mountains ; and besides the many interesting matters concerning climate, fauna, flora, resources, occupations, and other factors controlled by their form and altitude, questions will arise as to the relations of lofty mountain ranges to other parts of the earth. The first basis of correlation is found in the mountain structure. Mountains are prevailingly regions of crushing and elevation by constructional processes, whereby the rocks of the earth's crust are given a disordered attitude. For a time after the mountain making, much of the form and height due to the constructional processes of growth are preserved ; but this is only temporary, and for the rest of the mountain's life, form varies and height decreases from their initial values. Hence while all regions of crushed and disordered structure may be included under the general class of mountain regions, the maintenance of mountain height is a transient characteristic; mountains are lofty while young, but from that time on, unless rejuvenated by renewed processes of crushing or uplifting, they are worn down lower and lower, and finally only the lowland stumps of the original mountains remain. From the time of youth when massive constructional forms reared their summits to the clouds, to the time of maturity when the processes of sculpture have added variety to the simpler forms of early construction, and to the time of old age when denudation has reduced the region to a lowland surface of faint relief, there is a simple and systematic change of form. Unless renewed uplifts intervene to restore the altitude lost by erosion and thus delay the final consummation (and this, by the way, seems to have been a common exception to the simpler rule), there is no permanence in mountains. However permanent they may be in matters relating to human history, the real physical relation of mountains cannot be perceived without studying mountain history. Their growth, their wasting away, and their final extinction must be recognized. The chief postulates on which this statement rests are simply that the earth's crust suffers deformations; that destructive processes will attack surfaces which arise above the hydrosphere into the atmosphere; and that time is long. These postulates are all extremely safe.

I believe that all this general matter should be clearly in the mind of the teacher. How far he may pass it on to his scholars will depend on many things. He must consider their mental quality; not simply their standing in school, but their associations out of school, on which the success of teaching so largely depends. He must examine the opportunity for local illustration of relevant facts, such as the tilting and disorder of rock structure; abundant illustrations of disorder may be found all along our Appalachians; but in the Central states the rocks are not only generally covered over by loose materials, but when seen their strata lie horizontal. His advance will depend in part on the supply of diagrams and models, and more on his ingenuity in making them; but more than all, it will depend on his own familiarity with the facts of the case and his boldness in presenting them, whether mentioned in the text-book or not.

I believe that a teacher who has made a vacation excursion, on foot, if possible, across the mountains of Pennsylvania, and thus come to an appreciation of their extraordinary structure, as deciphered by the geologists of that state; who has extended the knowledge thus gained by a general study from books and maps of other mountain structures; who has in some way or other found or made a series of illustrations by which the facts that he wishes to refer to may be illustrated to his classes, and who has the good fortune to have classes of intelligent and well-taught scholars, — such a teacher will successfully present the problems here considered, with satisfaction and instruction to his pupils.

If the extinction of mountains by denudation, or by "base-leveling," as the word goes among geologists, were simply an ideal supposition, without actual occurrence; if its occurrence were known only in the remote regions of the world and did not concern our home geography, we might have little regard for it; its place would be better taken by something of local value. But fortunately for the variety of geographical teaching, the base-leveling of mountains is not an uncommon or remote fact. We here in New England live on an old base-leveled mountain region. Our rock structures are crushed to a degree that finds a close parallel in the structures of lofty mountain ranges. It is only an indolent conservatism that fails to recognize the former existence here of a mountain range of great height, perhaps as high as the Alps of to-day; and therefore as closely comparable with the Alps as the decaying trunk of a prostrate oak is comparable with a vigorous shoot from an acorn. They do not look alike, yet the Alps show us the past of New England, just as New England discloses the future of the Alps.

Climb to the top of any hill in central Massachusetts and notice the remarkable accordance of height among all the surrounding hills. They unite in a sky line of extraordinary simplicity. Look at their rocks, and recognize everywhere the signs of great disturbance and deep erosion. How can a disturbed and deeply eroded region possess a generally accordant upland surface unless that surface is the base-level down to which all the superincumbent mass has been reduced by denudation! It need not be imagined that the old mountains were absolutely worn out, and that a geometrical plane was produced. A low-land of gentle relief, an almost plain surface, a "peneplain," with here and there remnant hills and mountains rising some-what above its softly rolling surface, gives a fairer picture of the form to which mountain ranges fade in their old age.

No proper appreciation of our local geography can be gained until the observer has perceived this dominating upland surface, above which our Wachusetts and Monadnocks ascend five hun-dred or a thousand feet, and beneath which our present valleys sink by a similar measure. No one who believes that physical geography extends beyond the limits of descriptive geography towards an understanding of the natural relations of land forms will be satisfied with the recognition of this old peneplain as an unexplained fact. The meaning of the fact is reasonably desired ; fortunately its meaning already comes within the limits of our high-school teaching, and in the next generation, or sooner, I think it may be extended downward into the grammar schools.

It is not intended to present here a full account of the system of physical geography adopted in my college teaching, nor to give a full statement of the physical features of southern New England. A significant characteristic of this region is selected to illustrate the adopted system, which I have considered more fully on other occasions, and which can be touched on only lightly in a brief essay. Indeed, I trust that the reader has perceived a certain discrepancy between the conditions im-plied in the explanation of the upland of southern New England as an old base-leveled mountain region and the considerable altitude at which the greater part of it now stands above sea level. An old mountain region, reduced by the processes of denudation to a lowland of moderate relief, should stand close to sea level, and the streams should be powerless to sink valleys beneath its general surface. Residual mountain stumps might rise moderately above it, but valleys should not sink below it. The present altitude of our New England plateau and its dis-section by valleys, some of which are more than a thousand feet deep below the plateau upland, must therefore be taken to prove that since the base-leveling of the region it has suffered a gentle uplifting, whereby all its old rivers were given a new lease of life and their activities again quickened ; and in accordance with this opportunity they have all set to work to reduce the region to the present base-level, but they have not as yet advanced far in this task. The valleys are well begun, but the greater part of the plateau mass still remains to be consumed.

If one travels inland west from Massachusetts bay or north from Long Island sound, the upland surface of the plateau will be found to ascend gently, from sea level at the coast line to an elevation of sixteen hundred feet or more in northwestern Massachusetts, and even higher farther north. The uplifting of the old base-leveled lowland must therefore have been accomplished by a slight tilting; the part that we now live on rose above its former level, but another part sank, and is now under the Atlantic, — the two parts forming a single inclined plane.

The largest valley that has been excavated in the uplifted portion of the old lowland is that of the Connecticut, because its course follows a belt of relatively weak red sandstone across Massachusetts and Connecticut almost to the sea. This valley indeed deserves the name of a lowland of the second order, for its surface is generally of moderate relief, near present sea level, and it stands distinctly below the uplands of the plateau of harder crystalline rocks to the east and west. But at several points in the valley lowland we find ridges of hard volcanic rock that have withstood the erosion under which the red sandstones have wasted away; such are Mounts Tom and Holyoke in Massachusetts, and the Hanging Hills of Connecticut. These are residual mountains with respect to the surrounding valley lowland, just as Monadnock and Wachusett are residual mountains with respect to the upland plateau. Monadnock and Mount Tom are both residual mountains, but they belong to different generations of development; to different cycles of geographical evolution.

I have introduced this latter point as an illustration of the more detailed knowledge that I should hope the New England teacher would possess, but which might be omitted from his teaching; and yet I have hopes that, within a half century, precisely such facts as these will be the subject of ordinary instruction. Reference has already been made to the downward extension of high-school subjects into the future grammar schools. Such is the usual course of events. Microscopes were once the treasures of the few learned men; now they are familiarly employed in any ordinary school-teaching of botany or zoölogy. The isolation of oxygen was enough to make a chemist famous a hundred years ago; now it may be isolated in any school laboratory. The distances of astronomy and the remote ages of geology were obstinately denied by all but the most learned of earlier generations; now they are taught to our children, or if they are not, we regard the school from which they are excluded as misplaced in this end of the century. Modern scientific education above the primary grades includes subjects known for the greater part only to the few a short time ago. We need not doubt that the teaching of geography will be benefited by the introduction of newly discovered facts, just as the teaching of other subjects has been. Let us not hold back from this advance, but press forward to it. When our schoolmasters learn the modern developments of physical geography as they have learned those of botany and zoölogy, when our schools have geographical laboratories as well provided as are the laboratories of physics and chemistry in the best schools of to-day, then the extension which we are now urging will be the commonplace fact of public education.

VI

GEOGRAPHY IN GRAMMAR AND PRIMARY SCHOOLS

Geography is essentially a grammar-school study. It should be preceded in the primary school by such simple and local observations as the teacher there may have opportunity to introduce, and by descriptions of places in simple reading exercises; it should be followed in the later years of the grammar school and in the high school by history, for the extension of descriptive political geography, and in the high school by modernized physical geography, or physiography as some would call it, for the fuller explanation of natural geography. But general descriptive geography should be well acquired during the very acquisitive years of the grammar-school course.

If there is one thing more important than another in the teaching of geography in the grammar schools, it is that the facts of the subject be made vivid and real. Every means of the teacher's art should be employed to secure this end. Travelers who have seen much of the world can readily make a mental picture of an unseen region by reading a good description of it; but children in our schools have, as a rule, only the vaguest impressions concerning the places whose names they recite. How can it be otherwise when they generally have only the smallest experience with the world, and when the facts are presented to them in the briefest language in text-books that have been impoverished by compressing all their descriptions into short paragraphs for recitation? Let the teacher, therefore, strive to infuse some life and reality into the subject and bring it up nearer to the level of the scholar's intelligence. When the class is learning the succession of low headlands along our Atlantic coast, for example, let the teacher insert some little account of the manner in which the capes would appear one after another, if seen from a coasting vessel, each one guarded by a lighthouse at its extremity, or by a light-ship on the shoals offshore, with broad recessions of the coast between them. When telling of smaller streams branching from a trunk river, stop a little to describe how the valleys of the tributaries join the main valleys ; explain the importance of such points for early settlements and modern cities.

The class need not remember a word of this additional matter ; it is introduced only to expand the explanation and to maintain attention on the subject of the brief text, thus making it more real and more easily remembered. If the teacher finds difficulty in supplying explanatory narrative of this kind — that is, if her knowledge of the subject is but little greater than that which the class attains by reading the barren text, let her lessen the emphasis allotted to the subject, or let her, as soon as possible, increase her familiarity with it. Recitations of the mechanical kind make no progress in correcting the fundamental weakness of unreality in the study of geography. Examinations seldom detect it, because they are so largely occupied with questions of mere locality. Let us consider how a teacher may successfully labor to overcome this difficulty.

I believe that the first step is made in the desired advance when geography is taught, as our best teachers now teach it, as if it were a thing that live people talk about out of doors in the real world, and not as if it were merely the contents of a text-book that is closed when the scholars go home. Let the introduction of geographical topics in the primary schools be well correlated with the grade of work that is to be taken up in the grammar schools. Let the beginning of the study in the grammar schools be made by a somewhat more advanced quality of local observation, illustration, and narrative than the primary scholars could reach, until the listening and watching children perceive that they are learning more about a subject whose acquaintance they first made even before their earliest school days, when they began to walk alone. Teachers in the country especially should encourage excursions on half-holidays. Let there be a healthy rivalry developed among the children in learning the features of the surrounding district, its hills and valleys, its ledges and meadows, its ponds and streams, forests and fields ; let the divides between the streams be explored, and the descent of the slopes followed down to the brooks. Every element of form that is thus seen and reported by the children in school may be matched by the teacher with its larger fellows in the greater world, of which the class is now to learn something. This is geography; and such an introduction to it is far better than a recitation to order from the first page of a book. Excursions are more difficult in cities; but they are not impossible, as many enterprising teachers can testify. Some children in every class may at least afford a little journey into the country on an electric car, or a short voyage across a river or harbor on a ferryboat; and the things that these children see, when naturally talked about afterwards in school, gain a greater reality to the other children than the formal homilies of the first paragraphs in a book.

Turn the drift of the ideas obtained by excursion and narratives towards the first chapter of the text-book that is employed. Enlarge upon the theme of this chapter before the book is called for. Then open the book, and use it as a condensed abstract of the subject whose beginnings are already clearly in mind on a foundation of familiar facts.

By some such device, maintained throughout the course but varying with every teacher, the paragraphs of the book will take their proper place as the summary, not as the substance of the subject. Thus employed, any text-book is better than none; but when the "teaching" is all done by recitations, it might almost be said that no text-book is better than any. The barrenness of blank recitations from the books, and the vagueness of narratives, readings, and unwritten object lessons without a book, are both dangers that are avoided by the use of both methods. Recitations give precision after the subject has become real by illustrations of various kinds. When the class advances rapidly and there is a little time to spare, expand the account of the subject then in hand. When time presses, the text may be followed more closely; its brevity is then properly understood as only the shorter statement of what would be pleasanter if it were longer.

Now the fundamental requirement for such work as this, in which the text-book is subordinated to the teacher, is a teacher with an easy geographical mind ; not one who is timid when out of sight of the text, but a teacher whose familiarity with the facts of geography requires her continually to restrain the plentiful description, narrative, or anecdote with which almost every paragraph of the page might be illuminated. It will be only after years of effort that a teacher, under the manifold burdens of grammar-school work, can acquire such familiarity with geographical facts. The normal-school training that is accepted as fitting high-school graduates for grammar-school teaching is only a step towards the desired end, and sometimes only a short step. A longer step will be taken when the work is better done in these preparatory years, but no preparation that our younger teachers can bring to their work will excuse them from years of arduous study while teaching. The need of attaining an easy mind on several subjects besides geography at the same time is the most serious difficulty in the younger teacher's path ; and this difficulty must greatly embarrass our intermediate schools, until a practical method is invented by which there shall be a teacher for each subject instead of a teacher for each class.

The difficulties in the way of becoming experts in grammar-school subjects are truly formidable, but there is a way in which great assistance can be given in overcoming the difficulties. This is in teachers' meetings. It is disappointing to learn how seldom such meetings are held. The more thoughtful superintendents and principals advocate them. Conscientious teachers approve of them. Where they have been carefully tried, they are found so useful that they cannot be given up. If teachers' meetings can be had in no other way, it would be better for the scholars to have an extra half-holiday every fortnight, so that the teachers might have a spare afternoon for conferences, with suggestion and discussion in small parties. Then let it be understood that study in the high, normal, and training schools is only the beginning of the teacher's studious career. Let the mental activity of the individual teacher, as shown to her principal in the meetings, be recognized as one of the important tests of fitness for continued appointment. Give all subjects a due share of time in succession, geography along with the rest ; each subject being continued through a number of meetings, perhaps for half a year.

At nearly every meeting let every teacher contribute an item, an abstract, a narrative; a list of illustrations of one subject or another, found by a search through the files of some of our more accessible magazines; a method of explaining or introducing certain of the more troublesome matters, such as longitude, map scales, weather maps. In cities where as many as ten or twenty teachers can attend a fortnightly meeting, these specific contributions of matters of fact or method cannot fail to aid many another member. Avoid generalized lectures by outside experts; at least, do not let these take the place of the regular teachers' meetings. The essential to be gained comes only through the effort of the teachers themselves. But this is a theme that is larger than my whole subject, and I cannot pursue it further. It is plain that the training that a young woman may have before she begins to teach is only the beginning of her preparation for teaching; it serves to recommend her as a candidate who may be tried as a teacher; but real fitness is not to be expected in the beginner. Nor will real fitness be gained merely by years of teaching; it comes only from years of study while teaching. Nothing less than unceasing effort will develop the easy mind; and of all aids in this effort, I believe the teachers' meeting to be the best.

It is a sorry device to substitute methods of teaching for knowledge of fact. It is of little avail for the poorly prepared teacher to trust to psychological principles. Indeed, from what I have seen of it, I believe that many teachers are as much harmed as helped by an effort to teach in accordance with a determined order of mental development in children. This absorbingly interesting matter of mental development is a difficult subject. It is much more difficult than imparting the simple facts of descriptive geography. It is a fine subject for deep study, but it is a dangerous subject for the inexperienced to trifle with. A clear knowledge of the facts to be taught and a sympathetic perception of the difficulties of the class will be of greater value to a teacher in a grammar school than the scheme of mental growth. The larger pedagogical principles too often tend to obstruct a teacher's progress in the simple studious acquisition of a subject. All serious students and teachers of pedagogy of course agree that the fundamental requirement for a teacher's success is knowledge. This is so much of a truism and so easily stated that it seems to make less impression on the average teacher than the later principles of pedagogical instruction, which are concerned with the mental processes of acquisition and memory. The fundamental requirement is therefore too often relatively neglected, apparently with the idea that a general understanding by the teacher of the way in which scholars should learn will take the place of the narratives, illustrations, and other devices that I have here referred to. This is all a sad mistake. There is no "method" that can replace knowledge. There is nothing but knowledge that will supply the teacher with a means of awakening and holding attention long enough upon the more important parts of a subject to allow them to sink deeply into the understanding. The more fully the teacher is possessed of her subject, the less will be heard of terms that imply a conscious analysis of mental processes; the more will be heard of the subject itself.

Dr. Rice, in one of his instructive articles in the *Forum* some years ago, gives an instance of too much consciousness of process. He heard a grammar-school teacher ask a class, "With how many senses do we study geography?" And the reply was, "With three senses, — sight, hearing, touch." Again, "How many senses are you using now?" "Two senses, — touch and hearing." This reminds one of the acquisition that Molière's Jourdain thought he had made when he learned that he had all his life been talking "prose." Seeing and hearing are as natural and should be as unconscious as breathing to a child in the observant grammar-school years. To teach that sight is used in studying geography merely enlarges the "morbid influence of consciousness." It has no useful result. As has been well said of manners, so we may say of the senses of perception in school children, "conscious study would tend to distort rather than to fashion them." The earnest teacher in the grammar schools, whether holding classes in geography or in other elementary subjects, may safely let what passes with many teachers as "psychology" carefully alone. Talk to the children in school as simply and naturally as you would talk to them out of school. Give sincere attention to the presentation of the facts of geography in a simple and unaffected manner; for this, as a traveler on a "Sentimental Journey" once said of a much more difficult subject, "leaves nature for your mistress, and she fashions it to her mind." Strive to be quick in perceiving the difficulties that the scholars meet; invent many devices with which to avoid or lessen these difficulties; but be as unconscious of fixed "methods" as the children are of their eyes and ears.

The best test of a growing reality of understanding is found in the increase of questions from the class; not questions that show a puzzled mind, groping for an understanding, but questions that ask for more information, or that display a healthy skepticism. When questions arise, a teacher distrustful of herself takes refuge in recitations; the questions are promptly suppressed, and the most teachable moments of the class are lost. The conscientious teacher, not knowing answers to the questions, frankly says so and promises to find out about them; but the class is not satisfied if the teacher has to postpone her answers too often. Jolly little boys and "peart" little girls are then naturally enough tempted to put questions just for the fun of "cornering" the teacher, not for the pleasure of learning more for themselves.

Spontaneous and genuine questions are only an encouragement to an experienced teacher, and after a few years of studious effort there will not be too many hard ones whose answers have to be postponed. When occasional hard questions come, a frank confession of ignorance does not weaken confidence, and a hearty interest in the novelty of the question may even strengthen it. There is hardly any part of teaching so delightful as those little excursions from the regular path, prompted by appreciative inquiries from growing boys and girls. Then, if ever, a teacher has her reward. Then the real nature of the children is shown. Many a little scholar appears "stupid" when trying to memorize his paragraphic text, half of which means little or nothing to him; but his sufficient ability will be disclosed if the subject of the text is naturally talked about to him, not in brief sentences in the style of the book, but in the ordinary style of simple talk with children. His replies rather than his recitations may be taken as a measure of his knowledge. When sufficient comprehension is gained in this way, recitation from the text is useful as a means of securing concise and definite statement; but if time is allowed, the verbatim recitation method might be given up altogether.

It is only in the easy mind of the well-informed but still studious teacher that the various parts of a subject take their proper proportions and receive their proper emphasis. I recall the laborious and ill-proportioned efforts of a teacher who was following a recommendation to introduce some local map drawing in an early stage of her geography class, in order that her scholars should afterwards better appreciate maps of larger areas. With ill-judged devotion she held the children on this relatively trifling matter as if they were taking a course in surveying and map engraving. Entirely too much time was given to the work, and other parts of the subject suffered. The drawing of local maps should be treated simply as a device by which the nature of a map is made clear. It cannot be expected that the untrained hands of young scholars shall do more than make rough outlines; and the more clumsy scholars can hardly do this. Yet even rough outlines will aid them to understand that the better-drawn maps in their text-book are, like their own rude work, representations of a part of the outdoor world, and not merely a kind of colored picture, from which many names have to be learned. In every school there may be some scholars whose maps are almost worthless; they should not be too much tormented by the requirement of better work than is within their reach; they can learn a useful share of what is needed by seeing the neater maps made by some of the better draftsmen in the class, and thus vicariously gain their experience.

Too much emphasis on illustrative work of this kind betrays the inexperienced teacher. It shows that she needs practice in map drawing herself. Let her utilize the opportunities afforded by summer vacations; let her reproduce on paper the route that she follows on some short trip out of town by train or down the river by boat, taking directions by compass and distances by time. Then she will appreciate that drawing a map from observation is not a very easy task. Both a linear and a fractional scale should be added. For some curious reason, the question of map scales is generally but half understood. I have seen a whole roomful of teachers hesitate — to say the least — when asked to determine for themselves the scale of an ordinary terrestrial globe. Certainly their minds were not easy on this point, and they were not ready to guide their scholars over it.

The proficiency that a teacher acquires by practice in map drawing from nature will be of great assistance in class work. A few lines may be added to help the slower scholars ; a higher grade of accuracy and neatness may be called for from the brighter scholars ; but the teacher's own knowledge of the difficulties of the work will prevent her from exacting too much from any of the young beginners. The whole affair will be held down to a grade of relatively easy accomplishment ; and thus it will subside into the subordinate position that it deserves. Map drawing from nature is a device that should never be omitted from the early part of the course, but it should not be carried far. At no time need the mere copying of elaborate maps from an atlas be allotted as a lesson in geography to any but those having a natural liking for drafting. The rest of the class can better occupy their time by reading.

The teacher who has an easy geographical mind will be fertile in inventing little artifices by which the class is, all unconsciously, carried over difficulties of understanding that block the path of children led by inexperienced teachers. Those early chapters of many text-books, teeming with verbal unrealities about mathematical geography, are only so many stumbling-blocks to children under teachers who have never gained a clear mental view of the rakish attitude of the whirling earth, as it marches around the sun. The figures commonly given in the text are not of much value, because of their distortion or foreshortening, and also because they are ready-made. But a teacher who has persevered through an elementary astronomy, who has watched the changes of the stars with the advancing seasons, who has made for herself the simple little models or diagrams by which all the necessary astronomical relations of the earth and sun may be exhibited, — such a teacher will find the year, the seasons, and the varying length of the day only a series of entertainments, well adapted for gradual presentation to her class.

It is a mistake to think that the greater knowledge of such a teacher will tempt her to lead her classes too far and to trouble them with unnecessary difficulties. It is true that her classes will advance farther than those led by a teacher who is puzzled by the facts about which her scholars recite in unmeaning words; but the farther advance of the better-taught scholars will be made more easily than the apparent advance — really the mystification — of the others. The teacher who knows much of the subject, and who has moreover a sympathetic experience with school children, will wisely select the essential elements from her abundant store and teach them easily; but a teacher who is puzzled as to the real meaning of " the inclination of the earth's axis to the plane of its orbit" has no power of selection, and her teaching is heavy. Unhappily there is many a teacher who is thus puzzled. Recitation from the text is her only refuge; the chapter is soon passed and the danger is over. The children, however, have learned very little. Better omit the chapter altogether, or else teach it clearly, by improvising all sorts of observations and illustrations.

One of the most interesting items of early geographical study is the determination by observation of the varying noon altitude of the sun. A great difficulty is often made of this simple matter. The trouble evidently is that the subject is really not clear in the minds of the teachers. And yet this is a truly eloquent subject for early teaching. In a well-arranged course of primary- and grammar-school work the discovery of the sun's varying path through the sky should come before the class meets a statement of it in the text-book. The approach of the winter months is accompanied by a loss of noon altitude; just before the Christmas holidays the loss becomes very slow and practically ceases; and on returning to school again the northward march has begun. This is continued almost until school closes for the summer; but the full height of the June solstice may be detected before vacation begins. The greatest and least angular altitude of the sun may be determined even in the primary school, if desired; and from these two quantities, placed on record in the book of school observations kept in possession of the teacher, the scholars may in later years easily be led to determine for themselves the inclination of the earth's axis, the latitude of their school, and all the limits of the zones. The advance must be gradual, but it is very easy. The extension of observation into mathematical geography should be slow. Every new fact should be allowed to rest quietly and settle firmly in the mind before another is added to take the attention from the first. But there can be no doubt that all this can be easily introduced into grammar-school teaching, provided always that the whole problem is perfectly clear to the teacher, and that its mention does not in the least disturb her ease of mind.

There are certain profitable devices which some might regard as lacking in candor, but which may, I believe, be properly used in order to secure a desired sequence in the presentations of the facts. Suppose, for example, that a class of young children has been studying the continents upon a globe, as their first study of continents should always be made, and it is then desired to make a more careful examination of North America on a map of a larger scale. Place a wall map, rolled up on its stick, in the corner of the room before the school opens. Begin the lesson in geography with the globe, and ask various questions about North America, leading at last to some question, such as the length of the smallest of the Great Lakes, which cannot be determined on a globe of ordinary size. Even the best scholar in the class will be at a loss ; and if the proper relations are established between the teacher and her class, the embarrassment of the scholars will be frankly expressed. Then the teacher may say, " Sally, bring me the map that is rolled up in the corner of the room there. Tom and Harry, lift that table alongside of this one, so that we can spread out the map and look at it." Small divisions of the class may then in turn inspect the new map, and answer questions that could not be answered from the globe. The scale of the map may be determined, and compared with that of the globe. As on the globe, so on the map, while it is still lying flat, the outward course of the larger rivers from the continental interior may be noted and accepted as an indication of the general descent of the land from the central part towards the surrounding oceans.

At the opening of the next lesson in geography, the map of North America may be again spread on the table and a map of South America may be in a closet near at hand. South America has already been seen on the globe. Some simple comparison may be made between the two great divisions; for example, their western mountains and their three great eastern rivers. Then let the teacher ask the big boy of the class to help her hang the map of North America on the wall, out of the way; while another scholar is sent for the map of South America, which takes its turn on the table. The object of these harmless subterfuges is to introduce new facts and illustrations as far as possible only when the want of them is felt by at least some members of the class. This is a much more natural and intelligent method of procedure than one which takes up a new subject because it follows the last one on the page of a book. Moreover, the presentation of the wall map first in a horizontal position on a table will avoid the misunderstanding that teachers sometimes encounter as to the uphill course of northward flowing rivers. As the Mackenzie was first seen running out from the continental center, much in the same fashion as the Mississippi, there will be no question about its flowing uphill when the map is placed where it belongs on the wall. Again, until the map is needed, it is out of place in the schoolroom; as much out of place as the apparatus for the later part of a course in physics would be on the lecture desk in the opening lecture. It is less laborious for the teacher to place the maps on the wall, once for all; but it is monotonous for the scholars to have the same furnishings in the schoolroom all the year.

There is one aspect of geographical teaching in this country that is not generally recognized. Few persons suspect that the proper teaching of geography in the grammar schools is greatly hampered by an insufficient investigation and a prevailing ignorance of the facts concerning our own country. I do not mean ignorance on the part of teachers, but an absolute ignorance that cannot be removed until the facts are investigated by trained observers on the ground. The poverty of home illustrations is therefore not due to the lack of natural material, but to the general ignorance concerning the abundant material that undoubtedly exists. Consider the case of the Empire State. In the first place, there is no respectable map of its area! There is no map to which the teacher can turn for a clear picture of its beautifully varied features. There is not only no map; there is not even a good written description of its surface forms. We may of course find various accounts of the state in encyclopedias and gazetteers, but not one of them discloses the facts in the light of modern geographical science. There is no one who withholds the facts. No one has yet learned them, except in a fragmentary way, here and there. The same is more or less true of nearly all the other states. Some of them are well mapped, but not many. None of them are adequately explored and described geographically. The wealthy states of New York, Pennsylvania, and Ohio are about as poorly off in this respect as the western territories.

I have addressed the National Geographic Society on this subject, and suggested that the geological surveys of the various states should be asked to consider the feasibility of undertaking a direct geographical study of their territory, and reporting on the results in a style that would be easily understood by our common-school teachers. If such reports were made in successive annual chapters, they might be reprinted in the reports of the state boards of education and thus placed more generally in the hands of teachers. The gradual accumulation of good material in the course of a decade would furnish a highly prized source of home knowledge. Text-books would be refreshed by the incorporation of the new information. Teachers would be greatly aided by employing it as a basis for their descriptions and illustrations. It would compete with teachers' meetings for a chief place in the improvement of geographical teaching. I wish that superintendents and teachers all over the country would join me in the movement to secure this result.

Perhaps the impression that I may make by frequent repetition of the recommendation that the teacher must study unceasingly is that the teacher's life ought to be even more wearisome than it is at present. It must certainly be laborious if it is to be successful; but the consciousness of an easy geographical mind is a good return for all the labor that it has cost to gain it ; and surely the easy mind is a delightful substitute for the anxiety and drudgery of teaching a half-known subject. Indeed, I believe there is nothing that will so surely soften the hard lines of a teacher's life as the freedom from thraldom to the text-book, and the recreation afforded by a change of device and illustration from time to time.

VII

PHYSICAL GEOGRAPHY IN THE HIGH SCHOOL

Limitation of the Subject. A review of the older books on physical geography, and of some of the newer books also, will show that their various authors have not reached a clear agreement as to the limits of the subject. It has been allowed to run over upon physics and astronomy on one side and on geology, botany, and zoölogy on the other. As a result the central and truly geographical parts of the subject have as a rule been compressed below the space that they should occupy when properly developed. A way out of this confusion is found in a report recently made by the Committee on College Entrance Requirements to the National Educational Association. The reporting members of the sub-committee concerned with our science unanimously agree that "it should be the aim to exclude a number of subjects frequently treated under physical geography, but more appropriately included under other heads; for example, purely astronomical matter, certain principles of physics, the classification of animals and plants, and tables of geological periods. Important and interesting as these subjects are in their proper connections, it is believed that a better mental discipline will be obtained from physical geography when all its parts are closely joined to its leading theme," namely, "the physical environment of man," under which the principal headings are "the earth as a globe," "the atmosphere," "the oceans," and "the lands."

The agreement upon this limitation of the subject by the teachers present at the meeting of the sub-committee, and the approval of their agreement indicated by the publication of their report by the National Educational Association, mark a decided step forward from the indefiniteness of earlier years. Although slow in coming, the limitation is really an outgrowth of Ritter's teaching that geography is the study of the earth in relation to man, from which one may naturally deduce the definition of physical geography — or physiography — as the study of those features of the earth which are involved in the relation of earth and man; that is, the study of man's physical environment. In later years of education the physics of the atmosphere, the forms of the land, and other branches of the subject may be studied for themselves alone under the general name of terrestrial physics, or under such special names as meteorology, geomorphology, and so on, without special regard for their human relations; but when first encountered the limitation of the subject to man's physical environment has the great advantage of holding all its topics close to their most important and interesting theme. The earth's form and size, its rotation and revolution, are geographical as well as astronomical topics; but a list of planets, their dimensions, distances from the sun, and periods of rotation and revolutions are astronomical topics. Let the teacher introduce these interesting items if her interest turns towards astronomy, and if time can be spared for the purpose; but the space that they would occupy in the text-book should be saved for the fuller presentation of strictly geographical topics. To illustrate this by personal experience, I may note that the nebular hypothesis held its inherited place in my lectures only so long as the richness of the rest of the subjects was not sufficiently developed to crowd out so irrelevant an astronomical theory.

The forms of the land can be well seen only through the eye of the understanding, which shows them to be the product of agencies that have operated for long periods of past time; the "shut-in" valleys of the St. François mountains of Missouri and the Baraboo ridge of southern Wisconsin are never appreciated until they are seen as involving long stretches of time in their preparation. Thus far time is an element of geographical as well as of geological consideration; but the specific subdivision of past time into periods and the consideration of the events that occurred during those periods in their historical order is purely geological. By all means let the inventive teacher bring in abundant and helpful illustrations from all pertinent fields of knowledge, but let the teacher also recognize that there is a well-defined theme in physical geography whose logical development must govern the selection of topics that really constitute the framework of the course. A fact may be interesting and important, but it must also be pertinent to our science if a place is to be given to it in a well-organized text-book of physical geography.

Geographical Evolution. The contrast between older and newer methods of treatment is as well marked as between the older and newer limitations of our subject. In the days of Ritter many subdivisions of physical geography, and especially the chapters devoted to the forms of the lands, were treated empirically, because no adequate explanation had then been found for them; and the relation between organic forms and their inorganic environment was explained, when explained at all, by the philosophy of teleology, — the philosophy which, among other things, regards the earth as prepared for man, — because no conception had then been gained of the duration of the past time or of the development of the various forms of life. Since those days two great principles have been discovered, both of vast importance to geography. One is the evolution of land forms, contributed from geology; the other is the evolution of living forms, contributed from biology. Great advances have also been made in the physical study of the atmosphere and the ocean. As a result it is now possible to treat all aspects of physical geography in a rational manner, and at the same time to show the fundamental importance of the relation between physical environment and life. The changes thus wrought by the century are revolutionary in physical geography as well as elsewhere, and it is incumbent upon us to see that our pupils reap full advantage from the new opportunities thus broadly opened before them.

Causes and Consequences. There is no better measure of the degree of modernization in the treatment of physical geography than the evenness with which a rational or explanatory treatment is applied to all its parts. In the earlier books, explanation was offered only for the more active phenomena, such as winds, currents, and volcanoes; geographical features that were not evidently the result of active processes were merely described.

In the newer books the attempt is made to extend explanation uniformly all over the field of study. A review of older and newer methods is especially interesting in regard to the forms of the lands. Sand dunes, for example, have nearly always been mentioned in connection with their simple and evident origin by wind action; but the erosive action of weather and water in shaping valleys has been slowly and incompletely introduced. Cañons have been given too much importance, and only the more recent books have instanced wide-open valleys and worn-down mountains as illustrating the advanced stage of destructive development in which cañons are but the younger stage. It is undoubtedly true that many items of the subject are not yet fully explained, but there are many others for which good explanation is well assured. Let the latter be selected to form the body of the subject in elementary teaching, while the former are left aside for the present, or given at most only a subordinate place. The judicious application of this principle will not impoverish the subject by reducing it to scanty dimensions, but will enrich it by the addition of intelligent explanations. The pupils will from the outset gain the habit of looking at the subject in a rational way. They may to advantage even be prejudiced with the opinion that all its parts are within the reach of explanation; then, if an unexplained fact is encountered later, it will be attacked vigorously in the belief that explanation can surely be found by persistent study.

Equally significant with explanatory treatment is the applied treatment; that is, the presentation of every item as an element of the environment in which the life of the earth has been developed, and by which it is still conditioned at every turn. This second test of modernized treatment is as valuable as the first. When the applied treatment of the subject is understood it will be recognized that plants, animals, and man should not be given special chapters for themselves in the modern limitation of the contents of physical geography, for the very sufficient reason that mention of them is distributed all through the subject. Gravity determines the "standing" position of plants and animals. Latitude and longitude should be taught as devices by which man takes advantage of the form and rotation of the earth to determine his position on it, not as abstract mathematical problems. The chapters on temperature and moisture give opportunity for mentioning many appropriate consequences as to the distribution of plants. Under the description of the shallow border of the oceans, where the waters lie upon the so-called "continental shelf," proper opportunity is found for referring to these waters as the habitat of food fishes and therefore as valuable fishing grounds. A general account of the larger land forms leads up to the control exerted by continents, mountains (especially the Himalaya), and deserts (especially the Sahara) upon the distribution of man and animals. Under "mountains," reference is made to their significance as refuges for conquered tribes or peoples. Avalanches and landslides are not finished with a description and explanation of inorganic phenomena alone; they are also presented as dangers to which people living in mountain valleys are subjected. Here we may well introduce Guyot's eloquent sentence as a practical guide in our work : "To describe without rising to the causes or descending to the consequences is no more science than merely and simply to relate a fact of which one has been a witness." The phrase "causes and consequences" thus comes to serve as a touchstone by which both the explanatory and the applied treatment of the subject may be easily tested. Just as a topic that is beyond explanation had better as a rule be omitted, in order to give fuller attention to topics that can be explained, so a topic that has no connection with the manner in which organic forms are distributed or with the occupations in which men are engaged should in nearly all cases be excluded as of less importance than those topics in which such connection is manifested. Neither test of the touchstone should be applied rigidly or arbitrarily ; but the habit of looking for causes and consequences is a most useful aid in the development of the subject. No one need fear that the reasonable application of this test will deprive physical geography of anything that rightly belongs to it.

The omission of "man," "animals," and "plants" as chapters in physical geography frequently causes objection on the part of those who hold to the older plan of treatment. Against such objections I would urge the following considerations : The necessity for the study of man comes largely because the treatment of geography proper has been too empirical and unintelligent; when this old fashion is corrected there will be no need of a chapter on man in physical geography. Plants and animals are properly subjects for zoölogy and botany; their structural features and their classification cannot be taught merely as chapters in another subject. On the other hand, palms and pines, elephants and polar bears, may be freely mentioned in a treatise on physical geography as exhibiting in their distribution the effects of climatic control; wheat and corn fields are appropriate products of the rich soil on our prairies, in contrast to the forests which grow on the stony soils of our Appalachian mountains and uplands. It is not necessary to have studied the biological relations of these organic forms in order to make intelligent use of them as illustrations of the effect of environment. But the actual distribution of useful plants and animals is strictly a geographical subject, and no intelligent or effective treatment of political or economic geography can be reached if the facts of distribution are omitted from it.

Physical Geography Abroad. It is interesting in this connection to glance at the treatment of physical geography abroad, in contrast to the treatment recommended by the sub-committee of the National Educational Association. As to limitation of content there is the same wide diversity that has hitherto existed here, but without any strong movement now apparent to reduce the subject to better definition. Absence of proper limitation is most apparent in the " physiography " of the South Kensington examinations in England, where the subject is a sort of extension of a very elementary treatment of physical geography. It reaches as far as spectroscopic observations of stars and nebulæ, evidently because of the presence of an astronomer on the committee in charge of this division of the examinations; and the physical geography of the lands is almost lost sight of, evidently because no physical geographer is on the directing committee. This is the more remarkable and regrettable when it is remembered that the term "physiography" has been adopted because of Huxley's use of it as a title for a series of lectures in 1869 and 1870. The lectures were reduced to book form in 1878, and in the preface then published we find the following interesting statement :

I borrowed the title of " physiography " as I wished to draw a clear line of demarcation, both as to matter and method, between it and what is commonly understood by " physical geography." Many highly valuable compendia of physical geography, for the use of scientific students of that subject, are extant; but, in my judgment, most of the elementary works I have seen begin at the wrong end, and too often terminate in an omnium-gatherum of scraps of all sorts of undigested and unconnected information, thereby entirely destroying the educational value of that study which Kant justly termed the " propædeutic of natural knowledge." I do not think that a description of the earth, which commences by telling a child that it is an oblate spheroid, moving round the sun in an elliptical orbit, and ends without giving him the slightest hint towards understanding the ordnance map of his own county, or any suggestion as to the meaning of the phenomena offered by the brook which runs through his village, or the gravel pit whence the roads are mended, is calculated either to interest or to instruct. And the attempt to convey scientific conceptions, without the appeal to observation, which can alone give such conceptions firmness and reality, appears to me to be in direct antagonism to the fundamental principles of scientific education. " Physiography " has very little to do with this sort of " physical geography." My hearers were not troubled with much about latitudes and longitudes, the heights of mountains, depths of seas, or the geographical distribution of kangaroos and *Compositæ*. Neglecting such points of information — of the importance of which, in their proper places, I entertain no doubt — I endeavored to give them, in very broad, but, I hope, accurate outlines, a view of the " place in nature " of a particular district of England, the basin of the Thames, and to leave upon their minds the impression that the muddy waters of our metropolitan river, the hills between which it flows, the breezes which blow over it, are not isolated phenomena, to be taken as understood because they are familiar. On the contrary, I have endeavored to show that the application of the plainest and simplest processes of reasoning to any one of these phenomena suffices to show, lying behind it, a cause, which again suggests another, until, step by step, conviction dawns upon the learner that to attain to even an elementary conception of what goes on in his parish, he must know something about the universe ; that the pebble he kicks aside would not be what it is and where it is unless a particular chapter of the earth's history, finished untold ages ago, had been exactly what it was. It was necessary to illustrate my method by a concrete case ; and as a Londoner addressing Londoners, I selected the Thames and its basin for my text. But any intelligent teacher will have no difficulty in making use of the river and river basin of the district in which his own school is situated for the same purpose.

It is said that much disappointment was felt by those interested in the development of rational methods in education, on finding that teachers in various parts of England were following Huxley in taking as their text the Thames instead of their local river! Still greater disappointment may be felt on seeing how far the spirit of what Huxley meant by the name "physiography" is lost sight of in the books that undertake to present the requirements of the South Kensington examinations on that subject. It may, I believe, be fairly claimed that the recommendations of the conference on geography, above referred to, much more nearly represent the "sort of physical geography" in which the great English naturalist was interested than do the outlines issued by the most authoritative board of examinations in England to-day.

An explanatory treatment is usually applied in German and French schoolbooks to the active phenomena of the earth, but the treatment is not uniformly characteristic of all parts of the subject. Applied treatment is almost universally lacking in European schoolbooks on physical geography; and when encountered it seems to be introduced by accident rather than as the result of a systematic plan. Its omission is especially characteristic of the German books, whose comprehensive thoroughness is often remarked, but whose plan would place them rather under the heading of terrestrial physics than under physical geography, as here defined. Hence it may be said that when the recommendations in the report of the National Educational Association reach the stage of general and practical application, physical geography will be better organized in this country than in Europe, — a result that may be placed to the credit of the unofficial educational organizations of the country, which are so generally influential in bringing about reforms, and which are here very much less hampered by the restrictions of a centralized or bureaucratic control of educational matters than is the case abroad.

Let us now turn to the problem of the arrangement of topics under the four chief headings of our subject.

Systematic Treatment: the Atmosphere. It is important that a careful arrangement as well as a judicious selection of topics should be made, in order that the subject should advance systematically, in as logical a progress as actually prevails in geometry or Latin, or as is possible in botany or zoölogy. Passing "the earth as a globe" for lack of space, an example of the arrangement may be given under the heading "the atmosphere," by which the correlation of the prevailing winds and general distribution of rainfall may be impressively presented. First comes the general circulation as determined by the difference of temperature prevailing between the equator and poles, and as affected by the eastward rotation of the globe. Well-defined consequences as to the distribution of pressure and the oblique movements of the upper and lower currents are reasonably deduced from accepted physical principles governing such movements, but the difficulty here is that the real explanation of the winds cannot be presented in an elementary fashion; the problem is inherently complicated, and only the more important results are appropriate for high-school pupils; hence the general principle that cause must be presented with fact cannot here be fully carried out. Difference of temperature and the rotation of the earth may be mentioned as the chief controls of wind movement and direction, but the logical connection of cause and effect cannot be fully explained. Nothing need be said about the distribution of atmospheric pressure unless the text and the teacher are prepared to explain the low pressures of high latitudes. It is true that it has become fashionable in recent years to copy Buchan's pressure charts in elementary books, but it would be more philosophical to postpone them to more advanced study. Variations of pressure at sea level are not of importance as factors of geographical environment; and it is difficult to give a simple explanation of the observed variations. The winds determined by general differences of equatorial and polar temperatures may be called planetary, because such winds are to be expected on all planetary bodies, and the chief members of the planetary circulation may be described along with the rainy and dry belts that they control. The second step is more intelligible, as it involves the effect of seasonal changes of temperature, themselves well explained by the changing declination of the sun; relatively simple modifications of the planetary wind system (and of its rainy and dry belts) are thus described, to which the name terrestrial winds is to be given. The shifting of the equatorial calm belts and the associated development of monsoon winds and sub-equatorial rains in the summer hemisphere find mention at this stage ; also the relaxation of the westerly winds of the temperate zone of the summer hemisphere, and their acceleration in the temperate zone of the winter hemisphere, with the correlated migration of the tropical calm belt and the associated occurrence of the winter sub-tropical rains. The third step is made by considering the irregular distribution of land and water, from which it appears that the systematic development of the terrestrial winds is better seen in the southern hemisphere, while strong modifications of winds and rainfall are associated with the great alternations of land and water areas of the northern hemisphere. It may be fairly claimed for this method of presentation that it binds together all the elements of the problem — temperature, pressure, winds, and rainfall — in a rational association, by which the memory as well as the understanding is greatly aided. Nearly all the topics introduced under " the atmosphere " may be appropriately attached to the scheme of treatment here outlined ; and all may be led forward to important consequences.

The Ocean. Under the heading " the ocean," the sequence of items is fairly well agreed upon. They are : the form of the ocean basins ; the composition and temperature of ocean water ; the deposits on the ocean floor ; movements in the form of waves, currents, and tides ; influence of climate ; and control over distribution of organic forms. The only point on which I would lay special emphasis here is that tides should follow waves (with currents between, as the consequence of winds and temperatures), so that the tidal currents may be explained as the orbital movements of the water in the tidal waves. Under tides, a good explanation of the tide-making forces may be given to pupils who have studied geometry and physics ; otherwise, it is hardly worth while to attempt explanation. It should suffice to point out that the tides run on lunar time, and hence must in some way be associated with the moon. An explanation that does not explain is not worth its time.

Activities of the Lands. Under the heading "the lands" there is as yet no general agreement as to the order of topics, or indeed as to the topics themselves. After various experiments in this division of the subject, I have adopted the scheme indicated in the following statement. A general account of the activities or habits of the lands opens the subject, and here we find the best warrant for the previous consideration of the deep ocean floors, in themselves so remote from relations with man, but so excellent a foil for the presentation of the real characteristics of the lands. The sea floors are cold and dull, for no sunlight reaches them, though they may have some illumination from phosphorescent animals, as is indicated by the eyes and the color patterns of abyssal fauna; their oozy deposits are almost as monotonous as their gently undulating form; they are silent, and without change of weather or variety of climate. The lands are alternately light and dark, warm and cold, even and uneven, active and quiet, noisy and silent; here is one composition, there is another, with great differences of weather and climate in time and place, and the surface is nearly everywhere wasted and furrowed by valleys, down which the loss of the land is carried away by rain-fed streams to become the gain of the sea. Now that evolutionists as well as poets recognize that variety is the very spice of life, there is little wonder that the land surface and not the sea floor has come to be the home of the higher animals, higher in organization, in instincts, and in intelligence, with man at their head. A general chapter on the land may thus be made of much interest and value. Special emphasis should be given to a brief account of weathering and washing, topics of great importance in their later applications : the systematic relation of parts in valley systems as well as in river systems deserves much attention as a general characteristic of the lands ; but it is not desirable here to enter into details, for the reason that the closer knowledge of rivers and valleys requires a previous understanding of the initial land forms on which the rivers have worked and in which the valleys are carved. As at present advised, I should also include in this preliminary chapter some brief mention of the slow movements of the earth's crust, whereby the outline of the land areas is slowly varied through the ages. Here a sea-floor border is added to a continent by a movement of elevation; there a land border is submerged beneath the sea by a movement of depression. It is true that these statements are empirically introduced in this connection, and that no explanation of them can be attempted, for the cause of crustal movement is a puzzle even to the advanced student of geology. The sufficient reason for introducing brief mention of crustal movement at this early stage is that examples of their effects, encountered a little later, may be then understood more easily.

Features of the Lands. The lands are next to be treated in several chapters. Through each chapter the development of the land forms there considered should be treated from the point of view of geographical evolution, a problem too large for presentation here. In recent years I have made a particular point of beginning this division of the subject with the chapter on coastal plains, because of all land forms they are most easily apprehended; that is, the origin of young coastal plains, the position that they occupy with respect to their surroundings, the developmental changes produced by the destructive attack of weather and water can all be readily understood by young scholars without more preliminary study than is given in the general chapter on the activities of the lands. The great advantage resulting from a full and clear understanding of the first example of land forms is that a serious beginning is thus made of treating land forms genetically and rationally. Although not usually allowed much space, coastal plains, modern and ancient, young, mature, and old, uplifted and depressed, include a great variety of forms; the reasonable explanation that can easily be given to all these forms affords the pupils good grounds for the expectation that plateaus, mountains, volcanoes, and other forms in the following chapters may be no less rationally treated. This expectation is not disappointed in the chapter on plateaus, or in the earlier examples that may be given of simple mountain forms; but when disordered mountain ranges are reached, it is not desirable to attempt an explanatory discussion of their greatly deformed structures, or of all their complicated forms. Fortunately, the pupil will not complain of lack of material if nothing more is attempted under this subdivision of the chapter than the description, with some explanation, of peaks, ridges, spurs, passes, ravines, valleys, and slopes. The treatment of subdued and worn-down mountains that follow young and vigorous mountains is much simpler and may be readily enough understood. Worn-down mountains, now uplifted and again undergoing dissection, include examples of many regions whose description and explanatory treatment to-day is a refreshing contrast to the inattention of earlier years.

Volcanoes form a chapter that may naturally follow mountains; but it is important to distribute earthquakes through both these chapters in order to remove the old idea that they have only to do with volcanic action. "Volcanoes and Earthquakes" as a chapter heading has no logical place unless it is paralleled with " Mountains and Earthquakes" as another. Neither heading is a good one; it would be as appropriate to say volcanoes and eruptions, or mountains and dislocations; for eruptions and earthquakes are both subordinate topics under volcanoes, as dislocations and earthquakes are under mountains. Furthermore, earthquakes are associated only with growing mountains and volcanoes, and not with the old stages of these forms; hence the permanent association with either land form indicated by chapter headings is inadmissible.

Rivers and Valleys. Under all the topics thus far mentioned, rivers and valleys have had an essential place, for it is impossible to treat the development of land forms, or to describe existing forms in a rational manner, without constant reference to the valleys that have been worn in them and to the rivers by which the waste is washed away along the channel in the valley floor. From the very first, rivers and valleys have been made characteristic parts of the land surface; lakes are directly associated with rivers because, when considered in their true light, they are but "ephemeral phases in the history of rivers." Rivers and lakes, and the valleys and basins they occupy, are therefore considered wherever need be in connection with plains, plateaus, mountains, and volcanoes. But there are numerous details of interest and importance that deserve special consideration under the guidance of a scheme of river development; hence a chapter on rivers and valleys may advisedly follow those already mentioned, reviewing and extending what has already been presented. The development of meanders and cut-offs, the migration of divides and the resulting rearrangement of drainage systems by river capture, the peculiar features of valleys whose streams have been beheaded, are details of this kind. This is a strong departure from the English method, sanctioned by the South Kensington examinations, as at present planned, of placing lakes and rivers under the same general division with the oceans, because they are all water : a method that cannot be too strongly condemned by those who desire to see a reasonable treatment of physical geography introduced. As well take clouds and rain from the study of the atmosphere as lakes and rivers from the study of the lands.

The Waste of the Land. There is a chapter that naturally follows rivers and valleys in which I have become increasingly interested during the past ten years on account of its growing richness ; the more it is considered the more it seems to contain. It may be entitled, " The Forms assumed by the Waste of the Land on the Way to the Sea." Like the chapter in which rivers are especially considered, this one repeats certain items already met with under the four chapters on the chief classes of land forms ; but many other items which there was then no sufficient opportunity to describe without too long a delay may now be taken up deliberately. The process of weathering, whose importance is so great that it was presented as an essential characteristic of the lands, is now reviewed, thus leading to a consideration of the sheet of rock waste or discrete, as Gilbert calls it, with which so much of the land is covered, and more particularly to an examination of the forms assumed by the slow-moving waste as it creeps and washes down the slopes to the valleys, and as it is carried along by streams. It may be fairly claimed for this chapter that it gives a greatly broadened view of familiar facts and presents them in their true relations. We are all familiar with the forms assumed by the waters of the land on the way to the sea, — springs, brooks, rivers, lakes, and falls ; we should be equally familiar with the forms assumed by the waste of the land on the way to the sea, — talus slopes, alluvial fans, flood plains, deltas.

Climatic Control of Land Forms. Thus far it has been tacitly implied that the development of land forms always goes on under what may be called a normal climate; that is, a climate in which the precipitation, chiefly in the form of rain, is sufficient to fill all basins to overflowing. All that precedes concerning land forms may be regarded as a consideration of the control of land forms by normal climate. Attention must now be given to two other climates, the arid and the glacial. Wind in one case, and ice in the other, replaces water as the chief agent of transportation; and peculiar land forms are developed under these peculiar controls. Here are placed those peculiar regions known as interior drainage basins, in which certain highly specialized correlations of form and process are found; correlations that are very little understood by explorers, if one may judge by the unappreciative method of description often adopted. Nothing is more significant of advance in the rational treatment of geography than the recognition lately allowed to forms of glacial origin; and it is truly gratifying to find that there are children now in schools who know a drumlin when they see it, and who can give it a name that will concisely suggest the meaning desired to a hearer of like intelligence. Additional interest attaches to the chapter on the control of land forms by special climatic conditions when it is shown that climate is not constant, but that in certain parts of the world the climate of the recent past (as the earth counts time) has been different from that prevailing to-day, and that many marks of the past climate are still distinct in the existing topography. Thus topographical forms produced under the former normal climate of many basins now arid, and under former glacial climate of many regions now normal, are appropriately introduced, on branches that depart in an orderly fashion from the main theme; and this I hold to be just as important in geography as in geometry.

Shore-Lines. The chapter on shore-lines may be advisedly placed at the end of a general course on physical geography, for it cannot be introduced earlier without interrupting the sequence of chapters just sketched, and because it fittingly follows all of them. It is entirely inappropriate as a part of the study of the oceans, although it was there placed by Peschel. The natural association of this topic is with the forms of the land. One of the most pleasing results of the rational study of shore-lines is the discovery that their development may be treated just as systematically as that of land forms; and indeed that many general principles established in the study of land forms as affected by the sub-aërial agencies of erosion are equally applicable to the seashore, when allowance is made for the marine agencies of erosion there in action.

Plants, Animals, and Man. It may be noticed that no place is given in the list of topics here considered to plants, or animals, or man. This is because organic forms do not in themselves constitute any part of the content of physical geography, however largely they may enter into geography proper. It is therefore proper not to place Plants, Animals, and Man as chapter headings equivalent to Plains, Rivers, or Shore-lines, unless merely with the intention of gathering in one place and emphasizing the "consequences" already presented in connection with their physiographic controls; but, on the other hand, it is extremely desirable that plants, animals, and man should receive frequent mention in every chapter, in illustration of the organic consequences that follow from controls exerted by physical environment or organic opportunity. Herein the method of the American school, if the recommendation of the sub-committee of the National Educational Association may be so called, differs distinctly from that of the European, in which the physical features of the earth are considered for themselves alone and without regard to the conditions, favorable or unfavorable, that they offer for life, be it low or high. The omission of "consequences" seems to me almost as unfortunate as would be the omission of "causes."

Regional Geography. There is another omission from the content of the subject as outlined above that may excite comment. The regional study of the several continents, as made up of physical features of various kinds, is not attempted. This is because it is not possible to give both a general and regional course on physical geography in a single year. Neither part of the course could be properly developed in so short a time. It is true that some knowledge of the physical geography of North America and Europe is very important ; indeed, that it ought not to be sacrificed to the impossible by attempting to present the physical features of all the continents as a supplement to the general principles of physical geography in a single year. Instead of teaching the regional physical geography of even North America and Europe in the general course, it is better to use many features from these grand divisions as type examples in the several chapters to which they belong, always locating the examples by reference to maps. Clear ideas of some few things will thus be gained, instead of vague and imperfect ideas of many things. If there is time to spare, a following course on the physical geography of the continents would be interesting and profitable ; but as part of a general course this subject cannot receive adequate attention.

VIII

THE NEED OF GEOGRAPHY IN THE UNIVERSITY

Geography should have a place in the list of studies of our colleges and universities because the recognition implied in giving it a place is an essential part of the round of attentions that the subject deserves. At present there is nearly everywhere a break between the work on the elementary, ordinary, and rather old-fashioned geography of the schools and the work of the investigating and professional geographer in his explorations or other advanced studies. In consequence of this break, the general subject of geography is not advancing as so important a subject ought to advance.

As a result of the break between school geography and professional geography, our professional geographers are all self-made men. They have had to bridge over the gap from their school studies to their professional labors in such ways as they could best devise. They have consequently had to begin their higher work with preparation inferior to that which they should have had; and they have generally concluded it without coming personally, or through their writings, in close contact with our teachers of geography, who, of all persons in the community, should be most promptly supplied with everything which is new concerning their subject. The break in the study and development of the subject is therefore both in the ascending and descending order of educational attentions, and this I shall now endeavor to show more fully.

It is not a little curious that a subject of such fundamental importance and wide application should so seldom be regarded as affording material for serious collegiate study. There is, to be sure, not infrequently an elementary course in physical geography announced in college catalogues; but this is in nearly all cases given by men whose first attention is turned to other subjects. The course, as given, can do nothing more than open the study, as a simple elementary course in history or botany might open these attractive subjects. But while the higher study of history and botany is well provided for, opportunity for continued study in geography is seldom allowed; and geographical investigation is hardly known among us.

Perhaps one reason for this unfortunate neglect is the assumption that geography proper is finished in the schools, and that physical geography is completed in the single course that is allowed in the colleges, and that there is therefore no material for further teaching. Judging by the scarcity of geographical text-books of advanced quality in our language, good argument might be made to this conclusion, especially by those professors of other subjects who have the college courses in physical geography in their hands, and who cannot of course be expected to develop or originate higher courses, but only to reproduce the subject about in the form that it is left by others.

Another reason that might be offered for the discontinuance of geographical studies is that geography is properly continued in history and that physical geography finds its later development in geology; but this view cannot be accepted by those who recognize the fullness of geography as a subject in itself, or by those who know how completely the geographical element is subordinated in the usual presentation of history and geology. It might as well be urged that geography is sufficiently continued in zoölogy or botany, because the study of animals and plants involves the study of their distribution over the earth. In order to perceive more clearly this break in the ascending order of attentions, let us briefly trace the position of geography through our educational system.

At first, in the lower classes of the grammar schools, geography is a congeries of subjects including, besides a central body of real geographical material, various side issues about astronomy, physics, mineralogy, geology, zoölogy, botany, history, government, and economics. This is as it should be; under the broad subject of elementary geography the young scholar naturally makes acquaintance with related subjects that are afterward considered separately. Perhaps the distinguishing mark of the newer order of things in school geography is the increased share of explanatory and rational physiography that it includes, as contrasting with the empirical descriptive geography of earlier methods; and this replacement is a hopeful sign of what must eventually follow, but of which there is as yet not very much indication. A prevailing deficiency of existing elementary methods is the failure to make enough use of the natural illustrations of the subject that abound around all schools in the city and country. There is valiant effort made by many earnest teachers to escape from subjection to the text-book, but the small variety of available elementary literature on geographical subjects makes this effort a difficult one.

In the later grammar-school years geography is generally replaced with history, the natural successor of political geography, for this is only history in its most elementary form. The replacement continues in the high school, and here the various other subjects first encountered under geography are, as a rule, also given individual place, — astronomy, physics, physical geography (including meteorology), botany, zoölogy, and occasionally mineralogy and geology; although the last subject is too often unhappily treated by beginning with a book instead of in the field, the natural geological laboratory with which country schools at least are so well provided. As far as physical geography is concerned, the high-school course suffers from lack of illustrative material as well as from the small variety of good books for side reading. Normal schools too often fail to give a clear understanding of the physiographic aspects of geography to their embryonic teachers, because they place so little emphasis on the needed geological basis of the subject, and especially on the field study of geology. They likewise fail to familiarize their students by observation sufficiently with elementary facts about the apparent movement of the sun, the winds, and other commonplace phenomena which are of great educational value in the early stages of geography. As a result, most children learn from a book, and not from the sky, that the sun's noon altitude and the length of the days change with the seasons. This not only teaches the subject badly, but also dulls the child's observation and intelligence by failing to give him a legitimate opportunity for exercise. I believe that in most cases it would be more advantageous to the teacher's future worth to devote less time in normal schools to comparatively abstract philosophical and psychological studies, and more time to subjects that will have an immediate application in school work.

All the branches from elementary geography that are specialized in the high school have more or less recognition in college and university studies, but geography itself has practically none, and physical geography has too little for its needs. Yet who can doubt that the very subjects which constitute the core of school geography are worthy of broader treatment in college, and of investigation in the university. The geography of the grand divisions of the lands is susceptible of expanded collegiate treatment such as it receives at not a few German gymnasia and universities. Economic geography, a consideration of the larger aspects of commercial geography, might be made a most useful collegiate associate of economics. So with physical geography, and especially with the modern aspects of the subject for which many prefer the special name of physiography. Here is a subject, the outgrowth of modern geology, whose educational values are as yet hardly sounded, but whose attractions are everywhere admitted; nevertheless it is seldom allowed adequate recognition by being made the first responsibility of a college professor. Still less frequently is it made the field of investigation in higher university work, although its promise of fruitful return is not exceeded by that of any other of the subjects to which attention is now so generally turned by means of advanced courses, laboratory facilities, and especially prepared teachers. In all this we are not behind the English universities, but we are far behind those of Germany, where professorships in geography are not uncommon.

In another branch of educational ascent the insufficient attention allowed to physical geography is painfully marked. This is in those scientific schools which teach engineering, and whose students furnish the topographical surveyors by whom our national and state surveys are made. So strongly is the attention of the faculties of these schools turned toward the mathematical and technical sides of the instruction that is required as preparation for methods of work employed by the topographer and engineer, that little time is left for the study of the great subject of the topographer's attention; namely, the surface of the earth and the expression of its wonderfully modulated forms. The young men who are graduated from scientific schools and who undertake the responsible task of mapping our country in state and national surveys must, with few exceptions, begin the work with no adequate understanding of the subject they are to work upon, although they may be well instructed as to the use of the level and the plane table with which they are to work.

There is one phase of this subject of map making that is not generally understood. It is too commonly supposed that a map is made entirely by measurement; that it is necessarily accurate because the topographer carefully measured the forms of the land before him when the map was made. Now, while it occasionally happens that an elaborately measured survey has been made, — as, for example, of the area of Central Park in New York City, for the use of the landscape gardener by whom its natural beauties were so well utilized, — it is practically never the case in this country that a minutely elaborate method is employed on government surveys of large areas. The surveyor fixes by accurate measurement a certain number of points, but between these points he must sketch the intervening space. In sketching, he has to reduce the area of the ground before him to a much smaller area on his map sheet; and he must therefore omit many details and represent only the more important features. The process of selection and omission should involve intelligent and systematic generalization based upon an appreciation of the meaning of the landscape and on an understanding of the relation of its primary, secondary, and subordinate features. Without such generalization the map produced is inexpressive, a poor piece of work. If the topographer actually measured every line that he draws, he might be as unintelligent but as faithful as a camera; but he *must* generalize, and to do this he must have an intelligent understanding of this subject — "*l'intelligence du terrain*," as a competent French writer has lately expressed it. But at present the topographer receives only the barest introduction to this division of his life work in the professional school. The instruction that he may have had in physical geography is largely concerned with the larger features of the distribution of land and water and with the greater relief forms of land which he never sees as a whole, and too little concerned with a careful study, classification, and explanation of the more minute land forms with which he will be chiefly occupied all his life. He therefore goes into the field unprepared for some of his most important duties, and if he ever learns them (some topographers never do), it is only at the expense of many seasons of costly experience. The larger features of the world deserve all the attention that they receive in his education, but their value is chiefly in contributing to the development of his general intelligence, not of his professional skill. The smaller features of land form are not systematically taught in any engineering school in this country, as far as I have been able to learn. Until they are, the topographer will be graduated with one important side of his professional education neglected.

Now, in contrast to the existing condition of geographical teaching, let us briefly consider the ideal sequence of geographical studies from the bottom to the top of the educational system, and sketch out at the same time the ideal equipment necessary for the best work in each step of the ascending scale.

The grammar schools would, as a rule, follow their present plan as to time, but their geographical work would be better done. Great care would be taken to give just ideas, especially at the beginning of the study. More use would be made of outdoor observation of many kinds. A greater share of physiographic work would be introduced, thus emphasizing the rational side of the study and displacing something of the empirical descriptive and political geography that now takes up too much time. The teacher would be expected to have practical knowledge based on manual exercises and field observation of the various practical steps in the education of her scholars; and in every step her experience should have a greater, broader extension than can be expected of the boys and girls in her charge. As to equipment, there would be a great increase in the number of available text-books, manuals, and readers, and, let us hope, a general improvement in their quality as well. We should hope to find every grammar school provided with a good topographical map of its district and a good topographical map of its state, with a well-illustrated text explanatory of the latter and therefore including some account of the former. State maps are already distributed in the schools of New Jersey and Rhode Island, but they are not accompanied by explanatory texts, and their usefulness is therefore greatly decreased. Good models of typical land forms would be of great value, but practically none are now on the market. A good collection of wall maps is essential. Small elementary globes for hand study by each scholar are of great importance, not so much for teaching what used to be called "the use of the globes," but for implanting correct introductory ideas of the forms and distribution of land and water. In the private libraries of those teachers who felt a special fondness for this division of their work, we should expect to see maps and texts upon adjacent states. There should be, if possible, a projecting lantern, and a general collection of geographical lantern slides, and some of the governmental maps of the kind referred to below. Current weather maps should be accessible during part of the year at least, and simple meteorological records should be made to serve as the foundation of later systematic study. Besides the thermometer usually kept in the schoolroom for hygienic purposes, another should be provided for outdoor observations.

In the ideal high-school course the geographical basis of history, zoölogy, and botany should be carefully presented whenever those subjects are taught. Physical geography in its more modern form, based on simple geological principles, would replace the more descriptive treatment of the subject now in vogue. Meteorology might well have a half year to itself, for it is a subject that is capable of most satisfactory use as a mental discipline. The teacher should of course be well versed in all the observational work that is expected of her scholars, and her experience in field study should cover a much wider range than is possible around the school where she teaches. What has already been said of normal schools will indicate something of the changes that seem to me most needed there. The teacher of geography in the normal schools should in every case have good training in geological field work. Through no other discipline can the necessary command of the subject be acquired.

In the high-school and normal-school libraries the map collection would include an extended series of wall maps and a whole set of large-scale topographical sheets of the state and perhaps of some of the adjacent states, as well as the general maps of the home state and its neighbors, each with its appropriate text. There would also be a selected list of lantern slides, particularly illustrative of the features of the home state. There should be a considerable number of various governmental maps, of which we now have so large a variety procurable at so low a cost, such as the charts of the coast, of the Mississippi river, and of various topographical features like cañons, mesas, bays, deltas, etc., in different parts of the country.[1] These are of great value in giving large-scale illustrations of actual and important geographical features. A collection of well-made models would also be extremely serviceable. For supplementary reading, a good journal of school geography is very desirable; a valuable publication of this kind exists in Germany, and we may in time have one in this country. It would be particularly useful in the normal schools, and from them would work its way into other schools.

Some indication has already been given of the nature of the geographical instruction that is needed in our colleges. The chief requirements of the desired courses would be that they should build upon the high-school preparation; that they should form the first duties of the professor or professors in charge of them; that they should be thus developed in greater variety and strength and breadth than is now possible; that they should be given not only library collections but laboratory

[1] See *Governmental Maps for Use in Schools*, by Messrs. Davis, King, and Collie. Henry Holt & Co., New York, 1894.

facilities as well, where maps, models, and pictures could be carefully studied. The specific courses most desired are general physiography, general economic geography, special geography of continental areas, the different sections of the last to be given, if desired, only in successive years. The geographical courses in engineering schools should be in grade similar to those of the colleges, but in subject they should be more strictly limited to the practical needs of the student. For the topographical engineer the most serious need is a thorough course in the physiography of the land, based on geology with field work. The chief characteristic of real university work is embraced in the word "opportunity." The opportunity comes partly in association with specialists, who give lectures and hold conferences while carrying on their own investigations, partly in the free use of the university collections, both these opportunities being essential to the vigorous growth of the young geographer. If he looks to physical geography as his chief study, he must be well grounded in geology, always including good field training ; if he specializes in economic or commercial geography, a good knowledge of history must be acquired. The associated subjects of meteorology and climatology call for preparation in physics and mathematics. Oceanography, an undeveloped specialty, requires knowledge of mathematics, physics, chemistry, and biology. In any one of these lines of work the advanced student should always strive to make some original contribution to his subject.

The geographical collections of colleges and universities would of course include practically all that has already been mentioned, and in addition a number of the more important geographical journals : *Petermanns Mittheilungen*, the *Geographisches Jahrbuch*, the (London) *Geographical Journal*, the *Scottish Geographical Magazine*, and of course all the important geographical journals published in this country. Books of travel should be well represented in the college library. Furthermore, a series of grouped sheets of foreign topographical surveys, selected for their illustration of special features, will be found of service. Geographical lantern slides and models are also of great value in collegiate as well as in the earlier stages of instruction; such elaborate models as those made by Heim of Zürich would be especially appropriate in college laboratories. University collections, as differing from college collections, should give greater opportunity for original research ; and for this purpose, besides an extended collection of geographical literature, a series of topographical maps of various countries is of great service. The expense of such a collection is, however, very great.

I shall not attempt to measure the relative importance of these various geographical courses in college and university, for on that question my testimony would probably be prejudiced ; but it may be safely contended that they deserve more attention than they now receive. It is, however, plainly out of the question for all of our colleges and universities to undertake the whole round of geographical studies here outlined and do equal justice to other subjects at the same time. Even our largest universities fall short of the ideal here indicated, and there is no likelihood that all of them will reach it in any short time. Moreover, educators who are interested in other subjects generally contend that they also need and deserve a fuller attention than they receive. It is not probable that any one institution will be so fortunate as to be able to treat all subjects with the fullness that the specialists in each could desire. The solution of the difficulty is not so likely to be found in enormous endowments as it is in the wise distribution of efforts among neighboring institutions. When several colleges in a single state recognize that they cannot all teach all subjects, they may perhaps agree to develop individually, one in some scientific direction, another as a classical institution, a third as a historical, and a fourth as a mathematical center. Each might then give due attention to the general need of more elementary studies, and each might become well equipped in the field that it especially cultivates. The serious student could then resort to the institution which gave his preferred studies the greatest care ; he might follow the practice, not uncommon abroad, of going in his later college years from one institution to another, in order to get from each what it could give best. Hearty cooperation instead of silent or ill-concealed rivalry might then prevail. If four or five colleges or universities, well distributed over the country, included geography along with geology under the group of scientific subjects that they would cultivate most highly, geographers should for many years be well content. It is not to be expected that advanced geographical courses should be largely attended. They will never "pay" for the cost of their establishment, but fortunately this criterion is not one that will determine the advisability of establishing them in the more liberal universities. When geographical courses come to be recognized as important parts of collegiate and higher study, they will be provided for, even if not attended by large classes of students.

It is not, however, my intention to give at this time so much attention to the outlines of geographical courses that are needed in our higher institutions of learning as it is to indicate the need that is felt for these courses both in the work of the professional geographer and in the teaching of geography in the lower schools.

Allusion has been made in several paragraphs to "professional geographers." They do not form a large class of the scientific or technical community, but they include so many different classes of workers that it seems best to enumerate them more in detail.

The topographical surveyor has already been considered. Next let us review the work of the cartographer, or professional map maker, even though he might not consider himself a professional geographer. He is a specialist in these modern days, for he does little work on other subjects than maps; hence, although an artist primarily, he is so distinctly concerned with geographical subjects that he may be included with geographers. His duty is, at first sight, merely to copy faithfully the original field map that is presented for publication, and as far as such copying goes, he is aided much by photography; but when his copying involves reduction of scale or redrawing, it may be far from successful if the artist has no appreciation of his subject. If the map is to be reduced in scale, problems of selection and generalization are presented to the map maker not unlike those encountered by the topographer; and one has only to compare different small-scale maps of the same region to see what caricatures they often are of the true outlines. It would often seem as if the artist had no idea that river courses, shore-lines, and mountain ranges have individual expressions which must be intelligently preserved, when shown at all, if the map is to be faithful to nature, even though its scale is small. There are, of course, some map makers who are well prepared for their profession, but few of them are in this country. We do not often read here, as we may, not infrequently, in the advertisements on *Petermanns .Mittheilungen:* " Wissenschaftlicher Kartograph, vielseitig gebildet, durchaus selbständige Kraft, wünscht kartographische Arbeiten zu übernehmen ; " or " Kartograph, tüchtiger Zeichner mit geographische Fachkenntnissen, " etc. We shall not produce the highest class of maps until scientific as well as technical preparation is expected of the draughtsman. Although few persons enter this profession, and although they seldom attain individual reputation outside of their craft, nevertheless their works are widespread, and from beginning to end of educational progress they determine a large number of geographical conceptions ; hence the work should be good and the workers well prepared for the work. But until the cartographer is educated to select, omit, and generalize with appreciative skill, his maps will be inexpressive. Many an example of inexpressive maps in school books might be given, and a few examples of good school maps might be found to present by way of contrast ; but to that I shall not turn here, reserving it for a special article elsewhere.

The explorer so often directs his attention to other subjects than careful description of the lands over which he travels that he cannot in all cases be called a geographer ; but most explorers have geography as a prime subject before them, and they ought therefore to be trained geographers ; but unfortunately this is seldom the case. The usual accounts of travel in remote regions by brave and energetic searchers after novelty give little indication of careful preparation for geographical observation. The untrained traveler does not, in the first place, really see nearly all the facts that are before him ; for seeing requires trained sight. He may look at them day after day, but many of them make no conscious impression. Although he, of course, recognizes the more important elements of form, he is generally ignorant of their natural associates, and hence fails to search for them ; or, if he finds them by chance, he does not record them systematically. The records that he makes are in untechnical language, partly because he is seldom well versed in the limited number of technical geographical terms already invented, partly for the more serious reason that there is as yet so little development of scientific geographical terminology that the art of accurate geographical description necessarily remains for the present in a backward state. If the explorer finds something which he attempts not only to describe but to explain, the chances are that he will make a mistake, for he is not trained in the interpretation of past processes through present forms. The only way in which these deficiencies in the explorer's work can be corrected is by systematic geographical training of high collegiate grade.

The reports of our state and national surveys, as well as those of Europe, usually contain chapters of more or less detail concerning the physical geography of their districts. These are of course written by geologists, for it is not yet the practice for such surveys to recognize the geographer as a specialist distinct from the geologist, nor even to require that a knowledge of the two subjects should be combined in the geologist. The chapters referred to hardly constitute more than a fair beginning of what is wanted, although in recent years there are certain notable exceptions to this statement. In those state surveys that are concerned with the general natural history of their domain, careful study of geographical features by well-prepared specialists is as worthy an object of attention as the careful study of petrography, or as the study of birds, or Crustacea. This is particularly true when it is remembered that the survey reports are prepared not simply for use by professional experts, but for the body of intelligent, yet not professional, people of the state. That this is so is often indicated by the presence of several general explanatory chapters by way of introduction to the more technical parts of the reports. To this class of readers, geographical descriptions are particularly appropriate.

Again, for our school-teachers : it is too much to expect them to struggle through the technical chapters on geology, petrography, and paleontology, in search of information about their home state for use in teaching. But they would eagerly study geographical chapters, and would, moreover, use them to the great improvement of their school work. It is curious that our state surveyors have not recognized that, by attracting the interests of a large body of teachers, they would secure a new support for their legislative appropriations; and that additional support is often wanted is only too plainly shown by the instability of many of the surveys. Nothing would so generally secure this as chapters on local geography, prepared expressly for the use of the teachers of the state. At least some of the geologists on the surveys ought to be geographers as well.[1]

Writers of geographical text-books ought, of course, to be geographers, yet it is only too manifest, on examining such books, that their authors are seldom trained in the scientific phases of their fundamental subject. It is hardly surprising that they are untrained, for, if not self-taught, the training that they need can be had at very few places in this country.

It is perhaps on account of the lack of opportunity for professional training in geography that professorships in this subject are not more generally established; but this can hardly be more than a subordinate reason. If geographers were actively called for, they would certainly be forthcoming, even if special study in Europe were necessary for their preparation. Such was the case with petrographers a few years ago, but there is no lack of them now, and no lack of opportunity for their instruction in our own colleges.

There is much said about the connection between history and geography; but inasmuch as few, if any, historians are proficient in minute geographical knowledge, except so far as it concerns the mere location of various important points, it seems warrantable to suppose that a new light may be shed on the connection between the two studies when it is examined by experts who are well qualified in the two subjects that are concerned. The young historian, who inquires for a field in which he may gather

[1] I have elsewhere enlarged upon this subject: "The Improvement of Geographical Teaching," *National Geographical Magazine*, V (1893), 68; "A Step toward Improvement in Teaching Geography," Leaflet No. 11, January, 1894, Harvard Teachers' Association; "Geographical Work for State Geological Surveys," *Bulletin of the Geological Society of America*, V (1893), 604-608.

a neglected harvest, can find it in the space between these two generally separated areas of study, or rather in the space where the two ought to overlap.

It appears, then, that explorers, topographers, cartographers, teachers, and writers on geography all lack adequate preparation in their chosen subject. Compare their opportunities in school and college with those opened to students who decide on a career as chemists, physicists, zoölogists, or botanists. In these subjects there is an elaborate series of courses of instruction under carefully prepared instructors, all aided by well-equipped laboratories, all supported by extended collections of text-books, periodicals, and advanced memoirs. The young man or woman who wishes to enter upon a life work in any of these studies may prepare for it by as many years of well-directed study under experts as his or her purse will allow. Any one of these subjects may be pursued all through many of our larger colleges as the chief object of attention; and in the larger universities, graduate courses are provided in the several subjects, which may easily occupy two or three years. If the student's funds are exhausted, there are generally fellowships for the aid of those who give promise of excellent work. At the close of such a preparation the student has a wide knowledge of the subject in general, and a precise knowledge of certain parts of it; and in his own particular line he is often in advance of the world. He is ready for professional service in scientific bureaus, state experiment stations, colleges, and schools. He has, of course, still much to learn, but what he lacks chiefly is experience and the broader views of the relations of things that come only with living through a period of perhaps ten or twenty years after graduation.

The advanced instruction in these various subjects is not maintained because it is financially profitable, but because it is the plain duty of the university to offer to those who wish it an opportunity for study in as many of the lines of higher research as possible. Students who specialize in these subjects do not look forward to great fortunes, but rather to the satisfaction of living an intellectual life, hoping of course that it may lead to some reasonable measure of home comfort. Geography calls for and deserves as good an opportunity as that which its associated sciences enjoy. When this opportunity is offered by certain universities and is widely known, explorers will be expected to prepare for their work systematically, studying geography, if they wish to be geographical explorers, as assiduously as they now study botany, if they wish to be botanical explorers. Topographers will then be expected to enter their work reasonably well informed on the meaning of the most important subject that will come before them. Map publishers will not engage the services of young cartographers who cannot work intelligently. Teachers in all grades of geography will be held to a higher quality of work than they can now reach. The result of all this will be the gradual introduction of a higher standard in all that pertains to geographical matters; and the reaction from this result will be most favorably felt in a better understanding of the foundations of life and work all around us. When this time comes, the ascending order of attentions that geography deserves will be better filled out.

Let us next consider the effect of this geographical regeneration on the descending order of attentions by which the results gained through the professional investigators may be passed down into the lower schools, thus contributing their share to the enrichment of the early years of education.

It is generally recognized that improvements in methods of consideration and presentation in the lower schools are introduced chiefly by those who have studied in higher grades than those in which they teach. The recent report of the Committee of Fifteen emphasizes this principle by urging that all teachers in the elementary schools shall have had a high-school education, and that the high-school teachers shall have had a college course. The manner in which the requirements for admission to college determine improvement of teaching in the schools is also a case in point. Greater attention to English composition, Latin at sight, laboratory methods in physics, and ability to deal with original problems in geometry, — all are associated either with the suggestions of college faculties or of school-teachers who are college graduates. It is especially through the broadening influences of college and university work that traditional methods are refreshed and that the newer contributions to a subject are infused into the lower grades of teaching. Geography truly shows some signs of awakening to the need of modern knowledge and better methods on the part of its teachers, but little is as yet accomplished in this direction because of the break between the investigators and the teachers of the secondary schools. This is the interruption in the descending order of attentions, across which newer and better and broader views now pass so slowly.

As this interruption is lessened by giving a larger share to geographical subjects in higher instruction, two good results may be confidently expected. In the first place, the method of treatment of the subject as a whole will improve, for there is no place where so thorough a consideration is given to the various relations of a subject as in the advanced classes of a university. Professional experts are apt to work for themselves or for each other, and their manner of treatment therefore fails to include the relation of the higher and the lower parts of their subject. Teachers in the secondary schools are, as has already been pointed out, very rarely acquainted with investigation or investigators; they have little share in or association with origination; they are in nearly all cases closely limited to reproducing the statements of text-books. The university professor has an exceptional position between these two extremes. He is nowadays, fortunately for himself, expected to be a producer; he is expected to be personally familiar with investigation and investigators; he is increasingly involved in relations with the secondary schools, and he thus becomes acquainted with their limitations and their needs. Not less important is his close association with the select body of advanced students with whom he continually discusses new problems as they arise; and this is highly advantageous to all concerned, for in these discussions it is pretty certain that crudities of manner or matter will be thrashed out. This style of treatment is not found in any other part of the round of attentions that the well-cared-for subject receives. Discussions in scientific societies where expert meets expert are brief, and too often insufficient for thorough scrutiny. They truly have the advantage of being as a rule between persons of what would be commonly called "equal standing"; but the discussions between a professor and his advanced student, carried on around a table where all sit on chairs of the same height, familiarly gathering together week after week, are by no means always unequal contests. They are admirably adapted to searching out the strong and weak points of a subject.

The product of university discussion is a body of seasoned and tested knowledge, well arranged for use. The knowledge comes in part by inheritance from earlier years ; but fresh additions are constantly made by contemporary experts, by the professors themselves, and by their advanced students. The seasoning and testing of this body of knowledge is peculiarly the function of the university ; a study that is unfortunate enough not to receive this phase of attention will certainly remain in a backward condition. No other treatment that a subject receives can replace the attention bestowed upon it in the university. The recognition of geography as a fitting subject for higher instruction and investigation must therefore not only result in improving the education of those whose occupations call for a thorough knowledge of the subject; it will also improve the condition of the subject itself, so that future work upon it can be done both by school-teacher and expert to greater advantage.

The effect of a better-ordered condition of any subject as developed by university presentation and discussion is especially apparent in secondary schools. Improvement in the schools is of high importance not only because it reacts favorably on all later studies, but also because it affects a greater number of persons than can be reached anywhere else through the educational system. It is largely for these reasons that the university study of geography seems to me to be especially important. It will not only serve to improve the condition of geography in general and to give better preparation to professional geographers of all kinds, but it will also have a peculiarly invigorating effect on the fundamental subject of geography in the schools.

The progress of university influence on geography from the higher institutions into the schools will be easily traced. It will be from among those students who specialize in geography in the universities that new professorships of geography will be filled in the colleges and professional schools. The students of geography in college will take places as teachers of geography and the allied subjects in high schools and normal schools. The graduates of these schools will carry the better understanding that they have gained of the subject down into the grammar schools, and thus at last the subject will be begun aright at its beginning. In that good time coming, college students who look forward to becoming teachers of geography in high and normal schools will study geology, including field work, along with their geography, and they will hereby gain a sense of the real meaning of geographical facts. Thus equipped they will carry their pupils much farther than they now advance, and consequently such of the high-school pupils as look forward to becoming teachers in the grammar schools will be able to enter their work with a much better understanding of it than is now commonly possessed by school-teachers of that grade. Thus guided the young scholars will find their native intelligence fully exercised in the study of the wonderfully varied facts of geographical form and distribution and in the understanding of the interesting correlations by which these facts are associated with others. This will be better for school children than the dulling or blunting of their intelligence that has been so often practiced in the empirical study of a rational subject.

IX

PHYSICAL GEOGRAPHY AS A UNIVERSITY STUDY

The Logical Method in Geography. Success in the study of geography, as in the study of other subjects, depends largely on the share of mental light with which the facts are illuminated. For example, during the two weeks in which my class in physical geography has recently been occupied with the tides, a long roll of tracing linen has been hanging on the laboratory wall, containing copies of a half-month of tidal curves at Honolulu, Boston, Philadelphia, Port Townsend (Oregon), and Point Clear on the gulf of Mexico. The essential facts of tidal oscillation are thus exhibited with great clearness. While these curves were illuminated only by the light that came in through the laboratory windows, the facts were but imperfectly perceived. The more peculiar variations of the curves involved in the diurnal inequality of tidal amplitude and interval could not be discovered by eyesight alone, at least not by the simple eyesight of such observers as are found among average college students; but during the same week that the class was examining these tidal tracings in the laboratory, and thereby gaining an approach to a simple inductive knowledge of the principal facts of the subject, the problem was taken up from the other side in lectures, which discussed the theoretical consequences of the interaction of two bodies, and deduced from the theory of gravitation a number of special results that ought to occur if the theory of the tides is correct. As an aid in this deductive discussion I placed three great circles of paper around a globe so as to represent the theoretical arrangement of tidal deformation, with the high-tide poles and the low-tide equator and their relation to the latitude circles of the earth. Now, returning to the tidal diagrams with the results of the tidal theory in mind, it is only the poorly trained, the dull, or the stolid student who feels no mental satisfaction in the successful meeting of the facts of observation and the consequences of theory. Facts before noted, but not understood, now gain meaning; facts before disconnected now fall into their natural relationships; facts before unnoticed are now searched for and found, and wonder is even excited that they were not seen sooner. Neither induction nor deduction alone satisfies the mind. However full the series of facts, however extended the deductions from theory, both facts and deductions are of small value while they remain unmated. Properly confronted, they pair off, and each one reacts on its mate most favorably. If the facts are well observed and recorded, if the theory is justly based and logically extended to its consequences, the inductions and deductions mutually complete each other, and the mind is satisfied. The window light then seems a dull illumination of the tidal tracings compared to the light that shines on them from the understanding.

As with the tides of the ocean, so with the forms of the land. They are but half seen if examined only by daylight. They are less than half appreciated if seen without an understanding of the generalizations by which they are correlated. The more complete the mental scheme by which an ideal system of topographical forms is rationally explained, the more clearly can the physical eye perceive the actual features of the land surface and the more definitely can it record them in mental impressions. Topographical forms are so varied, and often so complicated, that the outer eye alone is no more competent to detect all their intricacies and correlations than it is to discover all the peculiarities of the tidal curves. It is true that with exceptionally keen powers of observation and with unusual opportunity for deliberate examination, the unaided eye may come to see more and more of the ultimate facts; but these conditions are so rare that they need not be considered. The average eye and the usual time allowed for observation do not suffice; they must be supplemented by the quickened insight that comes from rational understanding.

No better confirmation of this conclusion can be found than in the experience of those who have to employ engineers who are untrained in geology and geography to make topographical maps.

The work that such surveyors produce is rigid, mechanical, unsympathetic, inaccurate, inexpressive. If time were allowed them to run out all their contours by actual measurement, an exact map might be produced, but neither time nor money can be devoted to so slow and expensive a method. Even the best surveys are necessarily sketched in great part, and the topographer must appreciate his subject before he can sketch it. He must have a clear insight into its expression; his outer eye must be supplemented by his inner eye. Then he can make up a valuable, even though not an expensive, map. I do not mean for a moment that he is to invent and not to observe; that he is to make a fancy picture instead of a true likeness. My point is simply that the difficulty of making a true likeness is so great that all aids toward it must be employed; and one of the chief aids to sharp outsight is clear insight. How can a clear geographical insight be gained?

An analogy with the study of the tides may still serve us. The facts of the tides are first presented in what seems like a bewildering, even an overwhelming, variety, without suggestion of order or meaning. While these facts are studied and classified, let the system of the tides be deduced in accordance with accepted physical laws. Let the tidal theory be followed far enough to discover consequences so numerous and so intricate that they cannot be imitated by chance. Neither the inductive nor the deductive work should have precedence. They should advance together, but without confusing one with the other. When both processes are well advanced, let the facts be reëxamined in the light of the theory, and summon a critical judgment to determine how far the reports of outsight and insight agree. Success in such study requires that the facts shall have been closely observed, clearly described, and fairly generalized, the inductive results thus gained being held apart by themselves. It requires, also, that the theory shall have been logically extended to its legitimate consequences, the deductive results thus secured being stored away in a special mental compartment. Then, in due order, bring forth the corresponding members of the two classes of results and judge of the success of the theory by the agreements thus discovered.

Let the same method be applied in the study of geography. Set an abundant array of facts before the class in the laboratory. Let the facts be examined and classified as far as possible, simply according to their apparent features and without regard to explanation. At the same time, present an outline of a deductive geographical system in the lecture room. During the advance of the two lines of work, compare their results frequently, but do not confuse them. In a few months a large array of facts may be examined, an extended deductive system may be developed, and the two may be compared in the most thorough manner. Every comparison aids further advance in both parts of the work. Both outsight and insight are cultivated. A geographical understanding, based on a proper combination of many mental faculties, is aroused and strengthened. The real study of geography is well begun. The several steps involved in this plan of work may now be traced in some detail.

Introductory Illustration of Facts. It is well at the outset to present a collection of varied geographical illustrations, in order to bring prominently before the mind the great variety of the facts with which we have to deal. At the same time a preliminary exercise is gained in the interpretation of different means of geographical representation. The following list will serve to indicate the class of materials from which selection may be made for a first week's laboratory work :

Heim's model of an Alpine torrent ; Harden's model of Morrison's cove, Pennsylvania, or a photograph of this model, or of Branner's model of Arkansas ; Jackson's photograph of the deep valley of the Blackwater in the plateau of West Virginia ; Hölzel's oleograph of the Hungarian plain ; Becker's elaborately colored and shaded relief map of the canton Glarus, Switzerland; a group of contoured map sheets, as the twelve that embrace the Berkshire plateau and the Connecticut valley in western Massachusetts, or the nine that embrace the zigzag ridges northeast of Harrisburg, Pennsylvania, mounted as a wall map for better convenience in study; a hachured map, such as that of the Scotch Highlands, in a group of sheets of the British Ordnance Survey, also mounted as a wall map ; a tinted relief map, as of New Jersey, from the topographical atlas of that state, etc.

The need of the systematic study of geography is apparent from the difficulty that most students have in expressing the facts portrayed in these various illustrations. Words are not easily summoned to describe them. Many of the illustrations are on a much larger scale than is commonly employed in atlases, and the ordinary accounts of direction and distance, usually employed in describing similar maps, are at once felt to be insufficient to express the varied reliefs here exhibited. How can the student best approach a perception and an understanding of the facts before him and at the same time gain an ability to describe them in fitting language?

Insufficiency of Inductive Study. The ordinary fund of geographical terms does not suffice to describe good maps and models with sufficient exactness. Further than this, a few questions from the instructor will show that many facts plainly set forth are not seen at all. Interpretations and correlations are not even suspected. This is perfectly natural when it is remembered that most college students have never been taught to observe closely or to express themselves clearly in well-chosen words. It is still more natural when it is remembered that the little knowledge of geography that they have brought from school is hardly more than a confused memory of an unsystematic, empirical text-book. Whether their observation is directed to the semblance of facts in maps, views, and models, or to the actual facts of outdoor nature, observation is attempted only with the outer eye; the inner eye has never been opened. The idea that all the forms of the land are systematically developed has never been implanted in their minds. They possess no general and well-tested deductive understanding of the development of land forms, no system of terrestrial morphology. The facts of observation excite no harmonious response from the corresponding members of a deductive geographical scheme.

While the study of geography remains in this incomplete and illogical condition, it is a blind study, although it is carried on chiefly through the eye. While the life of the features of the earth's surface is not perceived, geography is a dead study. The features of the land that the outer eye sees will awaken no sufficient sympathy in the understanding until the scientific imagination has deduced a whole system of geography, filled with mental pictures of all kinds of forms in all stages of development, among which the report from the outer eye may find its mate. However faithfully mere observation is carried on, the impression on the retina might as well be the record on a photographic plate, as far as appreciative insight and understanding are concerned. Let us therefore strive to complete a deductive geographical scheme, even as we strive to complete our deductive tidal scheme, until it shall at last be ready to meet not only all the actual variety of nature, but all the possible variety of nature. Only when such a scheme as this is well advanced is the student ready to appreciate the materials presented in the laboratory work. The maps and models shown in the first week are therefore repeatedly introduced with others in the systematic advance of the course, and the student may gauge his progress by the increased meaning that these illustrations gain on every return.

Let us next consider the development of a deductive geographical scheme, by which external observation is to be supplemented and completed. Let it be understood at the outset that to exceed the variety of nature is an extended enterprise, a remote and ideal goal, toward which we strive. Let no excessive flight of theory carry us far from the earth and overcome us in mid-air. Let us carefully guard against an unwarranted wandering of the imagination by frequent conferences with the facts of observation, hoping to return, like old Antæus, strengthened for new efforts after every touch of Mother Earth.

The Deductive Geographical Scheme. It is the fundamental generalization of elementary geology to note that the lands are wasting away under the destructive attack of the weather. The hardest rocks decay; their waste creeps and washes down to lower and lower levels, never satisfied till it reaches the sea. However broad a plateau, however lofty a mountain range, it must, if time enough be allowed, be worn down to sea-level under the weather; and the unceasing beat of the sea on its shores must reduce it still lower to a submarine platform. Since the remote beginning of geological time there has been time enough and plenty to spare to reduce all the lands to such a submarine platform; but as high lands still exist, it must be concluded that they are revived from time to time and from place to place by some forces antagonistic to those of sub-aërial denudation. In whatever way a new mass is offered to the wasting forces, let us call the forces that uplift it "initial forces," and the forms thus given "initial forms." Let all the forces of wasting be called destructional forces; let the sea-level surface — down to which a sufficiently long attack of the destructional forces will reduce any initial form — be called the ultimate base-level; and let the portion of geological time required for the accomplishment of this task be called a physiographic cycle. Initial forces, destructive forces, base-level, and cycle are our primary terms. A full understanding of the destructional processes requires deliberate study of mineralogy and lithology, chemistry, and structural geology; a good understanding of initial forces and processes has not yet been gained, but a review of the advance made towards it carries the student through a wide range of geological theories in which physics and mathematics are continually appealed to, — perhaps sometimes with too great a confidence in the applicability of their conclusions concerning an ideal earth to the case of the actual earth.

If the cycle of destructive development is not interrupted, any initial form will pass through a series of sequential forms and will ultimately be reduced to a monotonous base-level plain of denudation. This is a broad abstract statement. It is simply the first framework of the geographical scheme. It is a mere sketch in faint outline, needing all manner of finishing before its full meaning can be made out. It must be filled in by the gradual addition of details. The first step involves the recognition of the systematic series of sequential forms produced during the accomplishment of the destructive work. This should be considered before classifying the various kinds of initial forms on which the destructional processes begin their tasks. Whatever initial form exists at the beginning of the cycle, there is a certain general succession of sequential features common to nearly all cases of physiographic development. The understanding of this succession calls for the study of river systems and the general drainage of the land under their guidance, because it is so largely under the control of these processes that the destructive forces do their work.

Initial Drainage. At the beginning of a cycle there are relatively broad, massive forms on which the carving of the destructive forces has made no mark. The unconcentrated drainage, or wet-weather wash, takes its way down the steepest slopes of the initial surface, until the supplies from either side meet obliquely in the trough lines, forming initial streams; these unite, forming initial drainage systems. If the trough lines are systematically arranged, as among the corrugations of mountain folds, the initial drainage system is definitely located; if the trough lines are faintly marked and lead irregularly about, as on the nearly level surface of a plateau, the drainage is essentially vague and unsystematic. If the general descent of the trough lines is here and there reversed into ascent, lakes are accumulated in the basins thus determined; and this is very common. If the descent of the trough lines is locally intensified, initial falls or rapids are developed; but this is relatively rare.

Consequent Drainage. The initial streams run down their troughs, carrying along the waste that is washed into them, and trenching channels beneath the initial surface, or filling initial hollows; that is, degrading or aggrading their course, as the necessities demand. As soon as they thus depart from their initial arrangement, they may be called consequent streams. It is true that the initial phase of a drainage system endures only a moment; yet it seems advisable to recognize this phase by employing a special name for it before introducing the term " consequent," which indicates the much longer phase that next follows. As long as a stream flows on a line that is essentially the perpetuation of its initial course, it may be called a consequent stream; the trench that it cuts and the valley that is formed by the widening of the trench may be included under the name "consequent valley." Initial features are encroached upon as the consequent features make their appearance. An initial lake decreases in size by filling at the inlet and cutting down at the outlet; while thus dwindling away it is a consequent lake. A fall or cascade recedes from its initial position, but as long as it endures it is a consequent fall.

Subsequent Drainage Features. As the consequent streams deepen their valleys beneath the initial surface, it often happens that they discover structures of unequal hardness. If, in passing downstream, a weak structure succeeds a hard structure, the valley will be quickly deepened in the former and slowly in the latter; a local increase of slope appears and a fall or cascade is the result. This is a subsequent fall on a consequent stream. It endures until the harder structure is worn down or back so far that it overtakes the deepening of the stream bed below the fall. The extinction of falls is accomplished in adolescence on large streams and on tilted rocks, but it may not be reached until maturity on the smaller streams in regions of horizontal strata.

A further consequence of the discovery of the variable resistance of internal structure is the variable rate at which the narrow young consequent valley widens into the more mature open valley. If the consequent stream crosses a local transverse belt of hard rocks, the gorge-like form of the valley walls may there be retained into the maturity of the region as a whole. If it crosses a belt of weak rocks, the consequent valley may there widen so greatly as to develop other valleys on either side of its path. Thus many a transverse consequent stream, cutting its valleys across belts of harder and softer structures, allows the development of longitudinal valleys on every belt of weak structure that it traverses, while the intermediate belts of harder structure stand up as longitudinal dividing ridges. The longitudinal streams and valleys are then called subsequent branches of the transverse consequent streams and valleys. Each of the subsequent streams deepens its valley only as fast as the downstream deepening of the consequent valley permits.

It is extremely important to recognize the difference thus indicated between consequent and subsequent streams. The first control the drainage of a region in its early stages of development. The second are of increasing importance in the secondary and later stages of growth, when they share the drainage of the region with the surviving consequent streams. Subsequent falls frequently appear on consequent streams, but they are rare on subsequent streams.

It is manifest that the development of subsequent streams will progress to the greatest extent in regions of disordered and complicated structure, in which the attitude of the rocks is varied, and in which contrasts of hardness are well marked. Such is the case in mountainous regions. On the other hand, regions of horizontal structure have no normal subsequent streams. All the branch streams are either perpetuated consequent streams, or else they are developed under accidental controls, of which no definite account can be given. It is to these self-guided streams that I have applied the term "insequent."

Divides. The initial divides waste slowly and become consequent divides. They are well defined in a region of distinct initial relief; they are vague or practically absent on the even surface of young plains where the drainage areas are really undivided. As subsequent streams develop, especially in regions of tilted structure, they frequently split a consequent divide and make two subsequent divides, between which lies the growing subsequent valley. As the subsequent divides are split farther and farther apart, lateral subsequent streams are developed down the internal slopes of the subsequent valley, and these are in headwater opposition to the lateral streams on the diminishing slopes of the adjacent consequent valleys. During changes thus produced in the position of divides, they migrate by slow creeping as long as the competing streams are in headwater opposition; but if, as sometimes happens, the head of an encroaching subsequent stream pushes its divide back until it cuts into the side of a consequent stream, then the divide leaps around the consequent headwaters above the point of capture, and a considerable area that had been tributary to the captured stream is suddenly transferred to the capturing stream.

A limit of these rearrangements is gradually approached. The persistent consequent streams and the successful subsequent streams come to an understanding about their drainage areas. The divides as well as the streams are then maturely adjusted to the structures on which they are developed, and thenceforward further change is slow.

Stream Profiles. Let us next examine the changes produced in the initial profile of the troughs where the first streams settled. The irregularities of the initial profile which determine lakes and falls are in most cases soon extinguished. The profile of a consequent stream may for a time possess unequal slopes at its subsequent falls, but it soon attains a tolerably systematic curve of descent, steeper near the headwaters, flatter near the mouth. While the young stream has abundant fall and rapid current, with moderate load delivered from the relatively simple initial and consequent slopes of its basin, it deepens its trench rapidly. But as the profile becomes flatter and the current runs slower, and as the area of wasting slopes increases by the deepening of the consequent valleys and the development of subsequent valleys, a time will soon arrive when the carrying power is reduced to equality with the load; and from this time on the deepening of the valley is very much slower than before. It is only as the load from the wasting slopes decreases in amount that the deepening can go on. Following certain French writers, the profile of the stream when this balanced condition is reached has been called the "profile of equilibrium." The term is inconveniently long, but the idea is of essential importance. Mr. Gilbert has recently suggested to me that a stream in this condition of balance between degrading and aggrading might be called a "graded stream," and its slope a "graded slope."

It is sometimes said that streams in this condition have reached base-level; but this introduces a confusion of ideas that should be avoided. For example, given two initial areas of similar form and altitude and under equivalent climatic conditions, let one be made of resistant rocks and the other of weak rocks. The base-level is the same for both. The streams will cut deep into the harder mass, producing strong relief before reaching a graded profile, because its waste is shed so slowly that the streams can carry it on a faint slope. They can cut only shallow valleys in the weaker mass, for its waste will be shed so rapidly that a steep slope is needed by the streams to carry the waste away. The contrast between the two areas is strengthened if the region of harder structure has a plentiful rainfall and the region of weaker structure has a light rainfall. All of these points of difference are with difficulty stated, if the streams are said to have reached base-level when their carrying power is reduced to equality with their load.

In certain cases it seems to be possible for a stream to cut down its profile to a gentler grade in its early adolescence than is suitable to later adolescence and maturity. If we conceive that the load offered by the waste from the valley slopes continues to increase after the grading of the stream has been reached, then the grade must be steepened again by the deposition of the excess of load, thus increasing carrying power and decreasing load and maintaining an equilibrium. Local examples of this relation are often seen in valleys among mountains, where a lateral stream is depositing an alluvial fan in the larger valley that it enters. The larger valley was deepened before the lateral valley had gained a considerable area of wasting slopes; but as the lateral valley grows headwards and discharges an increasing volume of waste, it cannot all be carried by the main stream, and hence the main valley is clogged up, and its grade is somewhat increased.

Stages in the Cycle of Geographical Development. Following the terminology of organic growth, it is convenient to speak of the successive stages in the physiographic cycle as infancy, youth, adolescence, maturity, old age, and perhaps second childhood. Let us consider particularly the activities of the drainage system as determined by the topographical form of a region in its different stages.

In infancy the rainfall is slowly concentrated from the broad initial surface; it is only gradually collected into streams; it is often delayed in lakes. Much of it is lost by evaporation, and the ratio of discharge at the river mouth to rainfall over the river basin is relatively low. The initial streams simply adopt the courses offered to them, without the least consideration or foresight regarding the difficulties that these courses may involve in the process of valley trenching. The load that they have to carry is relatively light, being only the waste that creeps and washes down the broad initial slopes under the guidance of the unconcentrated drainage.

In youth and adolescence the drainage lines are increased in number and greatly improved in their ability to gather and discharge the rainfall quickly. Numerous little trenches are incised in the broad initial surface, and the distance that the land waste washes and creeps under the guidance of unconcentrated drainage is much lessened; delay in lakes is decreased; the steep lateral slopes of the young consequent valleys furnish an increasing amount of load to the streams, although they still as a rule have carrying power to spare in their impetuous currents. A good beginning is made in the search for the best location of subsequent streams. As the subsequent streams become better developed in later adolescence, the original, broad initial forms are minutely carved, many subsequent divides are established, the discharge of rainfall is very prompt, and the load of waste that the streams have to carry is notably increased.

In maturity the relief retains much of the intensity of adolescence and adds thereto a great variety of features. The valley lines are closely adjusted to the structure of the region, this condition having been gained by a delicate and thorough process of natural selection, in which the most suitable drainage lines survive, and the less suitable ones are shortened or extinguished. The impetuosity of youth has disappeared ; all the larger streams have developed grades on which their ability to do work is nicely adjusted to the work that they have to do ; the lower courses already show signs of age, while the upper twig-like branches are relatively youthful. The whole drainage system is earnestly at work in its task of base-leveling the region, and the forms that the region has assumed bear witness to the close search made by the streams for every available line of effective work.

From this time onward there is a general fading away of strength and variety, both of forms and activities. The deepening of the valleys progresses even more slowly than the slow wasting away of the hilltops ; the relief fades ; the load offered to the stream lessens. The rainfall slowly decreases as a normal consequence of decrease of altitude ; the ratio of river discharge to rainfall decreases ; the small headwater branches shorten and dwindle away ; the close adjustment of stream to structure is more or less lost, especially by the larger rivers, which meander and wander somewhat freely over the peneplain of denudation. Extreme old age or second childhood is, like first childhood, characterized by imperfect work ; activities that were undeveloped in the earlier stage have been lost in the later stage.

All this should be so carefully imagined and so frequently reviewed that the orderly sequence of changes may pass easily before the mind. The mind should come to be in so close a sympathy with the progress of the cycle as to forget human measures of time and catch instead the rhythm of geographical development, even to the point of almost wishing to hurry to one place or another where some change of drainage or of form is imminent for fear of failing to be in time to see it in its present stage.

Shore-Lines. While the sub-aërial forces are denuding the surface of the land, the waves are beating on the shore and reducing the land mass to a submarine platform. They begin their work on a level line, contouring around the slope of the land mass as it is offered to them. The contour is simple if the sea lies on a rising sea-bottom, evenly spread over with sedimentary deposits ; the contour is irregular if the sea lies on a depressed land, more or less roughened by previous denudation. The waves of a great ocean work rapidly on a leeward shore, especially if it has a steep slope and if its rocks are not too hard ; but if the descent to deeper water is very gradual, the waves may for a time spend their force chiefly on the bottom, building offshore bars with the material they gather up, and thus deepening the water outside of the bars for a better attack on the land later on. The shore-line is generally simplified as the attack advances, but it may for a time become more irregular if the waves are strong and the land structure is of diverse resistances. Its changes deserve as careful an analysis as is given to the forms of the land, but they cannot be traced here for lack of space.

Illustrations of the Deductive Scheme. However much the advance of a deductive scheme of study may be aided by reference to concrete illustrations during its progress, its statement should be abstract, in order to emphasize the essentially deductive side of the study. It is difficult to follow such a method without artificial aids. Hence, in discussing the theory of the tides, a model of certain theoretical tidal circles was introduced for the convenience of definition and argument. It was found to be an effective aid in reaching certain geometrical consequences that follow from the rotation of the earth on an axis that is not coincident with the axis of the tidal circles. This model was an illustration of the same order as the diagrams employed in text-books on geometry. In the same way a series of some thirty rough paper reliefs, constructed several years ago to illustrate a course of lectures to teachers, under the auspices of the Boston Society of Natural History, are introduced to aid in giving clearness to the conception of the geographical scheme. They are roughly made, hardly better than blackboard diagrams, except in having three dimensions, yet they certainly serve a good purpose as aids in following deductive statements. Being two or three feet in length and yet light enough to handle easily, they are frequently brought into the lecture room, although they are used chiefly in the laboratory, where they can be examined and described deliberately. Nearly all the points thus far mentioned are illustrated in one way or another by these models, but I can here give account of only a few of them.

While occupied with the first considerations of the cycle and its systematic variations of relief, both in intensity and variety, use is made of three simple models, which are found to be of particular value in fixing the fundamental ideas. The first shows a broad upland, traversed by a main river with a few branching streams, all in valleys of the cañon type. The form of the second is well diversified, there being about as much of lowland in its wide-open valleys as there is of upland on its well-separated hills. The third is a broad lowland for the most part, but low hills rise above the general level near the headwaters of the streams. The main river has essentially the same course in all three models, and there is a manifest relation in the position of the streams and inter-stream hills of the series, plainly showing genetic relationship. The three models are different forms of the same region at certain stages in its cycle of development. Exercises are held in the simple description of these forms, and of other forms that might be interpolated in the series. It is suggested that the duration of a cycle should be divided into a hundred equal parts, and that the stages occupied by the three models should be designated by appropriate numbers. After some discussion it is agreed that they may be represented by five, twenty, and forty, thus impressing the idea that maturity is reached long before middle life, and that the passage through old age is extremely slow compared to the advance from youth well into maturity. These exercises are accompanied by others, in which illustrations of actual geographical forms are presented, as will be explained later ; but it is important that the different character of the two should be clearly kept before the mind.

Complications of the Simple Scheme. The difficulty of finding examples of actual forms in the various stages of development of a single cycle suggests that the departures from the ideal uninterrupted cycle should be examined. These are of two kinds, which I am accustomed to call "accidents" and "interruptions." Such departures as do not involve a change in the attitude of a land mass with respect to its base-level may be classed under the first heading as accidents ; those which do involve a change with respect to base-level will fall under the second heading as interruptions.

The most important accidents are climatic and volcanic. Climatic accidents include changes from humid to arid, and from cooler to warmer conditions, independent of the normal climatic change due to loss of relief from youth to old age. A study of such a region as the Great Salt Lake basin, or as the glaciated district of northeastern America, assures us that these accidents may succeed each other rapidly, — very rapidly compared to the rate of normal climatic change dependent on loss of relief from a deformational beginning to a destructional end. Volcanic accidents include the building of cones and the outpouring of lava flows. Both the glacial and the volcanic accidents may occur at any stage of a cycle. They both in a way involve constructional processes ; both may be regarded as furnishing examples of new initial forms ; but when looked at with respect to the surface on which these accidents are imposed, and with respect to the relatively brief endurance of the effects of the accidents, they are seen in their relatively subordinate character. When sheets of drift are heavily spread over a country of low relief, or when heavy lava floods cover and bury some antecedent topography, the accidents assume such proportions that they may be considered as revolutions, after which a new start is made in the processes of denudation.

A cycle is interrupted when the land mass rises or sinks, or when it is warped, twisted, or broken. Like accidents, interruptions may happen at any stage of development. It is then convenient to say that the sequential form attained in the first incomplete cycle shall be called the initial form of the new cycle, into which the region enters, more or less tilted or deformed from its former shape. Assuming for the moment that the interrupting process is so rapid that its duration may be neglected, it follows that in cases of simple vertical movement, up or down, the rivers and streams at once proceed to adapt their activities to the new conditions. They are shortened and betrunked if the interruption is a depression ; they are revived and extended if the interruption is an elevation. These two special conditions are illustrated by paper models. One model exhibits a rolling country, into which a branching bay enters, a stream descending into the head of every branch of the bay. No flats occur at the heads of the bays ; no cliffs are seen on the headlands. Hence it is said that on reaching maturity this country was depressed, and that the depression occurred very recently. The numerical expression of this example would be 20, −, 0 ; the minus sign not indicating subtraction, but merely signifying depression, and the zero indicating that no advance has been yet made in the new cycle. Another model exhibits a broad, gently undulating upland, traversed by a very narrow cañon. This is interpreted to signify that an elevation occurred in the old age of the region, and that since then the streams have simply entered a new youth, incising young valleys in the uplifted peneplain. The formula of this example would be 60, +, 3. Examples involving deformation of a land surface, and the accompanying possibility of antecedent streams, are more complicated and cannot be here introduced.

It is convenient to use the term "episode," for slight interruptions, so as to express their relative unimportance. I have also attempted the use of the term "chapter" for an unfinished cycle ; but in talking with students this specialization of terms hardly seems necessary. Any region whose surface has been developed partly in relation to one base-level and partly in relation to another, — that is, any form whose development has involved two or more incomplete cycles, — is said to have a composite topography. Many examples of such forms are encountered.

Special Features of Second or Later Cycles. It is interesting to notice that, in certain cases, the adolescent stages of a second or later cycle, following the elevation of a region well advanced in a previous cycle, present features that did not characterize its first adolescence. One case of this kind is seen in meandering river gorges. Young rivers in their first cycle may cut crooked gorges, but they then follow consequent courses, and these cannot manifest the close relation between volume and radius of curvature that is seen in true meanders. This relation is found only in oldish rivers, which develop systematic meanders on their own flood plains. But if the region on which these rivers flow is introduced into a new cycle by uniform elevation, the rivers may cut down their meandering channels and produce meandering gorges. The Osage in Missouri, the north branch of the Susquehanna in Pennsylvania, the Seine in northwestern France, and the Moselle in western Germany may be cited in illustration of this kind of occurrence.

Another case in which a second adolescence is unlike the first is found in regions of tilted structure, where the strata is of diverse resistance, thus giving good opportunity for the development of subsequent streams. In the beginning of the first cycle there are no subsequent streams. All the drainage is initial, antecedent streams not being now considered. In adolescence the drainage is chiefly consequent, although subsequent side streams are then beginning to bud forth from the consequent streams. In past-mature stages the subsequent streams may have acquired a considerable part of the drainage area. Now, if a region of this kind, with consequent and subsequent drainage, is bodily elevated, all the streams are revived; they all cut down new trenches toward the new base-level. But in this case the revived subsequent streams begin the new work at the same time as the revived consequent streams, and they will go on rapidly in acquiring still more drainage area. Therefore, in the adolescence or maturity of the second cycle, the drainage area acquired by the subsequent streams will be proportionately large — much larger than at the same stage of the first cycle. Much faith may be placed in this deduction. If the drainage of an adolescent region is largely subsequent, and but little consequent, the region may be regarded as almost certainly in a second cycle of development, after a first cycle of well-advanced age.

Illustrative Material. One of the greatest difficulties in the way of teaching physical geography arises from the failure of the student to know what the teacher is talking about. The teacher may have traveled and observed extensively; a large variety of geographical forms are in his memory, ready to be summoned by name when picturing the stages of the deductive scheme; but no amount of description suffices to place these mental pictures before the class. The best means of overcoming this difficulty is found in the use of the projecting lantern; and now that the electric light may be used in projecting slides on the screen, and the room kept light enough for the class to take notes while the pictures are exhibited and explained, the only thing left to be desired is a good series of views, carefully selected to present typical examples of land forms in various stages of more or less complicated development. These views are not intended primarily to furnish localized examples of geographical forms, although, of course, they have much value in that direction. Their greater value comes from the vividness of the conceptions by which the different kinds of forms and different stages of development of the deductive scheme are held in the mind. The collection of slides that I now use includes a large variety of views; although very useful, it is still imperfect. It should be extended by the addition of many views taken expressly to meet its needs, for the photographs and slides commonly to be had of dealers are as a rule taken with anything but geographical intention. As an indication of the character of illustrations used in a single lecture, I may mention the following examples and add an outline of the comments made on them.

When the general idea of a geographical cycle has been presented, including the initial forms with which it opens and an outline of the destructional forms by which its development is characterized, the next lecture may be devoted almost entirely to illustrations. First, a few slides to show various initial forms. Muir's Butte, a young volcanic cone in California, introduces a series; it is practically unworn. Its growth was so rapid and so recent that no significant advance in its denudation has yet been accomplished. Mt. St. Elias comes second; as described by Russell, it is an initial form slightly altered; an essentially young mountain mass. The considerable time required for accomplishment of so great an initial uplift may have been enough for the slight dissection already seen on its surface. While the building of a volcanic cone is spasmodic, almost instantaneous, the uplift of a great mountain is rather slow; its uplift is brief only when compared to the duration of the destructive cycle on which it thereby enters. When first describing the cycle, it was implied that the destructive forces make no beginning until the initial forces have completed their work. The view of Mt. St. Elias corrects that false idea. Several plains follow, — all dead level; all ending in even sky lines: the Llano Estacado of Texas, the lava deserts of southern Idaho, the littoral plain of southern New Jersey, the lacustrine plain of the Red River of the North. The areas included in these views show no signs whatever of destructive processes; the surfaces are essentially as flat as when they were born. A pair of drumlins in Boston harbor and a glacial sand plain in Newtonville, Massachusetts, as represented in a model by Mr. Gulliver, introduce examples of peculiar forms, which really belong among the "forms taken by the waste of the land on its way to the sea," under certain special conditions, and they will be reviewed in a later chapter of the course under that heading. The drumlins and the sand plain may also be regarded merely as evidence of a glacial accident during the denudation of the New England plateau.

Passing next to illustrations of young sequential forms, Mt. Shasta is exhibited, with great valleys worn down its flanks. It is at once pointed out that these gullies follow lines of constructional slope, that they began as the paths of initial streams, defined by some accidental irregularity in the form of the volcanic cone, and that they are now slightly advanced in their consequent growth. The Mancos cañon in Colorado illustrates the beginning of the dissection of a plateau, the consequent stream having here cut down a steep-sided consequent valley, but apparently not having yet graded its slope. A stream in Florida, hardly incised in the low coastal plain, illustrates the faint relief permitted in surfaces that stand but little above their base-level.

The Colorado, in its cañon, is another example of an early stage of development, but it possesses an extreme intensity of relief because of the great altitude of its plateau : not an old valley, but a precocious young valley; not a vast work, except in our inappropriate human measures, but the good beginning of a vast work. The Elbe above Dresden offers illustration of a later stage than the three preceding; it has the beginnings of a flood plain, now on one side, now on the other side of the river; from which it is inferred that the deepening of the valley has practically ceased, that the river is graded, and that the slower process of valley widening is now the determining cause of topographical change.

Views in the Jura mountains would serve as examples of adolescent forms, combining an interesting measure of consequent and subsequent features, but I have not yet succeeded in finding any satisfactory photographs of this region. Features of maturity, more or less advanced, are found in the retreating escarpments of the middle Ohio valley or of the central denuded region of Texas, and again in the minutely carved ranges of the central Alps. For yet older stages it is difficult to find examples still in the cycle in which their old age was reached; but the plain of the middle Wisconsin river and the plateau of the middle Rhine are ideally satisfactory illustrations of base-leveled surfaces, — one being an old plateau, and the other an old mountain region, — although both have lately been brought into a new cycle by elevation, allowing their rivers to cut narrow trenches beneath their even surfaces. By selecting views in which only the plain surface is seen, these examples make appropriate closing members of the series here described. At a later time, when the complications of the cycle are in discussion, other views showing the dells of Wisconsin and the gorge of the Rhine may be presented, thus giving a new meaning to old examples.

Systematic Examination of Facts. While the deductive geographical scheme is thus gradually extended, while its various elements are illustrated more or less completely by blackboard diagrams, diagrammatic models, and lantern slides, an acquaintance with the facts of the subjects is gained at the same time chiefly through the laboratory work of the course. This is for the most part devoted to the examination of maps and many other illustrations of actual geographical forms, introduced systematically to represent the kinds of construction and the stages of development that may be compared with similar kinds and stages in the deductive scheme. I regard it as essential that the two sides of the work should advance together. The theoretical considerations of the deductive scheme and the inductive observation, description, and generalization of the facts of nature continually react on each other to mutual advantage. They call different mental faculties into exercise. Neither one can be developed alone to the best advantage. It is true that the consideration of the two sides of the work at the same time leads to mental confusion on the part of untrained or careless students, but this does not seem to be unfortunate. It is, to be sure, rather disappointing for a young fellow to find in the middle of the course that his neglect of its beginning has left him hopelessly behind his better-prepared or more persevering comrades ; but it is much more disappointing to see how often collegiate instruction is degraded by allowing it to fall to the reach of students who do not know how, or who do not care to know how, to follow its proper quality. In work of the kind that I am describing, mental confusion soon overtakes those who are poorly trained for mental effort. I do not find that it makes much difference what subjects a student has been trained in, provided that he has been well trained.

Laboratory work is an important element in the study, because there is otherwise no opportunity for deliberate and close observation of geographical facts. Even if shown in the lectures, they cannot be clearly seen, and there is no time then for close study. No text-book or atlas contains illustrations in sufficient variety for collegiate work. But in the laboratory, numerous maps, views, or models may be exposed on walls, racks, or tables, remaining for a week together and thus giving abundant time for deliberate examination. From week to week a change may be made in the materials, the group for each week corresponding to the group of problems then in hand. Many of the illustrations shown in the first week are repeatedly brought forth again later in the course, always gaining new meaning as sharper outsight and insight are directed to them. Many facts of interest concerning population and occupations may be brought forward in this connection, but it is important that the geographical facts should first be clearly apprehended.

In the reports that are made on this laboratory work the students first describe the facts that they have observed in terms that have no suggestion of explanation. They should not say that a certain region is a base-leveled surface, but that it is a lowland of faint relief. They should not at first speak of old rivers revived into a second youth, but they may say that the rivers of a certain region run in deep, narrow valleys below an upland of generally uniform altitude, above which occasional isolated hills rise to greater elevations. This I regard as extremely important, in order to insure a careful observation of the facts in discussion; for until the facts are clearly perceived, they cannot be precisely explained. It is unsafe at first even to speak of the flat region at the mouth of a river as a delta. This term not only denotes the form of the surface, but connotes an explanation; and in the earlier weeks of the study it is by no means sure that the observer fully perceives all the facts of form that are denoted by the term, or that he fully appreciates all the features of the process that are connoted in its explanation. The outbranching of the distributaries near the river mouth, as contrasted with the inbranching of the tributaries farther upstream and the faintly convex form of the delta surface, may not be clearly observed unless they are concisely formulated in a description. The essentially balanced relations of carrying power and load involved in the explanation of the growth of deltas may not be perceived unless it is carefully discussed in making out the scheme of river development. There can be no thoroughness of work where observation and explanation are slurred over or confused. After observation and description are well advanced, explanatory terms may be introduced, it then being seen that such terms imply a pairing off of observed facts with the appropriate members of the deductive scheme. This mental process must become perfectly conscious; its several steps must be recognized in their proper relations. No strong grasp of the subject can be gained until the student sees clearly where every part of the work stands in relation to the whole.

Topographical Maps published by the United States Government Bureaus. It is difficult to secure a full series of facts for laboratory study. My plan at present is to select maps from our own surveys and from the surveys of foreign countries, with little regard to locality but with much regard to geographical features. The charts of our coast survey offer admirable illustrations of littoral forms : for example, the sand-bar cusps of capes Hatteras, Fear, and Lookout, and their offshore shoals, all formed between back-set eddy currents, rotating betwixt the Gulf Stream and coast ; or the blunted Canaveral cusp on the Florida coast, and its southward migration from a former position ; or the fiords and islands of Maine ; the sounds of North Carolina ; the delta of the Mississippi, a geographical gem. The maps of the Mississippi River Commission offer remarkable illustrations of the behavior of a large river on its alluvial plain. Its meanders, its cut-offs, and its oxbow lakes are shown to perfection. The eight-sheet map of the alluvial basin of the Mississippi, prepared by this commission, can be had for a merely nominal charge ; it exhibits the lower part of the great river in an admirable manner. It tells the curious story of streams that descend from the eastern bluffs, but are unable to ascend across the flood plain to the Mississippi ; they therefore unite and form the Yazoo river, which runs southward along the eastern margin of the flood plain, near the foot of the bluffs. It would have to pursue an independent course all the way to the Gulf, were it not that the Mississippi comes swinging across the plain and picks up the Yazoo at Vicksburg.

But it is the topographical sheets of the United States Geological Survey that afford the greatest variety of illustrative material for this country ; and it is not too much to say that the facts they present create a revolution in the student's knowledge of his home geography. We may well wish that they were more accurate, but, with all their imperfections, they present a great body of new information. Under the family of plains there are examples of low littoral plains in New Jersey and Florida, those of the latter state being so young that the initial lakes are not yet drained. The moderate advance in denudation of an upland — itself an old lowland of denudation — is seen in the meandering gorge of the Osage in central Missouri; the relatively uncut plateaus of Arizona are seen alongside of the beginning of their denudation in the Grand cañon of the Colorado. Maturely dissected plateaus are found in West Virginia and eastern Kentucky, and in northern Alabama and northern Arkansas; but the first two are of minute topographical texture; the second two are of coarser forms. Outliers of past-mature plateaus are shown on several sheets in central Texas. All manner of other illustrations are found in the same series of maps: the thoroughly adjusted streams of the Pennsylvania Appalachians; the superimposed streams of northern New Jersey; the Illinois river, the type of a medium-sized river in the abandoned channel of a large river — this being the only well-mapped example of the kind in this country; the warped intermontane valleys of Montana; Crater lake in northern California; glacial lakes in Massachusetts; flood plains slanting away from their river in Louisiana; fiords in Connecticut; moraines in Rhode Island; drumlins in Wisconsin; trap ridges in New Jersey; revived old mountains in North Carolina; half-buried mountains in Utah and Nevada. Every new package of these maps brings some new illustration, which is put in use as soon as opportunity allows. One of the latest is a peculiar case in southern California: a number of small rivers are here seen running down from the Coast range to the shore of the Pacific; but their mouths are all shut up by sand bars in the most summary manner!

These maps are simply indispensable. They call forth much interest from the class. At first hardly translatable into words, their meaning grows plainer and plainer, until at the close of the course they are as suggestive as they were uncommunicative at the beginning.

Foreign Topographical Maps. Not less valuable and far more accurate than our own topographical sheets are those of various foreign topographical surveys. Unfortunately, the relief in most of these is expressed by hachures, altitudes being given only for occasional points, or by widely separated contour lines; but the general expression of the surface is certainly admirably rendered in many of the surveys. The older maps are generally too heavily burdened with hachures, but the more modern surveys are very artistically executed. It has been my practice for several years past to select certain groups of sheets from the sets of foreign topographical maps in our college library and order extra copies of these groups, mount them on cloth and rollers, and thus prepare them for the most convenient use in the laboratory. Both the library and laboratory collections of this kind are increasing year by year, and I shall soon prepare a special account of the grouped sheets, in the hope that others may perceive their great value and introduce them as teaching materials as far as possible. Without specifying all that have been thus far secured, I may briefly mention some of the more interesting examples.

From the Army Staff map of France (1 : 80,000) there is a group of sheets showing the level plain of the Landes, with its exceptionally straight shore-line and its wide belt of littoral sand dunes ; the beautiful group of radial rivers flowing down the slopes of a great alluvial fan that has been formed where several large rivers emerge from the Pyrenees — this being one of the best examples of a simple, consequent river-grouping that I have found ; the plateau of the lower Seine, an old upland of denudation, with an excellent meandering river gorge of moderate depth cut through it, together with certain interesting features of young branching river valleys, and of rivers that have been shortened by the encroachments of the sea in cutting away the land. To these I intend shortly to add groups of sheets showing the dissected escarpment west of Rheims and Châlons, with its beautifully adjusted rivers, the delta of the Rhone, and the fiorded coast of Brittany.

From the Ordnance Survey of Great Britain (1 : 63,360) one set of sheets includes the central Highlands of Scotland, with the Great Glen and Glenroy ; two other sets include the fiords and islands of the southwestern and the northwestern coasts. These three sets agree in showing an old peneplain of denudation, once elevated and maturely dissected, but now somewhat depressed, with cliffs nipped on its land heads and deltas laid in its bay heads. Their formula, according to the plan already suggested, would be $75, +25, -2$. A glacial accident of late date is recorded by the upland tarns and the valley lakes. A group of sheets for southwestern Ireland exhibits bold mountain ranges running directly into the sea, forming a strongly serrated coast. The English sheets are of older date and are not of particularly good expression, and for this reason I have not yet ordered any of them, although the ragged escarpment of the chalk and of the oölite trending northeast on either side of Oxford should be represented, and the Weald offers excellent illustration of well-adjusted consequent and subsequent rivers on an unroofed dome of Cretaceous strata.

The map of the German Empire (1 : 100,000) supplies many examples of striking features. The plateau of the middle Rhine has already been mentioned as a subject for lantern slides ; it is represented in two map groups, one of which shows the transverse gorge of the Rhine ; the other includes the meandering gorge of the Moselle, with a perfect showing of its abandoned cut-offs among the hills. The flood plain of the Rhine about Mannheim exhibits the former meanders and the present controlled course of the river, foreshadowing the future control of the Mississippi ; the morainic country of Prussia is a medley of hills and hollows ; the Vistula turns sharply at its Bromberg elbow from the valley that it once followed, but which it now abandons to the little Netze ; long, curving sand bars form the two inclosed bays of eastern Prussia (the Frische and Kurische Haffe). From Norway (1 : 100,000) the district of the Christiania fiord is already received in ten sheets of most delicate execution, — the greater fiords of the western coast will be ordered as soon as fully published ; from Russia (1 : 400,000), the lakes of Finland and of the lower Danube ; from Austria, a portion of the flood plain of the Danube and a strip of the fiorded coast of the northern Adriatic. This is only a beginning of what I hope the collection may be in a few years.

I cannot speak too highly of the educative quality of these grouped sheets. It is, in the first place, a good thing for students to inspect, as closely as they may in laboratory work of this kind, the very best products of geographical art. Their ideals are thus raised above the commonplace level. Whatever they afterwards see will be compared with a high standard. A feeling of dissatisfaction will arise regarding the very inferior maps of their home states, to which they have been inured, and from this a demand will grow for the continuation and improvement of the mapping of our country that is now going on. In the second place, the facts of the subject are placed before the student so closely that he cannot fail to be impressed at once with their real features ; and these he will find so numerous and so varied that he will perceive the need of serious study for their apprehension. No verbal descriptions from the teacher suffice to replace the portrayal of geographical relief on good maps.

Classification of Initial Forms. It is only after the deductive scheme is well advanced, and after many examples of facts have been correlated with it, that I introduce a classification of initial forms. Some such classification is essential, but it is difficult to establish satisfactorily, because of the endless variety of structures found in nature. At present in the elementary course I recognize only plains and plateaus of horizontal strata ; mountains of disordered strata, with many minor subdivisions; and in a subordinate way, volcanic cones and flows, and glacial hills and moraines. Like the more difficult orders of plants in an elementary course on botany, mountains must be treated briefly in an elementary course on physical geography, and their fuller treatment left for more advanced study. After the various kinds of initial forms are treated, it is advisable to review the features of rivers, with their divides, lakes, waterfalls, flood plains, and deltas ; and in this connection a week or two may be given to the forms assumed by the waste of the land on the way to the sea. The distribution of different kinds of forms should be briefly given with their classification.

When thus developed, physical geography may worthily claim the dignity of a university study. Its subject-matter is of importance in itself, as well as in its relations to geology, zoölogy, and botany, or to history and economics. Its methods are of value in training various mental faculties : observation, description, generalization, imagination, comparison, discrimination, these are all cultivated to a high degree in the student who successfully utilizes the opportunities of the course.

X

METHODS AND MODELS IN GEOGRAPHICAL TEACHING[1]

In presenting to the Association certain considerations regarding methods of teaching geography, I venture to assume that your interests in educational matters extend so far down as to reach a subject which many scholars "finish" early in their course, and whose advanced study hardly receives its due place in our colleges ; certainly it has suffered from neglect. My own practice in the way of teaching it has been with college students in the division of physical geography, and not feeling entirely satisfied with the system of study as presented in the text-books in current use, I have endeavored to discover and supply certain elements by which instruction in the subject might be advanced.

The first element that should be supplied is one by which the conceptions which the teacher has in mind can be vividly transferred to the student. The teacher bases his mental pictures on something he has seen, if he is so fortunate as to have traveled and brought home with him fresh memories of the morphology of the earth's surface ; or if not an observer himself, he has at least had time to gain his geographical conceptions slowly, and with the aid of various descriptions and illustrations that he cannot present in their entirety to his class. How shall his ideas be passed on to his students ? Maps and pictures are of value, but as a rule they are of low quality, except for the larger parts of the world. They present no sufficient expression of the forms of moderate size on which we live. Photographs are excellent as illustrations of actual landscapes, yet they are too often chosen with other than geographical reasons for the choice, and but few schools have them in sufficient variety. Moreover, all these aids lack one element of great value, namely, the third dimension that

[1] A lecture delivered before the Scientific Association of Johns Hopkins University, February 13, 1889.

so strongly characterizes all geographical forms. I have therefore desired to use geographical models, which very easily give clear indication of the relief of a surface, and if without all its detail, still possess effective and suggestive form. Models are therefore to be taken as one of the means of improving the methods of illustrating what the teacher wishes to place before the class.

Again, physical geography as ordinarily defined is too largely merely descriptive, and not physical at all. Indeed, geography, which is supposed to treat of the form of the surface of the earth, neglects the form of the earth's surface to an unfortunate extent. We hear much about the connection between geography and history, for example ; but what *is* this subject that is connected with history ? Where is geography itself taught with the same thoroughness that characterizes the modern teaching of the biological sciences ? We recognize, of course, the vital connection between geography and history, just as the botanist recognizes the connection between botany and medicine ; but what botanist would be satisfied to conclude the teaching of his science, or even its elements, at the point that would suffice for the collector of medical herbs or for the doctor of medicine ? And why should the geographer be satisfied with so brief an outline of his science as will suffice for illustrating its connection with history ? The subject deserves study for its own worthy self ; it is in this line that the teacher of geography must wish to see it developed, and it is to this end that he must strive, just as his colleagues strive to advance the study of their respective sciences for their own sake, and not merely for the illustration of some other. For this reason I have endeavored to examine the forms of the land surface in detail, and to arrange them in their genetic relations, in order to come to a closer appreciation of the meaning of the form of the earth and its development. In this way, it seems to me, we may best study the fundamental material of geography. A year ago I had the pleasure of presenting some outlines of a geographical classification at a meeting of the National Geographical Society in Washington, and now I would add thereto some account of certain geographical models, designed for the Teachers School of Science under the Boston Society of Natural History, as a means of illustrating this classification. Some of the models illustrate the development of plains and plateaus; some present the various forms of volcanic cones and lava flows; others indicate the changes in the features of a river as it grows old, or as it is embarrassed by glacial or volcanic accidents. It is essential that we should study the surface of the land by means of types, for it would be as impossible for a scholar to learn all the individual forms of the land as it would for the young botanist to learn all the individual plants of the world, especially if they were brought before him in the order of their occurrence over the world, and not in accordance with some well-tried system of logical and natural classification. Botanists and zoölogists believe that it is time enough for their scholars to study the complex congeries of forms that constitute the fauna or flora of a country when they have mastered the rudiments of the subject by careful study of a moderate number of typical examples of plants or animals; and, indeed, in the modern development of the study of biology, one may see the strongest contrast with the older methods in this respect. I should be glad to see a similar change overtake the conservative science to which my studies are devoted.

In order to give specific illustration of the method of study by geographical types and the use of models, let me ask your consideration of that large group of land forms that may be included in the category of plains, plateaus, and their derivatives. There is a brief preliminary consideration.

Any mass of land constituting a single geographical individual, or a natural group of such individuals, must, as soon as it is exposed to the destructive forces of the atmosphere, begin its long sequence of development; and if no change of level happen to it, it must at length be worn down smooth and low to a featureless plain. When this work begins, with every mark of immaturity in its small accomplishment, we may regard the individual as young, that is, but little advanced in the long cycle of systematic change through which it is destined to pass. When much more work has been accomplished, and the variety of form resulting is at its greatest, the individual may be called mature; and finally, when the features of maturity weaken as the relief is reduced and intensity of form is lost, we find a resemblance to organic decay, and are warranted in the use of such a term as old age.

But you may say that all this is geology, not geography. Geological processes are indeed at work in carrying the geographical individual through its successive forms, but we are not concerned with the processes, only with the result. In organic growth, the process is chemical; but, for all that, biology is not chemistry. Moreover, if the several forms assumed by a geographical individual are geological affairs, we might expect to find them treated in the standard works on that science; but, except in brief outline, nowhere do they appear in such books. Geology is too much occupied with matters of underground structure, with questions of constructive and destructive processes, and with composition and fossil contents of rocks to be awake to another large question. The study of the form of the earth's surface, even though recognizing that the form changes, is geography. But, after all, geography and geology are one science, treating of the earth, and it is needless for us to embarrass our work by attempting unnecessary subdivision and limitation of the fields that the two branches shall occupy. Let each one take whatever will aid its attainment of the desired end. If we can understand geographical morphology better by some consideration of geological structure, let it be introduced, just as chemistry is introduced into physiology, or physics into meteorology. Surely geologists have employed geographical methods freely enough to warrant our reversing the relation. If some consideration of geological processes will serve our purpose and give better appreciation of the sequence of forms that geographical individuals pass through, then call freely on geology for such consideration, and use it to the best advantage. Do not hamper our endeavor to understand the form of the earth's surface by any arbitrary limitation of the means that we shall employ to the end. It is plainly apparent that geology and geography are parts of one great subject, as ancient and modern histories are, and they must not be considered independently. Indeed, it is only in this close relation that a satisfactory definition of the two terrestrial sciences is obtained. Mackinder has concisely said that geology is the study of the past, considered in the light of the present, and geography is the study of the present, considered in the light of the past. I can quote no better indication of the close connection of the two divisions of the world's history. Without going further into abstract considerations, we may now turn to our concrete examples.

The so-called "valley" of the Red River of the North in Minnesota and Dakota is a broad plain of exceedingly level surface. It is so truly level that it illustrates the curvature of the earth in the same way that it is seen at sea; for in crossing the plain, first a distant tree-top is seen above the horizon, then a house-top, and at last the body of the house rises into full view, just as the upper and lower sails and the hull of the ship are brought into sight in sailing toward it on the ocean. This broad plain is a lake bottom, whence the water in which its fine sediments were laid down has been drained away, and drained away by so curious a process that if, in teaching modern history, it were noted that some existing form of government were as curiously related to the past, no teacher would hesitate to make reference to it. The northern barrier that held the waters of the lake was the southward front slope of a great sheet of ice that for a time obstructed the open northward drainage; and in the lake thus created, fine sediments were spread out so plentifully that they buried the former surface of the land, and so evenly that when the waters were drained away as the ice melted, a dead-level plain was revealed.

The plain stands well above sea-level, and hence must suffer change as destructive processes attack it. Why, then, is it so smooth? Manifestly because it is young. There has not yet been time for streams to channel it. It is extremely immature, truly infantile in its appearance, with scarcely a sign of the variety of features that will be developed in its later history. Does not this consideration lend additional interest to the study of so simple and monotonous a district as a plain of the Red River of the North? Is there not a keener appreciation of its peculiarities gained by looking at them in the light of their development, instead of describing them simply as absolute forms, not otherwise considered?

The Red river plain has, however, begun its development. The Red river itself has incised a narrow, steep-sided trench twenty or forty feet deep in the surface of the plain, and the few side branches of the river have narrower and shallower channels.

These trenches and channels are simply young valleys, and they are growing so rapidly that their increase in length and width is noticeable even in the past few years of settlement. But still the streams have barely made a beginning of the great work of carrying away all the material of the plain above base-level, this being their manifest future task. So little has been done as yet in the way of preparing drainage channels that the rain which falls here is greatly delayed in reaching a stream course by which it may flow to its goal, the sea, and so much of it stands about idly, instead of quickly running off, that it is in good part evaporated and carried away through the air. Evidently we have here to do with a geographical individual that is just entering its career, that still retains its embryonic characteristics, so little has it advanced in its life history.

Can we not foretell something of the future history of this plain? As the rivers carve their trenches deeper and deeper, and the inclosing slopes are wasted away and widen out, and the little side gullies eat backwards and increase in length till they become ravines and the ravines grow into valleys, then the interstream surface, at first smooth and unbroken, is traversed in all directions by branching water courses; the rainfall is much more quickly led into the streams,—everything marks a more advanced stage, all of whose features are indicated in one of the models of the plain and plateau series. But we can not only predict the future of the Red river plains: we can find examples of other plains, born at an earlier time, that are now in the advanced stage that the Red river plains have yet to reach. Look at the coastal plains of the Carolinas. They are the old bottom of the Atlantic, laid bare by a relative uplift of the continent. They are well drained; many streams run across them, and many branches give ready discharge to the rainfall; the channels are deeper below the general level of the country than are those of the Red river plains, and the interstream surface is much more broken, yet still enough of it remains to make it clear that the present form is developed from an originally level, unbroken plain; and a close comparison will leave no doubt that the coastal plains of the Carolinas differ from the Red river plains chiefly in being further advanced in their cycle of development. They are closely related individuals, but they differ somewhat in age. They are like the egg of a caterpillar and the caterpillar itself, — not very similar at first, and not like what they will come to be later on, but closely comparable for all that; their differences only manifest their relationship; what one is, the other will be; what the other is, the first has been. Thus we can introduce into geography the element of growth, that is, systematic change, and greatly to the enlivenment of the study. It is often the reproach of geography that it does not deal with things having life, but this is true only if we do not take heed of the kind of life that it may consider. One may say that the changes here discussed are so slow that we need not take account of them, but this is predetermining what we shall and what we shall not study; let us rather see if the consideration of slow geographical life does not impart new meaning to an old study; let us question if this new meaning is not nearer the truth that we are striving for; then we shall be in a better position to judge if slowness of change is a reason for its neglect. No one makes objection to teaching a young scholar about the growth of an oak tree from an acorn, though it is safe to say that no scholar comes to the belief of the growth of an oak from witnessing it; he is convinced of a change that he cannot wait to see, partly by comparison with trees of a faster growth, and partly by seeing oaks of different sizes, and being led to make reasonable generalizations on his observations. It is the same with our understanding of geographical growth; we cannot see much of it, — not even the oldest of us, — and yet, after the conception is once gained, it becomes so vivid that one can hardly help expecting to find that a change is perceptible on returning after a time to some familiar locality. One may see a sand bank washed away by a heavy rain, and from this to the washing down of the largest mountain there is only a difference of degree, not of kind. A scholar may easily comprehend the change of form indicated by the differences between the two plains already described, and unless his natural intelligence is obstructed, he can then grasp the idea of geographical growth.

Let us next look at West Virginia, typified in the second model of the series; here the interstream hills are so high that they almost merit the name of mountains; the stream branches have become so numerous that no part of the original level upland surface remains; every part has an immediate slope to a stream, and the drainage system is advanced to its highest development. Indeed, we need some aid here from geology to be sure that we are dealing with an individual of the same kind as those already considered, so little likeness is there between this one and the others. But the aid from geology is conclusive; for West Virginia and a large area around it is made up of horizontal layers of bedded rocks that once were at the bottom of the sea, and that still retain the essentially horizontal attitude in which they were laid down; the whole mass of horizontal layers has simply been raised with respect to the surface of its parent ocean. This elevation occurred so long ago that the immaturity such as still characterizes the Red river plains is here long past; the adolescence seen in the Carolina plains is also long ago lived through. In West Virginia we have maturity; there can be no greater variety of form than is here presented. The relief of the surface is at its highest value; for while the interstream hills have not lost much of their original height, the valleys have been sunk about as low as they can be, and hence there is the greatest possible difference of altitude between hilltop and valley-bottom. The streams have become very numerous, and can hardly be more so; every part of the surface is intersected by them. There is no room for more.

From this time on the form of the surface becomes less pronounced. As the destructive changes progress further, the valleys can deepen but little, although the hill-tops must be reduced, and the valley slopes must widen out, and all the topographical expression must weaken as old age is approached. This is the character of central Kentucky, and appears in the third model of the set. Excepting where the valleys are inclosed in especially hard rocks, they are wide open, and the variable height of the intervening hills makes it clear that they retain no longer all of the height that they once possessed. They are weakening, passing into forms of less and less emphasis, losing variety, becoming old and feeble.

In the next stage we may expect to find the valleys so far widened that they should form broad plains, smoothly rolling, essentially a lowland of faint relief, but occasionally diversified with hills of moderate height ; and thus the very opposite of the Carolina plains, where the surface is an upland, with occasional valleys. Such an old plain may be seen about the headwaters of the Missouri, in eastern Montana ; the general surface is extremely monotonous, gently rolling, and one roll like the next, so that one may easily lose his way in the absence of landmarks. But here and there over the plain mesas of considerable elevation still remain, the reason for their endurance being seen in the layer of hard lava that protects them and retards their destruction, while the rest of the country has wasted away more rapidly. These lava caps are old flows from once active volcanoes ; the lava at the time of eruption undoubtedly ran down from its vents to the lowest ground that it could find, and yet it now occupies the highest ground, in virtue of its obstinate refusal to waste away. Every such lava cap is a witness to the greater mass of material over the whole country when the eruption took place, and the destruction of this greater mass must have progressed through the several stages illustrated by the present condition of the Red river plains, the Carolina plains, the mountains of West Virginia, and the hills of central Kentucky, before it could have reached a surface of faint relief. It requires great faith in the evidence here adduced to believe that so stupendous a piece of work has really been accomplished. It is well-nigh incredible, and the observer on the ground is fully justified in doubting it as long as he can, but it cannot be doubted when the evidence is once well seized. It is by no means unparalleled, and much nearer home we may find examples as extraordinary, and as far from easy belief, but as necessary to the convictions of the well-ordered geographer.

Such a plain as that of the upper Missouri may be called a base-level plain, because it has been worn down to the controlling level of drainage, or to what is called the base-level of the region ; this being in distinction to an initial or new plain, whose smoothness is due to the short time that its original form has been exposed to developing agencies. A base-level plain represents the ultimate stage in the sequence of a simple cycle of development.

Certain elements of importance yet remain to be considered. If the plain be raised to a moderate height over sea-level, it can never acquire great intensity of relief, for the streams are then allowed but a small depth to which they can cut. If, on the other hand, the elevation is great, and rapid enough to be for the most part acquired before the destructive processes have made great headway, then the vertical element is strong, the topographical relief is intense. Our coastal plain is an example of a region of mild form; it has but slight elevation, and hence, however long the rivers flow across it, they can never cut out deep valleys. The plateaus of Utah and adjacent parts of the West are of another sort; here the elevation is excessive, and the depth of cutting allowed to the rivers is correspondingly great. Marvelously have they taken advantage of their opportunity. The valley cut by the Colorado and its tributaries is in some places a mile deep, and yet when we see the enormous mass of land still lying on either side of the valley above base-level and waiting to be carried down to the ocean, we cannot doubt that the time thus far employed in doing so great a piece of work is a small part of the whole cycle of growth. The upper plateau surface is still broadly level, except for certain irregularities to be referred to later on; the valley is narrow, even to notoriety, and must therefore be called young. It is a case of precocious adolescence. Intensity or faintness of relief are therefore variations on the general scheme, and it is my intention that these variations shall also be represented by models when new members are added to complete the present series; a young plateau of intense relief, a middle-aged plain of mild relief, will thus become definitely intelligible terms to our mind. Along with this, it must be perceived that two mature plains need not be of the same age, if measured in years, for the development of maturity in a high plateau requires more time than in a lowland.

There is another element of variation that must be considered. Sometimes the simple cycle of development that has been described is interrupted: the land does not lie quiet long enough to pass through a complete series of changes without disturbance. Indeed, this interruption is, except in very young plains, the rule and not the exception; and several of the examples already given illustrate it. The coastal plain of the Carolinas has suffered a moderate depression since its valleys were defined pretty much in their present form, and their lower courses are thereby slightly submerged. Thus arise the estuaries that characterize our Atlantic coast, and these are presented in a fourth model. The old base-level plain of the upper Missouri no longer stands at the low level in which it was worn down, but has been elevated a thousand feet or more, and hence all its rivers, that had settled down to a quiet old age of little work, have been rejuvenated, and are now beginning a second cycle of life. They run swiftly in well-defined, narrow valleys, even though the inclosing rocks are soft; and they are sometimes interrupted by waterfalls, even when their volume is as large as that of the Missouri above Fort Benton. Manifestly, therefore, the elevation of the old plain is relatively recent; very little advance has yet been made in the development of its second cycle. The same kind of complexity appears in the high plateaus of Utah and Colorado: the high-level surface in which the cañons are cut is not an original surface of construction, but is a surface of considerable irregularity, as has already been mentioned; part of the irregularity is due to great fractures which have broken the country into massive blocks and lifted them a little unevenly, and part is due to the incomplete base-leveling of the region during a previous cycle of development, when the elevation was less than now. The combination of old and new forms thus explained is the subject of a fifth model. A wonderful addition is made to our appreciation of a country when all these factors in its history are recognized as contributing essentially to its topography.

Is it not worth while to try to acquire the broader comprehension of geography that comes from understanding its meaning? Can we not make immediate practical use of such terms as infantile, young, adolescent, mature or middle-aged, old, and very old? Do they not recall all the significance of certain selected or idealized typical examples that have been studied, being in this respect like the terms that the botanist employs to so great an advantage? No botanist would admit the superiority of paraphrases over terms; compactness, accuracy, and intelligibility would all be sacrificed if terms were given up. And yet nearly all geographers employ paraphrases instead of terms. Let us take an example to illustrate this from the description of certain counties in Missouri in one of the geological reports on that state, to which, as in other states, we must generally go for the best geographical materials.

The region is one of horizontal structure, and therefore comes under the general heading now considered. Of Miller county it is said : " Near the Osage and its larger tributaries the country is generally very broken and rocky, excepting immediately in the valleys ; but farther back the slopes usually become more gentle, with fewer exposures of rock, until we reach the higher districts, more remote from the streams, where the surface is comparatively level, or but slightly undulating." Again, of Morgan county : " The surface of the elevated region near the middle of the county is beautiful, comparatively level or undulating prairie land. South of this the slopes are first gentle, near the head branches of the Gravois, but as we descend these the face of the country becomes more hilly, and almost everywhere near that and the main creeks, as well as their principal tributaries, and especially near the Osage, it is very broken and rocky. North of the main divide, the high, nearly level prairie land extends, with a slight descent, for some distance northward between the streams flowing in that direction, but near most of the larger streams the surface is more or less broken, and sometimes rocky, but generally not so much so as on the south side."

What is meant by this ? Manifestly, the country is an adolescent plain of moderate intensity of development and apparently of simple history. The horizontal attitude of the rocks and the level surface of the uplands show us that the region belongs to the family of plains or plateaus ; the irregular courses of the streams and the steepness of their banks decide with equal clearness that the development of the plain has not advanced very far.

Now in the same report the writer says that there are oak trees in the forests. Why does he not say that there are tall vegetable growths of irregular bifurcations, bearing green appendages at the attenuated extremities, these appendages being strongly scalloped in outline, and so on ? He also speaks of pines.

Why not of other vegetable growths, with straight vertical axes, from which lateral arms spread out with some regularity, bearing long, slender spicules on their minuter divisions? Instead of this, he says oak and pine. This is not because all oaks and all pines are of precisely one pattern. Their variations are infinite, but for all that they vary only through a moderate range, and can all be brought under typical forms. They may be young or old, large or small, well grown or deformed, living or dead, but they are still oaks or pines. How well it is, therefore, that they should be known by a definite term or name. How well it would be if geographical forms were equally well named; and why should they not be? The many plains that we have described do not differ more greatly among themselves than the oaks or the pines; they deserve recognition as constituting a family, naturally related, not by inheritance from descent, as with the trees, but by similarity of the physical processes under which they have been developed. The natural association of their features deserves just such recognition as is implied by giving them names, distinctive and well defined.

Do we not gain a better understanding of the earth's surface, of the primary object of geographical study, by thus looking at the meaning of land form, as well as at the form itself? Is not the possibility of accurate description greatly increased thereby, and does not the description, when made, carry more of the desired meaning than ordinary geographical narration in which there is no definite standard recognized for comparison? The reason of this is not far to seek. Our conception of the unknown is based on the conception of the known, either by likeness or contrast. Ordinary geographical description has not sufficient accuracy because its terms are vague; they do not bring up to the mind the recollection of any well-defined type or standard. Plain, rolling country, hilly country, broken country, have no precise meaning; they "denote" but do not "connote." But when we examine a series of geographical forms related by community of structure, though contrasted in age, and give to every one a name, such as a young plain, a mature or middle-aged plain, these terms bring certain well-marked conceptions before us, — conceptions that have been elaborated in our study of the type or standard of reference, — and we readily form a mental picture in which all the many essential features of the region described are clearly appreciated. An adolescent plain, for example, is a surface of broad, even uplands, here and there trenched across by streams which follow valleys of moderate width ; the general continuity of level from one interstream surface to another comes to mind ; also the relative scarcity of the smaller stream channels ; and the relation of the region to its fellows of greater or less age.

It is immaterial what names are used for the present in describing plains and plateaus, for none as yet are authoritatively accepted by geographers, but it would be to our common advantage if experiments were made on the use of a larger set of terms than is commonly employed. The important point is that terms based on natural relationship should be used, and that they should be familiarized by the study of type forms. Experiment will alone decide what terms shall be finally adopted. My own experience with students of undergraduate age has shown me that the idea as here outlined is a valuable one, and that the terms here employed are suggestive and satisfactory. I am very desirous of hearing the experience of others in the same experimental line.

A few words may be said as to the method of using the models, a method that seems to me adapted to young as well as to more advanced scholars. A series of models is laid out on the tables of a room which, in the schools of the future, may, I trust, be called the geographical laboratory. Each student is asked to describe what he sees ; to note if he can recognize any features of the miniature landscape that are already familiar to him from his own observation. He is then told to try to draw a map of the surface represented, or a part of it if the whole is somewhat complicated. More or less aid must be given here, as so many students are untrained in the simplest delineation. When the map is drawn, show the class a map of some actual region of the same kind as that typified in the model ; ask them to notice how far the features that they have drawn from the model are features on the actual map ; let them search for additional features, generally small ones that may appear on the map, but which are not shown on the model.

Next produce the second model, and go through the same process, but without any suggestion that the first and second models are related. Finally, ask if any one perceives a connection or relation between the two regions thus considered. Few can fail to see it, and when perceived it should be described by every member of the class for himself. I have great faith in the scholar's own careful expression, both in drawing and in writing, of what he has himself seen or thought. Note here that the scholar need not discover how the change from one form to the next has been produced, he need only recognize it ; then the teacher may supplement the recognition as far as he wishes with simple geological explanation of processes. This need not go far, and merely opens the way to further study of geology. The word "geology" need not be mentioned.

If the class be somewhat mature, the teacher may, before bringing out the third model, ask for predictions of the form of future stages of the region ; or, if this seem venturesome, the simpler inductive method may still be followed. At last the models showing complications and interruptions in a single cycle of change may be introduced, all the examples being illustrated by maps of actual relations, as well as by models, views, descriptions, and in every other way that the ingenuity of the teacher devises.

When thus familiarized with the general conception of geographical change, let the scholars attempt to make full statement of all they have learned from the work so far concerning geographical relationships. The brighter ones will here manifest some perception of the generalizations that may be based on the facts thus far presented, and from this time on geographical form has a new and a fuller meaning to them. Additional examples of the various stages of development may be introduced at the discretion of the teacher, and, if time allow, they can best be taken from books of travel and exploration, reports of state and government surveys, and the like, in order to give some freshness and reality to the study. It is apparent enough that in its fully expanded form it will take a long time for the better geographical teaching to enter the larger public schools, but in schools where teachers are numerous enough to give every scholar a good share of personal attention, I do not despair of seeing geographical laboratories and a rational inductive method of instruction employed.

Comparisons have already been made between the methods employed in teaching biology some forty or fifty years ago and during the last decade. It seems to me that physical geography is still in the undeveloped condition that biology has outgrown. Our text-books of physical geography attempt to describe the whole earth, just as the old natural histories tried to describe the whole animal and vegetable kingdoms. Since the publication of Huxley and Martin's Biology, this plan has been abandoned in the better schools, and the pupil now studies the few typical forms that give him a knowledge of the great resemblances of animals, and does not dwell on their minute differences. He learns a good deal about a few animals instead of a very little about a great many. I should like to see the same change introduced into the teaching of physical geography. It is impossible for a scholar to learn anything definite about the form of the earth's surface if he attempts to study all the continents. He might as well attempt, in his botany lessons, to learn about the distribution of forests instead of studying the structure of plants. Something of the grosser continental forms should of course be considered, just as it is interesting to know something of the distribution of forested and of desert regions; the general distribution of land and water, its relation to climate, history, and so on, — all this is of great interest; so are the generalizations concerning evolution and the speculations concerning migrations in which the biologist may indulge, but they do not form the chief matter of our best elementary methods, for they cannot be sufficiently original with the ordinary student. When a boy grows up and travels over the country, he never sees the grosser continental forms; they are too large. He sees only small forms, corresponding to the individual plants of the forest. Why not, then, instruct him in such a way that he shall appreciate these small forms, these geographical individuals, just as he is taught to understand something of botanical individuals? Let him understand that there is a geographical morphology, perhaps not so precise as that of the organic world, but none the less interesting;

let him feel that these geographical forms are the results of
definite orderly processes, working systematically, and carrying the geographical individual through a determinate sequence
of changes nearly as definite as that passed through by any
animal or plant in its life development, but more complicated
from the combination of the records of several cycles of life
often being found in one individual. Let him learn that every
feature of a geographical individual is significant and expressive,
full of meaning to those who look at it aright. Do not hesitate
to call on geological processes when they are needed to aid his
understanding ; do not postpone the few necessary and simple
geological conceptions until he reaches a geological course of
study. Do not be discouraged because the earth's surface contains
many complicated individuals ; there are many simple ones also,
which a student may appreciate and enjoy, and from which,
when thus understood, he may form a better idea of unseen
regions. Of course there are many complicated forms that he
will not easily comprehend ; but so there are plants of difficult
analysis, yet this is not held to be an excuse for giving up the
teaching of systematic botany. Few scholars may be able to
analyze all the Compositæ, or to recognize all the species of
oaks, even if they have learned their lessons well in school, and
yet we do not doubt that there is profit in the teaching of systematic botany. So there may be in teaching the elements of
systematic geography. Let the scholar learn a few simple forms
well, as he surely can without difficulty ; he will recognize these
when he sees them, and finding meaning in their form, he will
be convinced that there is meaning also in the more complicated
forms that his slight study has not deciphered. He may even
come to conceive that he has not "finished" geography, and
that it is capable of advanced study for its own sake.

XI

PRACTICAL EXERCISES IN PHYSICAL GEOGRAPHY

I

There is coming to be a general recognition that physical geography must not be taught by recitations alone; that laboratory and field work should be systematically developed for the better understanding of the principles and examples set forth in the text; and that a proper assignment of space in the school building and of time in the school curriculum should be made for the accomplishment of these practical exercises. There is a growing movement in favor of practical exercises : a movement whose strength is to be measured not by the number of teachers who are standing still, indifferent to this innovation on traditional methods, but by the number and character of the teachers who are striving, often against difficulties and discouragements, to promote the rational development of their subject. There was a time, only ten or fifteen years ago, when a "geographical laboratory," as the name for a room specially set apart and equipped for practical exercises in geography, had no place in the school architect's plans; but if one may judge from the amount of inquiry and correspondence as to what a geographical laboratory should be and as to what it should contain, such a time is passing by. Let me then devote this essay to certain considerations regarding practical exercises in physical geography, in the hope that my suggestions may find some application in the construction of new school buildings, as well as in the remodeling of old ones, in the arrangement of new school courses, and in the appointment of new school-teachers.

First, as to the place in which practical exercises are to be carried on. An ordinary schoolroom, fitted with desks of the usual size, one for every pupil, is unsatisfactory in not affording proper accommodation for the maps and models which the pupils are to study, describe, or copy. Broad tables near good-sized windows, and movable or suspended racks, are well-nigh indispensable. Hence the importance of having a room specially set apart for work of this kind, a laboratory in which dust-proof racks, cases, and closets give convenient storage for materials not in use, a laboratory adjoining the class room in which recitations and lectures on geography are given. The laboratory need not be so large as to contain table space for an entire class, for the class may to advantage do much laboratory work in small sections — indeed, if no special laboratory is provided, the enterprising teacher will do all he can on ordinary desks, but it is a pity to hamper good work by unfavorable conditions. A combination of class room and laboratory is practicable in schools of moderate size, but in large schools a geographical laboratory is as important as a physical laboratory, and in the modern school buildings, where so much consideration is given to every need of the teacher, the geographical laboratory is, we are glad to say, coming to be included in the architect's plans.

The practical teaching of geography needs furthermore a flat space on the roof for observation of the sky, a basement room where experimental illustrations of land and water may be made without danger of injuring the ceiling of a room below, and a reservation in the school yard where a meridian line may be marked and various outdoor exercises may be carried on. It needs also a field for outdoor work, and this is, fortunately, always at hand without expense to the school committee; it is curious to note how generally the school-teachers' needs are now served by electric railways, which so greatly reduce the difficulty of transportation.

Let us next consider the subdivision of practical exercises as to kind. It is desirable that this part of the work in a course on physical geography in the high school should be closely parallel with the bookwork, for the reason that the main outline of the subject is best presented definitely and specifically in printed form; but it must be recognized that many obstacles stand in the way of the easy attainment of this ideal. In the first place, exercises on certain subjects must be very deliberately carried on, requiring even a whole school year for their proper inductive development. These must either anticipate the high-school course, or they must advance independently of the text in which their equivalent is stated in printed form. The study of the weather finds some of its best applications in observation of storms and other special conditions at the time of their occurrence. These must be taken up in the order of their happening, and reference must then be made forward or back to their systematic treatment. Our climate is such that the open-field season comes in the fall and spring, while many topics under the important heading of land forms will often be taught from the book in the winter, when field work is difficult or impossible. Indeed, even in fall and spring, an excursion, well planned to illustrate the text in hand at the moment, may have to be postponed on account of bad weather, thus disorganizing our best intentions. It is true that laboratory work may often supplement or replace field work, but not sufficiently to smooth out all the difficulties noted above. Simple parallelism between text and practical exercises is therefore out of the question, and we must be content if some effective correlation between the two is gained instead.

In general, however, the classification adopted should follow that of the text-book in use in the school; as a rule it will contain four chief groups, — the earth as a globe, the atmosphere, the oceans, and the lands. To these four some would add human conditions as a fifth, but my preference is to distribute this subject over all the others, so that it shall never be separated from them in the minds of the pupils. Latitude would then be taught, not as an abstract mathematical problem, but as an ingenious and practical device which man uses in order to indicate his place with respect to poles and equator. The sea-bottom would then be described not merely as a dark, cold, quiet, monotonous plain, but as a contrast to the light and dark, cold and warm, quiet and active, ever-changing surface of the land on which is found that variety which even poets recognize as the very spice of life, and which biologists recognize as the inspiring cause of all its higher growths, culminating in the development of man himself. It is, however, not necessary to give more space here to determine whether the classification shall be fourfold or fivefold, but it is worth while to point out that the exercises devoted to the several groups differ very widely in character. The earth as a globe must be dealt with geometrically; if formal geometry has not been studied by the class in physical geography, let the work proceed by inspectional geometry. The variety of work here provided is greater than is usually supposed, and is by no means dry or uninteresting or abstract. Some practical suggestions as to its character may be found in the latter portion of this essay. Let me specially urge on the attention of those who are attracted by this division of the subject the exercises by which latitude, longitude, the length of the year, the obliquity of the ecliptic, and the declination of the sun are determined by the scholars themselves, without assistance from nautical almanacs or other external aids. No high degree of accuracy may be reached, but a real comprehension of these problems and their applications may be gained, such as is never acquired by text-book study.

The atmosphere must be dealt with physically. If the class has not already studied physics, let them get a good introduction to its nature by the measurement of temperature, rainfall, and other climatic elements; but in the absence of a good physical basis, do not attempt to explain such problems as the general circulation of the atmosphere; that is impossible. Practical exercises on the atmosphere naturally lead to the construction and study of the weather maps with which this country is so highly favored; climatic charts are also susceptible of much more practical and useful study than is ordinarily given to them.

The study of the ocean is both physical and geometric. This part of the subject should be handled with a light touch; it is not worth while to give elaborate attention to the ocean in inland schools, but, if time is allowed, depths, waves, currents, and tides all afford excellent material for practical exercises by which useful lessons may be impressed. A tank in the basement may here be employed to advantage.

The study of the lands must be of a kind that will lead pupils to understand what they see in a landscape. For this reason, continents, mountain ranges, and plateaus are too large to serve as units. The items that are studied must be small enough to be seen, for it is only by putting together visible units that a good idea of larger areas can be gained. The units must be studied rationally ; shown to be the product of ordinary processes, not ready-made articles or the results of a mysterious past. All exercises on land forms should be directed to this reasonable end, not only for the sake of impressing a great truth regarding physiographic development, but still more for the sake of enabling the pupils to see things better. There can be no question whatever that observation is aided by intelligent understanding. Much of this part of the work, indoors and out, must be of a nature that is by many called geological, though it is not altogether clear why geographers are so generally content to leave to geologists all treatment of matters so eminently physiographic as the weathering of rocks, the wasting of soils, the transportation of land waste by streams, the abrasion of land margins by sea waves. If these activities had occurred only in the remote past, geologists alone might lay claim to them, but, as a matter of fact, they are all part of the very living present. A geographer might almost as well be ignorant of the downstream direction of river flow as of the downstream transportation of land waste. From the very first teaching of geography, the young pupil should regard a river as the discharge of the water and the waste of its drainage basin, not of pure water alone, though the ordinary definitions might give him that idea. It is chiefly in this connection that field work is so useful. Children may naturally enough believe that weathering and erosion take place only in books, if they are never led to see the commonplace operations of these processes in the home field. They may reasonably infer that the physiographic development of land forms is an abstraction, if they are never shown the results of such development in the hills and valleys about their home. All the habitual activities of the lands should be studied outdoors. Further illustration of certain processes should be given in the school basement or the school yard with clay or sand and a hose. Maps, models, and pictures of the land forms that have been fashioned by these processes, as well as the briefest series of minerals and rocks that chiefly make up the lands, may be studied in the laboratory.

A well-founded belief in the reality of geographical facts is one of the smallest of the good results that follow from the performance of field and laboratory work as contrasted with recitations from a text. Greater and better results are the development of an intelligent self-confidence in the place of a too docile submission to a printed statement ; the discovery by a young pupil that he or she is, like the author of the text-book, a reasoning being, capable of finding out things by looking and thinking as well as by reading; above all, the formation of a habit of appeal to the facts of nature by direct observation in order to lay the foundations of science, and of appeal to reason in order to find out the meaning of the facts. If the study of geography is to serve for the education of something more than post-office clerks and express messengers, if it is to contribute a proper share toward the development of intelligent citizens, then the attention that is now sometimes given to the names of the counties along the southern or eastern boundary of a state should be relaxed, and fuller attention be given to the observation of facts that have a more enlarging interest and application.

Though it is physical geography in the high school that here takes our attention, it should not be forgotten that many exercises of a practical nature should be given in the lower schools. The observational determination of the length of the year, of the mean temperature of a month, and of the weathering and washing of land waste ought to be made before the high school is reached. Then the pupil in the high school can do something better ; for example, he can by observation and correspondence determine the difference of longitude between his school and some other school ; he can similarly measure the size of the earth, measure the inversions of temperature that occur during anti-cyclonic winter weather, discuss the development of land forms as affected by the wasting and washing of their rocks. Before a satisfactory scheme of high-school exercises can be planned, appropriate schemes for the lower schools must be adopted ; and if this state association desires a useful task for some of its members, let a committee be appointed for the more precise formulation of the physiographic work that ought to be done in successive school years. Let me counsel such a committee to be ambitious and not to content itself with recommendations that can be immediately carried out, but rather with such as will call for some effort on the part of the average teacher. Let us compare notes on the results of such efforts ten years hence. In the meantime, it is evident that much educational waste can be stopped by a well-arranged scheme of work for successive years. Each year should include the work best adapted to it ; older pupils will then not have to do elementary exercises. The work of each year will be usefully built on by the work of late years ; it will thus be kept as fresh as possible in the pupil's memory. No work will be unnecessarily repeated, and valuable scraps of time will be gained in an economy of this kind. Coördinated work is as important in practical physiographic exercises as it is in arithmetic, algebra, and geometry.

An important question is encountered in considering the equipment of a high school for good practical work in physical geography. We must all agree that the first item in the equipment, ranking above laboratory and apparatus, is a good teacher ; and by a good teacher, I mean one who has, among other things, actually performed a large variety of practical exercises, has really learned what field work means, and is competent to explore a new district and to discover its field resources in so far as they are related to school-teaching. If I may judge from the teachers who have attended my summer course in geography at Harvard University during past years, such preparation is rare, because of the novelty of practical work in geography. There is plenty of interest and capacity, but little experience or confidence. We must wait for about two school generations — about twenty years — before such preparation will be general, and we may not always find it even then. The best thing to do now is to give existing teachers every chance to improve themselves, and to give intending teachers every encouragement to make serious preparation for their future work.

The material equipment of a physiographic laboratory is to-day under active discussion. There is no standard equipment yet devised. There is at present no school-furnishing firm ready to supply a complete set of materials, all prepared, leaving the teacher only to make such additions as will serve his individuality or his locality. Here is room for enterprise. In the meantime, we should all expect to find globes and wall maps in a geographical laboratory or class room; it is now coming to be customary to find also certain large-scale maps, such as are published by our government bureaus, and an occasional model; but when it comes to details, it is evident that the practical exercises must be first planned, and the materials for their accomplishment must then be secured. Your proposed committee has therefore a double task, — first, to devise the exercises, and second, to devise appropriate materials for performing them.

Before closing I wish to consider some of the external conditions that will help or hinder the attainment of our ideals. Foremost here is the responsibility of the normal schools. It will be at once admitted that an energetic normal teacher of physiography, well trained in his subject, imbued with the scientific spirit and possessing the teaching instinct, may greatly promote the progress that we have at heart; all the more, if he is sympathetically sustained by the principal of the school to the point of gaining a good material equipment. But I fancy that one of the great discouragements that such a teacher suffers is the ease with which normal graduates imperfectly prepared in physical geography secure positions in our schools. Hence we must look next to the superintendents or other appointing powers, and urge them to require of a candidate as high a degree of proficiency in physical geography as in any other subject; or, still better, to require a specialization in physical geography of any one to whose hands this growing subject is to be intrusted in high schools and academies. A conference among normal teachers, superintendents, and masters, to determine what shall be done in the school courses in physiography, and what preparation shall be expected of new teachers during the next five years, would be of value if it resulted in raising the present standards; but it would be a hindrance if it gave authoritative approval to the unsatisfactory conditions now existing and took no steps to better them.

An effective external aid to observational teaching is the preparation of local guidebooks for field work. The physiographic resources of many districts cannot at present be so well set forth by school-teachers as by experts of a larger experience.

Lectures and excursions for teachers, such as are often given by university professors of geology, are very helpful, but their value would be increased if they could be set forth in printed form with due regard to their actual use in schools. For the object here considered, it is not enough that a local guidebook shall present an accurate account of the home district; the account should be presented in the order in which it will be used in the schools, so that it will serve as an immediate aid in school-teaching. Local scientific societies could do excellent work in supporting the publication of such guidebooks, and thus they would greatly promote their own success in a later generation of members.

II

In order to give specific indication of the character of various practical exercises and of the correlations that may be established between such exercises and bookwork, the second part of this essay may be devoted to a presentation of some examples appropriate to the study of that interesting chapter of physical geography which is often given a forbidding appearance under the name of " mathematical geography."

The Earth as a Globe. It is seldom that justice is done to the opportunity for practical work under the heading of " the earth as a globe." The difficulties that stand in the way of various observational exercises may certainly be overcome if their accomplishment rather than the maintenance of a set order of school periods is made the object in view. Many series of observations that cannot and need not be made by a whole class may be made by scholars singly or in pairs; the avoidance of such exercises, because of the disorder that they may create, does not speak well for the discipline or for the spirit of the school. Several of these exercises are best performed under the name of nature study in lower grades than the high school; they are mentioned here because if, as is too often the case, they have not been performed in their proper place, they should be given place in the high school; but it is manifest that such a plan disarranges the high-school course in physical geography and retards the attainment of the grade that it deserves.

Shape of the Earth. The only observational proof of the globular shape of the earth that is within the reach of young scholars is offered at the time of an eclipse of the moon. Such an opportunity should not be lost sight of. The edge of the earth's shadow always having a curved outline, the earth must be round, as Aristotle perceived four centuries before the Christian era. The time-honored proof afforded by the gradual disappearance of ships at sea is available only at the seashore ; it is interesting to note that this proof was first mentioned by Strabo. Accepting the globular form as a fact, the horizon plane, touching the earth's surface at the observer's station, extends indefinitely on all sides — the visible sky lying above, the invisible sky lying below, the plane. As long as the earth is thought of as a large body in comparison to the dimensions of the sky vault, it will probably be more or less consciously believed that the smaller half of the sky is above, and the larger part is below, the horizon of an observer. But when the earth is stated to be very small in comparison to the distance to the stars, the two parts of the sky separated by a horizon plane will be recognized as equal. The horizon planes of observers at different points on the earth will cut the sky into different halves, as may be shown by the aid of a hand globe. The uneven border of the sky against hills should be called the sky line, not the horizon. All this is as much astronomy as geography, but it is all essential to the clear understanding of matters that are constantly taught in geography, such as latitude and the seasons ; no safe entrance into such matters can be made without careful attention to fundamental concepts.

The discovery, attributed to Eudoxus, that an observer traveling north or south sees that stars change their position with respect to his horizon, will be considered in connection with measures of the size of the earth further on.

The causes and consequences of the earth's shape are better presented in the text than in practical exercises. Among the consequences are the essentially uniform value of gravity at all points on the earth's surface, and the absence of immense ascents and descents that must occur on an earth of any other shape. The nearly globular form of the actual earth has been of enormous importance during long-past ages in facilitating the migration of plants and animals from one region to another, and in recent centuries in permitting the migrations of mankind and the development of commerce.

Rotation. The vague ideas in the minds of adults regarding the earth as a rotating globe suggest that no good ground was provided in their school days for a correct understanding of this fundamental problem. The problem pertains equally to geography and to astronomy ; but as it should be encountered before these two subjects are differentiated, it is naturally classified under the first and more usual school subject. Very simple apparatus suffices. A pointer, pivoted at one end and sighted at the sun at different hours through the day, enables a young observer to gain a definite idea of the sun's (apparent) daily movement across the sky. (Actual sighting at the sun is not necessary ; when the pointer is held so that its shadow is no larger than its cross section, it is properly directed.) Record of successive observations may be made by setting up stakes so that their tops shall just touch the end of the pointer in the successive sights at the sun. On the following day the sun may be seen again in the earliest position observed on the first day, the period thus measured being a natural unit of time which civilized nations divide into twenty-four hours. It is important to notice that the sun's return to its original position has not been accomplished by going backward, but by continuous motion, as if in a circuit. The idea of rotation is thus clearly presented in spite of the fact that much of the sun's diurnal path is out of sight. It should not be understood that these observations give school children their first knowledge of the movement of the sun in the sky ; that they have long known. But the vagueness of ordinary knowledge on this point is now advanced to well-defined knowledge, and this is an important step.

Regularity in the movement of rotation is easily shown by making observations at regular intervals of one or two hours and noting that equal angles are moved over by the pointer, or that equal arcs are measured between the stake tops in equal time intervals. It is, I believe, well understood by teachers to-day that no preparatory study of formal geometry is needed as a basis for inspectional geometry of this kind. A little more advanced treatment is given by making observations at irregular periods, noting the time intervals between them, and proving by a continued proportion that angles and times bear a constant ratio. The angle of complete rotation (360°) will be found to bear the same ratio to the time of a complete rotation (twenty-four hours) as that which obtains between partial angles and times; hence the movement of the sun while it is beneath the horizon must be at the same angular velocity as while it is within reach of observation above the horizon. Daytime observations of the old moon (about third quarter) and evening observations of stars at home may be used to extend the results gained from the observations of the sun. If the moon is studied, the teacher should be prepared to explain the questions that may arise if the difference in length of solar and lunar days is detected. The chief point to be determined by star observation is that a star must make a circuit of the sky in about twenty-four hours, because on the second evening it comes from the eastward to the position from which it departed with a westward motion the night before, — an elementary matter truly, but one which is less clearly known to many civilized adults than it was to their barbarous ancestors.

Axis and Meridians. As a result of these observations it is recognized that "something" must turn. Whether it is the earth or the sky that turns need not be decided at once, if the teacher has the patience to let this archaic problem really take possession of the pupils' minds. In either case, the fact of turning demands an axis on which the turning shall take place, and if the pupils have any serious difficulty in discovering and stating the attitude of the axis, the teacher may be sure that the difficulty lies chiefly in the form of her questions, for the problem is essentially easy to living boys and girls, however difficult it may seem when clothed in words to which they are not accustomed. When the "slanting" attitude of the axis of turning is clearly recognized, all problems of size, latitude, and longitude are greatly simplified. By whatever short cut the teacher presents the conclusion that the earth and not the sky really turns, the axis must be conceived as passing through the earth's center, and as defining two significant points, the poles, where it "comes out." The discovery of the north pole of the sky near the north star (really more than two moon diameters from it toward the end of the Dipper handle) leads to a clearer understanding of the diurnal paths of the stars in smaller or larger circles.

The shadow cast by a vertical pole on level ground by the midday sun shows us the direction in which one must travel to reach the north pole. The prolongation of this line around the earth gives a meridian circle. The meridians are standard lines of direction. The equator is the great circle that cuts all the meridians in halves, midway between the poles. A series of meridians drawn at equal distances apart at the equator divide the earth into equal areas, conveniently arranged for measuring the relative easting or westing of places. A small hand globe may be appealed to in this connection, but constant reference should be made to " outdoors " as a part of the real earth on whose surface the imaginary circles are to be traced. " There " on a hand globe is not so useful as " there," pointing out the window toward the equator. The latter may arouse a live sense of directions, always useful in self-orientation, whatever is one's path in life ; the former may leave the subject an unreality.

Latitude. The determination of local solar time and of magnetic variation may be introduced in this connection, but more important is the estimation of one's position on the earth's surface with respect to the pole and equator. No mention of the term "latitude" need be made till this question is solved. It may be solved even in the grammar school by means of the sun circle, marked out by stake tops, as above described. First, some general considerations. To an observer at the pole the sun or the stars would travel around the sky once a day, in circles parallel to the horizon. The position of the star circles remains fixed wherever the observer goes and however much his horizon changes from the position that it had at the pole. As the observer moves along any meridian toward the equator his horizon must progressively tilt from the position that it had at the pole, and the amount of tilting may be measured by the angle between the tilted horizon and any one of the star or sun circles. This is, in essence, the method of Eudoxus, already referred to. A third way from pole to equator the angle would be 30°; halfway, 45°; two-thirds way, 60°; at the equator, 90°. The rotation of the earth is thus of great assistance in determining the relative positions of places. Bearing these principles in mind, let the sun circle be determined and represented by a series of stakes in a school yard, as in Fig. 1. Stand about thirty feet to one side of the stakes, in such a position that the tops of all of them fall into a slanting straight line when the observer's head is lowered to the height of the highest stake ; estimate or measure the angle *CAD*, by which the horizon is depressed beneath this slanting line ; and as the angle thus determined is to 90°, so is the distance from the pole (measured along a meridian from the pole to

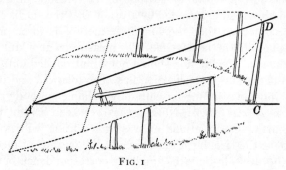

FIG. 1

the observer) to the entire quadrant of the meridian from pole to equator. Latitude is counted from the equator toward the pole ; it will therefore be the complement of the angle just measured. It should be noted that latitude may be thus determined at any time of year and without knowledge of the sun's angular distance from the sky equator (declination). In order to avoid misunderstanding, it may be pointed out that the pivot does not lie in the plane of the sun circle, and the slanting line *AD* does not measure the sun's noon altitude, except at the equinoxes. The noon altitude of the sun varies through the year, but the slanting line (the slant of the plane of the sun circle) is constant through the year, whatever the declination of the sun. In all this method of determining latitude it is assumed that the motion of the sun in declination in a single day will not be detected by the rough methods of record here employed.

An interesting feature of this elementary method of latitude determination is its novelty to many teachers. It involves nothing that grammar-school pupils who have learned by seeing and thinking, not by recitation, cannot easily apprehend if they are gradually led up to it by a well-graded flight of steps; the steps are not difficult and the flight is not long. The fear that they are so, on account of which many a teacher dreads to introduce fundamental work of this kind into her teaching, only goes to show the obscurity and confusion in which the chapter on so-called "mathematical geography" is often enveloped. Leave out this forbidding name, teach slowly on the basis of gradually accumulated observations, and the imagined difficulties will disappear.

The determination of latitude by the altitude of the pole star should always be preceded by a proof that the star is close to the pole; but even then the sun-circle method is to be preferred as being possible in the daytime. The measurement of latitude involving the sun's declination should not be introduced until the movement of the sun in declination has been followed and its greatest northing and southing measured by a simple method given below.

Size of the Earth. Nothing has yet been said of the size of the earth. Observations at a single station will not serve to measure the size, but the essence of the method of measurement may be usefully imitated, and, by correspondence between two schools, actual measurement may be made, much to the edification of the pupils. The relations of the local horizon to the plane of the sun circle, as involved in the measurement of latitude, enable the scholar to "see," if not to demonstrate, that an angle of one degree must separate the local horizons of two stations on the same meridian, whose latitude differs by one degree. Similarly, if observations of the sun's midday (meridian) altitude were made at two such stations on the same day, the altitudes would differ by one degree. Then, measuring the distance along the meridian arc between the stations, a simple proportion gives the circumference of the meridian circle:

$$1° : 360 :: \text{length of arc} : \text{circumference}.$$

This imitates the method employed by Eratosthenes. Two parties of scholars stationed at the ends of a short meridian

arc in a school yard or in an adjacent common may each determine the noon altitude of the sun and measure the distance between their stations in imitation of the genuine method of earth
measurement, and they may be convinced that if their observations were minutely accurate, the size of the earth could be estimated from even so short an arc as that which they can pace
during a recess interval. If a hill rises near the school, the convexity of the hill may be taken to imitate the rotundity of a little
earth. Two parties stationed out of sight of each other on the
north and south slopes of the hill, and on a north and south line,
may determine the sun's noon altitude with reference to the
slopes of the hill (which imitate the curved, level surface of a
little earth), and then, measuring the arc between their stations,
the size of a small earth to which such a hill would fit may be
determined. In the absence of a hill, a useful substitute may be
provided in a school yard by placing two tables or boxes in a
north and south line fifty or a hundred feet apart, tilting their
upper surfaces away from each other, and then proceeding on
the pretence that the table surfaces are parts of a little earth,
whose convex meridian may be indicated by the tops of a row
of stakes between them. The curved surface of a globe in a
schoolroom may be used to explain the geometry here involved,
but outdoor work should not be altogether replaced by such indoor substitutes. Nothing can so well give the sense of the real
great earth as outdoor observations.

Two schools can profitably coöperate to measure the size of
the earth. On a certain day agreed upon beforehand the midday
altitude of the sun is determined at each school. The length of
the meridian arc between the latitude circles of the two schools
may then be measured on a good map and the proportion of
Eratosthenes again employed to find the unknown quantity. If
each school determines its own latitude, the difference of latitudes replaces the difference of the sun's midday altitude on a
given day, and then no agreement as to the day of observation
is necessary. Why is it that nature study of this kind, so appropriate to the inhabitants of a rotating globe, is not introduced
in our lower schools ? Is it because of the supposed difficulty or
the actual simplicity of the necessary observations ; on account

of a recognition or a neglect of their value ; on account of a confidence in the innate ability of young scholars or a mistrust of their powers ; or on account of preparation or lack of preparation on the part of the teachers ? To the best of my belief, this is merely one of the many cases in which the real mental activity of school children is benumbed by substituting recitations of words for live performance.

Longitude. Difference of longitude (introduced under any name that is suggested by the pupils when talking freely of the relative positions of places on a rotating globe — the technical name to come in later) can be determined between two schools in any one of the three historical methods. As Strabo employed an eclipse of the moon to determine the relative easting or westing of certain points bordering the Mediterranean, so school children in different parts of the country may employ a lunar eclipse to-day to determine the relative positions of the meridians on which their homes are situated, previously determining their local solar time, and subsequently comparing the recorded time of any phase of the eclipse by correspondence. As governmental parties a hundred years ago made chronometer expeditions between neighboring national capitals, so school children may to-day send a watch from one school to another by express, and thus make a very good determination of difference of longitude. As modern observers employ the telegraph for time comparisons, even if separated by the whole breadth of a continent or of an ocean, so school children may to-day delegate some of their number to go to a telegraph office and send " time signals " from their watch (previously set to local solar time by their own observations) to an expectant party at the other end of the line. The two parties may have to wait half an hour or so to get the line " clear," but such a trifling delay should be no obstacle to success ; and even such delay may be avoided if a long-distance telephone is used ; then the time signals may be counted aloud by one party and directly heard by the other. Surely it is not the lack of capacity on the part of the pupils ; it is not the expense involved ; it is not the difficulty or the uselessness of the work that keeps such practical experiments as these out of our schools. What is the real difficulty in the way of their introduction ?

Indoor Exercises. Practical exercises of another kind on the earth as a globe may be performed indoors. A meridian section of the earth as a sphere and as a spheroid may be drawn to scale in order to show how vanishingly insignificant the polar flattening really is. Geographically, its value is negligible in a high-school course, however important and interesting it is in astronomy and however valuable it is historically as a proof of the earth's rotation. The height of the highest mountains, the depth of the deepest oceans, the mean altitude of continents, the mean depth of sea floors, and the rate of increase of interior temperatures may all be shown on this earth section. Comparisons of local and general distances and heights may be made by drawing them to scale.

Several methods of map projection may be illustrated. First the necessity for projection should be shown by the impossibility of smoothly laying a paper, cut to match a continental outline, upon the surface of a globe. The mercator (or stovepipe and cannon ball), the conical, and the gnomonic projections may be easily constructed; their difficulties may be magnified if clothed in mathematical language, or minified if talked about familiarly. After a network of meridians and latitude circles is drawn out a continental outline may be platted from a table giving the latitudes and longitudes of a number of points on the coast line. Greenland and South America on Mercator projection, Greenland on Mercator and conical projection, the margin of the unexplored areas in the Arctic and Antarctic regions on gnomonic projections all afford good practice for platting. Comparison of distances on globes and on maps serves to detect the distortion characteristic of each kind of projection. A great-circle sailing course between San Francisco and Yokohama, as determined on a globe, may be transferred to any projection by the latitude and longitude of a number of points on its path. The same may be tried on a polar gnomonic projection of the great southern ocean for a voyage from Cape Horn to Tasmania. The results in the two cases are interesting and instructive. From my own experience with school-teachers in problems of this kind, it is necessary to conclude that geometry must, as a rule, have been very badly taught to them.

Terrestrial magnetism affords some interesting exercises, if time can be allowed to them. The local variation of the magnetic needle has already been determined. Charts published by the Coast Survey and elsewhere give, by means of lines of equal variation, the values of local variation at any desired point. Local values thus obtained may be copied off on the blackboard, and the pupils may then write in the values on a Mercator map of the world (of their own construction, if desired), or on an outline map of the United States. The values thus charted afford practice in drawing lines of equal variation. The accuracy of the work can be tested by comparing the results with the original chart. A variation on this exercise may be made by drawing arrows at various stations to represent the local direction of magnetic north. Extend the arrows, curving them, if necessary, so that they shall not cross each other; they will then represent magnetic meridians. The north magnetic pole, in the neighborhood of Hudson bay, may be thus discovered. The meaning of magnetic charts can hardly be made clear without performing exercises of this kind.

The point that deserves special emphasis with regard to all the exercises thus far described is not so much their importance, although all are important, but rather their practicability. If the shape and size of the earth, latitude and longitude, and terrestrial magnetism are taught at all, practical exercises should replace recited definitions as far as possible. In all stages of the work excellent practice in English composition is afforded by calling for written description of observations and for careful formulation of results.

The Atmosphere. The study of the atmosphere suggests a great variety of practical exercises, many of which are now familiarly introduced in our schools. Local observations, without and with instruments, are made and discussed systematically. They are correlated with the larger phenomena of the weather maps, but the work in this direction often falls far short of its possible measure. In this connection I may refer to a book by my colleague, R. De C. Ward, entitled "Practical Exercises in Elementary Meteorology," in which the teacher and the pupil will find precise directions for the solution of a large number of problems that I am sure will be of great value in giving fuller appreciation of the treasures stored up in, but not always taken from, the daily weather maps. This guidebook being now accessible, I need here refer only to certain problems that are associated with the seasons. Here, as under the subject of the earth as a globe, it is too commonly the practice to learn definitions, instead of developing a real knowledge of the subject by the study of gradually accumulated observations. The need of plenty of time, only to be secured by carrying on observations during one or two years, is nowhere better illustrated than in this chapter of the subject. It is impossible to compress the necessary observations into the short time during which a high-school course would be concerned with the atmosphere. Adequate attention to the subject can be obtained only when the work is distributed over a long period in the grammar school, associated either with geography or with nature study.

The Seasons. The procession of phenomena observable in the annual succession of the seasons may be appreciated in early school years. The observations here described are intended to connect the simplest seasonal phenomena with their causes, which are to be found in the revolution of the earth around the sun, and in the resultant northing and southing of the sun (or its movement in declination, — declination in the sky being the equivalent of latitude on the earth).

The fact of seasonal change having been already recorded in a most elementary way, let a second record be made in connection with a search for the causes of change, as follows : at intervals of a fortnight or a month determine the midday altitude of the sun. At similar intervals determine the time, and, if possible, the compass direction, of sunrise and sunset. Again, at similar intervals, have the scholars, or at least the brighter ones, note the star groups that appear in the east shortly after the time, and opposite to the point, of sunset.

It is manifest that this requires observations outside of the school session and sometimes at rather inconvenient hours. But I would protest against the implication contained in objections to outside work, that lessons are so distasteful that none of the scholars will willingly give a little of their free time to such details as are here suggested. Early summer sunrise can be timed from sunset when it has been discovered during the winter that sunrise and sunset occur symmetrically before and after midday, or the moment when the sun reaches its highest altitude (meridian culmination). The general adoption of standard time introduces some confusion here, for it is desirable that sunrise and sunset should be recorded in local solar time. A watch kept to such time by observations of the sun at midday is useful in this connection. The watch will then give the necessary correction for the steeple clocks and factory whistles, by which some scholars may have to make their morning and evening records.

A pocket compass for measuring the direction of sunrise and sunset may be lent to those scholars whose homes give the best view of the horizon. Compass readings should be corrected for local variation of the needle to give true bearings. The direction of early sunrise may be determined from that of late sunset when it has been discovered that the two are symmetrical with respect to the true meridian.

All the facts thus determined vary systematically and in correlation with one another. The discovery of their system of change and of the correlations in the system should, if possible, be reserved for the scholars. Their intelligence is only half developed if the discoveries that they can make are made for them. In such case it may be claimed that time is saved, and that the results reached are the same; but it should be seen, on the other hand, that the scholars lose much appreciation of the result if they do not find it for themselves, and that they will fail entirely to acquire the power and the habit of discovering if they have no practice in it. If American schools are developed on a truly democratic basis, as befits republican institutions, one of their chief values will be that they aid in giving every boy and girl in the land a chance to emerge from the mass, where individuality is lost, and to reach a position in which they can do the most good for themselves, their homes, and their country. The cultivation of intelligence is as essential to this end as the acquisition of knowledge. The observations and correlations now in discussion may be made to contribute usefully to both these attainments.

The sun's midday altitude should be tabulated, and the change in its value should be indicated graphically. Records thus kept are in themselves educative, not only in forming habits of accuracy and neatness, but still further in familiarizing the pupils with the several methods of record, each best for its own purpose. Graphic record may be made on a diagram in which horizontal measures represent time (dates) and vertical measures represent angular altitude (Fig. 2). As the line connecting successive points of observation is seen to be not straight but curved, let expectation be aroused as to the probable result of further observations, thus developing the habit of thinking forward from a basis of observations in the past and present. Test the expectations by comparison with later observations, and thus

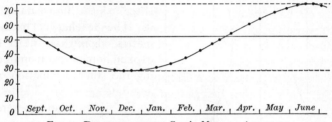

FIG. 2. DIAGRAM OF THE SUN'S MIDDAY ALTITUDE

develop the more important habit of not jumping at conclusions. The frequency of sun observations should be increased as the solstices are approached, in order to give good determination of those important dates. Few pupils will fail to await with interest the first observations after the Christmas holidays, or to continue observations with unflagging interest even into the hot weather of late June. It is conceivable that some children might even carry on observations of this kind through the summer vacation in order to complete their curve for the year. A graphic bisection of the upper and lower culminations of the curve, by lines drawn through the middle points of horizontal chords, will give good determinations of the dates of the solstices. When the upper and lower limits of the curve are well determined, draw horizontal lines tangent to them, and draw a third horizontal line midway between these tangents. Lead up to the discovery that this middle line represents the sky equator, that the date of the equinoxes is given at the two intersections of the equator and the sun's path, and that the angular distance (declination) of the sun north or south of the equator can easily be roughly determined for any day of the year by measuring up or down from the equator line to the curved sun path. Then, and not properly till then, are young geographers ready to use the noon altitude and declination of the sun in determining their latitude. When this stage is reached, better values of the sun's declination may be taken from the Nautical Almanac for the current year, accessible in the larger public libraries. If it is not accessible there, ask the librarian to get it. The teacher of mathematics should be able to explain how to use it in finding the sun's declination on any date.

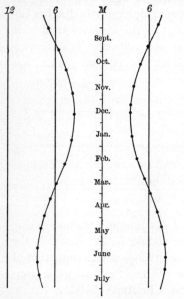

FIG. 3. DIAGRAM OF SUNRISE AND SUNSET HOURS

The Year. The time and direction of sunrise and sunset should be tabulated and diagramed. The correlation of the day's length, the direction of the sun at rising and setting, and the changes in midday altitude are most instructive. Each quantity affords occasion for prediction and verification of its future values. All the changes in these quantities are run in a period of 365 days, and in the same period the star group first seen in the east shortly after sunset is again seen there at the same hour. Now let the scholars try to explain this return to a previous condition, suggesting to them that a line may be imagined starting at the sun, passing through the earth, and extending to the distant stars. This line has been found to sweep through the sky, pointing to one star group after another, and to return to the original group in the same period as that in which the noon altitude and its correlated quantities run through their variations. Then the earth must go around the sun once in 365 days. The time unit, called a year, has long been familiar to the scholars; they have probably heard or read that the earth goes around the sun in a year, but those words are now fuller of meaning than they were ever before. The sensible constancy of the sun's apparent diameter (determined by letting a ray of sunlight pass through a pin hole in one sheet of paper and fall upon another sheet at a fixed distance from the pin hole) should serve to give a good idea of the form of the curve or orbit that the earth runs around.

In order to give a more satisfactory determination of the length of the year than can be obtained merely by general inspection of the eastern constellations after sunset, the following plan may be adopted: a series of observations in September and October will show that the stars occupy more and more western positions at a given hour on successive evenings. Let the more skillful scholars make record of the position of some recognizable star with respect to a roof or chimney at a certain hour on a certain evening, then ask them to discover when the star will again be in that position at that hour. It will be well to have records of this sort made on several different evenings, so as to lessen the possible trouble from cloudy evenings in the following year.

Inclined Attitude of Axis to Orbit. The facts regarding noon altitude and the correlated quantities can all be explained if it be suggested that the axis on which the earth has been found to turn does not stand vertical to the plane of the orbit in which it has been found to revolve. Here again a globe is of value as a mental aid and an aid in visualizing the necessary geometrical relations. So are the diagrams that one usually finds in text-books, although they are much less serviceable than globes. Whether children of under fourteen years of age can discover this solution of the problem or not remains to be proved. At least they should have a good chance to show their capacity to discover it, a carefully prepared chance, approached by the slow accumulation of pertinent observations, all familiarized by repetition.

A simple construction of the earth's orbit is also serviceable at this stage. Draw upon a sheet of paper about a foot square a line through its middle parallel to one side. Locate the middle point of the line. Construct a scale whose units are $\frac{1}{200}$ of the side of the paper, so that two pins, three units apart, can be driven into the middle line symmetrically on either side of the middle point. Lay a loop of thread or fine string 189 units in perimeter over the pins, stretch it tight with a pencil, and draw a curve thus guided. This nearly circular curve shows the true pattern of the earth's orbit, the units of the scale being millions of miles. Take out one of the pins, and around the other draw a little circle, a trifle less than a unit in diameter, to represent the sun; a good-sized pin head will not be much too small for it. Assuming that the north star is above the plane of the orbit (or paper), the earth moves around the orbit so as to pass from right to left when viewed from the sun. Find the point on the orbit that is nearest to the sun (it must lie where the orbit is cut by that half of the middle line which passes through the sun). Conveniently for our memories, the sun celebrates New Year's Day by passing through this "near sun point," or perihelion. July 1 sees the earth at the opposite "far sun point," or aphelion. Go backward along the orbit from perihelion one ninth of a quadrant arc; this is the point occupied on December 21, the date of the sun's least midday altitude, or the winter solstice. Draw a line from this point through the sun; it intersects the orbit at the summer solstice, which the earth passes on June 21. Draw a line through the sun at right angles to the solsticial line; it intersects the orbit in the equinoctial points. Set up a small ball on a vertical axis to represent the earth at the winter solstice; the sun can then be imagined to illuminate the near half of the earth; the day-and-night circle will separate the illuminated half from the dark half of the earth. As the earth now stands, with a vertical axis, the plane of the equator passes through the sun, but this has been shown by observation to be impossible at the time of the winter solstice. On that date the sun is 23° south of the equator. The axis of the earth must therefore be tilted 23° from the vertical and away from the sun in order to imitate actual conditions.

As the prolonged axis meets the sky in the same point at all seasons of the year, the attitude of the axis must always be parallel to its initial position. Carry the earth around its orbit, holding the axis properly on the way, and observe the relative attitude of the day-and-night circle at different times of year. All the peculiar variations of the sun's midday altitude, of the times and directions of sunrise and sunset, and of the length of day and night can be explained by this little working model; hence it may be fairly said to present the conditions of nature. It is well that the scholar should know that it is entirely on the basis of such agreements between hypothesis and fact that text-books make statements about the inclination of the earth's axis, the duration of its annual revolution, and so on. There is no other door by which one can really enter the domain of knowledge, where the motto is written: "Truth for authority, not authority for truth."

XII

FIELD WORK IN PHYSICAL GEOGRAPHY

The character of the practical exercises in a course in physical geography that follows a course on geology will be very different from that in one which precedes a course in geology, or which stands alone. The first of these arrangements is so unadvisable that it need not be considered; the second is common enough for those students who go to colleges after finishing a high-school course; the third is still more common, and will remain so for years to come; hence the third alone will be considered here. Furthermore, as our title refers only to those practical exercises which are involved in field work, laboratory exercises will not here be discussed. The problem is thus narrowed down to the selection of outdoor exercises in physical geography for a class of students who have not studied, and who may never study, geology. It will be still further narrowed by agreeing that exercises concerning the earth as a globe, the atmosphere, and the ocean are not at present in consideration, and hence that exercises on the lands, where physical geography and physical geology run so close together, are alone to be examined.

The first point to bear in mind is that the exercises should be so planned as to lead towards their object, namely, a real understanding of the existing lands on which we live, with particular attention to those elements which are of consequence as environments, controlling our way of living. This at once makes a distinction between exercises for a course on physical geography and exercises for a course on physical geology, even though the exercises lead over the same paths and stop at the same places; for exercises in geology have as their chief object the interpretation of the past history of the earth through its present condition, and this object should always be borne in mind if geology and not geography is to be taught. It may be noted, however, that as the history of the past cannot be really understood until the processes of the present are made familiar, it is eminently appropriate that physiographic field work, in which emphasis is laid on present conditions, should precede geological field work, which is laid on the sequence of past events. It was with this principle in mind that the Committee of Ten recommended, some years ago, the postponement of geology to the college course, and the general introduction of practical exercises as a part of physical geography in the high-school course.

Another important point is that field exercises in the autumn, when the text-book work is only just opening, should relate to general characteristics of the lands as illustrated by specific facts, and that the study of different kinds of land forms should be as a rule postponed to spring excursions, after a larger view of the subject has been acquired through the winter months. Let the students then be asked in September and October to look about them to try to discover what are the most general characteristics of the lands, and where and how they may be best illustrated by local examples. At the close of field exercises running through two fall months, it should have been observed, or reasonably inferred, that the lands are those parts of the earth's rocky crust that rise above the seas, and that are thereby directly exposed to sunshine, to atmospheric action, and to stream work (thus being strongly contrasted with the sea floors); that in consequence of this exposure the land surface is under changing conditions of light and darkness, of heat and cold, of aridity and humidity, of movement and rest, of chemical and organic processes; that chief among the consequences of these activities is the progressive disintegration of the surface rocks, thus forming rock waste and soil, and the progressive down-slope removal of the waste from higher to lower ground, and ultimately to the ocean, — or, in brief, that the waste of the land is the gain of the sea ; that the action of rain-, snow-, and spring-fed streams is particularly important in the transportation of waste, to such a degree that the pathway of the streams is usually worn down below the adjacent land surface, just as a much-used and poorly-cared-for road is worn down, but with the notable differences, that while the road may go uphill and downhill, the pathway or channel of the streams is always downhill, and that while roads may run crosswise and form a network, streams tend to join each other and thus form a branchwork.

While local observations are accumulating, it is for the teacher to emphasize their importance by telling something of the results of observation elsewhere. Rocks, weather, soil, wash, streams, valleys, and hills are of world-wide distribution. They all vary in many respects from place to place over the lands, yet they all maintain their essential characteristics. The capacity to see facts of these kinds can be acquired almost anywhere and utilized almost everywhere. It is of the utmost importance that this aspect of home field study and its relation to the study of the world should be appreciated. Just as soon as a group of home facts is well apprehended and generalized, let the teacher confirm its value by telling something of the wide distribution of such facts over the world, instancing examples where their value is greater or less than, or equal to, their value in the home field. Local field work may be greatly enriched in this way.

During the establishment of the fundamental generalizations, special attention may be given to some of the commoner minerals and rocks in the local field, and to the manner in which they are disintegrated, but the study of mineralogy as such should be set aside for another occasion. Familiarity should be gained with the processes whereby the disintegrating rock waste creeps and washes downhill to the streams, constantly removed and constantly renewed, and whereby the streams comminute the waste and transport it along their valleys toward the sea; attention should be given to the forms assumed by the waste of the land on its way to the sea, and the use made of the slowly moving waste by plants and animals. Gradually the great generalization may be reached that if destructive processes of these kinds should go on forever, the lands would in time be worn to nearly featureless lowlands, close to sea-level, and that this result would already have been reached had the crust of the earth stood still from the beginning; and then follows the reasonable inference that inasmuch as the lands still possess abundant relief, the earth's crust cannot always have stood still: it must have changed position, perhaps slowly rising and falling, now here, now there ; and then it dawns upon the inquiring student that the lands possess their present forms because they have for ages been the theater of the opposing processes of deformation and denudation ; that every part of the lands may be supposed to owe its existing form to the stage now reached by the process of denudation in overcoming the work of deformation, and that no better way of describing a land form can be found than to explain it in terms of its origin. Thus the essential principle of the geographical cycle is reached, and a sound foundation is laid for all further work. Truly, it still remains to demonstrate the correctness of all these inferences and suppositions, but real demonstration is, I fear, not to be accomplished in the time allowed for school exercises, and with students of the age appropriate to the exercises here considered. Demonstration may be quoted, if desired, in abundance, but the most that can be expected in the way of first-hand work is to show that the conclusions here announced are reasonable ; and on this foundation, text-book work may proceed with good effect through the winter.

It should be clearly understood that work of this kind is not limited merely to matters of observation and record. These are truly the first steps, but they must be followed by abundant thinking ; indeed, the soul of the work is gained only when the thinking that is inspired by the observations is logical, searching, critical. It is chiefly by this means that a sound disciplinary value is added to outdoor exercises, and that they become essentially scientific, for we here take it to be understood that observation is by no means the whole of science, although it is an essential part thereof. The thought as well as the facts should be written out, but inference and argument should be carefully separated from observation and generalization. Thus the work may be made as rigorous as is desired, and its educational value may be made second to none ; but much progress must be made in our schools before this ideal is reached.

Let it be here noted that field work of the kind above suggested is entirely out of reach of a teacher inexperienced in the field. It is nothing more than a travesty of observational exercises that is gained when they are conducted by a teacher who cannot "walk alone" in comfort out of doors. Hence, when superintendents wish to introduce work of this kind, it is incumbent upon them to engage a teacher who is competent to conduct it. The acceptance of an unprepared candidate is demoralizing in more ways than one ; not only will the educative and disciplinary elements of field physiography be greatly weakened, but those conscientious students who are preparing themselves to teach real physiography by devoting a good share of time to the study of the subject will be discouraged by seeing that ill-prepared candidates gain responsible positions. This is to-day a serious difficulty, and it lies more with superintendents than with any one else to correct it.

Let it be further noted that every competent teacher should be left free to plan field work with due regard to local field opportunity, and hence that field exercises must vary greatly in different schools, and that they should not be submitted to any uniform or rigid examination set by a state board of education. On the seacoast field observations may be directed to a whole series of problems that are reached only through the text-book or the laboratory at a school in the interior of the country. A lowland district in a dry climate suggests different exercises from a mountain district in a wet climate. The piedmont district of the southern Appalachians, with its deep weathered soils and its normally developed drainage systems, could be more simply treated than the glaciated uplands of New England, where the irregularly distributed drift and the many special or abnormal drainage features will require a very ingenious treatment before the best advantage can be taken of them in elementary work. It would be a mistake to impose a detailed outline of work upon a teacher situated in any one of these districts, for real success requires that every competent teacher should plan local field work for himself ; hence the following outline of a few items for autumn work in a Vermont high or normal school should be taken as a suggestion and not as a prescription ; as a beginning, and not as a whole course.

Autumn. General characteristics of the land. 1. A weathering ledge : decomposition of certain minerals, action of temperature, moisture; products of disintegration; their rapid removal, chiefly by falling from steep rock faces which are thus left bare for continued active attack of the weather; here only lichens, etc., grow; the accumulation of fine waste on little rocky shelves which are thus somewhat protected from the weather; here plants of higher order gain a root-hold; yet even here slow down-slope movement (creeping) is caused by washing, and by changes of temperature, etc. The prevalent coarsely crystalline texture of the rocks and the frequent occurrence of wrinkled foliated structures may be at once introduced as evidence that much material has already been removed from this region by erosion; for coarse crystalline texture and wrinkled foliated structure cannot be produced by any known processes that operate at the earth's surface; they are explained only by conditions that may occur at depths of many thousands of feet beneath the surface. Hence the visibility of such rock structures suggests that the surface has been worn down to them by the removal of rock masses that once covered them, probably to the depth of thousands of feet. In time the steep-faced ledge will be weathered back to such a slope that its waste will form a continuous cover over it; the waste will be cloaked over with plants, which delay but do not prevent its removal; the finer particles of waste directly on the surface will wash and creep down the slope fastest, while new fragments are slowly weathered off the ledge beneath the soil cover. If the processes of removal are very weak, so that less is removed from the outer surface than is added by weathering the rocks beneath the under surface of the waste cover, then the cover increases in thickness and thus decreases the effectiveness of under-weathering; if removal of waste at the surface is active, the waste cover is thinned and its slope is decreased, while under-weathering is accelerated; thus in time an essential balance comes to be struck between supply and loss, and the waste cover becomes a general and permanent feature of the surface. The flatter the surface is worn, the slower the removal of the waste, the finer its surface particles, and the greater its depth. The piedmont district of the southern Appalachians exhibits abundant examples of this condition of things; their absence in Vermont must be considered later.

2. A small stream. Explore and map its drainage area; note that its velocity is at every point just sufficient to dispose of the volume received; that it flows faster with a slender current on steeper slopes, and slower with a stouter current on gentler slopes; that in a cross section of a straight channel the current is fastest near the middle and at (or very close to) the surface; but in a curved channel the line of fastest current is displaced from the middle of the stream toward the outer side of the curve (convex side of stream, or concave bank); that the greater depth of the channel is usually nearly under the line of fastest current. Note the distribution of cobbles, gravel, sand, silt, along the stream bed. How are these materials related to the velocity of the stream and to the form of the channel? By attentively watching the stream bed, particles of waste may be seen dragged along the bottom; by studying the bed and the banks, inferences may be made as to the progressive action of the stream in the past and the future, and the origin of its present channel may be discovered. A second visit should be made just after a rain, when the stream is swollen, hurried, and turbid; this is the time when most of the stream's work is done; it has a vacation in fair weather. The waste is first received in great part from the banks, and it is supplied to the banks by washing and creeping from the adjoining hillsides; a very small part of its load of waste comes originally from its bed; but once in the power of the stream, the waste is slowly washed down the channel, making many stops on its way to the sea, sometimes being laid down in a bar, sometimes on the inner bank of a curve, to be taken up again for a further journey at some later time. Especially at time of flood is the channel scoured and the waste carried forward; as the flood subsides and the current weakens, the coarser waste is laid down first and the finer waste later. Trace a stream to its junction with another; note that the two streams come together at accordant grade. This is an almost universal relation, and is one of the chief arguments for the erosion of valleys by the streams that flow along them (see passage from Playfair, cited in Russell's "Rivers of North America," p. iii). The long-continued action of streams must necessarily produce this relation; the occurrence of the relation proves the long-continued

action of the streams. But the streams alone would cut vertical-walled trenches. The widely opened form of the valleys prevalent in Vermont, as indicated by the moderate slopes of the valley sides, suggests that a great amount of material must have been weathered and washed from them down to the streams, and carried by the streams to the rivers and the sea; and thus some confirmation is found for the conclusion already stated, based on the texture of the rocks.

Most streams in New England exhibit alternations of rushing rapids on rocky ledges and slow-flowing reaches in meadows. In the reaches, the depth to which the channel is cut is controlled by the ledge at the rapids next down the valley; and the stream is just balanced between the average supply and removal of the waste. Farther deepening of the balanced channel can be allowed only as the controlling ledge is slowly worn down. So delicate an adjustment of the balanced stream to the ledge can only be the result of the stream's own action on its original valley. If the original valley upstream from the ledge had too gentle a slope, the stream would have run slowly through it (or the stream might have been much delayed, as in a lake basin occupying a depression in the general path of the valley) and the channel (or lake basin) would have been filled up or aggraded with waste, thus producing the existing balanced slope. If the channel were originally of a stronger slope, the stream would have run more rapidly and would have worn down or degraded its bed until the present slope was gained. A channel that has a balanced slope may therefore be said to be *graded;* the stream may be said to be in a graded condition, or at grade; and the slope of the balanced stream may be described (in a slightly different sense of the same word) as having a steep or a gentle grade.

The ledge at the rapids is slowly worn or degraded chiefly by the rasping of waste over it at time of flood. Where a stream is actively deepening its channel in a ledge of weak rock (a rare condition in Vermont, but common enough in New York), the channel is worn chiefly downward, and lateral wearing is at a minimum. Where a stream is flowing at a grade through a meadow, downward wearing is at a minimum, and lateral wearing on the outer bank is at a maximum; as a result the meadow

stream is constantly changing its channel by wearing away the
outer bank and laying down the wash thus gained on the inner
bank of a curve farther forward; a meandering channel is thus
formed. Where the curves are well pronounced it may be noted
that the wearing action of the stream is extended forward from
the concave (outer) bank of a meander so as to include something of the up-valley side of the meadow lobe that enters the
next meander; and that the depositing action is extended forward from the convex (inner) bank of a meander so as to include
something of the down-valley side of the meadow lobe; hence
the meander system is migrating downstream at the same time
that it is wandering laterally. Much of the meadow or flood
plain may have been worked over by the shifting stream, and
hence it will be underlaid by stones and gravel such as are to-day
found in the stream channel, however fine may be the silt that
is strewn over its surface at time of overflow.

The ledge that determines a rapid serves as a local base-level
to the graded reach next upstream; that is, its surface determines a level base, to which the stream approaches very closely,
but which it cannot quite attain. If no ledge occurs between
the point of observation and the sea, then the stream will be
graded with respect to the general base-level of the ocean surface.
Most rivers are to-day graded with respect to local or general
base-levels; it is chiefly the smaller streams that are detained in
ungraded lakes or hurried in ungraded torrents. This illustrates
a general principle of wide application. Whenever the processes
that are in operation upon a land form tend to change it to
another form, then it cannot endure long, as the earth counts
time; but when the acting processes tend to maintain the form,
then it endures through ages. Lakes and rapids soon disappear
by the action of their streams; streams that possess such features are young, as the earth views them. Graded reaches persist, for they are self-perpetuating; streams that possess them
are mature or old. The relatively short life of exposed ledges
on hillsides and the long endurance of waste-covered or graded
slopes illustrate the same principle.

Local illustrations of processes and principles, such as these
just described, should be supplemented by citation of similar

illustrations in other parts of the world. The teacher should possess a mental fund of such parallel illustrations, ready for instant use. He should also possess a well-selected series of book references, many of them representing notes made in his own experience of reading, to which the more assiduous of his students may be referred for fuller information. Every item encountered in the local field may thus be shown to have its fellows elsewhere in the world, and the value of the local field is thus greatly increased. In this way every local item comes to aid the conception of an ideal type, the generalized representative of a class which includes many distant examples as well as the local example through which its acquaintance was first made. Field work thus becomes naturally associated with book work. As before noted, field work remains far below what it should be if it is limited merely to the observation of the examples that it immediately presents.

3. Drift. The hills and valleys of Vermont, and of New England in general, possess abundant deposits of unconsolidated rock waste known as drift. Note the varied composition of these deposits; they frequently contain rock fragments unlike the rock in the neighboring ledges. The rock fragments are frequently firm and unweathered; they are sometimes, especially in valleys, rounded as if waterworn; sometimes, especially on uplands, roughly faceted and striated, as if dragged under heavy pressure. The structure and form of these deposits is very varied. Those containing faceted and striated stones or bowlders are compact and unstratified, often wrapped over the rock hills as if packed upon them; sometimes reaching greater thickness and rising in oval hills of arched profile, independent of the rock beneath. Those containing rounded cobbles and pebbles, with sand, are stratified; they sometimes form small knolls or serpentine ridges; sometimes plains or terraces. The rock beneath the drift is usually firm and unweathered; its surface is often rounded and striated, as if it had been scoured under heavy pressure. Evidently the normal processes of weathering have not been active here, as they have been in the southern Appalachians. In place of the regular and well-graded slopes of gentle curvature, cloaked with abundant waste derived from the

underlying rock and always leading down to an elaborate branch work of well-established water courses, such as must characterize regions where normal weathering has long been in progress, the hills and valleys of Vermont present irregular forms; ledges are exposed here and there in disorder, irregularly distributed drift deposits of varied thickness, structure, and form lie on a firm and smoothed foundation of unweathered or little-weathered rock; the hillsides descend unevenly to water courses that exhibit in their ponds and rapids the most evident signs of an early stage of development. All these abnormal features are to be attributed to glacial action, whose geographical consequences in the northern states are so numerous and so important that every student of physiography should gain an early acquaintance with them.

As under weathering and streams, it is by no means advisable that every student should be expected to observe all the items here noted, or to formulate or invent for himself all the generalizations and explanations here quoted. The school year is too short for that. But there should be some observation, generalization, invention, and discussion on the part of every student, and in supplement to this the teacher should add enough to carry the class through a carefully prepared course in the appointed time. In particular is it necessary that the various classes of facts that lead to the most important generalizations and that call for the most frequent fundamental explanations should be illustrated by some well-selected examples, and that these examples should become familiar to the students by direct observation. The students should thus be led directly to discover or to recognize the chief principles and general ideas of land physiography — gradation, base-leveling, etc. — while in the presence of the facts to which these principles apply. Only in this way can abstract principles gain real and serviceable application. If it occur to any readers of these pages that the topics here suggested for field observation and study possess some measure of difficulty, more perhaps than is usually associated with work on geographical excursions, let them be assured that the results are worth the effort they may demand, and that only as physiography gains a seriousness of work comparable to that in classics and mathematics will it acquire the educational position that it deserves.

Spring. If it be true that field work for the autumn months must be planned for each school district, it is still more true for the spring months; for attention should then be given to those topics of the text-books which find local illustration near the school; not merely general topics, such as the gradation of river courses, but particular topics, such as the development of flood plains, the migration of divides, and the evolution of certain land forms. Any little stream that possesses a flood plain between the inclosing side slopes of its valley serves to review and to justify everything that has been learned about flood plains; the stage attained in the development of the actual flood plain should be determined with respect to the ideal scheme of flood-plain development. Every divide from which the two slopes are unsymmetrical is presumably a migrating divide. What changes will probably be brought about in stream courses and waste slopes if the migration continue? What examples from other parts of the world may be illustrated by the observed example? As to land forms, Vermont has an abundance of subdued mountains and of drift deposits; Kentucky illustrates the dissection of plains and plateaus in various stages; central Pennsylvania exhibits a beautiful variety of mountain ridges, with an extraordinarily well-adjusted drainage system; the Carolinas possess a beautiful variety of coastal features; Mississippi and Louisiana share the great flood plain of the " father of waters." Surely there is no lack of field material! Let us hear from the teachers who are making a success of their field work as to the examples of land forms that they are actually studying outdoors.

In closing, let me add a few more pieces of advice. While the field work in the fall leads up from various particular observations to several broad generalizations, the spring work should lead down from a broad scheme of classification to various particular examples that come under the scheme. Every observed fact should be associated with the class to which it belongs. As a member of this class, it should be compared with other members known through the text-book, or through outside reading, and representing earlier and later stages of development. Particular effort should be given to making this part of the work serious, definite, and accurate, for only in this way can a high disciplinary value be gained for field exercises ; otherwise they are apt to be vague, trifling, and uneducative. Let attention be frequently turned at all stages of the work to the controls exerted by physiographic factors upon organic life, both high and low ; not because physical geography includes biology, but because it is desirable to form the habit of recognizing the close correlation that surely exists between inorganic and organic nature. Controls illustrated in the field may be verified by examples from other sources, but care should be taken to avoid petty examples on the one hand and doubtful examples on the other.

Finally, let it be remembered that this is not an outline of a course in geography, but some suggestions for one part (fall and spring field work) of a year's course on one division (physical geography) of geography. Other parts and other divisions deserve equally careful and serious attention.

PART TWO

PHYSIOGRAPHIC ESSAYS

XIII

THE GEOGRAPHICAL CYCLE

The Genetic Classification of Land Forms. All the varied forms of the lands are dependent upon — or, as the mathematician would say, are functions of — three variable quantities, which may be called structure, process, and time. In the beginning, when the forces of deformation and uplift determine the structure and attitude of a region, the form of its surface is in sympathy with its internal arrangement, and its height depends on the amount of uplift that it has suffered. If its rocks were unchangeable under the attack of external processes, its surface would remain unaltered until the forces of deformation and uplift acted again ; and in this case structure would be alone in control of form. But no rocks are unchangeable ; even the most resistant yield under the attack of the atmosphere, and their waste creeps and washes downhill as long as any hills remain ; hence all forms, however high and however resistant, must be laid low, and thus destructive process gains rank equal to that of structure in determining the shape of a land mass. Process cannot, however, complete its work instantly, and the amount of change from initial form is therefore a function of time. Time thus completes the trio of geographical controls, and is, of the three, the one of the most frequent application and of a most practical value in geographical description.

Structure is the foundation of all geographical classifications in which the trio of controls is recognized. The Allegheny plateau is a unit, a "region," because all through its great extent it is composed of widespread horizontal rock layers. The Swiss

249

Jura and the Pennsylvania Appalachians are units, for they consist of corrugated strata. The Laurentian highlands of Canada are essentially a unit, for they consist of greatly disturbed crystalline rocks. These geographical units have, however, no such simplicity as mathematical units; each one has a certain variety. The strata of plateaus are not strictly horizontal, for they slant or roll gently, now this way, now that. The corrugations of the Jura or of the Appalachians are not all alike; they might, indeed, be more truly described as all different, yet they preserve their essential features with much constancy. The disordered rocks of the Laurentian highlands have so excessively complicated a structure as at present to defy description, unless item by item; yet, in spite of the free variations from a single structural pattern, it is legitimate and useful to look in a broad way at such a region, and to regard it as a structural unit. The forces by which structures and attitudes have been determined do not come within the scope of geographical inquiry, but the structures acquired by the action of these forces serve as the essential basis for the genetic classification of geographical forms. For the purpose of this article, it will suffice to recognize two great structural groups : first, the group of horizontal structures, including plains, plateaus, and their derivatives, for which no single name has been suggested; second, the group of disordered structures, including mountains and their derivatives, likewise without a single name. The second group may be more elaborately subdivided than the first.

The destructive processes are of great variety, — the chemical action of air and water, and the mechanical action of wind, heat, and cold, of rain and snow, rivers and glaciers, waves and currents. But as most of the land surface of the earth is acted on chiefly by weather changes and running water, these will be treated as forming a normal group of destructive processes, while the wind of arid deserts and the ice of frigid deserts will be considered as climatic modifications of the norm, and set apart for particular discussion ; a special chapter will be needed to explain the action of waves and currents on the shore-lines at the edge of the lands. The various processes by which destructive work is done are in their turn geographical features, and many of them are well recognized as such; for example, rivers, falls, and glaciers; but they are too commonly considered by geographers apart from the work that they do, this phase of their study being, for some unsatisfactory reason, given over to physical geology. There should be no such separation of agency and work in physical geography, although it is profitable to give separate consideration to the active agent and to the inert mass on which it works.

Time as an Element in Geographical Terminology. The amount of change caused by destructive processes increases with the passage of time, but neither the amount nor the rate of change is a simple function of time. The amount of change is limited, in the first place, by the altitude of a region above the sea; for, however long the time, the normal destructive forces cannot wear a land surface below this ultimate base-level of their action, and glacial and marine forces cannot wear down a land mass indefinitely beneath sea-level. The rate of change under normal processes, which alone will be considered for the present, is at the very first relatively moderate; it then advances rather rapidly to a maximum, and next slowly decreases to an indefinitely postponed minimum.

Evidently a longer period must be required for the complete denudation of a resistant than for that of a weak land mass, but no measure in terms of years or centuries can now be given to the period needed for the effective wearing down of highlands to featureless lowlands. All historic time is hardly more than a negligible fraction of so vast a duration. The best that can be done at present is to give a convenient name to this unmeasured part of eternity, and for this purpose nothing seems more appropriate than *a geographical cycle.* When it is possible to establish a ratio between geographical and geological units, there will probably be found an approach to equality between the duration of an average cycle and that of Cretaceous or Tertiary time, as has been indicated by the studies of several geomorphologists.

"Theoretical" Geography. It is evident that a scheme of geographical classification that is founded on structure, process, and time must be deductive in a high degree. This is intentionally and avowedly the case in the present instance. As a consequence,

the scheme gains a very "theoretical" flavor that is not relished by some geographers, whose work implies that geography, unlike all other sciences, should be developed by the use of certain of the mental faculties only, — chiefly observation, description, and generalization. But nothing seems to me clearer than that geography has already suffered too long from the disuse of imagination, invention, deduction, and the various other mental faculties that contribute towards the attainment of a well-tested explanation. It is like walking on one foot, or looking with one eye, to exclude from geography the "theoretical" half of the brain power, upon which other sciences call as well as upon the "practical" half. Indeed, it is only as a result of misunderstanding that an antipathy is implied between theory and practice; for in geography, as in all sound scientific work, the two advance most amiably and effectively together. Surely the fullest development of geography will not be reached until all the mental faculties that are in any way pertinent to its cultivation are well trained and exercised in geographical investigation.

All this may be stated in another way. One of the most effective aids to the appreciation of a subject is a correct explanation of the facts that it presents. Understanding thus comes to aid the memory. But a genetic classification of geographical forms is, in effect, an explanation of them; hence such a classification must be helpful to the traveling, studying, or teaching geographer, provided only that it is a true and natural classification. True and natural a genetic classification may certainly be, for the time is past when even geographers can look on the forms of lands as "ready-made." Indeed, geographical definitions and descriptions are untrue and unnatural just so far as they give the impression that the forms of the lands are of unknown origin, not susceptible of rational explanation. From the very beginning of geography in the lower schools the pupils should be possessed with the belief that geographical forms have meaning, and that the meaning or origin of so many forms is already so well assured that there is every reason to think that the meaning of all the others will be discovered in due time. The explorer of the earth should be as fully convinced of this principle, and as well prepared to apply it, as the explorer of the sky is to carry physical principles to the farthest reach of his telescope, his spectroscope, and his camera. The preparation of route maps and the determination of latitude, longitude, and altitude for the more important points is only the beginning of exploration, which has no end till all the facts of observation are carried forward to explanation.

It is important, however, to insist that the geographer needs to know the meaning, the explanation, and the origin of the forms that he looks at, simply because of the aid thus received when he attempts to observe and describe the forms carefully. It is necessary clearly to recognize this principle, and constantly to bear it in mind, if we would avoid the error of confounding the objects of geographical and geological study. The latter examines the changes of the past for their own sake, inasmuch as geology is concerned with the history of the earth; the former examines the changes of the past only so far as they serve to illuminate the present, for geography is concerned essentially with the earth as it now exists. Structure is a pertinent element of geographical study when, as nearly always, it influences form; no one would to-day attempt to describe the Weald without some reference to the resistant chalk layers that determine its rimming hills. Process is equally pertinent to our subject, for it has everywhere been influential in determining form to a greater or less degree, and it is everywhere in operation to-day. It is truly curious to find geographical text-books which accept the movement of winds, currents, and rivers as part of their responsibility, and yet which leave the weathering of the lands and the movement of land waste entirely out of consideration. Time is certainly an important geographical element, for where the forces of uplift or deformation have lately (as the earth views time) initiated a cycle of change, the destructive processes can have accomplished but little work, and the land form is "young"; where more time has elapsed, the surface will have been more thoroughly carved, and the form thus becomes "mature"; and where so much time has passed that the originally uplifted surface is worn down to a lowland of small relief, standing but little above sea-level, the form deserves to be called "old." A whole series of forms must be in this way evolved in the life history of a single region, and all the forms of such a series, however unlike they may seem at first sight, should be associated under the element of time, as merely expressing the different stages of development of a single structure. The larva, the pupa, and the imago of an insect, or the acorn, the full-grown oak, and the fallen old trunk, are no more naturally associated as representing the different phases in the life history of a single organic species than are the young mountain block, the maturely carved mountain peaks and valleys, and the old mountain peneplain, as representing the different stages in the life history of a single geographical group. Like land forms, the agencies that work upon them change their behavior and their appearance with the passage of time. A young land form has young streams of torrential activity, while an old form would have old streams of deliberate, or even of feeble, current, as will be more fully set forth below.

The Ideal Geographical Cycle. The sequence in the developmental changes of land forms is, in its own way, as systematic as the sequence of changes found in the more evident development of organic forms. Indeed, it is chiefly for this reason that the study of the origin of land forms — or geomorphogeny, as some call it — becomes a practical aid, helpful to the geographer at every turn. This will be made clearer by the specific consideration of an ideal case, and here a graphic form of expression will be found of assistance.

In Fig. 4 the base line $\alpha\omega$ represents the passage of time, while verticals above the base line measure altitude above sea-level. At the epoch 1 let a region of whatever structure and form be uplifted, B representing the average altitude of its higher parts and A that of its lower parts, AB thus measuring its average initial relief. The surface rocks are attacked by the weather. Rain falls on the weathered surface and washes some of the loosened waste down the initial slopes to the trough lines, where two converging slopes meet; there the streams are formed, flowing in directions consequent upon the descent of the trough lines. The machinery of the destructive processes is thus put in motion, and the destructive development of the region is begun. The larger rivers, whose channels initially had an altitude

A, quickly deepen their valleys, and at the epoch 2 have reduced their main channels to a moderate altitude represented by *C*. The higher parts of the interstream uplands, acted on only by the weather without the concentration of water in streams, waste away much more slowly, and at epoch 2 are reduced in height only to *D*. The relief of the surface has thus been increased from *AB* to *CD*. The main rivers then deepen their channels very slowly for the rest of their lives, as shown by the curve *CEGJ*, and the wasting of the uplands, much dissected by branch streams, comes to be more rapid than the deepening of the main valleys, as shown by comparing the curves *DFHK* and *CEGJ*. The period 3–4 is the time of the most rapid consumption of the uplands, and thus stands in strong contrast with the period 1–2, when there was the most rapid deepening of the main valleys. In the earlier period the relief was rapidly increasing in value,

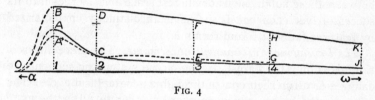

FIG. 4

as steep-sided valleys were cut beneath the initial troughs. Through the period 2–3 the maximum value of relief is reached, and the variety of form is greatly increased by the headward growth of side valleys. During the period 3–4 relief is decreasing faster than at any other time, and the slope of the valley sides is becoming much gentler than before ; but these changes advance much more slowly than those of the first period. From epoch 4 onward the remaining relief is gradually reduced to smaller and smaller measures, and the slopes become fainter and fainter, so that some time after the latest stage of the diagram the region is only a rolling lowland, whatever may have been its original height. So slowly do the later changes advance that the reduction of the reduced *JK* to half of its value might well require as much time as all that which has already elapsed ; and from the gentle slopes that would then remain, the further removal of waste must indeed be exceedingly slow.

The frequency of torrential floods and of landslides in young and in mature mountains, in contrast to the quiescence of the sluggish streams and the slow movement of the soil on lowlands of denudation, suffices to show that rate of denudation is a matter of strictly geographical as well as of geological interest.

It follows from this brief analysis that a geographical cycle may be subdivided into parts of unequal duration, each one of which will be characterized by the degree and variety of the relief, and by the rate of change, as well as by the amount of change that has been accomplished since the initiation of the cycle. There will be a brief youth of rapidly increasing relief, a maturity of strongest relief and greatest variety of form, a transition period of most rapidly yet slowly decreasing relief, and an indefinitely long old age of faint relief, in which further changes are exceedingly slow. There are, of course, no breaks between these subdivisions or stages; each one merges into its successor, yet each one is in the main distinctly characterized by features found at no other time.

The Development of Consequent Streams. The preceding section gives only the barest outline of the systematic sequence of changes that run their course through a geographical cycle. The outline must be at once gone over, in order to fill in the more important details. In the first place, it should not be implied, as was done in Fig. 4, that the forces of uplift and deformation act so rapidly that no destructive changes occur during their operation. A more probable relation at the opening of a cycle of change places the beginning of uplift at O (Fig. 4) and its end at 1. The divergence of the curves OB and OA then implies that certain parts of the disturbed region were uplifted more than others, and that from a surface of no relief at sea-level at epoch O, an upland having AB relief would be produced at epoch 1. But even during uplift the streams that gather in the troughs as soon as they are defined do some work, and hence young valleys are already incised in the trough bottoms when epoch 1 is reached, as shown by the curve OA. The uplands also waste more or less during the period of disturbance, and hence no absolutely unchanged initial surface should be found, even for some time anterior to epoch 1. Instead of looking for initial divides, separating initial slopes which descend to initial troughs, followed by initial streams, such as were implied in Fig. 4 at the epoch of instantaneous uplift, we must always expect to find some greater or less advance in the sequence of developmental changes, even in the youngest known land forms. "Initial" is therefore a term adapted to ideal rather than to actual cases, in treating which the term "sequential" and its derivatives will be found more appropriate. All the changes which directly follow the guidance of the ideal initial forms may be called consequent; thus a young form would possess consequent divides, separating consequent slopes, which descend to consequent valleys, the initial troughs being changed to consequent valleys in so far as their form is modified by the action of the consequent drainage.

The Grade of Valley Floors. The larger rivers soon — in terms of the cycle — deepen their main valleys, so that their channels are but little above the base-level of the region; but the valley floor cannot be reduced to the absolute base-level, because the river must slope down to its mouth at the seashore. The altitude of any point on a well-matured valley floor must therefore depend on river slope and distance from mouth. Distance from mouth may here be treated as a constant, although a fuller statement would consider its increase in consequence of delta growth. River slope cannot be less, as engineers know very well, than a certain minimum that is determined by volume and by quantity and texture of detritus or load. Volume may be temporarily taken as a constant, although it may easily be shown to suffer important changes during the progress of a normal cycle. Load is small at the beginning and rapidly increases in quantity and coarseness during youth, when the region is intrenched by steep-sided valleys; it continues to increase in quantity, but probably not in coarseness, during early maturity, when ramifying valleys are growing by headward erosion and are thus increasing the area of wasting slopes; but after full maturity, load continually decreases in quantity and in coarseness of texture, and during old age the small load that is carried must be of very fine texture or else must go off in solution. Let us now consider how the minimum slope of a main river will be determined.

In order to free the problem from unnecessary complications, let it be supposed that the young consequent rivers have at first slopes that are steep enough to make them all more than competent to carry the load that is washed into them from the wasting surface on either side, and hence competent to intrench themselves beneath the floor of the initial troughs. This is the condition tacitly postulated in Fig. 4, although it evidently departs from those cases in which deformation produces basins where lakes must form and where deposition (negative denudation) must take place, and also from those cases in which a main-trough stream of moderate slope is, even in its youth, oversupplied with detritus by active side streams that descend steep and long-wasting surfaces; but all these more involved cases may be set aside for the present.

If a young consequent river be followed from end to end, it may be imagined as everywhere deepening its valley, unless at the very mouth. Valley deepening will go on most rapidly at some point, probably nearer head than mouth. Above this point the river will find its slope increased; below, decreased. Let the part upstream from the point of most rapid deepening be called the headwaters, and the part downstream the lower course or trunk. In consequence of the changes thus systematically brought about, the lower course of the river will find its slope and velocity decreasing and its load increasing, that is, its ability to do work is becoming less, while the work that it has to do is becoming greater. The original excess of ability over work will thus in time be corrected, and when an equality of these two quantities is brought about, the river is *graded*, this being a simple form of expression, suggested by Gilbert, to replace the more cumbersome phrases that are required by the use of "profile of equilibrium" of French engineers. When the graded condition is reached, alteration of slope can take place only as volume and load change their relation; and changes of this kind are very slow.

In a land mass of homogeneous texture the graded condition of a river would be, in such cases as are above considered, first attained at the mouth, and would then advance retrogressively upstream. When the trunk streams are graded, early maturity is reached; when the smaller headwaters and side streams are also graded, maturity is far advanced; and when even the wet-weather rills are graded, old age is attained. In a land mass of heterogeneous texture the rivers will be divided into sections by the belts of weaker and stronger rocks that they traverse; each section of weaker rocks will in due time be graded with reference to the section of harder rock next downstream, and thus the river will come to consist of alternating quiet reaches and hurried falls or rapids. The less resistant of the harder rocks will be slowly worn down to grade with respect to the more resistant ones that are farther downstream; thus the rapids will decrease in number, and only those on the very strongest rocks will long survive. Even these must vanish in time, and the graded condition will then be extended from mouth to head. The slope that is adopted when grade is assumed varies inversely with the volume; hence rivers retain steep headwaters long after their lower course is worn down almost level; but in old age even the headwaters must have a gentle declivity and moderate velocity, free from all torrential features. The so-called "normal river," with torrential headwaters and well-graded middle and lower course, is therefore simply a maturely developed river. A young river may normally have falls, even in its lower course, and an old river must be free from rapid movement even near its head.

If an initial consequent stream is for any reason incompetent to carry away the load that is washed into it, it cannot degrade its channel, but must aggrade instead (to use an excellent term suggested by Salisbury). Such a river then lays down the coarser part of the offered load, thus forming a broadening flood land, building up its valley floor, and steepening its slope until it gains sufficient velocity to do the required work. In this case the graded condition is reached by filling up the initial trough instead of by cutting it down. Where basins occur, consequent lakes rise in them to the level of the outlet at the lowest point of the rim. As the outlet is cut down, it forms a sinking, local base-level, with respect to which the basin is aggraded; and as the lake is thus destroyed, it forms a sinking base-level, with respect to which the tributary streams grade their valleys; but,

as in the case of falls and rapids, the local base-levels of outlet
and lake are temporary and lose their control when the main
drainage lines are graded with respect to absolute base-level in
early or late maturity.

The Development of River Branches. Several classes of side
streams may be recognized. Some of them are defined by slight
initial depressions in the side slopes of the main river troughs;
these form lateral or secondary consequents, branching from a
main consequent; they generally run in the direction of the dip
of the strata. Others are developed by headward erosion under
the guidance of weak sub-structures that have been laid bare on
the valley walls of the consequent streams; they follow the strike
of the strata and are entirely regardless of the form of the initial
land surface; they may be called subsequent, this term having
been used by Jukes in describing the development of such
streams. Still others develop here and there, to all appearance
by accident, seemingly independent of systematic guidance;
they are common in horizontal or massive structures. While
waiting to learn just what their control may be, their independence of apparent control may be indicated by calling them insequent. Additional classes of streams are well known, but cannot
be described here for lack of space.

Relation of River Ability and Load. As the dissection of a
land mass proceeds with the fuller development of its consequent,
subsequent, and insequent streams, the area of steep valley
sides greatly increases from youth into early and full maturity.
The waste that is delivered by the side branches to the main
stream comes chiefly from the valley sides, and hence its quantity increases with the increase of strong dissection, reaching a
maximum when the formation of new branch streams ceases, or
when the decrease in the slope of the wasting valley sides comes
to balance their increase of area. It is interesting to note in
this connection the consequences that follow from two contrasted
relations of the date for the maximum discharge of waste and of
that for the grading of the trunk streams. If the first is not
later than the second, the graded rivers will slowly assume gentler slopes as their load lessens; but as the change in the discharge of waste is almost infinitesimal compared to the amount

discharged at any one time, the rivers will essentially preserve their graded condition in spite of the minute excess of ability over work. On the other hand, if the maximum of load is not reached until after the first attainment of the graded condition by the trunk rivers, then the valley floors will be aggraded by the deposition of a part of the increasing load, and thus a steeper slope and a greater velocity will be gained whereby the remainder of the increase can be borne along. The bottom of the V-shaped valley, previously carved, is thus slowly filled with a gravelly flood plain, which continues to rise until the epoch of the maximum load is reached, after which the slow degradation above stated is entered upon. Early maturity may therefore witness a slight shallowing of the main valleys instead of the slight deepening (indicated by the dotted line *CE* in Fig. 4); but late maturity and all old age will be normally occupied by the slow continuation of valley erosion that was so vigorously begun during youth.

The Development of Divides. There is no more beautiful process to be found in the systematic advance of a geographical cycle than the definition, subdivision, and rearrangement of the divides (water partings) by which the major and minor drainage basins are separated. The forces of crustal upheaval and deformation act in a much broader way than the processes of land sculpture ; hence at the opening of a cycle one would expect to find a moderate number of large river basins, somewhat indefinitely separated on the flat crests of broad swells or arches of land surface, or occasionally more sharply limited by the raised edge of faulted blocks. The action of the lateral consequent streams alone would, during youth and early maturity, sharpen all the vague initial divides into well-defined consequent divides, and the further action of insequent and subsequent streams would split up many consequent drainage slopes into subordinate drainage basins, separated by subdivides, either insequent or subsequent. Just as the subsequent valleys are eroded by their streams along weak structural belts, so the subsequent divides or ridges stand up where maintained by strong structural belts. However imperfect the division of drainage areas and the discharge of rainfall may have been in early youth, both are well developed by the time full maturity is reached. Indeed, the more prompt discharge of rainfall that may be expected to result from the development of an elaborate system of sub-divides, and of slopes from divides to streams, should cause an increased percentage of run-off; and it is possible that the increase of river volume thus brought about from youth to maturity may more or less fully counteract the tendency of increase in river load to cause aggradation. But, on the other hand, as soon as the uplands begin to lose height, the rainfall must decrease, for it is well known that the obstruction to wind movement caused by highlands is an effective cause of precipitation. While it is a gross exaggeration to maintain that the Quaternary Alpine glaciers caused their own destruction by reducing the height of the mountains on which their snows were gathered, it is perfectly logical to deduce a decrease of precipitation as an accompaniment of loss of height from the youth to the old age of a land mass. Thus many factors must be considered before the life history of a river can be fully analyzed.

The growth of subsequent streams and drainage areas must be at the expense of the original consequent streams and consequent drainage areas. All changes of this kind are promoted by the occurrence of inclined instead of horizontal rock layers, and hence are of common occurrence in mountainous regions, but rare in strictly horizontal plains. The changes are also favored by the occurrence of strong contrasts in the resistance of adjacent strata. In consequence of the migration of divides thus caused, many streams come to follow valleys that are worn down along belts of weak strata, while the divides come to occupy the ridges that stand up along the belts of stronger strata; in other words, the simple consequent drainage of youth is modified by the development of subsequent drainage lines, so as to bring about an *increasing adjustment of streams to structures*, which is highly characteristic of the mature stage of the geographical cycle. Not only so; adjustments of this kind form one of the strongest, even if one of the latest, proofs of the erosion of valleys by the streams that occupy them, and of the long-continued action in the past of the slow processes of weathering and washing that are in operation to-day.

There is nothing more significant of the advance in geographical development than the changes thus brought about. The processes here involved are too complicated to be now presented in detail, but they may be briefly illustrated by taking the drainage of a denuded arch, suggested by the Jura mountains, as a type example. *AB* (Fig. 5) is a main longitudinal consequent stream, following a trough whose floor has been somewhat aggraded by the waste actively supplied by the lateral consequents *CD, LO, EF*, etc. At an earlier stage of denudation, before the hard outer layer was worn away from the crown of the mountain arch, all the lateral consequents headed at the line of the

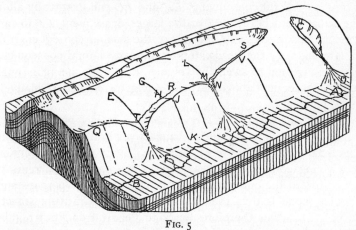

Fig. 5

mountain crest. But guided by a weak understratum, subsequent streams *TR* and *MS* have been developed as the branches of certain lateral consequents *EF* and *LO*, and thus the hard outer layer has been undermined and partly removed, and many small lateral consequents have been beheaded. To-day many of the laterals, like *JK*, have their source on the crest of the lateral ridge *VJQ*, and the headwaters, such as *GH*, that once belonged to them, are now diverted by the subsequent streams to swell the volume of the more successful laterals, like *EF*. Similar changes having taken place on the farther slope of the mountain arch, we now find the original consequent divide of the arch crest supplemented by the subsequent divides formed by the lateral ridges. A number of short streams, like *JH*, belonging to a class not mentioned above, run down the inner face of the lateral ridges to a subsequent stream *RT*. These short streams have a direction opposite to that of the original consequents, and may therefore be called obsequents. As denudation progresses, the edge of the lateral ridge will be worn farther from the arch crest; in other words, the subsequent divide will migrate towards the main valley, and thus a greater length will be gained by the diverted consequent headwaters *GH*, and a greater volume by the subsequents *SM* and *RT*. During these changes the inequality that must naturally prevail between adjacent successful consequents *EF* and *LO* will eventually allow the subsequent branch *RT* of the larger consequent *EF* to capture the headwaters *LM* and *SM* of the smaller consequent *LO*. In late maturity the headwaters of so many lateral consequents may be diverted to swell the volume of *EF* that the main longitudinal consequent above the point *F* may be reduced to relatively small volume.

The Development of River Meanders. It has been thus far implied that rivers cut their channels vertically downward, but this is far from being the whole truth. Every turn in the course of a young consequent stream causes the stronger currents to press toward the outer bank, and each irregular, or perhaps subangular, bend is thus rounded out to a comparatively smooth curve. The river therefore tends to depart from its irregular initial path (background block of Fig. 6) towards a serpentine course, in which it swings to right and left over a broader belt than at first. As the river cuts downwards and outwards at the same time, the valley slopes become unsymmetrical (middle block of Fig. 6), being steeper on the side toward which the current is urged by centrifugal force. The steeper valley side thus gains the form of a half-amphitheater, into which the gentler-sloping side enters as a spur of the opposite uplands.

When the graded condition is attained by the stream, downward cutting practically ceases, but outward cutting continues; a normal flood plain is then formed as the channel is withdrawn from the gently sloping side of the valley (foreground block of Fig. 6). Flood plains of this kind are easily distinguished in their early stages from those already mentioned (formed by aggrading the flat courses of incompetent young rivers, or by aggrading the graded valleys of overloaded rivers in early maturity); for these occur in detached lunate areas, first on one side, then on the other side, of the stream, and always systematically placed at the foot of the gentler-sloping spurs. But as time passes, the river impinges on the upstream side and withdraws from the downstream side of every spur, and thus the spurs are gradually consumed; they are first sharpened, so as better to deserve their name; they are next reduced to short cusps; then they are worn back to blunt salients; and, finally, they are entirely consumed, and the river wanders freely on its open flood plain, occasionally swinging against the valley

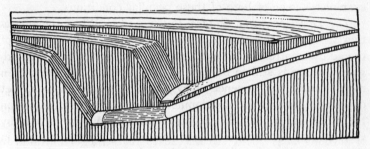

FIG. 6

side, now here, now there. By this time the curves of youth are changed into systematic meanders, of radius appropriate to river volume; and for all the rest of an undisturbed life the river persists in the habit of serpentine flow. The less the slope of the flood plain becomes in advancing old age, the larger the arc of each meander, and hence the longer the course of the river from any point to its mouth. Increase of length from this cause must tend to diminish fall, and thus to render the river less competent than it was before; and the result of this tendency will be to retard the already slow process by which a gently sloping flood plain is degraded, so as to approach coincidence with a level surface; but it is not likely that old rivers often remain undisturbed long enough for the full realization of these theoretical conditions.

The migration of divides must now and then result in a sudden increase in the volume of one river and in a correspondingly sudden decrease of another. After such changes, accommodation to the changed volume must be made in the meanders of each river affected. The one that is increased will call for enlarged dimensions; it will usually adopt a gentler slope, thus terracing its flood plain, and demand a greater freedom of swinging, thus widening its valley. The one that is decreased will have to be satisfied with smaller dimensions; it will wander aimlessly in relatively minute meanders on its flood plain, and from increase of length, as well as from loss of volume, it will become incompetent to transport the load brought in by the side streams, and thus its flood plain must be aggraded. There are beautiful examples known of both of these peculiar conditions.

The Development of Graded Valley Sides. When the migration of divides ceases in late maturity, and the valley floors of the adjusted streams are well graded, even far toward the headwaters, there is still to be completed another and perhaps even more remarkable sequence of systematic changes than any yet described: this is the development of graded waste slopes on the valley sides. It is briefly stated that valleys are eroded by their rivers, yet there is a vast amount of work performed in the erosion of valleys in which rivers have no part. It is true that rivers deepen the valleys in the youth and widen the valley floors during the maturity and old age of a cycle, and that they carry to the sea the waste denuded from the land; it is this work of transportation to the sea that is peculiarly the function of rivers, but the material to be transported is supplied chiefly by the action of the weather on the steeper consequent slopes and on the valley sides. The transportation of the weathered material from its source to the stream in the valley bottom is the work of various slow-acting processes, such as the surface wash of rain, the action of ground water, changes of temperature, freezing and thawing, chemical disintegration and hydration, the growth of plant roots, the activities of burrowing animals. All these cause the weathered rock waste to wash and creep slowly downhill, and in the motion thus ensuing there is much that is analogous to the flow of a river. Indeed, when considered in a very broad and general way, a river is seen to be a moving mixture of water and waste in variable proportions, but mostly water; while a creeping sheet of hillside waste is a moving mixture of waste and water in variable proportions, but mostly waste. Although the river and the hillside waste sheet do not resemble each other at first sight, they are only the extreme members of a continuous series, and when this generalization is appreciated, one may fairly extend the "river" all over its basin and up to its very divides. Ordinarily treated, the river is like the veins of a leaf; broadly viewed, it is like the entire leaf. The verity of this comparison may be more fully accepted when the analogy, indeed the homology, of waste sheets and water streams is set forth.

In the first place, a waste sheet moves fastest at the surface and slowest at the bottom, like a water stream. A graded waste sheet may be defined in the very terms applicable to a graded water stream; it is one in which the ability of the transporting forces to do work is equal to the work that they have to do. This is the condition that obtains on those evenly slanting, waste-covered mountain sides which have been reduced to a slope that engineers call "the angle of repose," because of the apparently stationary condition of the creeping waste, but that should be called, from the physiographic standpoint, "the angle of first-developed grade." The rocky cliffs and ledges that often surmount graded slopes are not yet graded; waste is removed from them faster than it is supplied by local weathering and by creeping from still higher slopes, and hence the cliffs and ledges are left almost bare; they correspond to falls and rapids in water streams, where the current is so rapid that its cross section is much reduced. A hollow on an initial slope will be filled to the angle of grade by waste from above; the waste will accumulate until it reaches the lowest point on the rim of the hollow, and then outflow of waste will balance inflow; and here is the evident homologue of a lake.

In the second place, it will be understood, from what has already been said, that rivers normally grade their valleys retrogressively from the mouth headwards, and that small side streams may not be graded till long after the trunk river is graded. So with waste sheets; they normally begin to establish a graded condition at their base and then extend it up the slope of the valley side whose waste they "drain." When rock masses of various resistance are exposed on the valley side, each one of the weaker is graded with reference to the stronger one next downhill, and the less resistant of the stronger ones are graded with reference to the more resistant, or with reference to the base of the valley side; this is perfectly comparable to the development of graded stretches and to the extinction of falls and rapids in rivers. Ledges remain ungraded on ridge crests and on the convex front of hill spurs long after the graded condition is reached in the channels of wet-weather streams in the ravines between the spurs; this corresponds nicely with the slower attainment of grade in small side streams than in large trunk rivers. But as late maturity passes into old age, even the ledges on ridge crests and spur fronts disappear, all being concealed in a universal sheet of slowly creeping waste. From any point on such a surface a graded slope leads the waste down to the streams. At any point the agencies of removal are just able to cope with the waste that is there weathered *plus* that which comes from farther uphill. This wonderful condition is reached in certain well-denuded mountains, now subdued from their mature vigor to the rounded profiles of incipient old age. When the full meaning of their graded form is apprehended, it constitutes one of the strongest possible arguments for the sculpture of the lands by the slow processes of weathering long continued. To look upon a landscape of this kind without any recognition of the labor expended in producing it, or of the extraordinary adjustments of streams to structures and of waste to weather, is like visiting Rome in the ignorant belief that the Romans of to-day have had no ancestors.

Just as graded rivers slowly degrade their courses after the period of maximum load is past, so graded waste sheets adopt gentler and gentler slopes when the upper ledges are consumed and coarse waste is no longer plentifully shed to the valley sides below. A changing adjustment of a most delicate kind is here discovered. When the graded slopes are first developed they are steep, and the waste that covers them is coarse and of moderate thickness; here the strong agencies of removal have all they can do to dispose of the plentiful supply of coarse waste from the strong ledges above, and the no less plentiful supply of waste that is weathered from the weaker rocks beneath the thin cover of detritus. In a more advanced stage of the cycle the graded slopes are moderate, and the waste that covers them is of finer texture and greater depth than before; here the weakened agencies of removal are favored by the slower weathering of the rocks beneath the thickened waste cover, and by the greater refinement (reduction to finer texture) of the loose waste during its slow journey. In old age, when all the slopes are very gentle, the agencies of waste removal must everywhere be weak, and their equality with the processes of waste supply can be maintained only by the reduction of the latter to very low values. The waste sheet then assumes a great thickness, — even fifty or a hundred feet, — so that the progress of weathering is almost *nil ;* at the same time, the surface waste is reduced to extremely fine texture, so that some of its particles may be moved even on faint slopes. Hence the occurrence of deep soils is an essential feature of old age, just as the occurrence of bare ledges is of youth. The relationships here obtaining are as significant as those which led Playfair to his famous statement concerning the origin of valleys by the rivers that drain them.

Old Age. Maturity is passed and old age is fully entered upon when the hilltops and the hillsides, as well as the valley floors, are graded. No new features are now developed, and those that have been earlier developed are weakened or even lost. The search for weak structures and the establishment of valleys along them has already been thoroughly carried out; now the larger streams meander freely in open valleys and begin to wander away from the adjustments of maturity. The active streams of the time of greatest relief now lose their headmost branches, for the rainfall is lessened by the destruction of the highlands, and the run-off of the rain water is retarded by the flat slopes and deep soils. The landscape is slowly tamed from its earlier strength and presents only a succession of gently rolling swells alternating with shallow valleys, a surface everywhere open to occupation. As time passes, the relief becomes

less and less; whatever the uplifts of youth, whatever the disorder and hardness of the rocks, an almost featureless plain
(a peneplain), showing little sympathy with structure, and controlled only by a close approach of base-level, must characterize
the penultimate stage of the uninterrupted cycle; and the ultimate stage would be a plain without relief.

Some observers have doubted whether even the penultimate
stage of a cycle is ever reached, so frequently do movements in
the earth's crust cause changes in its position with respect to
base-level. But, on the other hand, there are certain regions of
greatly disordered structure whose small relief and deep soils
cannot be explained without supposing them to have, in effect,
passed through all the stages above described — and doubtless
many more, if the whole truth were told — before reaching the
penultimate, whose features they verify. In spite of the great
disturbances that such regions have suffered in past geological
periods, they have afterwards stood still so long, so patiently,
as to be worn down to peneplains over large areas, only here
and there showing residual reliefs where the most resistant
rocks still stand up above the general level. Thus verification
is found for the penultimate, as well as for many earlier stages,
of the ideal cycle. Indeed, although the scheme of the cycle is
here presented only in theoretical form, the progress of developmental changes through the cycle has been tested over and
over again for many structures and for various stages; and on
recognizing the numerous accordances that are discovered when
the consequences of theory are confronted with the facts of
observation, one must feel a growing belief in the verity and
value of the theory that leads to results so satisfactory.

It is necessary to repeat what has already been said as to the
practical application of the principles of the geographical cycle.
Its value to the geographer is not simply in giving explanation
to land forms ; its greater value is in enabling him to see what
he looks at and to say what he sees. His standards of comparison, by which the unknown are likened to the known, are
greatly increased over the short list included in the terminology
of his school days. Significant features are consciously sought
for; exploration becomes more systematic and less haphazard.

"A hilly region" of the unprepared traveler becomes (if such it really be) "a maturely dissected upland" in the language of the better-prepared traveler; and the reader of travels at home gains greatly by the change. "A hilly region" brings no definite picture before the mental eyes. "A maturely dissected upland" suggests a systematic association of well-defined features; all the streams at grade, except the small headwaters; the larger rivers already meandering on flood-plained valley floors; the upper branches ramifying among spurs and hills, whose flanks show a good beginning of graded slopes; the most resistant rocks still cropping out in ungraded ledges, whose arrangement suggests the structure of the region. The practical value of this kind of theoretical study seems to me so great that, among various lines of work that may be encouraged by the councils of the great geographical societies, I believe there is none that would bring larger reward than the encouragement of some such method as is here outlined for the systematic investigation of land forms.

Some geographers urge that it is dangerous to use the theoretical or explanatory terminology involved in the practical application of the principles of the geographical cycle; mistakes may be made, and harm would thus be done. There are various sufficient answers to this objection. A very practical answer is that suggested by Penck, to the effect that a threefold terminology should be devised, — one set of terms being purely empirical, as "high," "low," "cliff," "gorge," "lake," "island"; another set being based on structural relations, as "monoclinal ridge," "transverse valley," "lava-capped mesa"; and the third being reserved for explanatory relations, as "mature dissection," "adjusted drainage," "graded slopes." Another answer is that the explanatory terminology is not really a novelty, but only an attempt to give a complete and systematic expansion to a rather timid beginning already made: a sand dune is not simply a hillock of sand, but a hillock heaped by the wind; a delta is not simply a plain at a river mouth, but a plain formed by river action; a volcano is not simply a mountain of somewhat conical form, but a mountain formed by eruption. It is chiefly a matter of experience and temperament where a geographer ceases to apply terms of this kind. But little more than half a century ago the erosion of valleys by rivers was either doubted or not thought of by the practical geographer; to-day the mature adjustment of rivers to structures is in the same position; and here is the third, and to my mind the most important, answer to those conservatives who would maintain an empirical position for geography instead of pressing forward toward the rational and explanatory geography of the future. It cannot be doubted, in view of what has already been learned to-day, that an essentially explanatory treatment must in the next century be generally adopted in all branches of geographical study; it is full time that an energetic beginning should be made toward so desirable an end.

Interruptions of the Ideal Cycle. One of the first objections that might be raised against a terminology based on the sequence of changes through the ideal uninterrupted cycle is that such a terminology can have little practical application on an earth whose crust has the habit of rising and sinking frequently during the passage of geological time. To this it may be answered that if the scheme of the geographical cycle were so rigid as to be incapable of accommodating itself to the actual condition of the earth's crust, it would certainly have to be abandoned as a theoretical abstraction; but such is by no means the case. Having traced the normal sequence of events through an ideal cycle, our next duty is to consider the effects of any and all kinds of movements of the land mass with respect to its base-level. Such movements must be imagined as small or great, simple or complex, rare or frequent, gradual or rapid, early or late. Whatever their character, they will be called "interruptions," because they determine a more or less complete break in processes previously in operation, by beginning a new series of processes with respect to the new base-level. Whenever interruptions occur, the preëxistent conditions that they interrupt can be understood only after one has analyzed them in accordance with the principles of the cycle, and herein lies one of the most practical applications of what at first seems remotely theoretical. A land mass, uplifted to a greater altitude than it had before, is at once more intensely attacked by the denuding processes in the new cycle thus initiated ; but the forms on which the new attack is made can only be understood by considering what had been accomplished in the preceding cycle previous to its interruption. It will be possible here to consider only one or two specific examples from among the multitude of interruptions that may be imagined.

Let it be supposed that a maturely dissected land mass is evenly uplifted five hundred feet above its former position. All the graded streams are hereby revived to new activities, and proceed to intrench their valley floors, in order to develop graded courses with respect to the new base-level. The larger streams first show the effect of the change; the smaller streams follow suit as rapidly as possible. Falls reappear for a time in the river channels and then are again worn away. Adjustments of streams to structures are carried farther in the second effort of the new cycle than was possible in the single effort of the previous cycle. Graded hillsides are undercut ; the waste washes and creeps down from them, leaving a long, even slope of bare rock ; the rocky slope is hacked into an uneven face by the weather until at last a new graded slope is developed. Cliffs that had been extinguished on graded hillsides in the previous cycle are thus for a time brought to life again, like the falls in the rivers, only to disappear in the late maturity of the new cycle.

The combination of topographical features belonging to two cycles may be called composite topography, and many examples could be cited in illustration of this interesting association. In every case, description is made concise and effective by employing a terminology derived from the scheme of the cycle. For example, Normandy is an uplifted peneplain, hardly yet in the mature stage of its new cycle ; thus stated, explanation is concisely given to the meandering course of the rather narrow valley of the Seine, for this river has carried forward into the early stages of the new cycle the habit of swinging in strong meanders that it had learned in the later stages of the former cycle.

If the uplift of a dissected region be accompanied by a gentle tilting, then all the water streams and waste streams whose slope is increased will be revived to new activity, while all those whose slope is decreased will become less active. The divides will migrate into the basins of the less active streams, and the revived streams will gain length and drainage area. If the uplift be in the form of an arch, some of the weaker streams whose course is across the axis of the arch may be, as it were, "broken in half"; a reversed direction of flow may thus be given to one part of the broken stream; but the stronger rivers may still persevere across the rising arch in spite of its uplift, cutting down their channels fast enough to maintain their direction of flow unchanged; and such rivers are known as antecedent rivers.

The changes introduced by an interruption involving depression are easily deduced. Among their most interesting features is the invasion of the lower valley floors by the sea, thus "drowning" the valleys to a certain depth and converting them into bays. Movements that tend to produce trough-like depressions across the course of a river usually give birth to a lake of water or waste in the depressed part of the river valley. In mountain ranges frequent and various interruptions occur during the long period of deformation; the Alps show so many recent interruptions that a student there would find little use for the ideal cycle; but in mountain regions of ancient deformation the disturbing forces seem to have become almost extinct, and there the ideal cycle is almost realized. Central France gives good illustration of this principle. It is manifest that one might imagine an endless number of possible combinations among the several factors of structure, stage of development at time of interruption, character of interruption, and time since interruption; but space cannot be here given to their further consideration.

Accidental Departures from the Ideal Cycle. Besides the interruptions that involve movements of a land mass with respect to base-level, there are two other classes of departure from the normal or ideal cycle that do not necessarily involve any such movements: these are changes of climate and volcanic eruptions, both of which occur so arbitrarily as to place and time that they may be called accidents. Changes of climate may vary from the normal toward the frigid or the arid, each change causing significant departures from normal geographical development. If a reverse change of climate brings back more normal conditions, the effects of the abnormal accident may last for some small part of a cycle's duration before they are obliterated. It is here that features of glacial origin belong, so common in northwestern Europe and northeastern America. Judging by the present analysis of glacial and interglacial epochs during Quaternary time, or of humid and arid epochs in the Great Salt Lake region, it must be concluded that accidental changes may occur over and over again within a single cycle.

In brief illustration of the combined interruptions and accidents, it may be said that southern New England is an old mountain region which had been reduced to a pretty good peneplain when further denudation was interrupted by a slanting uplift, with gentle descent to the southeast; that in the cycle thus introduced the tilted peneplain was denuded to a sub-mature or late-mature stage (according to the strength or weakness of its rocks); and that the maturely dissected region was then glaciated and slightly depressed so recently that little change has happened since. An instructive picture of the region may be conceived from this brief description.

Many volcanic eruptions produce forms so large that they deserve to be treated as new structural regions, but when viewed in a more general way, a great number of eruptions, if not the greater number, produce forms of small dimensions compared to those of the structures on which they are superposed; the volcanoes of central France are good instances of this relation. Thus considered, volcanoes and lava flows are so arbitrarily placed in time and space that their classification under the head of accidents is warranted. Still further ground for this classification is found when the effects of a volcanic eruption on the preëxistent processes of land sculpture are examined. A valley may be blockaded by a growing cone and its lava flows; lakes may form in the upstream portion of such a valley, even if it be mature or old. If the blockade be low, the lake will overflow to one side of the barrier, and thus the river will be locally displaced from its former course, however well adjusted to a weak structure that course may have been. If the blockade be higher than some points on the headwater divides, the lake will overflow "backward" and the upper part of the river system will become tributary to an adjacent system. The river must cut a gorge across the divide, however hard the rocks are there ; thus systematic adjustments to structure are seriously interfered with, and accidental relations are introduced. The form of the volcanic cone and the sprawling flow of its lava streams are quite out of accord with the forms that characterize the surrounding region. The cone arbitrarily forms a mountain, even though the subjacent rocks may be weak ; the lava flows aggrade valleys that should be degraded. During the dissection of the cone, a process that is systematic enough if considered for itself alone, a radial arrangement of spurs and ravines will be developed ; in long future time the streams of such ravines may cut down through the volcanic structures and thus superpose themselves most curiously on the underlying structures. The lava flows, being usually more resistant than the rocks of the district that they invade, gain a local relief as the adjoining surface is lowered by denudation ; thus an inversion of topography is brought about, and a " table mountain " comes to stand where formerly there had been the valley that guided the original course of the lava flow. The table mountain may be quite isolated from its volcanic source, where the cone is by this time reduced to a knob or butte. But although these various considerations seem to me to warrant the classification of volcanic forms as accidental, in contrast to the systematic forms with which they are usually associated, great importance should not be attached to this method of arrangement ; it should be given up as soon as a more truthful or more convenient classification is introduced.

The Forms assumed by Land Waste. An extension of the subject treated in the section on " Graded Valley Sides " would lead to a general discussion of the forms assumed by the waste of the land on the way to the sea, — one of the most interesting and profitable topics for investigation that has come under my notice. Geographers are well accustomed to giving due consideration to the forms assumed by the water drainage of the land on the way to the sea, and a good terminology is already in use for naming them ; but much less consideration is given to the forms assumed by the waste that slowly moves from the land to the sea. They are seldom presented in their true relations ;

many of them have no generally accepted names, — for example, the long slopes of waste that reach forward from the mountains into the desert basins of Persia. Forms as common as alluvial fans are unmentioned in all but the most recent schoolbooks; and such features as till plains, moraines, and drumlins are usually given over to the geologist, as if the geographer had nothing to do with them! There can be no question of the great importance of waste forms to the geographer, but it is not possible here to enter into their consideration. Suffice it to say that waste forms constitute a geographical group which, like water forms, stand quite apart from such groups as mountains and plateaus. The latter are forms of structure, and should be classified according to the arrangement of their rocks and to their age or stage of development. The former are forms of process, and should be classified according to the processes involved and to the stage that they have reached. The application of this general principle gives much assistance in the description of actual landscapes.

Lack of space prevents due consideration here of the development of shore-lines, a subject not less interesting, suggestive, and helpful than the development of inland forms; but I shall hope to return on some later occasion to a discussion of shore features, when it may be found that much of the terminology already introduced is again applicable. In closing this article I must revert, even though for a third time, to the practical side of the theoretical cycle, with its interruptions and accidents. It cannot be too carefully borne in mind that the explanation of the origin of land forms is not for its own sake added to the study of geography, but for the sake of the aid that explanation gives to the observation and description of existing geographical features. The sequence of forms developed through the cycle is not an abstraction that one leaves at home when he goes abroad; it is literally a *vade mecum* of the most serviceable kind. During my visits in Europe the scheme and the terminology of the cycle have been of the greatest assistance in my studies. Application of both scheme and terminology is found equally well in the minute and infantile coastal plains that border certain stretches of the Scotch shore-line in consequence of the slight post-glacial elevation of the land, and in the broad and aged central plateau of

France, where the young valleys of to-day result from the uplift of the region and the revival of its rivers after they had sub-maturely dissected a preëxistent peneplain. The adjustments of streams to structures brought about by the interaction of the waxing Severn and the waning Thames prove to be even more striking than when I first noticed them in 1894. The large ancient delta of the Var, between Nice and Cannes, now uplifted more than two hundred meters and maturely dissected, must come to be the type example of this class of forms. The Italian Riviera, west of Genoa, may be concisely described as a region of subdued mountains that has been partly submerged and that is now approaching maturity of shore-line features in the cycle thus initiated; one may picture, from this brief statement, the mountain spurs with well-graded slopes, limited by a very irreg-ular shore-line when first depressed, but now fronting in a com-paratively simple shore-line of cliffed headlands and filled bays. The peninsula of Sorrento, on its northern side, once resembled the Riviera, but it has now been elevated fifty meters, and its uplifted bay plains have cliffed fronts. The lower Tiber, whose mature valley floor is somewhat wider than its meander belt, is consequent upon a volcanic accident, for it follows the trough be-tween the slopes of the Bracciano volcanic center on the north-west and the Alban center on the southeast; farther upstream, as far as Orvieto, the river as a rule follows a trough between the Apennines and the three volcanic centers of Bolsena, Vico, and Bracciano. The Lepini mountains have along a part of their north-eastern base a young fault cliff, by which the graded slopes of the spurs and ravines are abruptly cut off; the fault cliff is easily recognized from the train on the line between Rome and Naples.

Botanists and zoölogists know very well that a trained observer can easily recognize and describe many small items of form that pass without notice from the untrained observer. It is the same in geography, and the only question is, How can the desired training be secured? Of the many methods of geographical training I believe that, as far as the forms of the land are con-cerned, no method can equal the value of one in which explanation is made an essential feature along with observation, for there is no other in which so many mental faculties are exercised.

XIV

COMPLICATIONS OF THE GEOGRAPHICAL CYCLE

Modern Geography. In earlier times, when it was thought that the past history of the earth was of a different order from the present, it was natural enough that the geography of the lands should be studied independently of geological methods. Now that it has been in more recent times recognized that the yesterdays of geology closely resemble the to-day of geography, and that the land forms of the present are the natural outcome of the past, it savors of an unnecessary conservatism to hold to empirical methods in geography instead of adopting the natural methods of geology. The rational and modernized treatment of geographical problems demands that land forms, like organic forms, shall be studied in view of their evolution, and that in so far as this method of study requires, the geographer shall be a geologist.

It is not enough, however, simply to see that land forms have been evolved by the interaction of internal and external agencies, — that is, of forces that deform the earth's crust and of forces that carve its surface : it must be noted also that the processes of evolution are in the main orderly, and that the evolved products are systematically related; for however disorderly the action of internal forces may be, the forces that carve the surface carry on their work in a regular fashion and thereby produce a systematic sequence of surface forms. The forms that we see are all members of this sequence, and are therefore fittingly described in its terms.

Ideal Cycle. In the scheme of the ideal geographical cycle a complete sequence of land forms of one kind or another may be traced out. The cycle begins with crustal movements that place a given land mass in a certain attitude with respect to base-level. The surface forms thus produced are called initial. Destructive processes set to work upon the initial forms, carving a whole series of sequential forms, and finally reducing the surface to its ultimate form, — a low plain of imperceptible relief. The sequential forms thus constitute a normal series by which the initial and the ultimate forms are connected. As a result, the sequential forms existing at any one moment are so largely dependent on the amount of work that has been done upon them that they are susceptible of systematic description in terms of the stage of the cycle which they have reached. Moreover, the correlation of all the separate forms appropriate to any one stage of the cycle is so intimate and systematic that any single form may be designated in an appropriate and consistent terminology as a member of the group of related forms to which it belongs, and thus, better than in any other way, the features of the lands may be systematically and effectively described.

Geographers do not as a rule recognize the correlation of forms here referred to, and as a result they do not use the principle of correlation as an aid in observation and description. This is the more to be regretted when it is noted that the failure to take advantage of the principle does not arise from any objection to its correctness, but rather from inattention to it.

A statement of the scheme of the cycle in its simplest form was presented before the Seventh International Geographical Congress at Berlin in 1899. I desire here first to consider briefly a few objections that have been urged against it, and second to set forth some of the modifications by which the ideally simple scheme may be adapted to meet the complications of nature.

The Term "Cycle." Objection has been made by some German writers to the term "cycle," because the scheme is not concerned with anything circular. It is a matter of relative indifference what term is used; and if any other word would be more generally acceptable than "cycle," priority of usage of this term and whatever currency it has already gained ought not to prevent the adoption of its belated superior. In any case, it is the scheme and not its name that is important, and it is a matter of regret that criticism of the latter should apparently detract from the discussion or the use of the former. If the name is, however, to be seriously reconsidered, it should be noted that there is in the

English meaning of the word "cycle" a sufficient reason for its being used as the name of the scheme here considered. Webster defines it as follows :

1. An imaginary circle or orbit in the heavens.

2. An interval of time in which a certain succession of events or phenomena is completed, and then returns again and again, uniformly and continuously in the same order ; a periodical space of time marked by the recurrence of something peculiar.

The ideal cycle, uninterrupted till its end, and then ready to run its course again, comes as near to its dictionary definition as need be. The actual and incomplete cycles, of which the lands give so many examples, depart from the ideal in the various ways to be considered below, and yet constantly, so long as they endure, hold fast to the essential features of the ideal cycle.

Some geographers have felt objection to the term "cycle" because the first member of the sequence of events that it includes is thought to be unlike the last. As far as plains and plateaus are concerned, this objection does not hold, for they begin and end their ideal cycle of changes as low, featureless expanses ; and if the views now coming into vogue regarding certain mountain chains prove generally applicable, as seems more and more likely to be the case, then mountains will also as a rule have low-lying plains for their initial and ultimate forms. In any event this objection to the term is based on a subordinate feature of the scheme ; its greater feature of orderly progress through a long period of time, repeated with every uplift, is the real warrant for the name.

Deductive Nature of the Cycle. The suggestion has been sometimes made that a scheme having a less proportion of imagined or deduced elements and a greater number of actual examples would be more generally acceptable to geographers. In reply it may be said that the scheme of the cycle is not meant to include any actual examples at all, because it is by intention a scheme of the imagination and not a matter of observation ; yet it should be accompanied, tested, and corrected by a collection of actual examples that match just as many of its elements as possible. It may be added that the fear expressed by some that deduction here goes too far is an illustration of a feeling which comes from adopting a very different point of view from that occupied by those who find profit in using the scheme of the cycle. Deduction may go wrong if it be illogical, careless, or incomplete, but if correct it cannot go too far. It seems to me that it would be just as appropriate to say, "In that work, observation goes too far," as to say, "In that scheme, deduction goes too far." The two processes are entirely distinct, and their results should never be confused. It is as desirable to complete the one as the other. Each process may supplement or reënforce the other, but neither one can wholly replace the other, and neither one should stop until it has covered the whole ground open to its advance. From the very difference between observation and deduction as to methods and results, it is essential that any science which attempts to explain the seen by the unseen should employ both these mental processes as fully as possible. For my own part, it is just as much a desire to carry the scheme of the cycle farther toward completion by the free use of accurate deductive methods as it is to carry the collection of actual facts farther toward completion by the free use of accurate observational methods. It cannot be too strongly urged that, while the results of the two methods should be carefully held apart, the two methods themselves should go hand in hand. Conscious cultivation of each method is a most desirable preparation for physiographic investigation, just as it is for physics or astronomy, and observation is greatly aided by thorough deduction, just as deduction is aided by thorough observation. To object to the scheme of the cycle because it is too deductive seems to me nothing less than a misapprehension as to the logic of the case — as well object to a report on field work because it is too observational.

Supposed Rigidity of the Cycle. It has been urged that the scheme of the cycle is so rigid and arbitrary that it cannot be of service in describing the manifold phenomena of nature. This criticism is a result of regarding the ideal cycle alone, without going on to the modifications by which it is easily adapted to natural conditions ; and as this misconception may have arisen either from inattention to the more advanced view of the scheme, or from too great an emphasis on the elementary statement of the scheme in the article above mentioned, it is all the more desirable now to present the scheme more fully and to consider the modifications by which it is so easily made to meet the complicated examples found in nature.

Elementary Postulates and their Modifications. The elementary presentation of the ideal cycle usually postulates a rapid uplift of a land mass, followed by a prolonged stillstand. The land mass may have any structure, but the simplest is that of horizontal layers; the uplift may be of any kind and rate, but the simplest is one of uniform amount and rapid completion; hence plains and plateaus have an early place in a systematic classification of land forms; but all sorts of structures and all sorts of uplifts must be considered before the scheme is completely worked out. In my own treatment of the problem the postulate of rapid uplift is largely a matter of convenience, in order to gain ready entrance to the consideration of sequential processes and of the successive stages of development, — young, mature, and old, — in terms of which it is afterwards so easy to describe typical examples of land forms. Instead of rapid uplift, gradual uplift may be postulated with equal fairness to the scheme, but with less satisfaction to the student who is then first learning it; for gradual uplift requires the consideration of erosion during uplift. It is therefore preferable to speak of rapid uplift in the first presentation of the problem, and afterwards to modify this elementary and temporary view by a nearer approach to the probable truth; and this has been for some years past my habitual method in teaching.

A special case necessitating explanation by slow uplift may be easily imagined. If an even upland of resistant rocks be interrupted by broadly open valleys, whose gently sloping, evenly graded sides descend to the stream banks, leaving no room for flood plains, it would suggest slow uplift; the absence of flood plains would show that the streams have not yet ceased deepening their valleys, and the graded valley sides would show that the downward corrasion by the streams has not been so rapid that the relatively slow processes of slope grading could not keep pace with it. In such a case there would have been no early stage of dissection in which the streams were inclosed in narrow valleys with steep and rocky walls; the stage of youth would have been elided and that of maturity would have prevailed from the beginning, but with constantly increasing relief as long as uplift continued. Examples of this kind must be rare; it is nearly always the case that a beginning of flood-plain development is made before the valley sides are completely graded to even, waste-covered slopes; and hence the usual supposition of rapid uplift — rapid as the earth views time — is probably essentially correct. Moreover, it should not be forgotten that uplift must usually be much faster than the downwear of general subaërial erosion, however nearly it may be equaled by the corrasion of large rivers. The original postulate of rapid uplift therefore requires only a moderate amount of modification to bring it into accord with most of the land forms that we have to consider.

The postulate of a stillstanding land, unmoved until it is worn down to a plain, is like the postulate of rapid uplift, a matter of convenience for first presentation; but it is also something more. It is essential to the analysis of the complete scheme because only in the ideal case of a land mass that stands still after its uplift can one trace out the normal series of sequential events in which the real value of the cycle scheme consists, and thus learn the systematic correlation of forms that characterizes each stage of the cycle. It is only after the normal series has been analyzed that the peculiar combinations of forms which result from two or more cycles of erosion can be understood. The recognition of the systematic correlation of individual forms appropriate to any given stage of the cycle constitutes a marked advance over that earlier stage of physical geography in which the various elements of form were described as if they had nothing to do with one another. One of the most notable features of this advance is the great increase in the interest that attaches to the study. The increase of interest is, however, a most natural result of the newer method, for interest is always aroused by closer approach to the true nature of things and by the perception that what had been mistaken for meaningless, inert forms are in reality actively engaged in a great series of meaningful changes. The marvelous interdependence of the various parts of a maturely organized drainage system must, indeed, when fully apprehended, awaken

wonder as well as interest; but it is only under the supposition
of an essentially stillstanding land that the mature organization
of drainage systems can be reached. Hence, however improbable
a prolonged stillstand of a land mass may seem, the consequences
of such a condition should be followed out with care as furnishing the norm of the scheme, and hence as forming the essential
introduction to all manner of complications that follow. Only
after the norm has been established can the effects of various
movements — uplift, depression, warping, breaking — be duly
considered.

Interruptions of the Cycle. Movements of the land mass may
evidently occur at any stage in the advance of the cycle. They
then interrupt the further progress of sculpturing processes with
respect to the former base-level by placing the land mass in a
new attitude as referred to the sea. The previous cycle is thus
cut short and a new cycle is entered upon. Such movements are
given the semi-technical name of interruptions, and the partial
cycles thus separated are by ellipsis spoken of simply as cycles.
The effects of interruption are chiefly observable in cases where
the newly opened cycle has reached a less advanced stage than
that of the previous cycle at the time of the interruption, — as,
for example, in western Germany, where the young or sub-mature
valley of the Rhine is carved in the old torso or peneplain of the
Schiefergebirge; or in western Pennsylvania, where the sub-mature valley of the Monongahela is incised in the floor of an older
valley in the much-dissected Allegheny plateau. If the opposite
relation obtains, the more advanced work of the new cycle will
obliterate the less advanced work of the previous cycle. It is in
connection with interruptions that such terms as "revived," "rejuvenated," and "drowned" have come into use; they are so convenient that, once adopted, they are not likely to be given up.
Certain it is that the conception of cycles and interruptions has
been extremely fertile; it has led to the recognition and ready
description of features that previously passed unnoticed, as in
the case of the Pennsylvania Appalachians.

Interruptions due to simple uplift or depression have been most
commonly considered, but tilting has been shown by Campbell
to have appropriate consequences in drainage modifications in

the eastern United States; the discussion of block faulting has been opened by Gilbert and Russell for the Great Basin region of Utah and Nevada; folding has been considered for the Alps, the Jura, and the Appalachians, and if the Jura mountains must now be withdrawn from the class of a one-cycle folded range, they will only join the majority as an example of a region of disordered structure once worn down and now broadly uplifted and maturely dissected in a second cycle of erosion.

Certain it is that when various kinds and degrees of interruption at various stages in a cycle have been considered, the variety of possible combinations becomes so great that there is no difficulty whatever in matching the variety of nature. The difficulty is indeed reversed; there are not enough kinds of observed facts on the small earth in the momentary present to match the long list of deduced elements of the scheme. A notable example of the deficiency of observation may be pointed out in connection with belted coastal plains. A number of examples are known in which the upland belt or cuesta is separated from the oldland by a continuous inner lowland, with appropriate drainage by longitudinal subsequent streams, diverted consequent headwaters, short obsequents running down the infacing slope of the cuesta, and beheaded consequents on the outlooking slope. The elastic scheme of the cycle easily matches these facts of observation, but there are no known examples of belted plains in earlier stages to match the several deduced phases of cuesta development which are familiarly included in the scheme of the cycle. Rigidity and deficient variety can therefore hardly be regarded as defects of the elaborated scheme of the geographical cycles.

Educational Value of the Elaborated Scheme. It is perhaps true that those who have already formed habits of study which do not include the apparently overlong deductive consideration of a scheme for the treatment of land forms may become impatient at what they regard as a too elaborative series of unpractical abstractions, and that they may prefer to treat each actual case in such a way as seems appropriate when the case arises, and thus allow a scheme of treatment to grow in the irregular order of accidental accumulation rather than in the more systematic order of deductive development. But, on the other hand, those who are now forming their habits of study gain great advantage from the more thorough consideration that the scheme of the cycle gives as compared with the less systematic methods of treatment. Beginners thus take up the study of land forms in their natural, genetic relations, and discover a fullness and continuity and reasonableness of meaning where explanation would otherwise be fragmentary or wanting. Moreover, even the preliminary presentation of the ideal cycle need not be wholly deductive or abstract; it may be enlivened by the frequent introduction of actually observed examples which confirm its deductions at every stage of progress; the method of presentation may be at any time changed from deductive to inductive, and a group of observed facts for which the scheme as then developed has no match may be empirically described as a means of exciting the further extension of the scheme. The only essential is that not merely the rigid ideal conception of a single cycle, but many combinations of interrupted cycles, should be familiarized by discussion and illustration until they are easily carried in the mind; for, as in the case of the Greek alphabet, of musical notation, or of contoured maps, so in the case of the cycle, it is only to those who reach the point of facility in using its complications that the scheme becomes of practical service in physiographic work.

Verity of the Cycle. Although it is thus shown that the complications arising from interruptions are of great practical importance, it is not true that the ideal cycle is only an abstraction. It is true that the consideration of actual examples frequently shows repeated earth movements or interruptions which result in a succession of partial cycles, some of which may be so short as to be merely brief episodes in an otherwise long history. It must not, however, be forgotten that cycles of erosion have in some cases reached at least the penultimate stage, without significant interruption, for the explanation of certain uplands as now uplifted and partly dissected peneplains is supported by a large array of strong evidence. However many interruptions the earlier history of such districts may have witnessed, a long cycle of untroubled calm seems afterwards to have settled upon them, in whose advanced progress all traces of previous cycles have been obliterated. However rare it may be to find peneplains still holding to-day the attitude with respect to base-level that they must have held while they were slowly worn down, the facts of observation on partly dissected uplands find no explanation save that which carries them all uninterruptedly through the stages of short youth and longer maturity far into very long old age. Thus in these cases at least there is full warrant for the original postulate of a stillstanding land mass. The verity of low-lying undissected peneplains to-day, and the reasonable inference of their more common occurrence in the past, belong with historical geology, where they are destined to play an important part in terrestrial physics, along with such matters as marine transgressions of widespread occurrence, like that of the Cambrian and Cretaceous seas.

Normal and Special Agencies. Thus far it has been tacitly implied that land sculpture is effected by the familiar processes of rain and rivers, of weather and water. It is certainly true that the greater part of the land surface has been carved by these agencies, which may therefore be called the prevailing or normal agencies; but it is important to consider the peculiar work of other special agencies, namely ice and wind. It is not to be implied that any special agency ever works alone, but that it dominates in its time and place, as ice does in Greenland, as wind does in certain deserts, and as the rain and rivers do in better-favored lands; it is indeed important to recognize that the various agencies work to a certain extent in combination, for frosty weathering and the active washing of rainy thaws on the higher peaks and ridges is a characteristic accompaniment of glacial erosion in mountain regions; and even in deserts occasional cloudbursts may provide short-lived but strenuous streams that develop and maintain valley systems, with their well-organized downhill lines, in defiance of the prevalent winds, which could never alone produce any such system of coördinated and ramifying slopes. It is only recently that the conception of a whole cycle of glacial erosion has been discussed, and a whole cycle of wind erosion is as yet a relatively neglected consideration; yet it cannot be doubted that both of these special ideal cycles deserve deliberate analysis, for until such analysis is made the next step, and one of more frequent application, cannot be safely taken, namely, the combination in a single cycle, uninterrupted by land movements, of a succession of normal and special agencies. Thus we come to the important complication of climatic changes.

Normal and Accidental Climatic Changes. The normal ideal cycle postulates no climatic change except such as accompanies the decrease of surface temperatures and the increase of precipitation caused by the initial (relatively) rapid uplift, and the gradual rise of surface temperatures and decrease of precipitation that accompanies the slow wearing down of the region to a lowland plain. That such climatic changes have taken place seems fanciful at first, but more deliberate consideration must change the fancy into matter of fact. It was a wild flight of the scientific imagination by which Tyndall was led to the brilliant suggestion that Alpine glaciation had decreased because the glaciers had worn the Alps down. The famous physicist mistook a short-lived climatic accident for a large part of a cycle. Yet it cannot be doubted that many mountain ranges of earlier geological times have been worn down in some way or other, and that the climate of their region has experienced changes appropriate to such changes in the topography. The distribution and indeed the specific modification of land plants and land animals must have repeatedly been influenced by such changes in land forms, for while short climatic accidents, like the several glacial epochs of post-Tertiary time, were rapid enough to cause migration or extinction of organic forms, the vastly slower change of climate normal to the ideal cycle may only provoke adaptations to new conditions.

It thus appears that climatic changes of the kind that have been most discussed in geographical literature are independent of the ideal cycle. Whether they are marked by changes from non-glacial to glacial, or from sub-arid to arid conditions, they occur at any stage of a cycle, and are therefore noted by the semi-technical term "accidents." The delicate shore-lines of lake Bonneville on the elaborately carved slopes of the Wasatch mountain block in Utah, or the relatively small terminal moraine that crosses the Cretaceous sky lines, the Tertiary slopes and valley floors, and the post-Tertiary trenches in the Pennsylvania

Appalachians, suffice to show how brief climatic accidents are in comparison with the cycles of erosion that wear down mountains.

Volcanic Accidents. Volcanic eruptions are accidents of another kind. They occur at any stage of a cycle and at any part of a surface, entirely irrelevant to the normal development and distribution of surface culture. They may reach so large a scale as to deserve the name of revolutions, as in Oregon or western India, but when of smaller dimensions, as in central France, the haphazard or accidental manner in which they interfere with the orderly sequence of normal processes is well illustrated.

The Cycle of the Shore-Line. There is still to be considered the work of the ocean on the shore-line of the lands ; but here, as before, the scheme includes an initial stage, when a movement of the earth's crust gives a new position to the shore-line, and a systematic series of normal sequential changes to an ultimate stage, in which all the land is worn away. This embraces all the possibilities of the ideal case. Like the processes of surface carving, the processes of shore-line development are subject to variation with climate, from the work of the ice foot in polar regions to the work of coral reefs and mangrove swamps in the torrid zone.

One significant peculiarity of the development of the shore-line is its immediate recognition of changes of level or interruptions ; not only changes in the local land mass, in which case the change is shown in its full measure, but in any part of the sea-bottom or sea-border, in which case every seashore line is also affected in some degree. This contrast leads to the inference that the product of long-continued work of the shore-line forces on a fixed level or on a uniformly changing level is less likely to be found than the product of long-continued work in an inland region, where a series of small and frequent interruptions (elevations and depressions) might hardly make themselves felt. The contrast is still more marked between the sensitive and fluctuating shore-line and the relatively fixed local base-level of a large interior drainage basin, which knows nothing of elevations and depressions except in the climatic variations they may cause, and which is subject to significant change only by warping or by the development of a drainage outlet to the sea. A case of the latter kind seems now to be in progress where the upper branches of Indian rivers are gnawing headward through the Himalayas and giving discharge to previously inclosed Tibetan basins.

The sensitiveness of a local shore-line to changes in the ocean basin or border all around the world makes extensive plains of marine abrasion of improbable occurrence; but the chief reason for interpreting as sub-aërial peneplains those areas that were formerly explained as the work of the seashore waves is that the unconsumed residual mountains, by which peneplains are so often adjoined, have no appearance of a sea cliff along their border, and have every appearance of the frayed-out base-line that sub-aërial erosion would necessarily produce. This is admirably shown along the inner border of the Piedmont peneplain in North Carolina and Georgia, where the residual mountains of the southern Appalachians give forth rambling, sprawling spurs, that interlock with wide-open, flat-floored, ramifying valleys. Mighty as are the destructive processes of the shore-line, they seem to have been too seldom allowed continued effort at a given level long enough to accomplish the great work of which they are undoubtedly capable. Richter was right in calling the coast plain of Norway, first explained by Reusch, the greatest single piece of shore-line work of which we as yet have definite knowledge.

Passive Masses, Active Agencies, Creeping Waste. The fully developed scheme of the cycle recognizes the passive mass of the earth crust, raised here and there, and thus exposed to the destructive processes; the various destructive processes or agencies by which the passive crustal mass is systematically carved; and the waste or " chips " that result from the carving processes. The waste is much less active in its creeping and washing movements than are rivers, glaciers, or winds in their flow, and yet the waste is much more active in its down-slope movements than is the passive mass on which it rests. The cloak of creeping rock waste that covers a graded hillside is as much deserving of systematic description as is the great rock mass of the hill as a whole, or the slender thread of the stream in the valley; and the suggestive correlations that result from giving a definite place in systematic physiography to the "forms assumed by the waste of the land on the way to the sea" are sufficient warrant for this element of the scheme.

Terminology of the Cycle. It thus appears that the scheme of the simple ideal cycle may be gradually and systematically modified until its deductions cover all manner of structures, agencies, waste forms, interruptions, and accidents. When thus conceived it is a powerful instrument of research, an invaluable equipment for the explorer. It is not arbitrary or rigid, but elastic and adaptable. It is a compendium of all the pertinent results of previous investigations.

A very natural accompaniment of the systematic development and elaboration of the scheme, along with the general advance of geology and geography, has been the introduction of a certain number of terms with which to name certain ideas as well as certain land forms of special importance. Cycle, stage; initial, sequential, ultimate; young, mature, old; interruption, accident; consequent, grade, adjustment, revived, drowned, and so on, are examples of ordinary nouns and adjectives thus used in a more or less new and special sense. The extension of the meaning of some of these words beyond their ordinary definitions is perfectly in accord with the normal growth of languages as an accompaniment to the growth of experience. "The ordinary processes by which words change their meanings are, then, essentially the same as the devices of poetry; or, to express the fact more accurately, the figurative language of poetry differs from the speech of common life mainly in employing fresher figures, or in revivifying those which have lost their freshness from age and constant use. Language is fossilized poetry which is constantly being worked over for the uses of speech. Our commonest words are worn-out metaphors."

Other terms are new-made, in the absence of any satisfactory existing words. Such are base-level, peneplain, obsequent, insequent, and a very few more. It is curious to note the disturbance that these few words have occasioned. Some go so far as to say that every new term is a positive detriment to science, as if it were possible to hold the new wine of discovery in the old bottles of ignorance. Others complain that they find it difficult to remember the different meanings of similar terms, such as subsequent and resequent, consequent and obsequent; but so far as I have looked into this difficulty, it is based on unfamiliarity with the ideas here concerned rather than with the words by which the ideas are named, and the sufficient cure for the difficulty is to give a more serious and sustained attention to the subject in which the terms are employed. Even so serviceable a term as "monadnock" has been objected to because it is not English; and yet the objector may complacently accept meander and atoll and a host of other foreigners without noting that they may have once seemed as strange and barbarous to his predecessors as monadnock now seems to him. "Islandmountain," literally translated from the term which German physiographers use for "monadnock," is not likely to be acceptable in English usage. Peneplain has been unjustly condemned as a badly formed hybrid, apparently on the ground that the Latin "pene" and the English "plain" ought not to be joined; yet this word was approved by expert philologists before it was announced, and it has a host of accepted analogues. If we happen to have kept the root in its Latin form in peninsula, we have not in promontory; peneplain is just as good as penult or promontory, in both of which the root is given in Anglicized form, while the Latin form of the prefix is kept unchanged.

With regard to all this matter of terminology, I allow myself here the pleasure of reciting a personal incident. An experienced geographer expressed to me on a certain occasion about ten years ago his regret that so many new and unnecessary terms had been introduced into the study of physiography. I replied that the terms did not seem to me unnecessary or unduly numerous. Some months later my friend wrote that he had looked more fully into the matter, and added:

It gives me pleasure to tell you that I now fully value the use of the exact terminology . . . and I beg of you kindly to excuse the remarks which I was too prompt to make . . . against the introduction of new terms.

Relation of Geology and Geography Some have urged that the scheme of the cycle is nothing more than a part of physical geology, and have thereby thought to criticise the scheme unfavorably. They are essentially right as to the geological quality of the scheme, but this is, to my mind, a high merit. Yet, although largely geological, the scheme of the cycle is at once something less and something more than physical geology. It is avowedly and necessarily geological in the sense stated at the beginning of this essay, because the time is now passed when the existing forms of the land can be considered apart from those of the past or apart from the processes and the changes that have accompanied the past into the present on the way to the future. It is an obsolescent system of the sciences that would set geography apart from geology, and it is a confused system that fails to recognize the relations and distinctions between the two. Geology is in fact made up of a countless number of geographies, horizontally stratified in relation to the vertical time line ; geography is, therefore, only one day's issue of the world journal whose complete file constitutes geology. Geology is, moreover, particularly concerned with changes recorded in the order of their time sequence, — that is, with the historical element of earth science ; geography is concerned chiefly with momentary views, and has, therefore, to do with the distribution of phenomena over the earth's surface at one time rather than with phenomena in their order of occurrence through the passing ages. Every epoch or moment of the past has had its own geography ; if we associate this name chiefly with the present, it is not so much because the geography of the present is inherently more important than the geographies of earlier times as because it is existent and visible.

The scheme of the cycle, by which land forms may be described, is, therefore, properly of a geological nature. It is, however, less than physical geology in that it does not study phenomena in their time sequence for the purpose of learning the history through which they have passed, but for the purpose of using this history in order to describe their present state. The geographer employs as much of geological methods as serves his needs in giving accurate statement of his facts ; yet he remains a geographer. In the same way the chemist employs physical methods in weighing his precipitates, yet he remains a chemist.

The scheme of the cycle is more than physical geology in that it attaches great importance to form as the product of process, and to the systematic correlation of normally associated forms, while physical geology, as ordinarily treated, is largely contented with the more independent and local study of process and product. It is obvious, however, that the scheme of the cycle may be used interchangeably as a means of geological investigation or as a means of physiographic description. The upland of southern New England may, on the one hand, be described as an uplifted and maturely dissected peneplain; or, on the other hand, through the forms thus described, determination may be made of a regional uplift that might otherwise elude recognition.

Practical Value of the Cycle. The elaborated scheme of the cycle provides a systematic, rational, genetic classification for land forms; the possession of such a classification promotes the collection and the description of observable facts; the understanding of the classification greatly assists the trained reader in appreciating the descriptions of the trained explorer.

XV

THE GEOGRAPHICAL CYCLE IN AN ARID
CLIMATE

Normal and Special Cycles. The scheme of the geographical
cycle is usually developed with respect to a land surface under
ordinary climatic conditions, not so dry but that all parts of the
surface have continuous drainage to the sea, nor so cold but that
the snow of winter all disappears in summer. The term "normal
climate" has been applied to such conditions, and "normal cycle"
to the scheme that embodies them. It is chiefly this scheme
that I have elsewhere treated on various occasions (*a, b, c, h*).

The general scheme of the geographical cycle needs adaptation to two special climates : one, glacial; the other, arid. The
glacial cycle received brief attention in my essay on "Glacial
Erosion in France, Switzerland, and Norway," but now needs
supplement in view of the later studies by Richter, de Martonne,
Lawson, and others, as to the forms of glaciated mountains, and
in view of the theory announced by Gilbert that glaciers are not
buoyed up while they rest on the sea-bottom, and that they may
therefore erode their channels deep below sea-level. The arid
cycle has not been considered as a whole, although special studies
of desert conditions have been made by various observers, notably
by Walther. The following general considerations are based on
the work of others as well as on my own observations in the arid
regions of the western United States and of western Asia; they
are presented for the most part in an intentionally and avowedly
deductive manner, but they are checked by facts from stage to
stage. My especial indebtedness to Passarge is stated below.

The Arid Climate. The essential features of the arid climate,
as it is here considered, are : so small a rainfall that plant growth
is scanty, that no basins of initial deformation are filled to overflowing, that no large trunk rivers are formed, and hence that
the drainage does not reach the sea.

The agencies of sculpture and their opportunities for work in arid regions are peculiar in several respects. The small rainfall and the dry air reduce the ground water to a minimum. In its absence, weathering is almost limited to the surface, and is more largely physical than chemical. The streams are usually shorter than the slopes, and act as discontinuously at their lower as at their upper ends. The scarcity of plant growth leaves the surface relatively free to the attack of the winds and of the intermittent waters. Hence, in the production of fine waste, the splitting, flaking, and splintering of local weathering are supplemented rather by the rasping and trituration that go with transportation than by the chemical disintegration that characterizes a plant-bound soil.

No special conditions need be postulated as to the initiation of the arid cycle. The passive earth's crust may be (relatively) uplifted and offered to the sculpturing agencies with any structure, any form, and any altitude, in dry as well as in moist regions.

Initial Stage. Let consideration be given to an uplifted region of large extent over which an arid climate prevails. Antecedent rivers, persisting from a previous cycle against the deformations by which the new cycle is introduced, must be rare, because such rivers should be large, and large rivers are unusual in an arid region. Consequent drainage must prevail. The initial slopes in each basin will lead the wash of local rains toward the central depression, whose lowest point serves as the local base-level for the district. There will be as many independent centripetal systems as there are basins of initial deformation, for no basin can contain an overflowing lake, whose outlet would connect two centripetal systems; the centripetal streams will not always follow the whole length of the centripetal slopes; most of the streams of each basin system will wither away after descending from the less arid highlands to the more arid depressions. Each basin system will therefore consist of many separate streams, which may occasionally, in time of flood or in the cooler season of diminished evaporation, unite in an intermittent trunk river, and even form a shallow lake in the basin bed, but which will ordinarily exist independently as disconnected headwater branches.

Youthful Stage. In the early stage of a normal cycle the relief is ordinarily and rapidly increased by the incision of consequent valleys by the trunk rivers that flow to the sea. In the early stage of the arid cycle the relief is slowly diminished by the removal of waste from the highlands, and its deposition on the lower gentler slopes and on the basin beds of all the separate centripetal drainage systems. Thus all the local base-levels rise. The areas of removal are in time dissected by valleys of normal origin; if the climate is very arid, the uplands and slopes of these areas are either swept bare, or left thinly veneered with angular stony waste, from which the finer particles are carried away almost as soon as they are weathered; if a less arid climate prevails on the uplands and highlands, the plants that they support will cause the retention of a larger proportion of finer waste on the slopes. The areas of deposition are, on the other hand, given a nearly level central floor of fine waste, with the varied phenomena of shallow lakes, playas, and salinas, surrounded with graded slopes of coarser waste. The deposits thus accumulated will be of variable composition and, toward the margin, of irregular structure. The coarser deposits will exhibit a variety of materials, mechanically comminuted, but not chemically disintegrated, and hence in this respect unlike the less heterogeneous deposits of humid climates from which the more easily soluble or decomposable minerals have been largely removed. The finer deposits will vary from sand and clay to salt and gypsum. The even strata that are supposed to characterize lake deposits may follow or precede irregular or cross-bedded strata, as the lake invades or is invaded by the deposits of streams or winds. While many desert deposits may be altogether devoid of organic remains, others may contain the fossils of land, stream, or lake organisms.

The Basin range province of the western United States gives examples of dissected mountains from which descend many withering streams that belong to separate drainage systems of the kind above described, and of basins aggraded with the waste from the dissected mountains. Trunk streams are rare. The initial relief has been decreased, although the basin floors are from three thousand to five thousand feet above sea-level.

Persia and Tibet give further illustrations of the same relation. In the latter region the intermontane basins often contain saline lakes; but the stage of development there reached is not yet clear, because the origin of the ranges and basins is not, as a rule, considered by Tibetan explorers. It should not, however, be inferred that the separation of the many drainage systems in regions such as those of Persia and Tibet is the result of any special peculiarity in the initial deformation of the surface essentially unlike the deformation of other regions of normal climate where large unified drainage systems are the rule. The latter regions may initially have had as many basins of deformation as the former, but the more plentiful rainfall of normal climate has enabled their rivers to cut down the basin rims. This principle has been pointed out by Penck (*a*, 87; *b*, 169) and others. The initial relief may be of coarse pattern, as in central Asia, where the vast aggraded plains of eastern and western Turkestan are separated by a broadly uplifted and deeply dissected mountainous area; or of finer pattern, as in the Basin range province just mentioned, where many small ranges separate nearly as many small basins. The progress of evolution through the cycle, and the arrangement of forms at successive stages, will be much affected by these unlike initial conditions.

Streams, floods, and lakes are the chief agencies in giving form to the aggraded basin floors, as well as to the dissected basin margins in the early stages of the cycle; but the winds also are of importance: they do a certain share of erosion by sand-blast action; they do a more important work of transportation by sweeping the granular waste from exposed uplands and depositing it in more sheltered depressions, and by raising the finer dust high in the air and carrying it far and wide before it is allowed to settle. Wind action is, moreover, peculiar in not being guided by the slopes or restrained by the divides which control streams and stream systems. It is true that the winds, like the streams, tend in a very general way to wear down the highlands and to fill up the basins; but sand may be drifted up-hill, — dunes may be seen climbing strong slopes and escarpments in Arizona and Oregon, — while fine dust carried aloft in whirlwinds and dust storms is spread about by the upper currents with little regard to the slopes of the land surface far below. Sand may be drifted, and dust may be in this way carried outside of the arid region from which it was derived. Wind erosion may, furthermore, tend to produce shallow depressions or hollows; for the whole region is the bed of the wind, and is therefore to a certain extent analogous to the bed of a river, where hollows are common enough; but in the early stages of the cycle in a region where the initial relief was strong, the action of the wind is not able to make hollows on the original slopes that are actively worked upon, and for a time even steepened, by streams and floods. Hence in the youthful stage wind-blown hollows are not likely to be formed.

It is important to notice that a significant, though small, share of wind-swept or wind-borne waste may be carried entirely outside of or "exported" from an arid region. It may be deposited on neighboring lands, where it will be held among the grass of a less arid climate, as long ago suggested by Richthofen; it may even be held down on coastal lands by the dew, as has been suggested for certain districts in Morocco by Fischer; it may fall into the sea, as is proved by the sand that gives a ruddy tinge to the sails of vessels in the Atlantic to leeward of the Sahara, and by the sand grains that are dredged up with true pelagic deposits from the bottom of that part of the Atlantic. It may therefore be expected that the progress of erosion and waste exportation in a desert region will be associated with the deposit of fine waste, as in loess sheets, on the neighboring less arid regions, especially down the course of the prevailing winds. In regions of weak and variable winds the process of sand and dust exportation must be extremely slow; in regions of steady winds it must still be vastly slower than the ordinary rate of waste removal in young or mature regions of plentiful rainfall and normal rivers. Yet it is by this slow process of exportation that the mean altitude of an arid region, such as is here considered, will be continually decreased; hence the earlier stages of the arid cycle are expectably longer than the corresponding stages of the normal cycle.

In the normal cycle the youthful stage is characterized by the headward growth of many subsequent streams, chiefly along belts of weak structures that are laid bare on the valley sides of the larger consequent streams. In the arid cycle subsequent streams have a smaller opportunity for development; first, because all the belts of weak structure under the basin deposits are buried out of reach; second, because in the absence of deep-cutting trunk rivers, many belts of weak structure are but little exposed. In so far, however, as the highlands are dissected by their headwater consequent streams, subsequent branches may grow out and diversify the slopes and rearrange the drainage.

Mature Stage. Continued erosion of the highlands and divides, and continued deposition in the basins, may here and there produce a slope from a higher basin floor across a reduced part of its initial rim to a lower basin floor. Headward erosion by the consequent or subsequent streams of the lower basin will favor this change, which might then be described as a capture of the higher drainage area. Aggradation of the higher basin is equally important, and a change thus effected might be described as an invasion of the lower basin by waste from the higher one; this corresponds in a belated way to the overflow of a lake in a normal cycle. There may still be no persistent stream connecting the two basins, but whenever rain falls on the slope that crosses the original divide, the wash will carry waste from the higher to the lower basin. Thus the drainage systems of two adjacent basins coalesce, and with this a beginning is made of the confluence and integration of drainage lines which, when more fully developed, characterize maturity. The intermittent drainage that is established across the former divide may have for a time a rather strong fall; as this is graded down to an even slope, an impulse of revival and deeper erosion makes its way, wave-like, across the floor of the higher basin and up all its centripetal slopes. The previously aggraded floor will thus for a time be dissected with a bad-land expression and then smoothed at a lower level; the bordering waste slopes will be trenched and degraded. At the same time the lower basin floor will be more actively aggraded. If there is a sufficient difference of altitude between the two basins, all the waste that had been, in a preliminary or youthful view of the case, gathered in the higher basin, will in time be transferred to the lower basin; and thus a larger relation of drainage lines, a longer distance of intermittent transportation, a more continuous area of bed rock in the higher areas, and a more general concentration of waste in the lowest basins will be established. The higher local base-levels are thus, by a process of slow, inorganic natural selection, replaced by a smaller and smaller number of lower and lower base-levels ; and with all this goes a headward extension of graded piedmont slopes, a deeper dissection of the highlands, and a better development of their subsequent and adjusted drainage. The processes of drainage adjustment are, however, at the best, of less importance here than in the normal cycle, because of the absence of main valleys, deep-cut by trunk rivers, and the resulting deficient development of deep-set subsequent streams, as has already been suggested.

Some changes of this kind have probably taken place in the Basin-range province of Utah and Nevada, but more field work will be needed before they can be safely pointed out. Indeed, it seems to be the case that certain changes of an opposite kind have taken place ; the long intermontane troughs appear to be here and there subdivided into separate basins by the undue growth of certain detrital fans where large valleys have been opened in the neighboring ranges ; but this condition of things will pass when the mountains are worn lower and the waste is discharged from them less actively.

As the coalescence of basins and the integration of stream systems progress, the changes of local base-levels will be fewer and slower and the obliteration of the uplands, the development of graded piedmont slopes, and the aggradation of the chief basins will be more and more extensive. The higher parts of the piedmont slopes may be rock floors, thinly and irregularly veneered with waste, as has been described by Keyes for certain basins (bolsons) in New Mexico ; here, as well as upon the aggraded slopes and plains, sheet-flood action will prevail, as explained by McGee. The area occupied during early maturity by the three different kinds of surface — dissected highlands or mountains, graded piedmont slopes of rock or waste, and aggraded central plains with playas, salinas, or lakes — will depend on the initial relief, on the rock structure and its relation to desert weathering, on the percentage of material exported by the winds, and on the climate itself.

It is worth noting that, although the activity of streams and floods decreases with the decrease of relief and of slope, the activity of the winds is hardly affected as maturity advances. The winds do not depend on the gradient of the land surface for their gravitative acceleration; they may blow violently and work efficiently on a level surface. Whirlwinds are, indeed, most active on true plains. It may be that smooth plains are never swept by winds so violent as the blasts which attack highlands and mountains; but it is probable that the effective action of the winds is greater on a generally plain surface than on one of strong relief, where the salient ridges and peaks consist largely of firm rock, and where the loose waste is sheltered in reëntrant valleys. Moreover, it is in very great part on the plains that the winds of ordinary strength drift the sand about, and from the plains that whirlwinds and dust storms raise the finest waste high enough for exportation. It may therefore be concluded that the work of the winds is but little, if any, impaired by the general decrease of relief that characterizes advancing maturity, and hence that their relative importance increases. Moreover, the scanty rainfall of an arid region will be decreased as its initial highlands, which originally acted as rain provokers, are worn down; hence, as the relief weakens, the winds will more and more gain the upper hand in the work of transportation. It is conceivable that the rate of exportation of sand and dust by the winds in maturity and all the later stages of an arid cycle is more rapid than the removal of fine soil, partly or largely in solution, from a plant-covered peneplain in the later stages of a normal cycle; thus the slower work of the earlier stages of an arid cycle may be partly made good by the relatively more active work in the later stages.

As the processes thus far described continue through geological periods, the initial relief will be extinguished even under the slow processes of desert erosion, and there will appear instead large rock-floored plains sloping toward large waste-floored plains; the plains will be interrupted only where parts of the initial highlands and masses of unusually resistant rocks here and there survive as isolated residual mountains. At the same time, deposits of loess may be expected to accumulate in increasing thickness on the neighboring less arid regions. The altitude at which the desert plain will stand is evidently independent of the general base-level — or sea-level — and dependent only on the original form and altitude of the region, and on the amount of dust that it has lost through wind transportation.

The most perfect maturity will be reached when the drainage of all the arid region becomes integrated with respect to a single aggraded basin base-level, so that the slopes lead from all parts of the surface to a single area for the deposition of the waste. The lowest basin area which thus comes to have a monopoly of deposition may receive so heavy a body of waste that some of its ridges may be nearly or quite buried. Strong relief may still remain in certain peripheral districts, but large plain areas will by this time necessarily have been developed. In so far as the plains are rock-floored, they will truncate the rocks without regard to their structure.

There is no novelty in the idea that a mountainous region of interior drainage may be reduced to a plain by the double process of wearing down the ranges and filling up the basins, and that the plain thus formed, consisting partly of worn-down rock and partly of built-up waste, will not stand in any definite relation to the general base-level of the ocean surface; yet the idea has seldom been applied in the interpretation of uplifts by the physiographic method. In the case of the plateaus that are now trenched by the Colorado river in northern Arizona, for example, it has usually been tacitly postulated that the base-level with respect to which they were widely denuded in the pre-cañon cycle was the normal base-level of the ocean, and from this postulate it has been argued that the cycle of cañon erosion was introduced by a strong uplift. My own opinion has agreed with that of Dutton and others in this respect. Yet it is not to-day easily demonstrated that the Arizona plateaus had exterior drainage at the time of their wide denudation; and until exterior drainage is shown to have obtained, the altitude of the plateau region during its denudation must remain uncertain. There are, however, several facts which point to the correctness of the generally accepted view : the course of the Colorado river through the Kaibab cannot easily be explained as having originated in the present cycle ; it appears to have been established earlier ; and it is doubtful whether there are late Tertiary basin deposits within the desert area, or wind-carried sand and loess deposits in the area to the eastward (leeward) of sufficient volume to represent the great volume of material removed in the degradation of the plateaus.

In the case of truncated uplands elsewhere — that is, uplands whose surface truncates their structure, as in the central plateau of France — it is generally a tacit postulate, if not a proved conclusion, that the climate during their truncation was not arid, and hence it is inferred that they were worn down as peneplains with respect to normal base-level, and that they have been uplifted since ; this aspect of the problem will be considered further on. In the meantime, there is another aspect of erosion in arid regions which has not, to my knowledge, until recently, received attention.

The Beginning of Old Age. During the advance of drainage integration the exportation of wind-borne waste is continued. At the same time the tendency of wind action to form hollows wherever the rocks weather most rapidly to a dusty texture would be favored by the general decrease of surface slopes, and by the decrease of rainfall and of stream action resulting from the general wearing-down of the highlands. Thus it may well happen that wind-blown hollows are produced here and there, through the mature and later stages of the cycle, and that they will, even during early maturity, interfere to a greater or less degree with the development of the integrated drainage described above. In any case, it may be expected that wind-blown hollows will in late maturity seriously interfere with the maintenance of an integrated drainage system. Thus it appears that, along with the processes which tend toward the mature integration of drainage, there are other processes which tend toward a later disintegration, and that the latter gain efficiency as the former begin to weaken. A strong initial relief of large pattern, a quality of rock not readily reducible to dusty waste, and an irregular movement of light winds might give the control of sculpture to the intermittent streams through youth and into maturity; in such a case maturity might be characterized by a fully integrated system of drainage slopes, with insignificant imperfections in the way of wind-blown hollows. In a second region an initial form of weaker relief, a quality of rock readily reducible to dust, and a steady flow of strong winds might favor the development of wind-blown hollows or basins, and here the process of drainage disintegration would set in relatively early and prevent the attainment of mature drainage integration. In any case, as soon as the process of drainage disintegration begins to predominate, maturity may be said to pass into old age.

This feature of the arid cycle has no close analogy with the features recognized in the normal cycle. In the latter case the drainage systems of maturity tend on the whole to persist, even though the streams weaken and wander somewhat — and according to theory lose some of their adjustments — in very advanced old age; in the former case, as old age advances, the integrated and enlarged drainage systems of maturity are broken up into all manner of new and local, small and variable, systems. The further results of drainage disintegration in the later stages of the cycle are even more peculiar.

Leveling without Base-Leveling. The later consequences of erosion in an extensive arid region have been, as far as my reading goes, first and recently stated by Passarge in connection with his studies of the arid regions of South Africa, as is more fully indicated below.

As the dissected highlands of maturity are worn down, the rainfall decreases, and the running streams are weakened and extinguished; thus, as has been suggested above, the winds in time would appear to gain the upper hand as agents of erosion and transportation. If such were the case, it would seem that great inequalities of level might be produced by the excavation of wide and deep hollows in areas of weak rocks. As long as the exportation of wind-swept sand and of wind-borne dust continued, no easily defined limit would be found for the depth of the hollows that might thus be developed in the surface, for the sweeping and lifting action of the wind is not controlled by any general base-level. In an absolutely rainless region there appears to be no reason for doubting that these abnormal in-equalities of surface might eventually produce a strong relief in a stillstanding land of unchanging climate, but in the actual deserts of the world there appears to be no absolutely rainless region ; and even small and occasional rainfalls will suffice, espe-cially when they occur suddenly and cause floods, as is habitual in deserts, to introduce an altogether different régime in the development of surface forms from the rock hills and hollows which would prevail under the control of the winds alone. The prevailing absence of such hill-and-hollow forms, and the gen-eral presence of graded wadies and of drainage slopes in desert regions, confirm this statement.

As soon as a shallow wind-blown hollow is formed, that part of the integrated drainage system which leads to the hollow will supply waste to it whenever rain falls there ; the finer waste will be blown away, the coarser waste will accumulate, and thus the tendency of the winds to over-deepen local hollows will be spontaneously and effectively counteracted. As incipient hollows are formed in advancing old age, and the maturely integrated drainage system disintegrates into many small and variable sys-tems, each system will check the deepening of a hollow by wind action ; hence no deep hollow can be formed anywhere so long as occasional rain falls.

It is conceivable that, in some special cases, there might be a peculiar balance of the various factors involved which would result in the development of wind-carved hills and hollows, even if the region were not absolutely rainless. The occurrence of permeable sandstones might favor such a result, because the rain falling on them would sink into the ground instead of run-ning off of it, while fine grains weathered from the sandstone would be disposed of by the winds. But for the present no desert sandstone region with hills and hollows is known, while such regions with hills and valleys are common. Hence it must be inferred that even in sandstone deserts the occasional rains suffice to wash the surface and to prevent the formation of any-thing more than very shallow depressions.

As the drainage becomes more and more disintegrated, and the surface of the plain is slowly lowered, rock masses that most

effectually resist dry weathering will remain as monadnocks —
Inselberge, as Bornhardt and Passarge call them in South Africa.
At the same time the waste will be washed away from the gathering grounds of maturity and scattered in the shallow hollows
that are formed here and there by the winds as old age approaches. The removal of the basin deposits by the winds may
be delayed where the hygroscopic action of saline clays keeps
the surface firm; but wherever the integrated centripetal slopes
are locally reversed by the hollowing action of the wind, some
of the central deposits will be washed back again and exposed
to renewed search for fine material by the wind, and thus a larger
and larger part of the central waste will be redistributed and
exported. As there is no relation of parts in the winds analogous to that of small branch and large trunk streams in river
systems, the surface eroded by the winds need not slope toward
any central area, but may everywhere be worn down essentially
to the same level. The surface ever wearing down, the waste
ever washed irregularly about by the variable disintegration of
the drainage system and continually exported by the winds, a
nearly level rock floor, nowhere heavily covered with waste and
everywhere slowly lowering at the rate of sand and dust exportation, is developed over a larger and larger area; and such is
the condition of quasi-equilibrium for old age. At last, as the
waste is more completely exported, the desert plain may be
reduced to a lower level than that of the deepest initial basin;
and then a rock floor, thinly veneered with waste, unrelated to
normal base-level, will prevail throughout — except where monadnocks still survive. This is the generalization that we owe to
Passarge; it seems to me secondary in value only to Powell's
generalization concerning the general base-level of erosion. So
long as the sea is held out, it would seem that a desert surface
might be worn even below sea-level, as certain writers have
pointed out in a general way (Penck, *b*, 167); but that such a
desert should persistently maintain a plain surface while it is
slowly worn lower and lower is a surprising result of deduction.
Little wonder that an understanding of the possible development
of rock-floored deserts of this kind, independent of base-level,
was not reached inductively in western America; for there has

been so much disturbance in the way of fracture and uplift in that region during Mesozoic, Tertiary, and Quaternary time that the attainment of arid old age has not been permitted; but that the problem was not solved deductively by the present generation of American physiographers before it was encountered and solved by others in Africa serves to show how insufficient still is the use of the deductive method among us.

Passarge writes that his attention has been called to the difficulty of explaining the vast plain surfaces of South Africa by wind action, because the wind has no base-level of erosion, and it therefore can and must excavate considerable hollows in rock areas whose waste it can easily remove. He adds that this difficulty disappears as soon as rain works with the wind, since the rain constantly seeks to wash waste into the hollows formed by the wind, whose tendency to make hollows is thereby counteracted.

The Verity of the Arid Cycle. The deductive method by which most of the preceding paragraphs are characterized may be regarded by some readers as reaching too far into the field of untestable speculation. It is true that the examples of observed forms, by which the deduced forms of every stage should be matched, are as yet not described in sufficient number; but this may be because desert regions have not yet been sufficiently explored with the principles herein set forth — particularly Passarge's law — in mind. On the other hand, the examples of desert plains in South Africa, described by Passarge as plains of the Bechuana (Betschuana) type, suffice to show that the stage of widespread desert leveling has actually been reached in that region, and thus justify all the earlier stages; for, however many land movements may have interrupted the regular progress of preceding cycles, the occurrence of widespread rock plains proves that at least the present cycle of arid erosion has been long continued without disturbance.

The levelness of the plains over wide areas is especially emphasized. Isolated mountains rise above the plains; and the combination of the two unlike forms is described under the term *Inselberglandschaft*, suggested by Bornhardt. Passarge states that these desert plains are not undulating with low hills, but are true plains of great extent, from which the isolated residual mountains rise like islands from the sea. The residuals may be low mounds only a few meters high, or lofty mountain masses rising several thousand meters above the plains. The plain surrounds the steep slope of the mountains with a table-like evenness; there is no transitional belt of piedmont hills, and no intermediate slope (b, 194). The mountains consist of resistant rocks such as granite, diorite, gabbro, quartzite, etc., granite being the most frequent; the plains are of more easily eroded rocks such as gneiss, schists, slates, sandstones, and limestones. The bedding of the rocks is not flat, but disturbed; the plain therefore truncates the rock structures. The rocks are not deeply decomposed, but are relatively fresh. The products of weathering are usually spread as a thin veneer on the plain; the waste does not lie in place on the rocks from which it was weathered, but has been drifted about by wind and flood and has gathered in slight depressions. The waste veneer increases the smoothness of the plain, but the rock surface is also a plain, as may be seen in the edge of water channels, as well as where the veneer is absent (b, 195). Neighboring areas contain extensive deposits of irregular strata whose composition and want of fossils indicate their desert origin, as will be referred to again below. Various additional details are given, with the conclusion as above quoted : these rock-floored plains are not uplifted peneplains, but are the product of desert erosion unrelated to normal base-level, in which occasional water action has coöperated with more persistent wind action.

The scheme of the arid cycle thus seems to be as well supported by appropriate facts as is the scheme of the normal cycle; it is, indeed, in one respect even better supported, for while the arid African plains are examples of old desert plains now growing still older, it is difficult to point out any large peneplain that still stands close to the base-level with respect to which it was worn down.

Contrasted Consequences of Normal Base-Leveling and Desert Leveling. While the theory of marine planation was in vogue, it was customary to interpret all evenly truncated uplands — that is, uplands whose surface truncates their rock structure —

as uplifted plains of marine abrasion, more or less dissected since they were uplifted. When the efficacy of sub-aërial erosion was recognized, it became equally customary to interpret truncated uplands as once base-leveled and afterward uplifted peneplains. If Passarge's views be now accepted, it follows that no truncated uplands should, without further inquiry, be treated as having been eroded when their region had a lower stand with respect to base-level; the possibility of their having been formed during an earlier arid climate as desert plains, without regard to the general base-level of the ocean, must be considered and excluded before base-leveling and uplift can be taken as proved.

It may at first appear sufficient to say that high-standing desert plains can have been made only in those regions which are now desert, but this easy solution of the problem is hardly convincing. Climatic changes are known to have occurred in the past, and inasmuch as they did not all affect areas in a way that is sympathetic with the present arrangement of the zones, the possibility of a former different distribution of deserts from that which now occurs seems to be open. Pleistocene climatic changes of the glacial kind were so modern and short-lived that they have little bearing on the possibility of earlier climatic changes of another order. The more ancient records of glaciation are so distributed as to demand significant rearrangement of the present climatic conditions. The existing deserts are, moreover, of two kinds with respect to cause: some deserts, like those of Africa and Australia, are arranged chiefly with respect to the trade-wind belt; other deserts, like those of central Asia and the southwestern United States, are dependent for the most part on the extent and configuration of the surrounding highlands. When we go back as far as Cretaceous time, it should only be by evidence and not by assumption that we are led to regard a truncated upland of that date as having been base-leveled during a cycle of normal climate and afterward uplifted and dissected, instead of having been leveled above base-level during a cycle of arid climate, and dissected in consequence of a change to a normal climate. A century ago demonstrated movements of the earth's crust were matters of astonishment; witness the surprise then felt at the discovery of fossilized marine shells in some of the loftier Alpine ranges. To-day the crust is raised and lowered on the evidence of dissected peneplains, as in the Appalachian region, without exciting remark; it is now the shifting of climatic conditions that would cause dissenting surprise. It is difficult to determine how far such surprise is well founded, and how far it simply reflects the fashion of our time. Even if the climatic zones have always belted the earth as they do now, the desert areas that depend on the configuration of land and water, and of highlands and lowlands, have certainly varied through the geological ages. It is therefore desirable, wherever the question of "uplifted and dissected peneplains" is raised, to scrutinize it carefully, and to determine, if possible, whether it is really the attitude of the earth's crust or the condition of climate that has been changed. It is likewise important to scrutinize desert plains, now standing above base-level, to see if they may not have been formed normally as lowland plains of erosion and afterward uplifted. It is therefore necessary to inquire into these features by which base-leveled peneplains and rock-floored desert plains may be distinguished, even though the former may be uplifted with a change to an arid climate, or though the latter may be depressed with a change to a humid climate.

Passarge holds the opinion that the plains of the *Inselberglandschaft* are smoother than any peneplain can be; for he describes the desert plains as true plains, not as gently undulating surfaces. He states that water is not competent to produce such plains; its power of erosion works chiefly downward, and only by exception laterally; and he concludes that although long-continued normal erosion may produce a peneplain, — that is, a low, undulating hilly surface, — it nevertheless cannot produce a surface like that of the plains in the *Inselberglandschaft*. But however difficult it may be to wait, in imagination, through the ages required to wear a low hilly region down to less and less relief by the weakened processes of weather and water erosion in the latest stages of the normal cycle, there are certainly some truncated uplands, ordinarily taken to be uplifted peneplains, whose interstream uplands are astonishingly even, and whose surface must have been, before dissection, very nearly plain over large areas; hence it does not seem to me altogether certain that a greater and a less degree of flatness can be taken to distinguish the two classes of plains.

A plain of erosion lying close to sea-level in a region of normal climate, and therefore traversed by rivers that reach the sea but that do not trench the plain, might conceivably be a depressed desert plain standing long enough in a changed climate to have become cloaked with local soils; but it is extremely unlikely that the depression of a desert plain could place it so that it should slope gently to the seashore, and that its new-made rivers should not dissect it, and that there should be no drifted sands and loess sheets on adjoining areas, and no signs of submergence on neighboring coasts. An untrenched plain of erosion in such an attitude would be properly interpreted as the result of normal processes, long and successfully acting with respect to normal base-level. There would therefore appear to be no serious danger of confusing an actual peneplain of normal origin, still standing close to base-level, with a depressed plain of desert origin. For the reasons above given I am not disposed to follow Passarge in the suggestion that the old land mass of Guiana may be an *Inselberglandschaft* in the process of destruction. He cites it as a flat, gently undulating surface of gneiss, above which rise knobs and mountains of granite; the divides are so low that one may pass in canoe between the headwaters of the Orinoco and Amazon systems (*b*, 194). Until further details are given, it would seem appropriate to regard this region, like the interior of Brazil to which Lapparent refers (*a*, 148), as an example of a normal peneplain not raised so as to be attacked by its rivers.

In the same way a high-standing plain of erosion in a desert region might be possibly explained as an evenly uplifted peneplain whose climate had in some way been changed from humid to arid, whose deep-weathered soils had been removed and replaced by thin sheets of stony, sandy, or saline waste, and whose residual reliefs had been modified to the point of producing shallow basins. But in this case there should be some indications of recent uplift around the margin of the area, either in the form of uplifted marine formations whose deposition was contemporaneous with the erosion of the peneplain, or in the form of fault escarpments separating the uplifted from the non-uplifted areas. Moreover, it is extremely unlikely that the uplift of an extensive peneplain could place it in so level a position that it should not suffer dissection even by desert agencies; hence a high-standing desert plain is best accounted for by supposing that it has been leveled in the position that it now occupies. According to Passarge, there are no sufficient indications of elevation associated with the South African desert plains, and their explanation as the result of long-continued desert erosion in a stillstanding region would therefore seem to be assured. Whether an appropriate deposit of wind-borne waste is to be found on neighboring regions is not yet made clear.

It should not, however, be overlooked that there is some danger of misreading the history of a depressed desert plain which has been by a moderate amount of normal weathering and erosion transformed into a normal peneplain, and of an uplifted peneplain which has been by a moderate amount of arid weathering and erosion transformed into a typical desert plain; the danger of error here is similar to that by which a peneplain, wave-swept and scoured during submergence, might be mistaken for a normal plain of marine abrasion. The consequences of error are, however, not so serious in these cases of actual plains as in those cases which may arise in connection with dissected plains; for this class of forms is of common occurrence, and mistakes in explaining their origin as uplifted peneplains or as changed-climate desert plains might therefore be of frequent and widespread occurrence. It is therefore desirable to search out those features by which normal peneplains, uplifted and dissected, may be distinguished from desert plains, dissected after a change to humid climate.

If a normal peneplain be uplifted, its already adjusted streams will carry their adjustments still farther in the new cycle. The high degree of adjustment of streams to structures in the Pennsylvania Appalachians and in the mediæval coastal plain of central England therefore suggests that the former surface of truncation, beneath which the present lower lands have been etched out, was a normal peneplain, uplifted. If a normal peneplain be tilted, its depressed part will soon be submerged and covered with marine deposits; and this part may, by later uplift, be associated with the elevated and dissected part. The marine deposits of our Atlantic and Gulf coastal plain, certain basal strata of continental origin excepted, seem to lie upon a depressed part of the Appalachian peneplain, and thus confirm the evidence of normal base-leveling derived from the adjusted drainage of the uplifted and dissected part of the same peneplain; the basal strata just mentioned contain fossil land plants of normal climate and confirm the conclusion. The now dissected uplands of Brittany and of the Ardennes are adjoined or overlapped by marine deposits which give strong suggestion of normal peneplanation, as shown by Lapparent (*b*). Disturbances of the arid cycle are followed by consequences of other kinds.

Interruptions and Modifications of the Arid Cycle. A land mass suffering erosion under an arid climate may, as in the normal cycle, suffer interruption in the regular progress of its changes by movement of any kind at any stage of development. If, for example, integration of drainage has advanced so far that the number of original basins is reduced by half, the number may be increased again by renewed deformation; or if the integration of drainage has reached a mature stage, the drainage may be thrown into disorder again by a more or less gentle warping by the region. In all such cases a new cycle may be regarded as having been initiated; its initial forms will be the eroded forms developed during the preceding incomplete cycle, and displaced by the movements through which the preceding cycle was closed. The work of the new cycle, thus initiated, then goes on as before; but with interruptions of this kind we are not here particularly concerned, because they offer no special difficulty of explanation or interpretation.

It is otherwise when interruptions or modifications of the arid cycle occur after old age is well advanced, for the desert plains then developed may, under certain conditions, come to imitate uplifted undissected peneplains, as has already been partly considered in the preceding section.

Uniform uplift or depression, by which a normal peneplain is so immediately and significantly modified, will not interrupt the regular process of degradation on a desert plain in an arid cycle. It is perhaps in part for this reason that actual examples of rock-floored desert plains appear to be more common than actual examples of peneplains. Depression would drown a peneplain, and elevation would cause its dissection; but, unless carried to an extreme, neither of these movements would greatly affect the slow degradation of a desert plain. Unequal movements, whereby a desert plain is warped or slanted, are of more importance and are probably of more common occurrence.

If an old rock-floored desert plain be gently warped or tilted, marine submergence is not likely to follow immediately, but the regular continuation of general degradation will be interrupted. The patches and veneers of waste will be washed from the higher to the lower parts of the warped surface; the higher parts, having an increased slope, may be somewhat dissected, and will certainly be exposed to more active degradation than before, until they are worn down to a nearly level plain again. The lower parts will receive the waste from the higher parts, and the continuance of this process of concentration will in time cause the accumulation of extensive and heavy deposits in the lower areas. Such deposits will be, as a rule, barren of fossils; the composition, texture, and arrangement of their materials will indicate the arid conditions under which they have been weathered, transported, and laid down; their structures will seldom exhibit the regularity of marine strata, and they may reach the extreme irregularity of sand-dune deposits. If warping continues, the desert deposits may gain great thickness; their original floor may be depressed below sea-level, while their surface is still hundreds or thousands of feet above sea-level.

Passarge gives a number of instances, which he groups under the Banda type (*b*, 200), that seem to illustrate this phase of the arid cycle, although he ascribes the barren sandstones of this type to a weakening in the activity of the winds rather than to a tilting of the region. Here the upper parts of monadnocks — *Inselberge* — rise above a broad deposit of barren continental sandstones; the intermontane plains, being buried, are matters of inference. Examples of this type are mentioned in West Australia as well as in Africa.

If a change from an arid toward a moister climate causes a drainage discharge to the sea, a dissection of the plain will ensue. The valleys thus eroded cannot expectably exhibit any great degree of adjustment to the structures, because the stream courses will result from the irregular patching together of the preëxisting irregularly disintegrated drainage. This peculiar characteristic, taken together with the absence of neighboring uplifted marine deposits, will probably suffice in most cases to distinguish desert plains, dissected by a change to a moister climate, from peneplains dissected in consequence of uplift; but there still might be confusion with peneplains dissected by superposed streams.

Passarge gives two types of desert plains with a modified climate. The first, or Kordofan type (*b*, 200), is marked by a slight increase of rainfall, sufficient to introduce a steppe vegetation, but not sufficient to form rivers that shall reach the sea. In this case the larger residual mountain masses come to be surrounded by washed deposits coarser near the mountain base, finer farther forward, and at last grading into swampy areas with dark rich soil. Such deposits are said to be well developed in Kordofan, where the buried eroded plain between the mountains has been revealed by well borings, and where basins in the buried plain are indicated by certain unusual accumulations of ground water. The second, or Adamaua type (*b*, 201), includes an example of more abundant rainfall, and therefore exhibits the dissection of what is taken to have been a desert plain with *Inselberge;* but the relation of streams to structures is not mentioned. Finally a Rovuma type (*b*, 202) is instanced on the authority of Bornhardt, in which marine Cretaceous strata of moderate thickness lie upon a plain whose erosion is ascribed to preëxisting desert conditions.

Diversion of Desert Drainage to Exterior Discharge. The development of desert plains without regard to normal base-level is possible only so long as they are interior basins without drainage discharge to the sea. The maintenance of this essential condition is imperiled by small area, great altitude, no inclosing mountains, strong exterior slopes to the sea, and the occurrence of heavy rainfall on the exterior slopes. A small desert island would have no room for the production of interior basins by the processes of initial deformation, or for their maintenance against the attack of exterior streams. The absence of inclosing mountains around a continental arid region would permit the development of escaping drainage systems, so that when mature integration was reached it might be developed with respect to normal base-level, instead of with respect to a local interior base-level; the Sonoran district of Mexico, as described by McGee, seems to offer examples of this kind. Great altitude of an arid region and strong exterior slopes would give strength to attacking exterior streams, and no advantage to the interior drainage; some of the basins of Tibet have already been invaded by the headwater erosion of Himalayan streams, for here the unfavorable conditions of great altitude in the basins, strong exterior slopes, and heavy exterior rainfall are all combined.

On the other hand, great area, moderate altitude, inclosure by mountain barriers, and small exterior rainfall are favorable to the leveling of interior desert plains; and to these favoring conditions should be added a long geological period of quiet. The greater the area and the less the altitude, the less the opportunity that exterior streams will have to establish relations with the interior streams. The higher the inclosing mountains, the longer the interior region will be left to itself, but the more dust it will have to export before a general rock floor can be developed; the desert of Gobi offers an example of this kind, for its surface must long continue to suffer aggradation before the lofty ranges around its depressed surface are worn down to its level. South Africa would seem to offer, according to the descriptions by Passarge, excellent opportunity for the successful advance of the arid cycle far into old age, because of the large extent of the land area, its sufficient height and inclosure, its long-undisturbed history, and its persistently arid climate.

It thus seems evident that the conditions necessary for desert leveling are actually present in greater or less degree in different parts of the world.

The Scheme of the Arid Cycle as an Aid to Observation. The normal cycle has now been practically used by so many observers, and with so many advantageous results, that it is not unfair to expect similar advantage from the use of the arid cycle as an aid to observation in regions where it may be appropriately applied. It is very certain that many observations now on record with regard to arid regions do not suffice to indicate clearly the stage of erosion in the arid cycle which such regions have reached; and this is true not because the observers had either reason or wish to dissent from the principles of the scheme, but because it was not consciously present in their minds when the observations were made. The same is often true of the scheme of the normal cycle. In both cases the failure of the observant explorer to refer the facts that he finds to some comprehensive scheme for their systematic treatment not only results in the accidental overlooking of certain significant facts and in the insufficient description of others, but it leaves the reader in great difficulty when he tries to visualize what the observer has seen. It is as if the writer and the reader had no common language in which the observations and thoughts of the one should be transmitted to the other. It would be far otherwise if the description of a desert region were undertaken systematically in view of what seems to be the essential sequence of changes in all deserts; that is, if the mountains and basins, the rock plains and waste plains, the stream channels, the playas, and the lakes, were all treated in view of their place in the cycle of changes through which they must be running. It is chiefly as an aid to observation and record, and as an aid to the understanding of observations thus recorded, that the scheme of the arid cycle may come to be of service.

It would be fitting to accompany an article of this kind with a larger number of actual examples than have here been introduced; but in the endeavor to find appropriate examples, the interpretation of the observations of various writers in view of the scheme here submitted has not seemed safe enough to make it worth while to undertake it. Safe interpretation needs the conscious application of the scheme by the observer in the field. When thus applied, it is to be hoped that the scheme of the arid cycle may lead to the detection of many facts concerning the evolution of land forms in desert regions that have thus far escaped notice. In the meantime the scheme must remain in great part speculative.

The Bearing of the Arid Cycle on Theories of Elevation and Depression. There is another aspect of the case which, to my mind, not only gives sufficient justification for all the speculation here presented, but makes one regret that it was not undertaken sooner; for in that case certain theoretical discussions would have earlier gained a firm foundation.

In a discussion of " The Bearing of Physiography on Suess's Theories" (*f*), I have urged that the occurrence of high-standing and isolated peneplains could not be the result of the depression of the surrounding lands — as is advocated by Suess — unless all the oceans and their associated lowlands on other continents were also depressed at the same time and by the same amount. The necessity of accepting world-wide crustal movements may, however, be avoided, if the high-standing truncated uplands are regarded as the result of local uplifts of formerly low-standing peneplains. This alternative conclusion is so simple and economical that it is accepted by many geologists and geographers; and it seems well based as long as one believes that the even uplands can have been truncated only by peneplanation close to sea-level. As soon, however, as it is recognized that leveling may be accomplished in an arid region without base-leveling, it is no longer necessarily the case that truncated uplands represent uplifted peneplains; the uplands may perhaps be parts of ancient desert plains, originally denuded at their present altitude; and until this possibility is excluded, their isolated position may be explained by the depression of the surrounding lands, as Suess has supposed, without corresponding change in the level of the oceans and the other continents.

In the case of the truncated uplands or *horsts* of central Germany, there appears to be good geological reason for associating them with the denuded areas of the Ardennes and of Brittany, as described by Lapparent (*b*), and thus concluding that they were all low-lying peneplains before they were uplifted. In the case of the plateaus of northern Arizona, the evidence of normal peneplanation is less complete; yet, as above stated, it still seems probable that these plateaus were denuded with respect to normal base-level, and that the cañon was cut across their surface in consequence of a later uplift with respect to sea-level. The

Bural-baś-tau, a flat-topped range, and the associated plateau-like highlands in the Tian Shan system, also need reconsideration in view of the possibility of desert leveling. I have treated the Bural-bas-tau (*e, f, g*), and Huntington has treated the associated highlands, as uplifted peneplains. Friederichsen, on the other hand, while recognizing the highland region as a *Denudations-fläche*, has hesitated to treat it as a once low-lying peneplain, because of the possibility of its erosion above base-level in a region of inland drainage. If such were the case, it need not have had that close relation to base-level that is to be expected in a normal peneplain. Nevertheless, the truncated highlands and mountain tops in the Tian Shan seem to be closely related to the still low-lying plains of erosion that are drained by the Ili river to lake Balkash, and also to the still lower-lying plain of erosion — apparently a true peneplain — that is drained by the Irtysh and the Ob to the Arctic ocean; hence the probability still seems great that the even highlands of the Bural-bas-tau represent a greatly uplifted plain, even though that plain may have been, at the time of its erosion, a desert plain, and not a normal peneplain. It is therefore exceedingly improbable that the even-topped Bural-bas-tau, standing twelve or thirteen thousand feet above sea-level, gives any close measure of the altitude which the whole region possessed while the great erosion that it has suffered was accomplished.

REFERENCES

Bornhardt. Zur Oberflächengestaltung und Geologie Deutsch-Ostafrikas. Berlin, 1900.

Davis, W. M. (*a*) "Geographic Classification, illustrated by a Study of Plains, Plateaus, and their Derivatives." *Proceedings of the American Association*, XXXIII (1884), 428–432.

(*b*) "Geographic Methods in Geologic Investigation." *Nat. Geog. Mag.*, I (1888), 11–26.

(*c*) "The Geographical Cycle." *Geog. Jour.* (London), XIV (1899), 481–584.

(*d*) "Glacial Erosion in France, Switzerland, and Norway." *Proc. Bost. Soc. Nat. Hist.*, XXIX (1900), 273–322.

(*e*) "A Flat-Topped Range in the Tian Shan." *Appalachia*, X (1904), 277–284.

(*f*) " The Bearing of Physiography on Suess' Theories." *Am. Jour. Sci.*, XIX (1905), 265–273.

(*g*) "A Journey across Turkestan." *Explorations in Turkestan* (Carnegie Institution Publications, No. 26, 1905), 21–119.

(*h*) " The Complications of the Geographical Cycle." *Compte Rendu*, *8me Congrès International de Géographie.*

Friederichsen, *Petermanns Mittheilungen*, XLIX, 136.

Huntington, E. "A Geologic and Physiographic Reconnaissance in Central Turkestan." *Explorations in Turkestan* (Carnegie Institution Publications, No. 26, 1905), 157–216.

Keyes, C. R. "Geological Structure of New Mexican Bolson Plains." *Am. Jour. Sci.*, XV (1903), 207–210.

Lapparent, A. de. (*a*) Leçons de Géographie Physique. Paris, 1896.

(*b*) " La Question de Pénéplaines envisagée à la Lumière des Faits Géologiques." *Verhandlungen des VII. Internationalen Geographischen Kongresses (1899)*, (Berlin, 1901), II, 213–220.

McGee, W. J. ": Sheetflood Erosion." *Bull. Geol. Soc. Am.*, VIII (1897), 87–112.

Passarge, S. (*a*) Die Kalahari. Berlin, 1904.

(*b*) " Rumpffläche und Inselberge." *Zeitschrift der Deut. Geol. Gesellschaft*, LVI (1904), Protokol, 193–209.

(*c*) " Die Inselberglandschaften im Tropischen Afrika." *Naturwiss. Wochenschr.*, new series, III (1904), 657–665.

Penck, A. (*a*) " Einfluss des Klimas auf die Gestalt der Erdoberfläche." *Verhandlungen des III. Deut. Geographentages* (1883), 78–92.

(*b*) "Climatic Features in the Land Surface." *Am. Jour. Sci.*, XIX (1905), 165–174.

Walther, J. Das Gesetz der Wüstenbildung. Berlin, 1900.

XVI

PLAINS OF MARINE AND SUB-AËRIAL DENUDATION

Introduction. Geologists to-day may be divided into two schools on the basis of the theories which they hold regarding the origin of regions of comparatively smooth surface from which a large volume of overlying rocks has been removed. These regions occur under two conditions : first, as buried "oldlands" on which an unconformable cover of later formations has been deposited, the oldlands being now more or less locally revealed by the dissection or stripping of the cover ; second, as uplands or plateaus whose once even surface is now more or less roughened by the erosion of valleys.

The older school, now represented chiefly by English geologists, follows the theory of Ramsay, and regards these even oldlands as plains of marine denudation. The newer school, represented chiefly by American geologists, but also by a number of continental European geologists, may be said to follow Powell, who first emphatically called attention to the possibility of producing plains by long-continued sub-aërial denudation. The present review of the question first cites a number of extracts from various representatives of the two schools, and then seeks for a test by which the rival conclusions may be distinguished, the test being developed from a study of the natural history of rivers.

The English School. Ramsay is believed to have been the first advócate of marine erosion as an agency for the production of broad plains of denudation. In describing the action of the sea on the land he wrote :

The line of greatest waste on any coast is the average level of the breakers. The effect of such waste is obviously to wear back the coast, the line of denudation being a level corresponding to the average height of the sea. Taking *unlimited* time into account, we can conceive that any extent of land might be so destroyed, for though shingle beaches and other coast formations will apparently for almost any ordinary length of time protect the country from the further encroachments of the sea, yet the protections to such beaches being at last themselves worn away, the beaches are in the course of time destroyed, and so, unless checked by elevation, the waste being carried on forever, a whole country might gradually disappear.

If to this be added an *exceedingly slow depression* of the land and sea-bottom, the wasting process would be materially assisted by this depression, bringing the land more uniformly within the reach of the sea, and enabling the latter more rapidly to overcome obstacles to further encroachments, created by itself in the shape of beaches. By further gradually increasing the depth of the surrounding water, ample space would also be afforded for the outspreading of the denuded matter. To such combined forces, namely, the *shaving away* of coasts by the sea, and the spreading abroad of the material thus obtained, the great *plain* of shallow soundings which generally surrounds our islands is in all probability attributable (*a*, 327).

At this early date Ramsay attributed not only the plains themselves, but also the valleys which now interrupt ancient and uplifted plains of denudation, in greatest part to marine action, and allowed but little effect to sub-aërial denudation. On this topic he said :

The power of running water has also considerably modified the surface, but the part it has played is trifling compared with the effects that have sometimes been attributed to its agency. . . . In the larger valleys, where the streams are sluggish, instead of assisting in further excavations, the general tendency is often rather to fill up the hollow with alluvial accumulations, and so help to smooth the original irregularities of the surface (*a*, 332, 333).

Thirty years later Ramsay ascribed greater results to sub-aërial agents. Referring to the generally even sky line of South Wales, he wrote :

The inclined line that touches the hill-tops must have represented a great plain of marine denudation. Atmospheric degradation, aided by sea waves on the cliffs by the shore, are the only powers I know of that can denude a country so as to shave it across and make a plain surface either horizontal or gently inclined. If a country be sinking very gradually and the rate of waste by all causes be proportionate to the rate of sinking, this will greatly assist in the production of the phenomena we are now considering.

When raised out of the water

the streams made by its drainage immediately began to scoop out valleys, and though some inequalities of contour forming mere bays may have been begun by marine denudation during emergence, yet in the main I believe that the inequalities below the [level of the plain] have been made by the influence of rain and running water (*b*, 497, 498).

Greenwood, an early advocate of the efficacy of "rain and rivers" (1857), directed his arguments against the prevailing belief of the time that valleys were carved by marine currents, but does not seem to have considered the possibility of producing plains by the long-continued weathering and washing of the land.

The important paper by Jukes, on the "Formation of . . . River Valleys in the South of Ireland," still finds many followers among English geologists. Like Ramsay, Jukes assumed an uplifted plain of marine denudation on which the rivers of to-day began their erosive work (399), but he did not specify slow depression during the marine denudation.

Lyell said little on the problem before us. His "Principles" do not discuss plains of denudation. His "Elements of Geology" allow only small valleys to stream work, and ascribe the larger valleys "to other causes besides the mere excavating power of rivers" (70). It is said that "denudation has had a leveling influence on some countries of shattered and disturbed strata" (71). Again, "in the same manner as a mountain mass may, in the course of ages, be formed by sedimentary deposition, layer after layer, so masses equally voluminous may in time waste away by inches ; as, for example, if beds of incoherent materials are raised slowly in an open sea where a strong current prevails" (70). The problem of sub-aërial denudation here discussed was not then formulated.

The writings of Sir A. Geikie offer several interesting quotations. When describing the general uniformity of the sky line over the Scotch Highlands in the first edition (1865) of the "Scenery of Scotland," he writes :

In other words, these mountain tops are parts of a great undulating plain or table-land of marine denudation. . . . The marine denudation probably went on during many oscillations of level, and the general result would hence be the production of a great table-land, some parts rising gently to a height of many hundred feet above other portions, yet the whole wearing that general tameness and uniformity of surface characteristic of a table-land where there are neither any conspicuous hills towering sharply above the average level nor any valleys sinking abruptly below it. . . . The valleys which now intersect it . . . have probably been dug out of it by the agencies of denudation. If, therefore, it were possible to replace the rock which has been removed in the excavation of these hollows, the Highlands would be turned into a wide, undulating table-land, sloping up here and there into long, central heights and stretching out between them league after league with a tolerable uniformity of level. And in this rolling plain we should find a restoration of a very ancient sea (*a*, 106, 108).

On earlier pages sub-aërial agents are described as producing valleys and cliffs, while the sea, aided by the atmosphere, produces a plain of marine denudation.

An essay, "On Modern Denudation," by the same author, recognizes that plains of denudation are reduced mainly by sub-aërial forces, but concludes that "undoubtedly the last touches in the long processes of sculpturing were given by waves and currents, and the surface of the plain corresponds with the lower limit of the action of these forces" (*b*, 186).

In the second edition (1887) of his delightful book on the "Scenery of Scotland," argument is still directed against the prejudice that mountains are due to local upheaval; in a word, against the prepossession that mountainous districts, like the Scotch Highlands, are constructional forms not significantly modified by denudation; but greater value is given to sub-aërial agencies than before:

The more we consider the present operations of sub-aërial denuding agents, the more we shall be convinced that a system of hills and valleys, with all the local varieties of scenic feature that now diversify the surface of the earth, may be entirely produced by denudation, without further help from underground forces than the initial uplift into land. No matter what may be the original configuration of the mass of land, the flow of water across its surface will inevitably carve out a system of valleys and leave ridges and hills between them (*d*, 94).

The possibility of producing a plain by a continuance of this process is not here alluded to, but on an earlier page the aid of shore waves is called on:

The limit beneath which there is little effective erosion by waves and tidal currents probably does not exceed a very few hundred feet. Worn down to that limit, the degraded land would become a submarine plain, across the surface of which younger deposits might afterward be strewn (*d*, 92).

On later pages the author continues :

The table-land of the Highlands has been the work not of subterranean action but of superficial waste. The long, flat surfaces of the Highland ridges, cut across the edges of the vertical strata, mark, I believe, fragments of a former base-level of erosion. In other words, they represent the general submarine level to which the Highland region was reduced after protracted exposure to sub-aërial and marine denudation. The valleys which now intersect the table-land . . . have been eroded out of it. If, therefore, it were possible to replace the rock which has been removed in the excavation of these hollows, the Highlands would be turned into a wide, undulating table-land ; . . . and in this rolling plain we should find a restoration of the bottom of a very ancient sea. . . . Its mountains were leveled ; its valleys were planed down ; and finally the region was reduced to a base-level of erosion beneath the waves. . . . Some central tracts of higher ground may have been left as islands (*d*, 137, 138).

In Geikie's " Text-Book of Geology " sub-aërial denudation is regarded as providing a greater amount of detritus than marine denudation, and a significant modification is made of Ramsay's interpretation of plains of marine denudation. In the actual production of such plains

the sea has really had less to do than the meteoric agents. A "plain of marine denudation " is that sea-level to which a mass of land had been reduced mainly by the sub-aërial forces, the line below which further degradation became impossible, because the land was thereafter protected by being covered by the sea. Undoubtedly the last touches in the long process of sculpturing were given by marine waves and currents, and the surface of the plain, save where it has subsided, may correspond generally with the lower limit of wave action (*c*, 434, 435).

Plains or peneplains of sub-aërial denudation, elevated into a new cycle of erosion without waiting to be planed off by the sea, are not explicitly considered. Under "terrestrial features due to denudation " it is stated that

table-lands may sometimes arise from the abrasion of hard rocks and the production of a level plain by the action of the sea, or rather [by] that action combined with the previous degradation of the land by sub-aërial waste. Such a form of surface may be termed a " table-land of erosion" (*c*, 939).

That an author who has so ably discussed the relative competence of marine and sub-aërial denudation should not give explicit account of plains worn down under the air and afterward uplifted and dissected, illustrates how strongly the doctrine of marine denudation has been impressed on the geologists of to-day. Brief citation may be made from a number of other books and essays.

The able article, "The Denudation of the Weald," in which Foster and Topley did so much to advance the modern understanding of the sub-aërial origin of valleys, assumed that the streams of southern England began to act on an uplifted plain of marine denudation, and from this arbitrary beginning explained the transverse valleys by which the chalk escarpments around the Weald are trenched (473).

Maw in his essay, "Notes on the Comparative Structure of Surfaces produced by Sub-aërial and Marine Denudation," contrasts hills and valleys carved by rain and rivers with plains of denudation carved by the sea.

In the same way, Wynne wrote "On Denudation with Reference to the Configuration of the Ground," and concluded that

rain seems to act vertically, its tendency always being to produce steep ground where it is not accumulating materials. Thus we are obliged, in the absence of anything more likely to produce them, to attribute the formation of plains to the action of the sea (10).

A little later Whitaker, when advocating the origin of cliffs and escarpments by sub-aërial denudation, said that nature "uses the sea to carve out continents and islands ; rain and rivers to cut out hills and valleys" (454).

Mackintosh in his "Scenery of England and Wales" (1869) carries the doctrine of marine erosion to an extreme and allows hardly anything to sub-aërial agencies. Even the inner Triassic lowlands of England, inside of the oölitic escarpment, are ascribed to marine denudation. "The sea must have mainly given rise to the inequalities of the earth's surface, so far as they are the result of denudation" (292).

It appears, therefore, that the active discussion in England, of which the above extracts give some indication, did not consider the possibility of sub-aërial base-leveling, but was concerned chiefly with the origin of valleys by rain and rivers. Since the settlement of this question, land sculpture has not received much attention from English geologists, as the following extracts from a later period will show.

Green says, "The even surface that would result from the action of marine denudation is called a 'plain of marine denudation'" (577). No appreciable wearing takes place below the level of the lowest tides. No mention is made of a cover of sediments as a characteristic accompaniment of the plain of denudation, and no consideration is given to the plains of sub-aërial denudation; only the lesser inequalities of land form are ascribed to sub-aërial agencies.

The edition of "Phillips' Manual of Geology," by Etheridge and Seeley (1885), briefly describes plains of marine denudation (131), and under sub-aërial denudation goes no further than to explain the origin of valleys.

Woodward, in his valuable summary of the "Geology of England and Wales," follows his predecessors in adopting the idea of marine denudation for the production of plains.

Jukes-Brown writes:

Plains of erosion are those which have been formed by marine erosion across the edges and outcrops of strata without reference to their inclination, flexures, or fractures. They are surfaces of planation formed by the march of the sea across the country. The limestone plains of central Ireland may be cited as an instance (620).

Sub-aërial agencies are not considered beyond the formation of valleys. For example: "As soon as this surface produced by marine erosion is elevated into dry land, it is subjected to the detritive action of the sub-aërial agencies already described, and is ultimately carved out into new forms of hill and valley (565)."

Detritive and erosive agencies are grouped under two heads:

(1) Marine agencies, which act along the margin of the land, and tend to produce an approximate level surface or plain; (2) sub-aërial agencies, which act over the whole surface of the land, and tend to produce a system of valleys and watersheds, hollows and relative eminences (564).

In discussing breaches in the escarpments and hill ranges of the Wealden district, the same author says:

The only explanation of these facts is . . . marine erosion first produced a surface of planation across the whole district while it was being slowly elevated, so that this original surface sloped gently from a central line toward the north and south. The primary streams naturally followed these slopes, . . . forming the transverse valleys (581).

Among continental geologists Richthofen is the leading advocate of marine erosion. He treated the origin of plains of denudation, independently of Ramsay's writings, in his great work on China, attention being led to the problem by the occurrence of unconformable marine strata lying on smooth foundations, as observed in his eastern travels. He concludes that the "oldland" platform cannot have been produced by atmospheric wasting or by running water; these agencies produce valleys separated by ridges. Truly, the valleys multiply and widen and the ridges weaken, but reduction to a lowland can be reached only locally and in small dimensions. Moreover, change in the altitude of land works against complete denudation; yet, although such a result is unattainable by sub-aërial agencies, it may be accomplished by the waves of the sea beating on the coast. Three cases are considered: a stillstand of the land for an indefinite period, a slow elevation, and a slow depression. The stillstanding land would be cut inward to a limited distance, after which the waves would be exhausted on the platform of their own carving. During elevation slight effect could result, for the work would always be beginning anew. Slow depression alone can produce regional abrasion, for then the power of the waves is maintained by the continued sinking of the bottom, while detritus accumulates on it. In contrast to structural plateaus (*Schichtungsplateaus*), plateaus of denudation have no relation to the structures across which they are cut or to the valleys which are sunk beneath their level after general elevation. As examples, the Ardennes and the uplands of the middle Rhine are first mentioned, these being explained as producible only by sea waves, never by flowing water or other sub-aërial agents. Another example given is the western slope of the Sierra Nevada of California, now uplifted and dissected (*a*).

The substance of the above is repeated in Richthofen's " Führer für Forschungsreisende" (*b*, 353–361), emphasis being given to the association of plains of denudation with unconformably overlying sediments, to which the English school directs insufficient attention. Sub-aërial agents are described as excavating valleys in uplifted plains of denudation, but not in producing the plains (*b*, 171–173, 670, 671). The prevalence of superposed streams in certain dissected uplands of abrasion is noted (*b*, 671, 672), but no contrast drawn between these examples and others in which the streams are systematically adjusted to the structures.

Cornet and Briart have made special study of the greatly deformed Paleozoic rocks of Belgium, which they believe once rose in lofty mountains. Although they regard sub-aërial agencies competent to produce the "complete ablation" of a land surface, they conclude that it was probably the waves of an encroaching sea that contributed largely to destroy what remained of their ancient mountains in Cretaceous time (72–113).

Philippson follows Richthofen in treating plains of denudation — *abrasionsflächen* — as the result of wave action (100).

The American School. Few American writers accept the belief of the English school. The first clear recognition of the importance of sub-aërial base-leveling should, I believe, be credited to our geologists in the western surveys. Marvine briefly presented the essence of the idea in 1873, but he made mention of marine action in a late stage of the process, somewhat after the fashion of the English school. Describing the east slope of the Rocky Mountain front range, he wrote :

> The ancient erosion gradually wore down the mass of Archean rocks to the surface of the sea, . . . the mass was finally leveled off irrespective of structure or relative hardnesses of its beds, by the encroaching ocean, which worked over its ruins and laid them down upon the smoothed surface in the form of the Triassic and other beds (144).

Powell's "Exploration of the Colorado River" (1875) brought the American view of the capabilities of sub-aërial erosion more prominently forward, yet the text does not furnish brief explicit statement directly to the effect that lowlands of denudation may be produced by sub-aërial agencies. Extracts would lose their flavor apart from their context, but in figuring a section of the wall in the Grand Cañon the beveled surface of the tilted older strata on which the horizontal Carboniferous strata lie is drawn smooth and even. The overlying beds "are records of the invasion of the sea ; the line of separation the record of a long time when the region was dry land" (*a*, 212). Here the implication is that the sea gained entrance by depression of the base-leveled land. The overlying strata are regarded as the ruins of some unrepresented land, not of the locally buried land. The explanation is precisely opposite to that given to similar structures by Richthofen.

In Powell's "Geology of the Uinta Mountains" (1876) there is a similar absence of explicit account of base-leveled plains, apparently because it was not necessary to expand truisms so simple; but the chapter on degradation very clearly implies the capacity of sub-aërial forces to wear down mountains, however high; indeed, its burden is to show that the destruction of a lofty range is so much accelerated by steep declivity that its life cannot be much longer than that of a low range. Mountains are "ephemeral topographic forms"; all existing mountains are geologically recent (*b*, 197). All this without once calling on the aid of sea waves.

Dutton's monograph on the "Tertiary History of the Grand Cañon District" (1882) is most characteristically American in treatment as in theme. Referring to the great unconformity near the base of the cañon walls in the Kaibab and Sheavwits plateaus, he says: "The horizontal Carboniferous beds appear to have been laid down upon the surface of a country which had been enormously eroded and afterward submerged" (207).

The erosion followed uplift, the deposition followed submergence when the erosion was essentially completed. Along the surface of contact there are

a few bosses of Silurian strata rising higher than the hard quartzitic sandstone which forms the base of the Carboniferous. These are Paleozoic hills, which were buried by the growing mass of sediment. But they are of insignificant mass, rarely exceeding two or three hundred feet in height, and do not appear to have ruffled the parallelism of the sandstones and limestones of the massive Red Wall group above them (209).

On another page Dutton says:

The meaning of this great unconformity obviously is that after a vast body of early Paleozoic strata had been laid down they were distorted by differential vertical movements, were flexed and faulted, and were elevated above the sea. They were then enormously eroded. . . . Still later the region was again submerged (181).

Over the rugged country thus ravaged, the later strata, perhaps fifteen thousand feet thick, were laid down.

Many other examples of the American view may be given. Most of them, as in the cases already cited, take no account of the possibility that the evenly abraded surface of the older terrane might be essentially the product of wave work, but tacitly assume that it resulted from sub-aërial erosion, followed by depression, with more or less tilting, so that the submerged area comes to be sheeted over with waste derived from some nonsubmerged area.

Irving concludes that in Wisconsin "an amount of material vast beyond computation was removed from this ancient land before the encroachment upon it of the sea within which the [Potsdam] sandstone was deposited" (402).

The buried oldland is referred to as a "sub-Potsdam land surface" (409).

Van Hise, writing of the great unconformities below and above the Penokee series of Wisconsin and upper Michigan, implies great sub-aërial erosion, by which an uplifted region was reduced to a peneplain; depression, submergence, and deposition of material eroded elsewhere then followed. The essentials of the explanation are that the Penokee series rests upon an ancient land surface, more or less modified by wave action at the time of submergence, but worn down from its constructional form almost entirely by sub-aërial agents (454–466).

Walcott, recognizing wave work at the margin of an encroaching sea as contributing to the formation of basal conglomerates, nevertheless explains the great pre-Cambrian land area of our country as "approaching the base-level of erosion over large portions of its surface" (562). Moreover, it was a result of continental depression and not of erosive encroachment of the waves that the upper Cambrian sea gained its extension over the great interior of the continent (565). The relation of sub-aërial and marine agencies are here, as in so many instances, just reversed from their proportionate activities in Richthofen's scheme.

McGee was the first to present a clear statement of the vast sub-aërial denudation of our Atlantic slope in Mesozoic time:

Before the initiation of Potomac deposition, but subsequent to the accumulation of the Triassic and Rhaetic deposits and to the displacement and diking by which they are affected, there was an eon of degradation during which a grand mountain system was obliterated and its base reduced to a plain which, as its topography tells us, was slightly inclined seaward and little elevated above tide. . . . There followed a slight elevation of the land, when the rivers attacked their beds and excavated valleys as deep as those to-day intersecting the Piedmont plain. . . . Then came the movement by which the deposition of the Potomac formation was initiated ; the deeply ravined base-level plain was at the same time submerged and tilted oceanward (142).

It appears from the foregoing examples that in denuded plains over which unconformable sediments have been deposited, some small share in the work of denudation may be allowed to the shore-waves as they advance over an already prepared peneplain ; but it is otherwise with those uplifted and dissected plains of denudation upon which there is no reason to think that unconformable sediments have ever been deposited. The plateau in which the Grand Cañon of the Colorado is cut is an extraordinary example of this kind. It is, moreover, notable for consisting of nearly horizontal strata, where acute observation has been needed to detect evidence of the long cycle of erosion passed through before the region was uplifted to its present altitude.

The great plateau is beveled obliquely across the Carboniferous and Permian strata, so that the undulating surface of the upland in its medial part presents Permian beds on the hills and Carboniferous beds in the hollows ; but to the south, where the strata gently rise, the whole surface is Carboniferous ; to the north, where the strata sink, the surface is entirely Permian.

We may suppose that this entire region, at the epoch at which the great denudation of the Mesozoic system approached completion, occupied a level not much above the sea. Under such circumstances it would have been at what Powell terms base-level of erosion. The rivers and tributaries would no longer corrade their channels. The inequalities which are due to land sculpture and the general process of erosion would then no longer increase, and the total energy of erosion would be occupied in reducing such inequalities as had been previously generated. During periods of upheaval, and for a considerable time thereafter, the streams are cutting down their channels, and weathering widens them into broad valleys with ridges between. The diversification so produced reaches a maximum when the streams have nearly reached their base-levels ; but when the streams can no longer corrade, and if the uplifting ceases, these diversifications are reduced and finally obliterated. Such, I conceive, was the case here. . . . The entire region was planed down to a comparatively smooth surface (Dutton, 119).

Willis first called attention to the occurrence of an uplifted and dissected peneplain of sub-aërial denudation in the mountains of North Carolina (*a*, 297), and Hayes and Campbell have since then shown the great extent and area of this ancient land surface (69). Willis and Hayes have described the northern and southern Appalachians, giving much attention to the essential extinction of the mountains, except in the Carolina highlands, in late Cretaceous time. The first author writes of the lowland thus produced: "The land was flat, featureless, and very slightly elevated above the sea" (*b*, 189). The second author writes: "The whole region was reduced to a nearly featureless plain, relieved only by a few groups of monadnocks where the highest mountains now stand" (*a*, 330).

Emerson writes of the Berkshire hills in western Massachusetts:

Erosion planed away the mountains to the general level, which can still be seen in the average level of the plateau, pitching slightly east. . . . When this peneplain was formed it was doubtless horizontal and near the sea-level, and was what is called a base-level.

Salisbury says that the even crest lines of the New Jersey highlands tell of "mountainous elevations reduced to a peneplain near the level of the sea (8)."

Not only the tilted rocks of the Alleghenies and of the older Appalachian belt, but the horizontal strata of the Allegheny plateau are regarded as having been base-leveled, or almost so, before their present uplift and dissection was gained. See, for example, the account of the Cumberland plateau in Tennessee by Hayes (*b*).

Griswold has recognized a greatly dissected peneplain in the even-crested ridges of the Arkansas novaculites, and has associated the warping of the great peneplain of which his special district was a part with the origin of the lower course of the Mississippi in late Mesozoic time (*a, b*).

Keyes and Hershey have recently described the upland of the Ozark plateau in Missouri as an uplifted and dissected peneplain. The region has an essentially horizontal structure, like the Allegheny plateau, with which it is in many ways homologous. The latter author tells of residual hills or monadnocks which still surmount the upland plain, and of faint inequalities of form that seem to mark "the hydrographic basins of the streams which flowed on the Cretaceous lowland plain"; but as a whole the region was "a low, marshy plain of very slight relief, probably nearly at sea-level" (338).

Darton describes the Piedmont area of Virginia as

an undulating plateau carved in greater part in crystalline rocks . . . traversed by rivers which flow in gorges. . . . It is now very clearly recognized that the Piedmont plateau is a peneplain of Tertiary age. . . There is a system of very low, flat divides coincident with those of the present drainage system (568–570).

Keith also describes the formerly even surface of the Piedmont belt in which the valleys of to-day are incised, as a Tertiary base-level of sub-aërial origin (369).

The beveled western slope of the Sierra Nevada, regarded as an upturned plain of marine abrasion by Richthofen, is ascribed by Gilbert, Leconte, Lindgren, Diller, and others to sub-aërial denudation ; but Lindgren makes it clear that when the region stood lower it was not worn smooth enough to be called a peneplain ; "the declivities and irregularities of the old surface are too considerable for that" (298).

Diller describes a peneplain formed on the upturned Cretaceous rocks of northern California and now dissected by various streams :

The production of such a broad, uniform plain by the erosion of rocks varying greatly in hardness could only be accomplished on a very gentle slope near the level of the controlling water body, and we may therefore properly consider this plain a base-level of erosion (b, 405).

Lawson presents an instructive account of an uplifted and dissected peneplain beveled across upturned strata in northern California. Waterworn gravels occur on the ridges of the dissected upland. They "can only be interpreted as remnants of the stream gravels of the ancient peneplain" (244).

G. M. Dawson describes an ancient peneplain, now an elevated and dissected plateau, in the Rocky mountain region of Canada :

Climbing to the level of this old plateau, or to that of some slightly more elevated point about the fiftieth or fifty-first parallel of latitude, the deep valleys of modern rivers with other low tracts are lost sight of, and the eye appears to range across an unbroken or but slightly diversified plain, which, on a clear day, may be observed to be bounded to the northeast, southwest, and south by mountain ranges with rugged forms, and above which in a few places isolated higher points rise, either as outstanding monuments of the denudation by which the plateau was produced, or as accumulations due to volcanic action of the Miocene or middle Tertiary period (11).

After explicitly considering the alternatives of marine and subaërial erosion, the author decides against the former, because the plateau district is not accessible to the sea, and because there are no marine strata thereabouts referable to the period when the peneplain was formed. The river system of the region,

aided by other sub-aërial agencies, cut down almost its entire drainage basin till this became a nearly uniform plain, with some slight slope in the main direction of the river's flow, but of which the lowest part approximately coincided with the sea-level of the time. . . . After reaching this base-level of erosion the rivers would, of course, be unable to do more than serve as channels for the conveyance of material brought into them from the surrounding country, which, wherever it stood above the general level, was still subject to waste. The valleys became wide and shallow, and the surface as a whole assumed permanent characters (13).

My own studies lead me to believe that sub-aërial denudation has reduced various mountainous or plateau-like uplifts to lowland peneplains.

A considerable number of extracts might be presented from the works of foreign writers to show that the idea of marine denudation is on the whole less favorably received by continental than by English geologists ; but the features of land form and the processes of land sculpture have not been studied in Europe with the attention that has been given to stratigraphic succession or to the problems of paleontology and petrography. Regions that are known to be uplands of denudation are often described with abundant detail as to their structure, but with the scantiest reference to the conditions of their topographical development.

A characteristic example of this manner of treatment is found in the valuable works by Lepsius on the mountains of the upper and middle Rhine, in which the Schiefergebirge and other ancient mountains are fully treated as to structure, although little is said of their form and still less of the origin of their form (*a, b*).

The following citations are from works in which land form and sculpture are more fully considered.

The increasing importance attributed by Sir A. Geikie to sub-aërial agencies in his later writings has already been noted. Professor James Geikie goes farther in this direction and says :

Valleys continue to be deepened and widened, while the intervening mountains, eaten into by the rivers and their countless feeders and shattered and pulverized by springs and frosts, are gradually narrowed, interrupted, and reduced until eventually what was formerly a great mountain chain becomes converted into a low-lying undulating plain (160).

Gosselet, in his comprehensive monograph on the Ardennes, says that the tilted, folded, and faulted strata of their uplands have been, as it were, planed down by the combined action of atmospheric disintegration and pluvial wearing. Both the Jurassic and Cretaceous formations are described as lying on oldland soils, where they overlap the Paleozoic strata (802, 808, 837).

The elaborate treatise on "Les Formes du Terrain" (1888), by De la Noë and de Margerie, clearly maintains that pluvial denudation may not only produce valleys, but it may wear down the divides between the valleys (106). The escarpments or cross valleys of the Weald in southern England may be explained without calling on marine erosion, as most of the English geologists have done (135, 136). Plateaus of abrasion, without a cover of unconformable strata, may be "simply the result of prolonged sub-aërial erosion." If unconformably covered, it still remains to be seen how far the abraded surface is

the modification by wave action of a hardly different surface, produced by the prolonged work of streams which had long before attained faintly graded slopes, and which had by the aid of atmospheric agents almost completely destroyed preëxisting inequalities of form (188).

Penck concludes that the final aim of sub-aërial denuding agents is to reduce a land almost completely to a plain (a), but his account of the Schiefergebirge of the middle Rhine does not explicitly state whether the *abrasionsplateau* of their uplands is of marine or sub-aërial origin (b). In his compendious volumes on the "Morphologie der Erdoberfläche" (1894), he considers plains of marine and of sub-aërial denudation, both as to process of origin and as to derivative forms, after elevation and dissection, but criteria for their discrimination are not discussed (c).

De Lapparent, president of the French Geographical Society, has advocated sub-aërial erosion as the means of denuding the Ardennes and the central plateau of France (a), and later says:

La notion des pénéplaines est extrêmement féconde, et ce n'est pas un de ses moindres mérites d'avoir porté le coup de grâce à la théorie des plaines de dénudation marine, si fort en honneur de l'autre côté du détroit (b).

Comparison of the Two Schools. It is noteworthy that, with few exceptions, the more recent writers here quoted do not discuss both processes by which smoothly abraded plains, whether buried or bare, may be produced, but directly announce their conclusion as to the origin — by marine or by sub-aërial agencies — of the surface under consideration. This, of course, implies that they regard the question as settled, just as for some time back it has been the habit of geologists on finding marine shells in stratified rocks to conclude, without reviving the discussions of earlier centuries, that the strata are of marine origin, and that their present position indicates a change in the relative attitude of the land and sea. But in this latter example all geologists are to-day agreed, while in the problem of the origin of plains of denudation each writer follows only the conclusion of his own school, not the conviction of the world. *It is chiefly to arouse attention to this aspect of the problem that the present review is undertaken.*

It is further noteworthy that, with few exceptions, the authors who discuss the matter at all do not attempt to discriminate between the two possible classes of denuded surfaces by searching for features peculiar to one or the other, but content themselves with a priori argument as to the possibility of producing plains by marine or sub-aërial agencies.

There is, however, a certain difference of attitude in the two schools regarding each other's doctrines. The English school hardly considers at all the ability of sub-aërial agencies to produce smooth plains of denudation; their discussion of the question turns really on the possible origin of valleys by sub-aërial agencies. The American school does not, as far as I have read, deny the ability of marine agencies, but attributes greater ability, especially far in continental interiors, to sub-aërial agencies; their discussion of the question postulates the sub-aërial origin of ordinary valleys as a matter already proved, and goes on from this to the possible ultimate result of the valley-making processes. Again, the English school denies, tacitly or directly, the probability or even the possibility of a period of stillstand long enough for essentially complete sub-aërial denudation close to sea-level, but assumes the possibility of a period of stillstand or of slight depression continuous and long enough to allow the sea waves to plane off the sinking lands. The American school tacitly questions the occurrence of great erosive transgressions of the sea during either a stillstand or a slow depression of the land, but admits the possibility of essentially complete sub-aërial denudation to an average sea-level, above and below which the land long hovers in many minor oscillations before a new attitude is assumed by great depression, elevation, or deformation. It should be borne in mind that the depressed and buried or the uplifted and dissected plains of denudation whose origin is in question are in no cases geometrical planes; they nearly always possess perceptible inequalities, amounting frequently to two or three hundred feet; but these measures are small compared to the inferred constructional relief of earlier date, or compared to the deep valleys often eroded beneath the plain if it has been uplifted. By whatever process the so-called "plain of denudation" was produced, an explanation that will account for a peneplain of moderate or slight relief is all that is necessary. Absolute planation is so rare as hardly to need consideration here.

In no respect is the contrast between the two schools more strikingly shown than in the beliefs concerning the cover of unconformable strata that lie or are supposed to have lain upon an oldland. The continental members of the English school generally regard these strata as an essential result of the process of marine denudation during slow depression; if such strata are absent from a dissected plateau, their absence is explained by denudation after uplift. The American school does not give the cover of unconformable strata an essential place in the problem; if present, it is generally ascribed to deposition following the submergence of a region already for the most part base-leveled by sub-aërial agencies.

Review of the A Priori Argument. It may be noted that the value of marine agencies gained a high reputation for effective work before sub-aërial agencies were recognized as significantly affecting the form of the land, and that from that time to the present the importance of the latter agencies has been steadily increasing in the minds of geologists. The manifest work of waves on a bold coast was perceived at a time when the production of valleys by rain and rivers was scouted. To-day it is not so much that the absolute strength of marine erosion is given a smaller value than heretofore, but that the relative importance of sub-aërial erosion is rated much higher than at the beginning of the century. While the sea works energetically along a line, sub-aërial forces work gently over a broad surface. Chiefly for this reason Geikie concludes that "before the sea, advancing at a rate of ten feet a century, could pare off more than a mere marginal strip of land between seventy and eighty miles in breadth, the whole land might be washed into the ocean by atmospheric denudation" (*c*, 432).

A slight movement of elevation usually sets the sea back to begin its work anew on the seaward side of its previous shore-line, but such an elevation only accelerates the work of sub-aërial denudation all over the elevated region. The waves on the sea-shore shift their line of attack with every slight vertical movement of the coastal region ; but the sub-aërial forces over large continental areas gain no notice of slight movements until a considerable time after they have been accomplished, and hence they perform their task only with reference to the average attitude of the land. Observers near a shore-line naturally have their attention directed to the unsteadiness of the land, as indicated by marks of many recent changes of land-level ; hence they are perhaps indisposed to admit that any land has ever stood still — or oscillated slightly above and below an average attitude — long enough to be nearly or quite base-leveled by sub-aërial agencies. They prefer to think that the sea is, in spite of its many stops and starts, the great leveler of the lands.

Some have intimated that the insular position of English observers has led them to exaggerate the relative power of the sea. Thus W. T. Blanford, after much experience in India and elsewhere, as well as at home in England, writes :

It is not surprising that the power of rain and rivers should be recognized with difficulty in regions where their effects are comparatively so dwarfed as in the British Isles, while the power of marine denudation is at its maximum from the enormous coast line exposed and the small amount of detritus furnished for its protection by rivers of small length and in which floods are of exceptional occurrence (158).

But even this well-practiced observer contended only for the sub-aërial origin of valleys, not of plains also. On the other hand, those whose studies have been directed chiefly to large interior areas seldom have occasion to observe the action of energetic shore waves, and hence are apt to attribute relatively little importance to their work. The small share of attention recently given by Powell to shore waves and coastal forms in a general discussion of physiographic processes and features is perhaps thus explained (c). The citation from Dawson, given above, is an especially good illustration of the manner in which large continental surroundings may affect the opinions of an observer who, from certain associations, might be expected to follow the insular school.

Although mature deliberation and good judgment may lead through a priori argument to a safe conclusion in many problems, the method is of difficult application here on account of the great number of variable factors whose appropriate values can hardly be determined. It is probably by reason of assigning different values to variable factors that the opposite conclusions summarized above have been reached.

Statement of the A Posteriori Argument. In attempting to decide by arguing from effect to cause whether evenly denuded regions have been worn down by sub-aërial or marine agencies, let us try to stand on a provisional Atlantis, hoping that it may give steady support long enough for us to gain an unprejudiced view of the opinions that are so generally accepted on the lands to the east and west. From this neutral ground let us attempt to deduce from the essential conditions of each explanation of the problem as many as possible of its essential consequences, and then confront these consequences with the facts. The measure of accordance between consequences of theory and facts of observation will then serve as a measure of the verity of the theory from which the consequences are derived. No final decision can be

reached in many cases, for however clearly the consequences
may be deduced, the facts with which they should be compared
are often beyond the reach of observation. In such cases it is
advisable to announce indecision as clearly as decision is announced in the others.

As far as I have been able to carry the analysis of the problems,
it is more difficult to find positive criteria characteristic of plains
of marine denudation than of plains of sub-aërial denudation ;
hence I will take up the latter class first. It should be remembered, however, that in each class of plains both classes of agencies
may have some share, one preponderating over the other.

Consequences of Sub-aërial Denudation. Imagine a region of
deformed harder and softer strata raised to a considerable elevation. Then let the land stand essentially still, or oscillate slightly
above and below a mean position. The rivers deepen their valleys, the valleys widen by the wasting of their slopes, and the
hills are slowly consumed. During this long process a most patient and thorough examination of the structure is made by the
destructive forces, and whatever is the drainage arrangement
when the rivers begin to cut their valleys, a significant rearrangement of many drainage lines will result from the processes of
spontaneous adjustment of streams to structures. This involves
the adjustment of many subsequent streams to the weaker structures and the shifting of many divides to the stronger structures.
Adjustment begins in the early stages of dissection, advances
greatly in the mature stages, and continues very slowly toward
old age, while the relief is fading away. Indeed, when the region
is well worn down, some of the adjustments of maturity may be
lost in the wanderings of decrepitude ; but this will seldom cause
significant loss of adjustment except in the larger rivers. Now,
if a region thus base-leveled, or nearly base-leveled, is raised by
broad and even elevation into a new cycle of geographical life, the
rivers will carry the adjustments acquired in the first cycle over
to the second cycle. Still further adjustment may then be accomplished. The master streams will increase their drainage area
in such a way that the minor streams will seldom head behind a
hard stratum. In a word, the drainage will become more and
more longitudinal, and fewer and fewer small streams will persist

in transverse courses. All this is so systematic that I believe it safe to assert that the advanced adjustments of a second cycle may in many cases be distinguished from the partial adjustments of a first cycle. It should be noted further that in the early stages of the second cycle the residual reliefs of the first will still be preserved on the uplands, and that they will be systematically related to the streams by which the dissection of the upland is in progress, as noted in the examples described by Darton and Hershey.

It is manifestly impossible to apply what may be called the river test to plains of denudation upon which a cover of unconformable sediments is spread; but before assuming that such buried plains are of marine origin, their uppermost portion next beneath the cover should be examined to see if it presents indications of secular decay before burial; and, if so, a sub-aërial origin for the plain may be argued. Certain aspects of this division of the subject have been discussed by Pumpelly (211). Another matter of importance is the character of the undermost layers of the cover. If these are fresh-water beds a sub-aërial origin for the plain on which they rest may be inferred. The Potomac formation offers an example of this kind (McGee, 137, and Fontaine, 61).

Consequences of Marine Denudation. Now suppose that a region of disordered structure is partly worn down by rain and rivers and is smoothly planed across by the sea during a time of stillstand or of gradual depression. The land waste gained in the later attack will be spread offshore on the platform abraded in the earlier attack. The basal strata of the unconformable cover thus formed must indicate their marine origin and must be appropriately related in composition and texture to their sources of supply. The drainage systems of the land will be essentially extinguished by the encroaching sea. When the region rises, with the cover of new sediments lying evenly on its smoothed back, a new system of original consequent streams will take their way across it. If the elevation be sufficient, the streams will incise their valleys through the cover of new sediments and in time find themselves superposed on the "oldland" beneath. As time passes, more and more of the cover will be stripped off; at last it may disappear far and wide, although the stripped surface of the oldland may still retain a generally even sky line as a memorial of its once even denudation. Now, in this case, the rivers by which the dissected plateau is drained will have at most only a very slight adjustment to its structure. Their courses will have been inherited from the slope of the lost cover; they will at first run at random across hard and soft structures; a little later some adjustment to the discovered structures will be made, but as long as the even sky line of the upland is recognizable, only the incomplete adjustments appropriate to the adolescent stage of denudation can be gained.

Examples of Dissected Uplands with Adjusted Drainage. This essay has already reached so much more than its expected length that it will not be possible to give extended space to the consideration of specific examples. This is, however, no great disadvantage, inasmuch as the number of examples in which the problem has been considered in relation to drainage arrangement and other discriminating features is very small. The various articles already referred to concerning the geographical development of the Appalachian region treat this aspect of the subject with some care; to these may be added my paper on "Certain English Rivers," in which it seems to me that there is shown some ground for the consideration of the alternative to the usual English view. Of the Ardennes it may be said briefly that systematic longitudinal and transverse streams are well developed in certain areas, and in those parts, at least, there does not appear direct evidence of marine transgression. Sheets 48 and 54 of the Belgian topographical map (scale, 1 : 40,000) exhibit these features very clearly. On the other hand, the branches of the Rhine and the Moselle in the Schiefergebirge suggest superposition from a lost cover, as mapped on the sheets of the Karte des Deutschen Reichs (scale, 1 : 100,000).

It is manifest that many plains of denudation, now uplifted and more or less dissected, may be found in which no simple test based on the presence of superposed streams will serve to settle the question of marine origin. Indeed, it appears to me a difficult matter to adduce any examples of extensive plains of denudation whose origin is demonstrably marine and to whose planation sub-aërial agencies have not contributed the greater work. A region may be almost reduced to base-level by sub-aërial denudation when the transgressing sea completes the work, extinguishing the adjusted valleys and introducing superposed streams in the next cycle of denudation. A region well base-leveled under the air may by quick depression suffer rapid ingression of the sea, whose shore waves will, during depression, nowhere reside long enough to perform a significant amount of abrasion. When the region is thus submerged and stands again relatively quiet, the waste from a non-submerged area, gained both by marine and sub-aërial denudation, may be spread over the denuded and depressed plain, and when this plain is afterwards elevated with an unconformable cover that will induce superposed drainage, all trace of former adjustments will be lost; yet here the planation was not marine. A district of superposed drainage in central New Jersey, where the Amboy clays once spread over the red shales and sandstones of the Trias, may probably be taken as an example of this kind. Superposed rivers cannot, therefore, always be taken to prove that the uplands which they dissect are uplifted plains whose denudation was chiefly performed by the sea.

Regions of essentially horizontal structure normally have wandering streams; no systematic arrangement of drainage is here to be expected. Discrimination in such regions has seldom been attempted between examples of one cycle of sub-aërial denudation, now adolescent or mature, and examples of two cycles, the first having reached old age and the second now being in its adolescence or maturity. The sky line would be smooth and even in examples of either class: in the first, because its original constructional form was a plain; in the second, because it was planed down essentially smooth at the close of the cycle preceding the current cycle. It is, however, sometimes possible in regions of horizontal structure to recognize the records of old age reached in a former cycle by a slight discordance between the general upland surface and the attitude of the strata; or by the association of the region with an adjacent region of tilted structure where indications of an earlier cycle of sub-aërial denudation are manifest, both these tests being applicable in the Allegheny plateau; or by the arrangement of the faint residual relief of the uplands, where not trenched by young or adolescent streams, this test having been applied in the Piedmont district of Virginia, in the Ozark plateau of Missouri, and in the Great plains of eastern Montana. Further study of many other examples is desirable.

REFERENCES

Blanford, W. T. Geology and Zoölogy of Abyssinia, 158, note. 1870.

Cornet, F. L., and Briart, A. "Le Relief du Sol en Belgique." *Ann. Soc. Geol. Belg.*, IV, 1877.

Darton, N. H. *Jour. Geol.*, II (1894), 568–570.

Davis, W. M. (*a*) "Relation of the Coal of Montana to the Older Rocks." *Tenth Census U. S.*, XV (1886), 710.

(*b*) "Topographic Development . . . of the Connecticut Valley." *Am. Jour. Sci.*, XXXVII (1889), 430.

(*c*) "Geographic Development of Northern New Jersey" (with J. W. Wood). *Proc. Boston Soc. Nat. Hist.*, XXIV (1889), 373.

(*d*) "Rivers of Northern New Jersey." *Nat. Geog. Mag.*, II (1890), 6.

(*e*) "Topographic Forms of the Atlantic Slope." *Bull. Geol. Soc. Am.*, II (1891), 557.

(*f*) "Physical Geography of Southern New England." *Nat. Geog. Mon.*, I (1895), 276.

(*g*) "Development of Certain English Rivers." *Geog. Jour.* (London), V (1895), 140.

Dawson, G. M. ". . . The Rocky Mountain Region in Canada." *Trans. Roy. Soc. Canada*, VIII, 1890.

Diller, J. S. (*a*) *Jour. Geol.*, II (1894), 34.

(*b*) *U. S. Geol. Surv.*, *XIV Ann. Rep.* (1894), 405.

Dutton, C. E. "Tertiary History of the Grand Cañon District." *U. S. Geol. Surv.*, *Mon. II* (1882).

Emerson, B. K. Hawley Folio, *Geol. Atlas U. S.* (1894).

Fontaine, W. M. *U. S. Geol. Surv.*, *Mon. XV* (1889), 61.

Foster, C. Le N., and Topley, W. "The Denudation of the Weald." *Quart. Jour. Geol. Soc.*, XXI (1865), 443–474.

Geikie, Sir Archibald. (*a*) Scenery of Scotland. 1st ed., 1865.

(*b*) "On Modern Denudation." *Trans. Geol. Soc. Glasgow*, III (1868).

(*c*) Text-Book of Geology. 2d ed., 1885.

(*d*) Scenery of Scotland. 2d ed., 1887.

Geikie, James. "Mountains, their Origin, Growth, and Decay." *Scot. Geog. Mag.*, II (1886), 160.

Gilbert, G. K. *Science*, I (1883), 195.

Gosselet, J. "L'Ardenne." *Mém. Carte Géol., France* (1888), 802, 808, 837.

Green, A. Physical Geology. 1882.

Griswold, L. S. (a) Geol. Surv. Arkansas, III (1890), 222.

(b) Proc. Boston Soc. Nat. Hist., XXVI (1895), 478.

Hayes, C. W. (a) "The Southern Appalachians." Nat. Geog. Mon., No. 10 (1895).

(b) Sewanee Folio, Geol. Atlas U. S. (1895).

Hayes, C. W., and Campbell, M. R. "Geomorphology of the Southern Appalachians." Nat. Geog. Mag., VI (1894).

Hershey, O. H. Am. Geol., XVI (1895), 338.

Irving, R. D. U. S. Geol. Surv., VII Ann. Rep. (1888).

Jukes, J. B. "Formation of . . . River Valleys in the South of Ireland." Quart. Jour. Geol. Soc., XVIII (1862), 378–403.

Jukes-Brown, A. J. Handbook of Physical Geology. 1892.

Keith, A. U. S. Geol. Surv., XIV Ann. Rep. (1894), 369.

Keyes, C. R. Geol. Surv. Missouri, VIII (1894), 330, 352.

La Noë, and Margerie, E. de. Les Formes du Terrain. 1888.

Lapparent, A. de. (a) "L'Age des Formes Topographiques." Rev. des Quest. Scient. (October, 1894).

(b) "La Géomorphogénie." Rev. des Quest. Scient. (April, 1895).

Lawson, A. W. Bull. Dept. Geol. Univ. Calif., I (1894), 244.

LeConte, Joseph. Bull. Geol. Soc. Am., II (1891), 327.

Lepsius, G. R. (a) "Die Oberrheinische Tiefebene und ihre Randgebirge." Forschungen zur Deut. Landeskunde, I (1885), 35–91.

(b) Geologie von Deutschland (1887).

Lindgren, W. Bull. Geol. Soc. Am., IV (1893), 298.

Lyell, Sir Charles. Elements of Geology. 6th ed., 1868.

Marvine, A. R. Hayden's Survey (Report for 1873), 144.

Maw, G. "Notes on the Comparative Structure of Surfaces produced by Sub-aërial and Marine Denudation." Geol. Mag., III (1866), 439–451.

McGee, W. J. "Three Formations of the Middle Atlantic Slope." Am. Jour. Sci., XXXV (1888).

McIntosh. Scenery of England and Wales. 1869.

Penck, A. (a) "Das Endziel der Erosion und Denudation." Verh. VIII. Deut. Geographentages (1889), 91–100.

(b) Länderkunde des Erdtheils Europa, I (1887), 316.

(c) Morphologie der Erdoberfläche, II (1894), 145, 181, 489.

Philippson, A. Studien über Wasserscheiden. 1886.

Powell, J. W. (a) Exploration of the Colorado River. 1875.

(b) Geology of the Uinta Mountains. 1876.

(c) Nat. Geog. Mon., Nos. 1 and 2 (1895).

Pumpelly, R. Bull. Geol. Soc. Am., II (1891), 211.

Ramsay, A. C. (a) "Denudation of South Wales." Mem. Geol. Surv. Great Britain, I (1846).

(b) Physical Geology and Geography of Great Britain. 5th ed., 1878.

Richthofen, F. von. (a) China, II (1882), chap. xiv, sec. 3.

(b) Führer für Forschungsreisende. Berlin, 1886.

Salisbury, R. D.   *Geol. Surv. New Jersey, 1894* (1895).

Van Hise, C. R.   *U. S. Geol. Surv., Mon. XIX* (1892), 454–466.

Walcott, C. D.   *U. S. Geol. Surv., XII Ann. Rep.* (1891), 562, 565.

Whitaker, W.   *Geol. Mag.*, IV (1867), 454.

Willis, B.   (*a*) " Round about Asheville." *Nat. Geog. Mag.*, I (1889), 297.
   (*b*) " The Northern Appalachians." *Nat. Geog. Mon.*, No. 6 (1895).

Woodward, H. B.   Geology of England and Wales.   2d ed., 1887.

Wynne, A. B.   " On Denudation with Reference to the Configuration of the Ground." *Geol. Mag.*, IV (1867), 3–10.

XVII

THE PENEPLAIN [1]

At the beginning of this essay I wish to emphasize the fact that the "peneplain idea" was not original with me. The name is of my invention, and, as has sometimes happened, the introduction of a definite name for a thing previously talked about only in general terms has promoted its consideration: witness the name "antecedent" for rivers that hold their courses against mountains uplifted beneath them. The idea of antecedent rivers had occurred to several observers who gave it no name, and unnamed it gained no general currency; but it became popular when Powell named it. Moreover, the ideas of antecedence and peneplanation were ripe in many minds about the time the names were suggested, and it is chiefly for that reason, as it seems to me, that antecedent rivers have been so frequently mentioned in the last thirty years, and peneplains in the last ten.

It was in Powell's "Exploration of the Colorado River" (1875) that the peneplain idea, along with a number of other important facts and principles, first came to my notice. The idea is not stated categorically, but when describing the even surface of deformed rocks beneath the horizontal Carboniferous strata in the Colorado cañon, Powell said that "aërial forces carried away 10,000 feet of rocks by a process slow yet unrelenting, until the sea again rolled over the land," and the evenly denuded surface is referred to as "the record of a long time when the region was dry land" (212). In his "Geology of the Uinta Mountains" (1876) the same author writes: "Mountains cannot long remain as mountains; they are ephemeral topographical forms. Geologically speaking, all existing mountains are recent; the ancient mountains are gone" (196).

[1] Revised form of a paper originally prepared as a reply to an article on "The Peneplain," published by Professor R. S. Tarr in the *American Geologist*, June, 1898.

Again :

In a very low degree of declivity approaching horizontality, the power of transporting material is also very small. The degradation of the last few inches of a broad area of land above the level of the sea would require a longer time than all the thousands of feet which might have been above it, so far as this degradation depends on mechanical process, — that is, driving or flotation ; but here the disintegration by solution and the transportation of material by the agency of fluidity come in to assist the slow processes of mechanical degradation, and finally perform the chief part of the task (*b*, 196).

Dutton referred to Powell's having given precision to the idea of base-level, an idea probably known previously in a general way to many geologists. "All regions," Dutton says, "are tending to base-levels of erosion, and if the time be long enough, each region will, in its turn, approach nearer and nearer, and at last sensibly reach it " (76).

I had expected to find some similar sentences in Gilbert's "Geology of the Henry Mountains," but discover instead the following statement :

It is evident that if steep slopes are worn more rapidly than gentle, the tendency is to abolish all differences of slope and produce uniformity. The law of uniformity of slope thus opposes diversity of topography, and if not complemented by other laws, would reduce all drainage basins to plains. But in reality it is never free to work out its full results, for it demands a uniformity of conditions which nowhere exists (115).

In Great Britain, where the literature very generally indicates a belief in plains of marine abrasion, a number of geologists have, without public announcement in any formal manner, gradually enlarged the share of work attributed to sub-aërial forces, until, as some of them have lately assured me, the peneplain idea has come to be for a number of years as familiar to them as to most American geologists ; and some of them certainly entertained it before the term "peneplain" was suggested. Several examples of the recognition of the peneplain idea by continental geologists might be given if time and space permitted.

The peneplain theory has been criticised on the ground that certain regions instanced as dissected peneplains have never really been lowlands of faint relief ; that the process of peneplanation is in itself an extremely unlikely one ; and that the so-called peneplains, all of which are now more or less dissected, are capable of other explanation; in brief, that peneplains are (A) unreal, (B) improbable, and (C) unnecessary. Several subdivisions of each of these headings will be made in replying to them.

A 1. *Certain Regions show no Trace of Peneplanation.* It has been stated that "one standing upon the crest of one of the mountains of central Maine would hardly find the evenness [of the sky line] sufficient to give the appearance of levelness even to the eye." But no one, so far as I know, has thought that the mountain tops of Maine mark the remnants of a peneplain. The mountains there are probably of the nature of monadnocks; it is only the general upland surface above which the mountains rise that can be regarded as a peneplain, uplifted and dissected, if the features that I have seen about Portland and at some other points along the coast may be extended inland. The White mountains have been, in my mind, tentatively classed as a group of monadnocks; they do not, as far as I have seen them in brief excursions, stand upon any distinct basement comparable to that of the uplands of New England farther south; but Mr. Philip Emerson, master of the Cobbett school, Lynn, tells me that he has in summer excursions traced what he thinks may be regarded as the extension of the more southern uplands around the White mountains on the east, north, and west. Northern New England is not to-day well enough mapped or studied to give either decided support or disproof to the theory of peneplains. Its ruggedness is generally so great that it is quite possible that the peneplain explanation does not apply to the greater part of the area. Little wonder that an observer whose attention is given to this mountainous district, under the impression that its mountain tops represent the remnants of a peneplain, should come to discredit such an explanation.

A 2. *The Uplands of Southern New England and of Northern New Jersey are not of Uniform Altitude.* It has been urged that a careful examination of the topographical maps of these regions disproves the accordance claimed for their upland altitudes. In answer, I should say that the lack of uniformity among the uplands—a fact perfectly familiar to those who accept the peneplain idea—is partly the result of tilting, as will be further considered below (see A 4); and that for the rest the unevenness of the uplands of to-day is a natural result of imperfect pene- planation followed by sub-mature dissection. The examination of the peneplain remnants by means of topographical maps is not a new method of investigation, as it was employed for New Jersey in 1888–1889, and for southern New England a few years later; but, like observation outdoors, it seems to lead different investigators to different results. Considerable as the inequalities of altitude are, frequent study of the maps and repeated views of the uplands from various hill-tops impress me much more with the relative accordance of their altitudes than with their diversity. I cannot admit that the appearance of ac- cordance from hill-top to hill-top is an optical deception. There is an important matter of fact behind the appearance.

The comparative evenness of the uplands in Connecticut was recognized and well described by Percival over half a century ago. The state being divided into eastern and western areas of primary rocks by the trough of Triassic strata, he said:

The eastern and western primary may both be regarded as extensive plateaus, usually terminating abruptly toward the larger secondary basin, but sinking more gradually toward the south, on the sound. These plateaus present, when viewed from an elevated point on their surface, the appear- ance of a general level, with a rolling or undulating outline, over which the view often extends to a very great distance, interrupted only by isolated summits or ridges, usually of small extent. These plateaus are also inter- sected by valleys and basins, which serve to mark the arrangement of their surface even more definitely than the elevations. This arrangement will be found to correspond very exactly with that of the geological formation, indicating that it was caused essentially by the original form of the surface of these formations, and not by any subsequent denudation (477).

The western primary . . . forms, within the limits of this state, a wide plateau . . . of so uniform an elevation that from many points the view extends across its entire width, and to a great distance north and south (478).

The eastern primary, viewed from its more elevated points, presents the same general appearance as the western: that of an extensive undulating surface of nearly uniform elevation, diversified by detached summits (482).

The peculiar conclusion of the first of the above quotations is interesting in contrast to modern views.

In eastern Massachusetts dissection has gone so far that it would be difficult to discover an uplifted peneplain on local evidence alone; but in the central and western parts of the state the uplands are generally well defined and very accordant. Looking eastward from the Berkshire hills across the Connecticut valley lowlands in northern Massachusetts, the sky line of the central plateau is astonishingly uniform, though its altitude is over a thousand feet.

A 3. *The Remains of Certain Peneplains are Fragmentary.* It has been urged that ten per cent of the original area of the supposed peneplain, now preserved in the uplands of Connecticut, is too small a fraction to serve as a basis of reconstruction. This does not strike me as a serious or a novel difficulty. Geologists are often compelled to work on fragmentary evidence; they are satisfied if the fragments can be logically built up into the complete structure. In most parts of the world rock outcrops occupy less than ten per cent — often less than one per cent — of the land surface, yet no field geologist hesitates to "color in" a formation over an area where scattered outcrops give reasonable proof of its occurrence. The surface area thus colored in is often but a small part of the entire body of the original formation, which may be largely covered by later deposits or destroyed by erosion; but the covered and eroded portions are reasonably inferred, and a formation thus established is a stock subject in historical geology. A high percentage of direct observation is less essential than a logical method of reconstructing the unseen whole from the observed parts. Here the dissected peneplain seems to me to stand on a par with many other things. Its fragmental condition is most natural; its discovered parts are connected and the lost peneplain is restored by a line of argument that is perfectly reasonable in itself, and that is objected to only because it runs counter to certain views that are held to be established principles in the science of geology. These views will be considered below (B 1, 2).

A 4. *Certain So-called Peneplains are now Inclined.* It has been stated that uplift or tilting "is an assumption rendered necessary to explain the difference in elevation of the supposed peneplain, but there is no evidence to prove it unless the peneplain be previously accepted." With this I fully agree. I have repeatedly insisted that it was only by recognizing the existence of a peneplain that uplift or deformation could be determined in certain cases; and that only in this way could certain stages of geological history be discovered, in the absence of what might be called orthodox geological evidence in the form of marine deposits. For example, it is by the remnants of an uplifted, inclined, and warped peneplain in the even crest lines of the Pennsylvania Appalachians that the post-Cretaceous uplift of the mountain belt has been determined; it was formerly supposed that the existing ridges were the unconsumed remnants of the ancient Appalachians, and, by implication, that no uplift of the region had occurred since the mountains were crushed, folded, and upheaved. So in southern New England: there was no means of determining the date of uplift, as a result of which the existing valleys were eroded, until the peneplain of the uplands was recognized and dated. Twenty or thirty years ago it was not uncommon to meet the suggestion that the valleys might be of glacial origin, so little understanding had then been reached of the geographical development of the region. Those who believe in the verity of peneplains will infer uplift where they see a high-standing and dissected peneplain as confidently as the geologists of the end of the eighteenth century inferred uplift when they found marine fossils in stratified rocks far above sea-level.

But it does not seem warranted to conclude that the peneplain theory is invalidated because certain peneplains are now uplifted on a slant. It is no objection to the peneplain idea to say that the crest of Kittatinny mountain is higher than the upland surface of the New Jersey highlands, or that the crest of the Palisades is lower. It would be as extraordinary to find no slanting peneplains as to find no inclined strata. Warped and faulted peneplains are no more unlikely products of crustal deformation than warped and faulted sedimentary formations; witness the dislocations of the plateaus trenched by the Colorado cañon, the plateau surface having been worn down to "a very flat expanse" before the uplift and displacements that have determined the altitudes and forms of to-day.

A 5. *Objections based on the Fragmentary Condition of Certain Peneplains further Considered.* If the best-preserved peneplains were not less fragmentary than those of New England and

New Jersey, the theory of peneplains might perhaps be over-thrown; but when these imperfect peneplains are considered in connection with many more nearly perfect peneplains elsewhere, the series becomes so well graded, from better to worse, that the theory seems to me unassailable. A few examples of the better-preserved peneplains may therefore be now considered.

The Piedmont belt of Virginia has been described by a number of observers in recent years. McGee writes: "The plain is not monotonously smooth; here it undulates in graceful swells, there it dips into rocky river gorges, winding across its width . . . . Such is the Piedmont plain within view of Monticello, and such is the province throughout its extent from New York to Alabama" (261). The Piedmont rivers "rush through narrow, rockbound gorges. . . . All the Piedmont rivers, large and small, are incessantly corrading their beds" (262). The plain "must be regarded as the basal portion of a vast mass of inclined rocks of which an unmeasured upper portion has been planed away" (263). In describing the same region, Darton writes: "The Piedmont plateau is a peneplain of Tertiary age . . . the plain has been deeply trenched by drainage ways, but wide areas are preserved

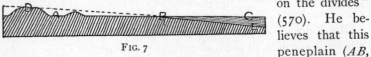

FIG. 7

on the divides" (570). He believes that this peneplain (AB, Fig. 7) continues across the inner strata (BC) of the coastal plain, and that it should therefore be distinguished from an earlier peneplain carved on the same ancient rocks, part of which is BE, preserved beneath the strata of the coastal plain, and part of which (DB) is generally hereabout destroyed by erosion. It is upon the older peneplain that the Potomac formation, with its fossil terrestrial flora, directly rests. Keith gives an elaborate account of a part of the Piedmont plain in his "Geology of the Catoctin Belt" and discusses its relations to various members of the coastal-plain series.

Any one who will follow up the foregoing references, or who will, better still, look over the region on the ground, will find a decidedly larger portion of the peneplain surface preserved than is the case in New England or New Jersey; and this is most natural, for the Virginia Piedmont plain is of distinctly later origin than the peneplain of the uplands farther north : the latter corresponds to the earlier peneplain (*DBE*) in Virginia. But it is not only the comparative continuity of the Piedmont plain that makes it a valuable example : the deep soils of the upland plain and the rocky walls of the narrow, steep-sided valleys are as important witnesses to the once lower position of the plain and to the uplift by which its present altitude has been gained as are the forms of the upland and the valleys. To explain this point more fully, a brief digression may be allowed.

The peneplain is only one element in the theory of the geographical cycle. The systematic sequence in the development of land forms through the cycle is a much larger and more important principle than the penultimate development of a peneplain, considered alone, for the former includes the latter. One of the elements of the cycle is the development of the graded condition of streams of water during maturity, whereby an essential agreement is brought about between the ability of a stream to do work and the work that it has to do. Another element, less generally recognized, is the development of the graded condition in the streams and sheets of rock waste or soil on sloping surfaces, where no running streams of water occur. By following out the ideal scheme thus suggested, it must result that just as the graded condition of water streams is normally propagated from the mouth towards the head, and in time reaches the source of all the branches, so the graded condition of soil-covered slopes is in time extended all over a land surface, from the valley floors to the divides. The supply of waste by the disintegration of the sub-soil rock is then everywhere essentially equal to its removal by all available agents of transportation. In a late stage of a cycle, when the surface slopes are small, agents of transportation are weak ; hence the supply of waste must then be slow and the waste to be removed must be of fine texture. In order that the supply shall be slow, the waste comes to have a great depth, and the upper parts greatly protect the rock beneath from the attack of the weather. At the same time, transportation is facilitated by the refinement of the surface soil during its long exposure to the weather. Hence, under ordinary climatic conditions, normal peneplains must have deep local soils of fine texture at the surface, and grading into firm rock at a depth of thirty, fifty, or more feet. Moreover, it is only on a lowland surface of small slope that such a depth and arrangement of local soil can be normally produced.

In contrast to the deep soil of a peneplain, the steep sides of young valleys, whose graded waste sheets are not yet developed, must frequently reveal bare, rocky ledges. Only as the valleys widen and their side slopes become somewhat more gentle will the ledges disappear; and even then the rock will be covered only by a relatively thin and coarse sheet of rapidly creeping waste. It therefore follows that the uplands of the Piedmont belt, with their deep soil, are of an essentially different cycle of development from the narrow valleys, with their bare ledges. The two elements of form remain mutually inconsistent until reconciled by the postulate of an uplift of the region between their developments. But if this postulate is accepted, the plain is shown to have been a lowland of faint relief before the existing narrow valleys were cut in it. It is this double line of argument, based on deep soil and bare ledge, as well as undulating plain and narrow valley, that has convinced various observers of the verity of the peneplain in the Piedmont belt.

The Great Plains of eastern Montana include an area of nearly horizontal Cretaceous strata on either side of the Missouri river, regarding which the evidence of peneplanation seems to me beyond dispute. Here and there volcanic buttes, dikes, and mesas surmount the plain by several hundred feet; on the south the Highwood mountains, a network of dikes among nearly horizontal shales and sandstones, rise in still stronger relief. Hence there can be no question that strata, measuring hundreds, if not thousands, of feet in thickness, have been broadly removed from the region by denudation. Yet the surface between the various eminences that rise above it is a true geographical plain. It is not absolutely level, but broadly undulating, with a sky line almost as even as that of the ocean itself. In this plain the Missouri river and its chief branches have cut narrow, steep-sided valleys several hundred feet below the general upland level. These valleys are so young that the Missouri itself has

not yet developed an even slope: witness its several leaps at
Great Falls. Innumerable wet-weather side streams are cutting
sharp ravines in the larger valley sides. It does not seem possible to avoid concluding that the upland plain is to-day in process
of destruction by an agency that could not have been in operation
while the finishing touches were given to its production. It was
upon this peneplain in 1883 that the necessity of believing in
penultimate denudation was first strongly impressed upon me.
Dr. Waldemar Lindgren, now of the United States Geological
Survey, who was with me in the field, may recall how the conviction grew upon our minds; if I am not mistaken, he accepted
it before I did. A brief account of the region is published in
Volume XV of the Tenth United States Census Reports.

The extended plains of central Russia, as lately described by
Philippson, have a gently undulating surface at a height of two
hundred or three hundred meters, broadly continuous, but here
and there dissected by relatively narrow, steep-sided young
valleys. The upland surface is not a structural plain, for it
bevels across formations of very different ages; it is therefore a
plain of erosion. In the south there is a partial covering of loess,
a thin veneer often absent and leaving the rock surface visible
over large areas. In the north the drift cover is heavier and
more continuous, but the plateau surface is still the continuation
of the same plain of erosion as in the south. There is no record
of marine action on the great plain, hence its erosion is ascribed
to the lateral swinging of the lower courses of large rivers; but
the origin of the rivers is unknown: it can only be said that
when the erosion was going on, the Russian "Scholle" must
have stood two hundred meters lower than to-day. The narrow
valleys have been cut since the uplift of the plain and are older
than the glacial period. This is the largest peneplain of which
I have found any account.

A 6. *The Asserted Discordance of Peneplain Surface and
Rock Structure is open to Question.* It has been said to be
questionable whether there is, after all, such a lack of sympathy
between topography and rock structure as has been represented,
and in evidence of this doubt one has urged that in the highlands of New Jersey there is "a very evident general sympathy

between the present topography and the rock texture." This objection to peneplanation does not meet the arguments advanced in its favor. Disregarding the weaker structures, which are now worn down beneath the inferred surface of the peneplain, it seems to me undeniable that the peneplain surface was strongly discordant with the hard structures that still preserve its remnants. It is a matter of necessity that the present topography of an uplifted and dissected peneplain should exhibit sympathy between form and structure, for where should better accordance of form and structure be expected than in such a region of adjusted drainage; but this is a matter quite apart from the present discussion.

Various gneisses, sandstones, and trap sheets, standing in a more or less inclined position, are truncated with good appearance of system by the gently slanting surface of the peneplain of northern New Jersey. The following description of the region is taken from one of Cook's reports.

The Highland mountain range consists of many ridges which are in part separated by deep valleys and in part coalesce, forming plateaus or tablelands of small extent. . . . A characteristic feature is the absence of what might be called Alpine structure [form?] or scenery. There are no prominent peaks or cones. The ridges are even-topped for long distances, and the average elevation is uniform over wide areas. Looking at the crests alone and imagining the valleys and depressions filled, the surface would approximate to a plane gently inclined toward the southeast and toward the southwest (27).

It is this indifference of the peneplain to the various structures that it systematically truncates that has always been the chief argument of those who thought they saw traces of a former lowland where there is to-day a dissected highland, whether they believed in marine abrasion or in sub-aërial denudation.

Special mention may be made here of certain features that will be referred to more briefly in a later section. Descending the Hudson from Haverstraw to Jersey City, one may see a gradual decrease of altitude in the Palisades, a ridge formed on a monoclinal sheet of dense, intrusive trap, from a height of about six hundred feet in the north to sea-level in the south. There is no corresponding variation in the thickness of the trap sheet. The uplands of schists and gneisses on the east of the Hudson have a similar descent from the Highlands to Long Island sound. In Connecticut the view from East Rock, New Haven, discloses the extraordinarily even crest line of Totoket mountain, the edge of a strongly warped sheet of extrusive trap. The crest line slowly descends southward and is continued by the somewhat lower crest line of Pond mountain, of similar structure. Furthermore, the descent of these crest lines agrees very well with the descent of the crystalline uplands next on the east. The systematic relation of these and many other crest lines and uplands suggests a peneplain, and the peneplain thus inferred is strikingly indifferent to the structures that it truncates. It might be urged that the observed discordance of form and structure is of some other origin than peneplanation, but the discordance does not seem open to question.

A 7. *The Rocks of Monadnocks are not proved to be more Resistant than those of the Adjoining Peneplain.* It has been urged that there is no proof of the durability of the rocks of monadnocks other "than that which comes from the necessity of such an explanation, made necessary by first accepting the existence of the peneplain." As far as my own work is concerned, there is some ground for this objection. I have as a rule given no particular attention to the composition of the monadnock rocks; indeed, it has generally seemed to me reasonable to infer their greater resistance on account of their form. But so far as attention has been given directly to this phase of the problem, the inference based on the peneplain theory is borne out by petrographic study. The buttes and mesas that surmount the plains of the upper Missouri are maintained by dense igneous rocks. The monadnocks of the Virginia Piedmont belt "are ribbed with siliceous schists or quartzites or other rocks that resist well the work of the weather . . ., while the rocks underlying the fertile fields of the plain are softer schists, easily weathered and worn away" (McGee, 262, 263). Near Atlanta, Georgia, the Piedmont area is a well-finished peneplain, rather strongly dissected, with deep soils overlying the uplands of gneiss and schist. Stone mountain, a superb monadnock of abrupt form, consists of fine homogeneous granite, quite unlike the rocks of the peneplain (Purington, 105–108). Van Hise, in describing the uplands of the ancient disordered and indurated rocks in north-central Wisconsin, says that they constitute "as nearly perfect a base-level plain as it has been my good fortune to see. . . . Above the valley of the Wisconsin river an almost perfect plain is seen . . ., large areas of which are but little dissected by any of the tributary streams of the Wisconsin." The upland plain is surmounted by Big Rib hill, a monadnock of exceedingly resistant quartzite. The upland of the Slate mountains in western Germany is a wonderfully fine peneplain of broad and gentle undulations, now undergoing active dissection by the branches of the Rhine, Moselle, and other strong rivers which have eroded their steep-sided valleys deep beneath its even surface. The upland is surmounted by several ridges or elongated monadnocks; and some of these at least are composed of a very resistant quartzite. In New England the "Monadnock" is, if my memory serves me, largely composed of an andalusite schist, which certainly has every appearance of being a resistant rock. Yet I must freely admit that, as far as I know, no artificial test has been made of its resistance as compared with that of many apparently resistant rocks around its base. It may be added that an appropriate test would be difficult to devise, inasmuch as exposure for ages to the weather would certainly be the best means of discovering the way in which long ages of weathering will affect a rock. In view of this difficulty I hope that those who regard the peneplain explanation as compulsory will not be left alone to devise appropriate tests to determine the resistance of monadnock rocks, but that others who are interested in the development of land forms, but who feel no such compulsion from the peneplain theory, will nevertheless turn their ingenuity in this direction. It is the truth of the matter that we are all striving for, not the maintenance of this theory or that; and it seems unfriendly, if not unscientific, to say that the burden of proof should rest with the advocates of the peneplain theory. We are not retained to argue for or against the theory; each of us follows the guidance of the best evidence he can find. It is of course difficult to avoid the appearance and even the style of the advocate or the enemy when writing earnestly in expression of one's convictions, but for my part I cannot say too emphatically that the peneplain idea shall find no "defense" from me. Let us all set forth the *pros* and *cons* to the best of our ability, and then the peneplain idea must look out for itself, and stand or fall according to its value.

The objections thus far discussed relate to actual examples of supposed peneplains. Attention may be next turned to a group of objections based on general considerations, leading to the belief that the production or occurrence of peneplains is improbable or even impossible.

B 1. *No Peneplains are now found standing close to Base-Level.* It has been stated that since no extensive peneplains are now known to exist in any part of the earth, in accepting the peneplain theory we must assume that during a part of the remote past the conditions have been different from those that have prevailed in any part of the known earth during the present and immediate past. As far as my own understanding of the problem is concerned, it was not at all as an assumption, but as a very surprising corollary, that I came upon the difference between the present and certain parts of the past with respect to peneplanation.

Although agreeing in the belief that the theory of peneplains involves a certain difference between the past and the present, I do not agree to the implication that the past, "whose history has been worked out by purely stratigraphic methods," is proved to be so like the present that the theory of peneplains must be wrong because it involves a past that is in some ways unlike the present. My opinion is that stratigraphic methods do not always disclose a past closely like the present (see B 4), and that, even at their best, stratigraphic methods are not so complete in their revelations but that all other lines of evidence concerning the nature of the past should have a careful hearing.

There are certain parts of the world in which frequent disorderly movements of the earth's crust appear to have continued during several geological periods, including the present; for example, the Alps. The teachings of Mesozoic and Cenozoic stratigraphy in such a region would lend no support to the theory of peneplanation, as little support would be gained from the teachings of denudation in the Alps. Indeed, I have been interested to learn that certain careful students of geomorphy in the neighborhood of the Alps have recognized that they were prejudiced against the theory because their experience was gained chiefly in an uneasy part of the world. But there are other parts of the world which have been relatively quiescent for long geological periods; for example, the upper Mississippi basin, where all represented formations, from the Cambrian down, are essentially horizontal and of moderate thickness. Stratigraphy, as there taught, would not be inconsistent with peneplanation; neither would geomorphy, and to illustrate this I have a little story to tell. During an excursion with a friend native to that part of the country, I pointed out the very even sky line of a dissected upland as an example of a peneplain. My friend dissented, thinking no such special explanation necessary; ordinary denudation would suffice, he thought, to produce the observed forms, without specification of control by different base-levels. A year later, on meeting the same friend, our talk happened to turn on peneplains, and he said, "I should like to show you an excellent example of that sort of thing," proceeding to describe the very region we had seen together. "How," I asked, "did you come upon that explanation?" "I cannot say precisely how," he replied; "it is nothing new." This incident seems to me to illustrate the unconscious encouragement given to the idea of peneplanation by a quiescent environment, in contrast to the discouragement given in such a region as the Alps.

Unrest and quiescence are not persistent characteristics of one region or another. Pre-Cambrian time was active enough in the Wisconsin-Minnesota region; and there are indications of relative quiet in the Alpine region before its Mesozoic and Cenozoic activity began. But this aspect of the problem is too large for consideration here. Suffice it to say that there is yet much to be learned about the past, and that I fully agree with McGee in believing that the world's history is to be read in denudation as well as in deposition. If the deciphering of trustworthy records of denudation leads to the conclusion that the present is in some respects exceptional, a peculiar chapter in the earth's history, then I should have to add that conclusion

to the other authenticated conclusions which go to making
up the history of the planet. Admitting the present to be
exceptional in the lack of peneplains close to their base-level of
production, and thus postulating general disturbances by uplift
and tilting in the recent past, I doubt if this condition is more
exceptional than that which permitted the widespread deposition
of the chalk of Europe upon its even foundation, or than that
which determined the formation of the coal measures of Europe
and North America. There does not seem to be any severe
strain upon the reasonably elastic form of the doctrine of uniformitarianism in meeting the requirements of the peneplain theory.

B 2. *The Earth's Crust will not stand still long enough for the
Slow Process of Denudation to produce a Peneplain.* It is justly
urged that according to theory the later stages of peneplanation
are much longer than the early stages of dissection, as Powell
clearly pointed out some years ago ; and it has been inferred
that the earth's crust will not stand still long enough for even
penultimate denudation to be accomplished. But the stability or
instability of the earth's crust can be learned only by comparing
the consequences reasonably deduced from one condition or the
other with observed facts. It seems to me a prejudgment of the
case to enter it with the conclusion that the lands do not stand
still long enough for peneplanation. Certainly they do not stand
still long enough in certain regions ; witness the manifest effects
of uneasiness in the varied and unconformable stratified deposits,
or in the repeated renewals of dissection in the Alps. But the
opposite conclusion is enforced by both lines of evidence in the
Piedmont region of Virginia.

Another example may be taken from the West. The upland
of the plateaus trenched by the Colorado cañon is by no means
a level surface ; but if the fault cliffs and the monoclinal slopes
by which it is dislocated, the cañons by which it is dissected,
and the volcanic cones by which it is embossed were subtracted,
the remaining relief could not, if one may judge by Dutton's
vivid descriptions, be so great but that the surface might be
called a peneplain, especially if due regard is had to the vast
volume of material removed in its preparation, as attested by the
huge cliffs of recession on the north. It is true that a certain

part of the upland seems to be a structural plain; that is, its surface agrees rather closely with that of the more resistant Carboniferous layers; but when looked at broadly, the upland is seen to bevel gently across the edges of the layers, which dip northward at a faint angle. In explanation of this great denuded upland, Dutton says that the evidence points decisively to a "period of quiescence" in Tertiary time; "while it prevailed, the great Carboniferous platform was denuded of most of its inequalities, and was planed down to a very flat expanse" (77). The supposition of a period of active uplift, during which the incision of valleys was begun, and a period of quiescence, during which the hills were worn away, "would give just such a country as we see at present" (225). Inasmuch as the platform is now in process of active destruction by the widening of the main and branch cañons, a strong uplift must be postulated after the period of quiescence during which the platform was denuded. In all this inquiry, the argument based on processes of denudation is fully as logical and as legitimate as the argument elsewhere based on the processes of deposition.

But it has never been my intention to imply an absolute stillstand of the earth's crust during an entire cycle of denudation. Any sort of movement that does not cause a distinct dissection of the surface below the peneplain level is admissible. Well-preserved peneplains, now dissected only by young, narrow valleys, give assurance that no significant valley cutting below the peneplain level was permitted before the uplift by which the erosion of the existing valleys was initiated. Even in so uneven a region as southern New England the gradual decrease of relief on approaching the coast makes it extremely probable that the deep valleys of the interior were not cut till after the peneplain was essentially finished. Any other supposition involves special conditions of oscillation and tilting that I believe are less probable than those involved in peneplanation, as may be seen by drawing a series of diagrams to represent the successive attitudes assumed by the land under different hypotheses.

It is sometimes suggested that before peneplanation, but after valleys like those of southern New England had been excavated, economy of work and time would be served by postulating a depression and a truncation of so much of the mountains as then remained above base-level. The truncated surface thus produced would, under this supposition, correspond to the New England uplands. This truly effects an economy of work, measured by area of base-leveling, but it effects no important economy of time; for it will require essentially as long a time to truncate or base-level a large cone as a small cone, structure and slope being equal. Moreover, unless very special suppositions were made as to the attitude of the land before, during, and after such a truncation of its mountains, the existing forms of southern New England could not be explained. During a submergence long enough to truncate the mountains remaining above base-level, many shallow valleys would be filled with marine deposits; and after elevation, the streams might frequently abandon their former valleys for new, superposed courses. The narrow, new valleys excavated on such courses, and the former valleys in which remnants of marine deposits might long linger, are not represented in southern New England.

Yet any supposition or process that will aid in the destruction of a land mass must be welcomed by those who believe that land masses have been destroyed, close down to base-level. The lateral swinging of large rivers, occasional incursions of the sea, changes of climate, anything that will contribute to the end, is a pertinent part of the theory of peneplanation. Still my own opinion is that, of all processes, sub-aërial denudation is the most important. This is not simply an opinion of preference: it is an opinion based on the arrangement of rivers in uplifted and dissected peneplains (Davis, 378–398). Such rivers frequently exhibit adjustments that they could not have gained from a disordered arrangement during the present cycle of denudation alone; adjustments that could have been gained for the most part only during the cycle of peneplanation, and that would have been lost if the rivers had wandered far, or if the sea had abraded much of the land during the later stages of that cycle. It is of course perfectly possible that a peneplain should be smoothed off by the sea after it had been worn down under the air: such appears to have been the case with the Cambro-Silurian plain of northwest England (see B 3); but it is not reasonable to suppose that every uplifted and dissected peneplain was thus smoothed before it was uplifted, although this supposition finds much favor with certain English geologists.

As to the arguments based on the slow progress of denudation during a brief period of observation or during post-glacial time, I can only reply that a geographical cycle must be so enormously longer than either of these intervals that their evidence is not of value. Truly, denudation is retarded when a capping of waste protects the rocks from the attack of the weather, but rather than side with Deluc, who concluded that waste-covered mountains are practically protected from further change, I should prefer to side with Hutton, who maintained that even the slow denudation of waste-covered slopes could produce great changes of form. As to the time that has elapsed during the denudation of dissection of peneplains, there is apparently no way of measuring it but by the work done. Hence the question returns to the verity of the peneplains; whether much or little time is needed to produce them is a secondary matter. Above all, a preconception as to the insufficience of geological time should not in this day be urged as a reason for not believing in the possibility of peneplanation. One sometimes hears a student say: "I should think that drumlin ought to be more eroded if it has stood there unprotected since the ice sheet disappeared." Evidently such an opinion is based on a preconception of too long a post-glacial interval; for how can the interval be measured except by what has happened to the drumlin during its passage! How can past time be estimated except by studying what has happened during the progress of its ages!

B 3. *No Part of the Earth reveals even an Approximation to a Peneplain.* It has been contended that as all the reputed peneplains now known are of the past, and that as all are now more or less fragmentary, "no part of the earth reveals even an approximation to this supposed condition." This seems to me an over-strong statement in view of the form of such districts as the Piedmont belt, above referred to; but leaving aside even the best examples of well-finished and slightly dissected peneplains, let us consider some examples of peneplains that were submerged and unconformably buried after their surface had been reduced to faint relief, and that are now more or less visible where valleys are cut into the compound mass in consequence of uplift. It is true that these peneplains are not to-day standing in the position in which they were formed, that they make a very small part of the earth's actual surface, and that they are imperfectly open to observation; but it seems to me that they give strong evidence of the verity of peneplains, and that they certainly suffice to set against the strong assertion quoted at the opening of this paragraph.

An excellent example of a plain of denudation is exposed in section on the walls of the Colorado cañon. It is well shown — to those who cannot see the cañon itself — in several photographs by Jackson; it is "the record of a long time when the region was dry land," as already quoted from Powell; and it is thus described by Dutton:

> The base of the Carboniferous has a contact with unconformable rocks beneath, which was but slightly roughened by hills and ridges. In the Kaibab division of the Grand cañon . . . we may observe . . . a few bosses of Silurian strata rising higher than the hard quartzitic sandstone which forms the base of the Carboniferous. These are Paleozoic hills, which were buried by the growing mass of sediment. But they are of insignificant mass, rarely exceeding two or three hundred feet in height (209).

This magnificent exposure of an unconformity is further referred to as a local illustration of the widespread erosion of a great mass of land, "afterwards submerged." As the cañon has an accidental position with regard to the buried surface, the single section may be taken as a fair sample of a much larger area than is actually exposed.

A buried plain of remarkably even form underlies the heavy Carboniferous limestones of northwestern England. It has been repeatedly described and figured by English geologists. An official report states:

> It is evident that these [Carboniferous] beds were deposited on an uneven floor of the Silurian rocks, for the line dividing the two formations runs sharply up or down 20 or 30 feet in places, while the bedding of the limestone keeps nearly horizontal. In other places . . . Silurian grit sticks up in a boss, against the west side of which limestone has been laid down in horizontal strata (Dakyns et al., 23).

The inequalities of the floor here referred to are very small in comparison to the heights that the Silurian strata must have reached after their great deformation, for the sections represent the contact surface by an essentially even line, parallel to the limestone beds, and so it may be seen on various valley sides; for example, in upper Ribblesdale. The actual contacts displayed in certain hillside quarries on Moughton fell are extraordinarily clear; one of them is well reproduced in the frontispiece to Bird's "Geology of Yorkshire." The heavy Silurian flagstones are so evenly truncated that a single layer of limestone stretches smoothly over them for a hundred feet or more across the quarry; the same limestone bluff may be traced for two or three miles around the side of the fell, close above the uppermost outcrops of the flagstones; and the same general division of the Carboniferous formation lies on the denuded surface over tens or scores of miles. As there is no residual soil on the firm rocks of the denuded plain, and as the overlying strata are heavy marine limestones (excepting local deposits of pebbly beds, one or two feet thick), the floor must have been swept and worn by the sea before Carboniferous deposition began. There seems to be no way of determining how much work was thus done by the sea, and how much had been previously done by sub-aërial agencies; but whatever the proportions, a well-finished plain of denudation, hundreds of square miles in area, had taken the place of a vigorous mountain range before the deposition of the limestones began.

Goodchild has repeatedly referred to this ancient plain of denudation, and to two others of later date in northwest England. He says that when the deformed Cambrian and Silurian rocks "were brought within the destroying action of the waves . . ., the end of it was that the whole surface of the country was shorn off to one general uniform level; depressions and elevations there were, beyond a doubt, just as there are both depths and islands left on a modern plain of denudation; but in the main the surface was tolerably uniform" (a, 92, 93). Many mountain slopes in the Lake district consist of reëxposed areas of this ancient plain, from which the weaker covering strata have been worn off again (b, 76). The plain extends, locally, with marvelous evenness of contour, across the edges of quite five miles of strata in the Lake district alone (*c*, 45).

B 4. *Stratigraphic Evidence is against the Occurrence of Peneplains.* It has been said that quiescence sufficient for peneplanation requires conditions different from "those of that portion of the past whose history has been worked out by purely stratigraphic methods." Although I am not sure of just what is meant by "purely stratigraphic methods," it seems fair to regard the two examples given in the preceding section as dependent on at least a mixed stratigraphic argument. These examples were, however, associated with marine strata, and hence the subaërial origin of the buried plains is not assured, although there can be little doubt as to the actual occurrence of the plains themselves. The following examples are more pertinent to the present discussion, for they point chiefly to the action of sub-aërial denudation in the production of peneplains.

The central plateau of France is a part of the ancient Hercynian mountain system of post-Carboniferous deformation that once stretched across west-central Europe. Judging by the strength of its foldings, its altitude may for a time have rivaled that of the Alps of to-day. The mountains were greatly denuded during secondary time, as is shown by the comparatively even overlaps of Jurassic and Cretaceous strata on the flanks of the central plateau and elsewhere; but of these buried portions no more need be said at present. Continued denudation at last reduced the region of the central area itself to a surface of moderate relief, and it was upon a surface thus prepared that several brackish Tertiary lakes, communicating with the sea on the north and south, laid down their sediments. Since then, the region as a whole has been much uplifted, its southern and eastern parts have been irregularly dislocated, volcanic action has diversified parts of the surface, and denudation has effected important changes in the complex, uplifted mass; but the northwestern part is free from dislocation and from volcanic action, and there the uplifted surface of denudation is well displayed in an even plateau (Depèret). If stripped of its volcanic cones and flows and "unfaulted" the plateau would have the form of a vast inclined plane, highest in the southeast, and descending very slowly to the northwest (Boule). The northwestern part of the plateau, unaffected by volcanic action and not covered by the lacustrine formations that elsewhere rest upon it, exhibits a surface of crystalline rocks interrupted only by closely folded troughs of coal measures, whose outcrops are sharply cut across at plateau height as if the whole structure had been rubbed down by a great leveling machine. The perfect regularity of the uplands between Montluçon and Creuse is an excellent representation of the form that the whole extent of the plateau region must have had about the beginning of Tertiary time, before it was uplifted and dislocated. Long-continued erosion had then reduced the region to a plain close to sea-level, thus destroying a great mountain chain and leaving in its place a lowland composed chiefly of long belts of granitic rocks (Vélain).

These extracts make it clear that French observers regard the stratigraphic evidence of the Tertiary lake deposits as confirming the conclusion reached from the study of form alone; both lines of evidence show that the uplifted, dislocated, and dissected plateau region of to-day was a lowland of denudation in Tertiary time.

The highlands of the Ardennes along the border of France and Belgium is another part of the ancient Hercynian range, greatly denuded. It descends southward, where it is overlapped by Mesozoic formations, among which the Cretaceous strata are of special interest in the present connection. A belt of coal measures extends from the Ardennes southwestward under the Cretaceous ; shafts have been sunk through the Cretaceous to the coal measures at many points, and thus the form of the buried denuded surface has been determined with much accuracy. Gosselet's elaborate "Mémoire sur l'Ardenne " (a) gives much information concerning both the buried and the unburied portions of the denuded mountains. The frontispiece shows the valley of the Meuse incised in the plateau, "everywhere leveled to the same altitude." Many sections in the text show the Mesozoic strata lying on the deformed and denuded Paleozoic rocks, but the basal deposits beneath the Cretaceous are usually not marine. Even under the Jurassic there is a ferruginous clay with limonite concretions, thought to be of terrestrial origin (802).

Under the Cretaceous strata the most general deposit is a layer of black pyritous clay with vegetal remains, taken to represent the soil of a pre-Cretaceous land surface. Fluviatile and lacustrine deposits are also recognized. The Carboniferous limestone is often pitted, and the pits contain non-marine materials and fossils. Where the intermediate deposits are wanting, the ancient rocks are perforated by boring mollusks and strewn with shells of oysters and serpulæ (808, 810). On the uplands at a considerable altitude, and far beyond the main overlap of the Mesozoic cover, there are scattered remnants of Cretaceous and Tertiary deposits, and these are all regarded as of earlier date than the elevation and dissection of the plateau (831). Fuller details as to the composition and distribution of these deposits are given in other papers by Gosselet (*b*, 100) and Barrois (340). Bertrand says that the buried pre-Cretaceous surface is a denuded plain, and that its existing irregularities are due, at least in great part, to subsequent movements that the chalk also has suffered (36).

The different parts of the ancient mountains of the Ardennes, overlapped by Triassic, Jurassic, Liassic, Cretaceous, and Tertiary formations, were doubtless exposed to denudation for different periods of time, and successively submerged in encroaching seas; it is quite possible that the dissected uplands of to-day were peneplained at a distinctly later date than was the floor beneath the Jurassic strata, and that the relation of the two is similar to the relation stated by Darton for the two parts (*AB* and *BE*, Fig. 7) of the ancient rocks of the Piedmont belt in Virginia. French writers do not seem to have occupied themselves especially with this question, either in the Ardennes or in the central plateau. But, on the other hand, there seems to be no question that the stratigraphy of both the marine and the terrestrial deposits proves the existence in northern France of a denuded surface of small relief, whose larger part is now buried, and whose smaller part is elevated and more or less dissected.

Bohemia offers another remarkably good example for citation, as summarized by Penck and here freely rendered. A great mountain range once rose there, probably reaching an altitude of five thousand meters. It was worn down to a comparatively even lowland before the incursion of the Cretaceous sea, by whose deposits it is now thinly covered, for fresh-water formations are everywhere found under the Cretaceous strata. This relation is repeated in many other parts of Europe, especially where truncated old mountains are found. Terrestrial formations are their first cover, and upon these rest the later marine deposits. It follows from this that the truncated mountains of Europe were not denuded by the surf of ancient seas, eating into their heights and gradually wearing them away; for before the sea rolled over the old mountains they were already laid low and covered with terrestrial formations (*a*, 23, 24).

While it may be true that there are to-day no extensive peneplains still standing close to the sea-level with respect to which they were denuded, the examples given in this and in the preceding section seem to me to prove that the earth contains many approximations to the peneplain condition, inasmuch as it preserves some excellent fossil peneplains; and that the stratigraphic as well as the physiographic method of investigation yields abundant and accordant evidence of their occurrence.

B 5. *Plains of Marine Abrasion as well as of Sub-aërial Denudation are Discarded.* It is worth while to point out explicitly that all these districts which have been for half a century past explained as uplifted and dissected plains of marine denudation (or of marine abrasion) by geologists and geographers in many parts of the world are to be otherwise interpreted by those who adopt the alternative theory stated below (C 2). The even sky line, discordant with structure, has been the leading evidence for plains of marine denudation ever since it was introduced by Ramsay in his description of the hills and mountains of South Wales. The marinists and the sub-aërialists differ as to the agency by which an elevated region may be worn down to a nearly featureless plain, a little below or a little above sea-level; but they are unanimous in recognizing the necessity of such plains when uplands of even sky line exist in regions of disordered structure. It must be remembered that the terms "plain of marine denudation" and "peneplain" are in nearly all cases hardly more than different names for the same thing. If the whole truth were known, it is probable that one or the other name might be appropriately applied in this or that case, but it is seldom that any one has succeeded in convincing all his contemporaries that he could distinguish a plain of marine denudation from a peneplain, or vice versa. On the other hand, all regions, heretofore explained as having passed through the condition of abraded or denuded plains, would be explained as never having reached a form of faint relief, if the alternative theory be accepted. It therefore demands careful consideration, to which we may now turn.

C 1. *The Alternative Theory aims chiefly to explain the Existing Forms of New England rather than those of Better-Finished and Better-Preserved Peneplains.* It is a matter of regret that a theory intended to replace the theory of peneplanation should have been tested by its author chiefly in New England, whose highest and most rugged parts are generally taken as examples of grouped monadnocks. I should not be at all disposed to say that the peneplains of New England and New Jersey have been most fully studied, and rest upon the firmest basis. Southern New England would have been a fairly satisfactory area, but when the White and Green mountains and the mountains of Maine are included, the example to be explained falls largely outside of the scope of peneplanation. However, if the alternative theory of mature dissection is really capable of supplementing the theory of peneplanation, it should suffice to explain not only rugged New England, but also the many better-finished and better-preserved peneplains in other parts of the world, some of which have been referred to above.

C 2. *The Sub-equality of Mountain Heights.* The development of a rough equality in the height of mountain peaks by the faster destruction of the higher summits, on account of the greater violence of weather changes and of the absence of tree and soil covering at great heights, has been announced by Penck (*b*) and by Dawson, and has recently been independently suggested by Professor Tarr. *ABC* and *ADE* (Fig. 8) are in this way changed to *FGH* and *FJK*. The processes appealed to are not identical in the explanations of the three authors, but not having the writings of the two former at hand, I cannot give details. The approach to equal height of many peaks of different structure in a given mountain group may be thus explained, as in the Alps, or in the Rocky mountains of Colorado;

if any one felt *per contra* convinced that this sub-equality might
be the result of the deep dissection of a greatly elevated peneplain, the discussion would doubtless be interesting.

The sub-equality of mountain heights being once gained, all
the mountains are then under essentially uniform climatic conditions, and for the rest of their lives difference of structure will
determine their rate of decay. All changes would truly be very
slow, but small differences in rate of wasting would suffice to
develop distinct differences of altitude while the mountains were
worn down from the tree line to the farm line. The uneven hill
and mountain districts about lake Winnepesaukee, New Hampshire, might be evolved in this way; but it seems to me very

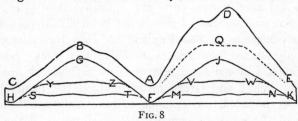

Fig. 8

doubtful whether any such equality of height as prevails in
central Massachusetts can be explained as an inheritance from
an equality determined by climatic control when the region had
a much greater elevation, for to-day these uplands are about
three thousand feet below the tree line, and their structure is
by no means uniform.

C 3. *Denudation and Beveling will be more Advanced near the
Coast than in the Interior.* It has been urged that near the coast
"mountains would have been more lowered than in the interior,
and, in the coastal region, there may well have been an approach
to the peneplain condition" and again, that "this beveling of the
hill-tops would be very much further advanced near the coast
than in the interior, thus coinciding with the conditions found
in New England."

The ancient mountain trends of southern New England are
obliquely traversed by the shore-line of Long Island sound.
The ancient mountain structures show no sign of weakening as
they approach the shore-line, and we may fairly suppose that

there has been about as much denudation to be done there as farther north. From southern New Hampshire, across central Massachusetts and Connecticut, there is no indication of a weakening of the rocks ; a good variety of more or less resistant gneisses and schists occur all across this district. Difference of climate cannot be appealed to as a cause of faster denudation and beveling near the coast, for the climate is more severe in the interior. The streams are larger and the valleys are necessarily lower and broader near the coast than in the interior, but the interstream uplands are under essentially similar conditions in the two regions. A rough equality of mountain heights being established, as *H, A, B* (Fig. 9), there is then no reason for the greater action of the weather on a square foot of surface at *B* than at *A*. The master streams having gained a graded slope

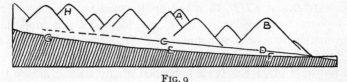

FIG. 9

GEF, there is no reason for the denudation of *A* to hesitate at the height *C*, a thousand feet above the streams, while *B* is reduced to *D*, only a hundred feet or less above the streams. The tilting of a previously denuded surface seems a relatively simple and safe way of accounting for the relation of the upland and stream profiles *CD* and *EF*, as has been suggested above (A 6); but tilting has no announced place in this alternative theory. The omission of so commonplace a movement is the more curious, inasmuch as frequent movement of some sort must be characteristic of a theory that requires no long periods of relative quiet.

C 4. *New England and New Jersey as Maturely Dissected Mountains, Rejuvenated.* It has been maintained that the regions especially under discussion have been lowered to the stage of full maturity, then elevated and made more rugged, and that although the surface has always been mountainous, it was once less mountainous than now, because of the recent uplift. There are various other parts of the world to which a similar description

might be applied: the indication of full maturity being found in
the well-opened valleys of the larger streams ABC (Fig. 10),
developed with respect to a former base-level MM; and the indication of "recent uplift" being no less apparent in the narrow

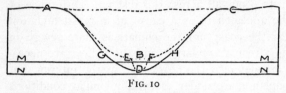

FIG. 10

gorges D, in-
cised in the
floor of the ma-
turely opened
valleys ABC,
with reference
to the new base-level NN. The essential evidence of such recent
uplift and rejuvenation is found in benches E, F, on the compound
valley slopes AED and CFD. If rejuvenation were so long ago
that this bench were destroyed by the development of continuous
slopes AGD and CHD, then the uplift could not be discovered
by topographical evidence. It is on evidence of this kind that
rejuvenation has been announced for the Susquehanna district
of the Pennsylvania Appalachians and for the Hudson valley;
but no description has been published of any such evidence for
the rejuvenation of New England. The deep valleys of many
rivers in Massachusetts and Connecticut have no persistent
benches on their slopes, and there is no visible reason for saying that any important pause was made in the elevation by which
the former base-level of the uplands AC was replaced by the present base-level NN of the valleys $AGDHC$. The rivers truly have
many falls and rapids, due to their displacement from better-
graded courses by the irregular distribution of glacial drift, but
this is quite
another matter.

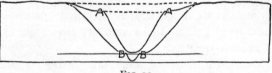

FIG. 11

The valley-
side benches
are important
items in the
present discussion, if they exist at all; for when fully established
they will define many interesting points. If high on the valley
sides, as at A (Fig. 11) (resembling the gorge of the Rhine), they
would show that the previous cycle had gone far beyond maturity
and well into old age before uplift occurred; if low down in the

valley bottom, as at *B* (resembling the Frazer river valley in British Columbia), they are of trifling importance as far as the present discussion is concerned. If the downstream slope of the benches were about parallel to the present profile of the rivers, a uniform uplift would be suggested; if distinctly not parallel to the present stream profiles, an uneven uplift would be implied. All these points should receive specific attention if the new hypothesis, which "requires no long periods of relative quiet," is to be accepted. As now stated, the recent rejuvenation of New England seems to me very open to question. There is no evidence of recent rejuvenation in the occurrence of a young coastal plain along the coastal border, such as ordinarily accompanies recent uplift, unless the post-glacial coastal plain of Maine be so considered; and that would hardly be permissible, for the existing valleys were eroded before the plain was formed.

C 5. *The Alternate Hypothesis takes no Account of Buried Peneplains.* The alternative hypothesis, which calls merely for a greatly reduced, but still markedly irregular surface, entirely fails to meet the case of well-preserved peneplains, like that of the Piedmont belt in Virginia, and even more entirely fails to meet the case of buried peneplains, such as have been described above. The first example cited — that of the even floor on which the Carboniferous rocks rest in the Colorado cañon — is entirely beyond the reach of a theory that does not carry subaërial denudation farther than the stage of maturity. If refuge is taken in the theory of marine abrasion, the several examples in France and Bohemia, where marine abrasion is excluded, remain to be explained. It must therefore be repeated that it is a matter of regret that a theory intended to supplant the theory of peneplanation should have been framed chiefly with respect to the rugged uplands of New England and New Jersey, and without sufficient consideration of the many other examples of better peneplains, buried and unburied, of which modern geological and geographical writings contain abundant descriptions.

The preparation of this essay has been greatly aided by the kindness of my geological and geographical colleagues in Edinburgh, London, and Paris. The completion of the essay in southeastern France has made it impossible to cite, as fully as I should like, certain pertinent examples, to which, however, there may be opportunity of returning if fuller consideration of the peneplain idea is called for by a continuation of this discussion.

REFERENCES

Barrois, C. *Ann. Soc. Géol. du Nord*, VI (1879), 340.

Bertrand, M. *Ann. des Mines* (January, 1893), 36.

Boule, M. Joanne's Dict. Géog. et Admin. de la France, IV (1895), 2538.

Cook, G. H. *Geol. Surv. New Jersey, Ann. Rep.* (1883), 27 ; see also pages 28, 29, 60, 61.

Dakyns, J. R. et al. " Geology of the Country around Ingleborough." *Mem. Geol. Surv. Great Britain* (1890), 23.

Darton, N. H. *Jour. Geol.*, II (1894), 570.

Davis, W. M. " Plains of Marine and Sub-aërial Denudation." *Bull. Geol. Soc. Am.*, VII (1896), 378–398.

Dawson, G. M. " Report on the Area of the Kamloops Map-Sheet, British Columbia." *Can. Geog. Surv.*, new series, VII, Rep. B (1896).

Depèret. *Ann. de Géog.*, I (1892), 369–378.

Dutton, C. E. "Tertiary History of the Grand Cañon District." *U. S. Geol. Surv., Mon. II* (1882).

Gilbert, G. K. Geology of the Henry Mountains. 1880.

Goodchild, J. G. (*a*) *Trans. Cumberland and Westmoreland Assoc.*, XIII (1888), 92, 93.

(*b*) Ibid., XIV (1889), 76.

(*c*) *Geol. Assoc.* (London), XI (1889), 45.

Gosselet, J. (*a*) Mémoire sur l'Ardenne. Paris, 1888.

(*b*) *Ann. Soc. Géol. du Nord*, VII (1879), 100.

Keith, A. " Geology of the Catoctin Belt." *U. S. Geol. Surv., XIV Ann. Rep.*, Pt. II (1894), 285–395.

McGee, W. J. *Nat. Geog. Mag.*, VIII (1896), 261–263.

Penck, A. (*a*) Ueber Denudation der Erdoberfläche, 23, 24. Vienna, 1887.

(*b*) Morphologie der Erdoberfläche. 1894.

Percival, J. G. Report on the Geology of the State of Connecticut. 1842.

Philippson, A. *Zeitschr. Ges. f. Erdk.* (Berlin), XXXIII (1898), 37–68, 77–110 ; see especially pages 38–42, 54, 55, 62.

Powell, J. W. (*a*) Exploration of the Colorado River. 1875.

(*b*) Geology of the Uinta Mountains. 1876.

Purington, C. W. "Geological and Topographical Features of the Region about Atlanta, Georgia." *Am. Geol.*, XIV (1894), 105–108.

Tarr, R. S. " The Peneplain." *Am. Geol.*, XXI (1898), 351–370.

Van Hise, C. R. "A Central Wisconsin Base-Level." *Science*, new series, IV (1896), 57–59.

Vélain, C. "Auvergne et Limousin, Géographie Physique." L'Itinéraire Miriam, 10. Paris, 1897.

XVIII

BASE-LEVEL, GRADE, AND PENEPLAIN

Thesis of this Essay. The attention given during the last fifty years to the processes and results of land sculpture has naturally resulted in the introduction of various new terms, three of which stand at the head of this article. It is desired to point out that too many meanings have been attached to the first term, "base-level," and that some of them should be transferred to the other two, "grade" and "peneplain."

The Original Meaning of Base-Level. Although the control exerted by sea-level on river action has long been recognized, the importance of the control was more generally perceived by American students of geology when it was explicitly formulated in the term "base-level" by Powell in 1875. The term soon became so popular, especially with American writers, that a divergence of meaning has arisen with regard to it. It is therefore proposed to trace its history, with the hope of inducing geologists and geographers to use it in a somewhat restricted sense.

Powell's original definition of base-level is as follows, the parenthesis being in his text:

We may consider the level of the sea to be a grand base-level, below which the dry lands cannot be eroded ; but we may also have, for local and temporary purposes, other base-levels of erosion, which are the levels of the beds of the principal streams which carry away the products of erosion. (I take some liberty in using the term "level" in this connection, as the action of a running stream in wearing its channel ceases, for all practical purposes, before its bed has quite reached the level of the lower end of the stream. What I have called the base-level would, in fact, be an imaginary surface, inclining slightly in all its parts toward the lower end of the principal stream draining the area through which the level is supposed to extend, or having the inclination of its parts varied in direction as determined by tributary streams.) Where such a stream crosses a series of rocks in its course, some of which are hard, and others soft, the harder beds form a series of temporary dams, above which the corrasion of the channel through the softer beds is checked, and thus we may have a series of base-levels of erosion, below which the rocks on either side of the river, though exceedingly friable, cannot be degraded (*a*, 203, 204).

Base-level, as thus defined, seems to include three ideas: first, the grand or general base-level for sub-aërial erosion is the level of the sea; second, a base-level is an imaginary, sloping surface which generalizes the faint inclination of the trunk and branch rivers of a region when the erosion of their channels has practically ceased; third, local and temporary base-levels are those slow reaches in a river which are determined by ledges in its course farther downstream.

There is some reason for thinking that Powell's intention may have been misunderstood with respect to the first and third of these ideas. The first, " the level of the sea," may have referred only to the actual area of the sea, and not to an imaginary extension of the sea-level or geoid surface under the lands. The third certainly referred to the faintly sloping reach of a river, and not to a level surface passing through the ledge of hard rock with respect to which the reach is worn down, although this latter meaning has become popular. The following citations will show that most writers seem to be agreed that base-levels may be local or temporary as well as general, but that there is no prevalent agreement as to the definition of either the general or the local base-level.

Definitions of Base-Level by Various Writers. The following authors adopt the first of the above meanings. Gilbert writes: " The land cannot be worn down below the level of the ocean. Geologists express this law by saying that the ocean is the 'base-level of erosion'" (*c*, 575).

Campbell says: " If the streams are in their old age, the surface of the land will constitute a peneplain, and in their extreme old age, this peneplain will approach very closely to base-level" (665).

Tarr writes to the same effect: " In no part of the valley can the stream cut below the sea-level, or below *base-level*, as it is called " (265).

Russell quotes Powell, as if adopting his definition, but concludes that

the real base-level toward which all streams are working is the surface level of the sea. . . . When a stream has lowered its channel nearly to

base-level, downward corrasion is retarded, but lateral corrasion continues.
. . . The ultimate result of erosion is to reduce a land area to a plain at sea-level (47–48).

Finally, Powell may be quoted again as follows : " The base-level of a plain is the level of the surface of the sea, lake, or stream into which the waters of the plain are discharged" (*b*, 34).

The second idea under the term " base-level " — that of the imaginary, undulating surface — does not appear to have been adopted by any of the many writers whose works I have looked over. It is perhaps on account of the elaborateness of this second meaning that it has not come more generally into use. Its partial adoption, however, is indicated by the following extracts. It should be noted that nearly all the writers here cited imply that after base-level is reached by a stream, downward corrasion ceases.

McGee describes the streams of the coastal plain at about the head of Chesapeake bay as "at base-level" (*a*, 617).

When describing the dissection of the Piedmont plateau of Virginia, Darton says : "As the cutting reached base-level a series of wide terraces were cut" (584).

Winslow writes : "The streams of the prairie country [in Missouri] . . . have, in large part, reached base-level, and are developing meander plains (310).

Fairbanks states that in southeastern California

erosion has reached an advanced stage with the production of excellent examples of base-leveling. . . . One of the best examples . . . is the western portion of a granite ridge lying south of the El Paso range. . . . It is bordered by long, gentle slopes of gravel and bowlders, which, extending upward into the shallow cañons, reach almost to the summit. Viewed from a distance of ten miles but little of the mountains appears to project above the plane of deposition (70).

Salisbury's statement is as follows :

The time necessary for the development of such a surface is known as a *cycle of erosion*, and the resulting surface is a *base-level plain*, that is, a plain as near sea-level as river erosion can bring it. At a stage preceding the base-level stage the surface would be a *peneplain*. . . . It is also important to notice that when streams have cut a land surface down to the level at which they cease to erode, that surface will still possess some slight slope, and that to the seaward. Along the coast a base-level is at sea-level. A little back from the coast it is slightly higher, and at a greater distance still higher. No definite degree of slope can be fixed upon as marking a base-level. The angle of slope which would practically stop erosion in a region of slight rainfall might be great enough to allow of erosion if the precipitation were greater. . . . The Mississippi has a fall of less than a foot per mile. . . . A small stream in a similar situation would have ceased to lower its channel before so low a gradient had been reached (*b*, 73, 79).

J. Geikie writes :

Running waters will continue to deepen their channels until the gradient by the process is gradually reduced to a minimum and vertical erosion ceases. The main river will be the first to attain this base-level,—a level not much above that of the sea (47).

Marr does not use the term "base-level," but says :

A river which has established equilibrium . . . is said to have reached its base-line of erosion, and no further work of erosion or deposit can occur until the conditions are changed (84).

Dryer states :

The lower Mississippi has reached its base-level, or the lowest level to which its current and load will permit it to reduce its bed. . . . In the lower reaches of a river the valley is soon cut down to base-level, where the slope is gentle and the current too slow to carry the full load of sediment it receives. Deposition occurs and downward corrasion ceases (79, 154).

In a discussion of reaches and rapids Powell makes the following statement : "The slow reach is a base-level, like that of a lake, below which the banks and hills on either side cannot be degraded" (*b*, 35).

Various other definitions, more or less aberrant from the original and discordant with each other, are found in the following citations.

Dutton took base-level to be a condition :

The condition of base-level is one in which the rivers of a region cannot corrade. As a general rule it arises from the rivers having cut down so low that their transporting power is fully occupied, even to repletion. . . . The recurrence of upheaval terminates the condition of base-level (224, 225).

According to Willis, base-level is a slope :

A base-level is the lowest slope to which rivers can reduce a land area (*a*, 189). The ideal lowest possible slope, which is called a base-level, is perhaps rarely reached (*b*, 27).

Hayes makes base-level a mathematical plane :

The term "base-level," synonymous with base-level of erosion, is [here] restricted to Powell's original use . . ., the general base-level being sea-level. There may be an indefinite number of *local* base-levels in any region, each being determined by the outlet of the stream whose drainage basin is considered ; but only one *general* base-level. . . . It should be clearly understood, then, that a base-level is not a topographic form, but a mathematical *plane* which may or may not, and generally does not, coincide with a land surface (21).

When describing erosion by rivers, Scott writes :

A stage must sooner or later be reached when the vertical cutting of the stream must cease. This stage is called the base-level of erosion or regimen of the river, and it approximates a parabolic curve, rising toward the head of the stream (98).

Rice makes the following statement : " The condition of balance between erosion and deposition [by rivers] has been called by Powell the condition of base-level " (140).

Brigham writes as follows :

A base-level is a plane to which denudation must reduce a stably poised land mass, and below which denudation cannot take place. The plane is that of the ocean surface. . . . The great river first cuts its bed close to the sea-level, and we say that a portion of the valley is reduced to base-level. It lacks a little of it, but the difference is so small that we neglect it. Gradually the valley widens, and the base-leveled strip extends up the stream toward the heart of the country (281).

Cowles gives a definition of base-level which, taken literally, gives it the meaning of a process : " Denudation of the uplands and deposition in the lowlands result in an ultimate planation known as the base-level " (178).

The derivative use of base-level as the name of a worn-down land surface does not seem to be so common now as it was some ten years ago. A few examples will here suffice.

Keith made frequent use of "base-level plain," or simply "base-level," as the name for a surface that had been reduced to faint relief, even though now uplifted and more or less dissected. He discusses the "considerable variation in the altitude of different parts of the base-level" or old Tertiary land surface in the Catoctin region district of Virginia (373). He mentions "hill tops marking the dissected base-level" of the Shenandoah valley (374). The term seems to be applied in at least one instance to a peneplain in saying, " It needs but little study of this base-level to discover considerable inequalities in its surface" (369).

Diller made equally free use of "base-level plain" and of "base-level" in his account of an ancient surface of erosion in northern California. He states that "the western edge of the base-level, where it enters the mountains, has an altitude of 2600 feet," and on a later page he suggests two ways in which the "deformation of the base-level may be studied " (406, 430).

Kümmel writes of the "long erosion which resulted in the Cretaceous base-level" of Connecticut (379).

Willis says :

The tendency is in time to reduce the land to a gently sloping plain, which extends from the sea to the headwaters of the rivers. Such a plain is called a *base-level*. . . . A surface which is almost, but not quite, a base-level is called a *peneplain* (*a*, 188, 189).

Hill describes a persistent bench near Panama as "representing an ancient base-leveled plain, which will be described as the Panama base-level" (197).

An essay by Van Hise describing a base-leveled plain is entitled "A Central Wisconsin Base-Level" (57).

I have had a small share in a similar use of base-level; for example :

The general upland surface of the Highlands [of New Jersey] is an old base-level, in which valleys have been cut in consequence of a subsequent elevation (*a*, 20 ; see also Davis and Wood, 384).

A review of the above citations, whose number might be greatly extended, shows that base-level is given very different meanings by different writers. These meanings are : an imaginary level surface in extension of that of the ocean (the convex geoid surface) ; an imaginary mathematical plane ; an imaginary surface sloping with the mature or old streams of its area ; the lowest slope to which rivers can reduce a land surface ; a level not much above that of the sea ; a slow reach in a stream ; a condition in which rivers cannot corrade or in which they are balanced between erosion and deposition ; a certain stage in the history of rivers when vertical cutting ceases and their slope approximates a parabolic curve ; an ultimate planation ; and a plain of degradation.

Limitation of the Meaning of Base-Level. The diversity of the above definitions may be better perceived when it is noted that they are expressed in terms of very unlike quantities : imaginary surfaces, level, plane, or warped ; a low slope ; a part of a river ; a condition of river development ; a stage in river history ; an ultimate planation ; and an actual geographical form. It is evidently desirable to associate base-level with at most only a few of these meanings, preferably with only one ; and to leave the others unnamed, or to associate them with other terms. It seems to me advisable to limit base-level to the first meaning, "an imaginary level surface," and to define it simply as the level base with respect to which normal sub-aërial erosion proceeds ; to employ the term "grade" for the balanced condition of a mature or old river ; and to name the geographical surface that is developed near or very near to the close of a cycle, a "peneplain," or "plain of gradation." The following paragraphs may make the need of this discrimination clearer.

A full understanding of the development of land forms can be gained only by tracing the progressive changes of a generalized example from the initial stage through the various sequential stages to the ultimate stage of an ideal geographical cycle. This problem is encountered in an elementary form at the beginning of the study of land sculpture in physiography or geology, and at the very outset it is necessary to make definite and simple statement regarding the limit with respect to which the processes of normal sub-aërial erosion (weather and streams, without significant aid from wind or ice) may act. If the limit is defined in terms of the slopes that the streams of the region will have gained when they have reached a maturely balanced condition, the definition will be of no service to beginners ; indeed, a limit thus defined is elusive and difficult of conception even by experts. The limiting surface is certainly of so great importance to the beginner that it must be briefly defined for him in terms of known factors, and the definition thus framed should remain serviceable through all later study. These conditions are satisfied when the beginner is told that the limit of sub-aërial erosion is the "level base" or "base-level" drawn through a land mass in prolongation of the normal sea-level surface. The fact that rivers erode their channels near their mouths below sea-level, and that special processes of erosion (winds and glaciers) may work below sea-level, does not invalidate the general statement at the opening of the whole discussion ; but these special conditions must be explicitly considered later, especially those concerning glacial erosion. It suffices at first to recognize that in the ideal undisturbed cycle of normal erosion the base-level must be more and more closely approached as time is extended.

This definition of base-level as a level base certainly has the advantage of being easily conceived. Once conceived in the study of the ideal cycle, it needs no modification so long as the relative attitude of land and sea remains fixed. If the land rise or fall with respect to the sea, the base-level takes a new position within the land mass, and further progress of erosion is then continued with respect to the new limit.

As the study of the cycle advances it becomes desirable to speak of various local or temporary controls of erosion : a rock ledge or a lake on a river course, the central basin of a dry interior basin either above or below sea-level, the surface of a lake in such a basin. Nothing can be simpler than to imagine a level surface passing through any one of these controls, and rising or sinking as the control rises or sinks ; and such a surface is naturally called a local or temporary base-level. With the enlargement of conceptions that is required when the aggradation of depressions is considered at the same time with the degradation of elevations, Powell's more general term "gradation" may replace "erosion"; the merit of this substitution will appear more fully in the following pages.

In view of the importance appropriately allowed to the idea of the level base with respect to which the erosion of valleys by rivers must proceed, it is curious that earlier writers did not give more explicit attention to it ; but as far as I have read, they were so largely occupied with controverting the various older theories of the origin of valleys that it did not occur to them to give special name to limiting surface of erosion. Their understanding of the important principle here involved is to be read rather between the lines than in explicit statements. For example, Greenwood's curious book on "Rain and Rivers," almost as remarkable for its admixture of jokes and polemics as for its many admirable expositions of rain and river work, contains the following account of the problems here considered :

Suppose a barrier of rock to run across any valley or river bed ; when the bed of the valley or river on the upper side of the barrier has been worn down to a horizontal level with this barrier, it can *not* go lower. . . . But as the barrier is cut through, the bed of the valley or river will be deepened *backward*, or from below upward, or towards the hills. . . . The passage of the detritus and soil from the inclined upper parts of valleys is checked in the horizontal lower parts of valleys, and soil accumulates there. This is the origin of alluvial plains ; and a river of any size, or any rapidity, may, at any distance from the sea, have *patches* of alluvial plain, where no lakes have ever been ; that is, above every rapid or accidental barrier of hard ground. . . . The only difference in the laws for the growth and gradient of these patches from those which regulate the growth and gradient of the plain at the level of the sea is that they have no *increasing* cause for rising equivalent to the *forward* lengthening of the delta of the lower alluvial plain. These flat, alluvial patches may be seen even in torrents, sometimes reaching from one cascade to the other. . . . It is easy to perceive that these patches must be liable to constant change. They must be perpetually shortened by the recession of the lower barrier, and lengthened by the recession of the upper one. . . . These principles are eternally at work on all valleys, from the smallest to the largest (174–176).

Greenwood's use of "horizontal" in describing the lower parts of valleys is curiously inexact in contrast to his keenness in recognizing the difference between what we should now call local base-levels and general base-levels, and also in recognizing that the aggradation of a flood plain is related to the "forward lengthening of the delta."

The Balanced Condition of Rivers. Turning now more particularly to the problem of river action, we find that the balance between erosion and deposition, attained by mature rivers, introduces one of the most important problems that is encountered in the discussion of the geographical cycle. The development of this balanced condition is brought about by changes in the capacity of a river to do work, and in the quantity of work that the river has to do. The changes continue until the two quantities, at first unequal, reach equality ; and then the river may be said to be graded, or to have reached the condition of grade. This condition cannot be understood without rather careful thinking on the part of the expert as well as of the tyro. The idea of grade is not of almost axiomatic simplicity, like the idea of base-level; its meaning must be gradually elaborated as it is approached. Moreover, a graded river does not maintain a constant slope; it changes its slope systematically with the progress of the cycle; but before taking up this element of the discussion, a few paragraphs may be given to the consideration of "grade," as a common word used in a technical sense.

It should be noted in the first place that it is a condition of river development, not a surface, nor a stage, nor a form, for which the term "grade" is to serve as a name. The condition of grade must not be confused with the limiting under-surface of erosion, with respect to which the graded condition is developed; the name for this surface is "base-level." Nor must it be confused with the stage in the history of river development in which the graded condition is reached; "maturity" is the name for that stage; but it may be noted in passing that the graded condition persists all through the old age as well as the maturity of an uninterrupted cycle. "Grade," meaning a condition or balance, must not be confused with the same word used with another meaning, namely, the slope or declivity of the river when the graded condition is reached; for "grade," meaning slope, varies in place and in time; while "grade," meaning balance, always implies an equality of two quantities. In fine, grade is a condition of essential balance between corrasion and deposition, usually reached by rivers in the mature stage of their development, when their slopes have been duly worn down or built up with respect to the base-level of their basin.

There can be no question that the balanced condition of mature and old rivers deserves a name. It was to this condition that Powell called attention in his original discussion of land sculpture, and to which he devoted one of the meanings of his term "base-level." A name had already been suggested for the balanced condition by various writers, who called it the "régime" or "regimen" of rivers, while the slope of a river under this regimen was called its *"pente d'équilibre"* by Dausse (759) and the

"*Erosions-Terminante*" by Philippson (71). But "regimen" may be better used as meaning the rule of river action under which the balanced condition is developed and maintained; while "slope of equilibrium" may be taken as a descriptive phrase, too cumbersome for ordinary or frequent use, but essentially synonymous with "graded slope." "Base-level" seems at best a very inappropriate name for a condition in which the idea of slope is essential; and when another and equally important use is made of this excellent word, its employment as the name for the balanced condition of rivers is all the more unsatisfactory. "Grade" is the most satisfactory term for the balanced condition or state of equilibrium of rivers on several grounds, in spite of certain objections that may be urged against it. Let us consider the objections first.

Origin and Use of the Term "Grade." One of my correspondents has objected to "grade" because, in the sense here adopted, the word means, etymologically, a step, and not a slope. This objection seems to me of small value on account of the freedom with which new meanings are given to old roots. Language does not grow by rule but by use; and use has decreed that one meaning of the English word "grade" shall depart somewhat from the meaning of its Latin ancestor. The chapter on Transference of Meaning, in a work on "Words and their Ways in English Speech," by two of my colleagues, Professors Greenough and Kittredge, may be consulted to advantage in this connection.

Another correspondent objects because the word "grade" is already in common use, meaning, among other things, a slope, and the ratio of the vertical to the horizontal in a slope; but as a matter of fact no practical inconvenience has arisen on this account. The context suffices to indicate which one of the several meanings of the word is intended. Moreover, if we should endeavor to escape the criticism of Scylla, by making up a new technical term in order to avoid the technical use of a common word in a new meaning, we should be met by the objections of Charybdis, who maintains that "every new technical term is a positive detriment to science." The objections to "grade" seem to me far outweighed by the many points in its favor, which may now be reviewed.

In favor of the term it may be noted first that "grade," like "base-level," is of a convenient form, ready for use as noun, adjective, and verb, after the handy fashion of the English language in many other cases. In the second place, the sense of the verb "grade," as employed by engineers (to prepare, by cutting and filling, a smooth bed of gentle slope for a railroad or other line of transportation), is closely analogous to the meaning here advocated for the verb " grade " as used by geologists and geographers; a river grades its course by a process of cutting and filling, until an equable slope is developed along which the transportation of its load is most effectively accomplished. In the third place, "grade" lends itself admirably to the formation of such terms as "degrade," "aggrade," and "gradation"; "degrade," in the sense of to wear down, has been in use for some time by geologists; "aggrade" is an excellent addition to our terminology, proposed by Salisbury (*a*, 103) in the sense of building up; while "gradation" is Powell's term for the general process of wearing down elevations and filling up depressions, in the production of lowland plains (*b*, 30). Finally, the word has already made a beginning towards acquiring a useful place in scientific writings.

The use of "grade" in the sense here advocated was almost reached by Gilbert in his description of hills of planation, covered with stream gravels: "The slope of the hill depends on the grade of the ancient stream, and is independent of the hardness and dip of the strata" (*b*, 130); and again in his account of how a river "tends to establish a single, uniform grade," and "an equilibrium of action " (*a*, 100). It was in consequence of a suggestion from this philosophical writer that I introduced "grade" as a substitute for various paraphrases in my own work in 1893 (*b*, 77).

McGee considers the control of the balanced condition of rivers under the "law of river gradation" (*b*, 265).

Mill uses "grade" as a verb, essentially in the sense here advocated: "Ultimately the river grades its course and flows uniformly along a uniform slope " (56).

Gannett has adopted "grade" as a technical term in Folios 1 and 2 of the *Topographic Atlas of the United States*. In the first he writes: "There finally comes a time when the river ceases to erode, or, rather, it deposits as much as it erodes. . . . A river is then said to be graded."

In the second a special sheet, with explanatory text, is devoted to "A Graded River," the example chosen being the lower Missouri :

> At this stage the lower portion of its [a river's] course has been eroded to almost as low a stage as possible, and its slope has become very slight, so that its cutting power is trifling. This part of the stream is said to be "graded."

Johnson uses "gradation" as involving both degradation and aggradation, and as producing a "graded slope," a slope of "equilibrium easily disturbed, yet constantly maintained" (620).

"Grade" may therefore be regarded as having already gained recognition in the sense here advocated, as a replacement of one of the meanings of "base-level."

There remain to be considered several reasons in favor of giving different names to the limiting base of sub-aërial erosion and to the balanced condition in which rivers spend most of their lives while approaching the limit of their work. The first reason is based on the persistence of the base-level surface all through the cycle, without change from its initially complete extension, in contrast to the gradual introduction and slow extension of the condition of grade during the mature and older stages of the cycle. The second is based on the fixity of the base-level surface in contrast to the variation in the slope of graded rivers. The third springs from the essential simplicity in the meaning of "base-level" in contrast to the complexity and variety of conditions ultimately gathered under the term "grade."

Base-Level is Complete from the Beginning and Permanent to the End; Grade is Slowly Introduced and Gradually Extended. The conception of the general base-level must be made at the outset as that of a completed surface extending beneath the land mass under consideration at the beginning of the cycle, and so remaining as long as the advance of the cycle continues undisturbed. In the ideal case, which provides the general scheme with respect to which all other cases are classified, the land mass once uplifted is supposed to stand still until it is worn down flat. This supposition is so artificial and does so great violence to much that is known as to the behavior of the earth's crust that some students are therefore disposed to discard the scheme of the cycle altogether in the study of the sculpture of land masses, overlooking the fact that however many movements of a land mass may be discovered, the many incomplete cycles that are separated by these movements must each be treated essentially according to the scheme of the ideal cycle. In every case the processes of land sculpture, quickened or slackened in consequence of the new attitude given to the region, go on with respect to the new attitude of the base-level within the land mass.

Even during the movement of the land mass, it must be conceived of as rising or sinking through a fixed and complete base-level surface, with respect to which its carving is even then begun, and long afterwards continued, during the ensuing time of relative or absolute rest. Hence, for every cycle or partial cycle of erosion, the imaginary base-level surface is immediately conceived as complete at the outset, and as thenceforwards remaining unchanged. Local base-levels are also complete, in extending at once as far as the imagination wishes to carry them; they rise or fall slowly with their control.

It is far otherwise with the development of the graded condition. The previous paragraphs have explained that the development of grade depends on the spontaneous adjustment of the capacity of a river to do work, and the quantity of work to be done by the river. It is well understood that this adjustment is realized by the larger streams relatively early in the cycle; by those of medium and smaller size at later and later stages; and hence that the condition of grade is deliberately introduced and systematically extended through all parts of a river system as the cycle advances. The condition of grade needs no mention when the scheme of the cycle is first presented. Truly, it might be considered as an accompaniment of the youth of a cycle in those special cases where a large river is running across a slowly rising region of weak rocks, for here the condition of grade may be continuously maintained during the period of uplift. But it is not in connection with special cases of this kind that a first acquaintance with the condition of grade is best made. Its fuller meaning is not likely to be well understood unless presented with something of the deliberation that characterizes the actual development of graded rivers. Indeed, the conception of grade is likely to be an embarrassment if presented too early.

The extension of the graded condition over all parts of a river system introduces a thoroughness of organization in the processes of land sculpture that warrants the use of the term "maturity" as the name of the stage of the cycle in which the organization of river systems is chiefly accomplished. The growth of organization goes with the development of grade. In every reach of a river in which the graded condition has been attained, the lowest point on the reach is always coincident with and dependent on a controlling base-level (as above defined), either general or local, and river action at any point in the graded reach is then delicately correlated with that at every other point. River action in such a reach may justly be said to be organized, inasmuch as a change in form or action at any one point involves a change at every other point. Adjacent reaches, separated by a fall on an ungraded ledge or by an unfilled lake, are independently organized; a change in one does not necessarily call for a change in the other. But when all falls and rapids are worn down, and all lakes are filled up, and the entire river system is graded, as is characteristically the case in the late-mature stage of a cycle, the organization of the system is so complete that all its parts are correlated. A change at any one point then involves a change, of infinitesimal amount perhaps, all through the system. It is this condition of organization that Gilbert alluded to in describing the "interdependence" that comes to be developed among the different lines of a river system, as a result of which "a disturbance upon any line is communicated through it to the main line and thence to every tributary" (b, 124).

The actual slopes of the different parts of a graded river system vary from a faintest declivity in the lower course of the trunk river to decidedly steeper declivities in the uppermost courses of the headwater streams. If any stream line is followed from head to mouth, its profile will show a curve, approximating theoretically to the flatter part of one wing of a parabola; but when studied in detail, the normally continuous decrease of slope downstream is found to be seldom realized. The entrance of a tributary is usually accompanied by a decrease of slope upstream and an increase of slope downstream from the tributary mouth; the spasmodic action of floods introduces some faint symptoms of disorder in otherwise simple slopes; and in this connection the inequalities due to what McGee has called "varigradation" are to be considered (*b*, 269; see also Oldham). All these complications in the slopes of a graded river system make it extremely difficult to conceive of a surface which shall generalize the river slopes. Indeed, it is hardly worth while to attempt this conception, for the reason that all the value of the imaginary surface is to be found in the actual slope lines of the graded river systems by which the surface is guided. It is with respect to the sloping course of a graded stream that the valley sides are to be worn down; it is with respect to the graded lines of a river system that its whole basin is to be worn down. This conception, as announced by Powell, is of fundamental importance; but it does not seem to gain in clearness or strength by expressing the control of erosion in terms of a warped surface, guided by the branching lines of the graded river system, instead of expressing it distinctly in terms of the branching stream lines themselves. Reference will be made again to this aspect of the problem further on.

Not only do graded streams vary in slope in different parts of a river system; the slopes may vary greatly in two neighboring river systems at the time of the general establishment of their grade. This may be illustrated by considering the unlike conditions obtaining in two rivers, alike in volume, but one flowing through an upland of resistant rocks, the other through a similar upland of weak rocks. The first river would have to cut down a deep valley to a gentle slope before grade was reached, because its load would be slowly delivered from the resistant rocks of its valley walls, and high walls would have to be produced by deep valley cutting before a balance could be struck between the increasing load from the walls and headwaters and the decreasing capacity of the river. The second river could not cut so deep a valley, however weak the rocks of its bed, because it would have an abundant load supplied by the rapid wasting of its valley sides, even when they were of moderate height, and a strong slope down the valley would be required in order to maintain a velocity with which the graded stream could bear the abundant load away. Only as the whole upland is worn down in the later stages of the cycle could the second stream wear down its valley to a gentle slope, and then the valley would be still shallower than when grade was first attained.

The principle here considered is clearly recognized by Gilbert, who instances the Platte as a river of the second kind, and states that Powell also had so described it (*a*, 100). The difference between the two kinds of rivers is not satisfactorily indicated in terms of base-level, but it is clearly presented by stating that one has developed its grade on a faint slope, the other on a stronger slope.

The incapacity of the Platte to deepen its valley leads Gannett to describe it as an "overloaded river"; but this phrase is not altogether satisfactory, because it overlooks the fact that rivers refuse to be overloaded. A river will most dutifully work up to its full capacity; it is ready to increase its capacity by increasing its slope through aggrading when necessary (as stated below), and thus it may become heavily loaded; but like the traditional llama it refuses to carry an overload. Like all streams with braided channels, the Platte is well graded, as well graded as the typical lower Missouri, although the quantity and texture of its load require it to maintain a relatively strong slope.

Base-Level remains fixed all through an Uninterrupted Cycle; the Slope of Graded Streams must vary as the Cycle advances. After a river system has attained a maturely graded condition, it will maintain a graded condition through all the rest of the undisturbed cycle; but it is important to recognize that the maintenance of grade, during the very slow changes in volume and load that accompany the advance of the cycle, involves an appropriate change of slope as well. Instead, therefore, of having to do with a fixed control of erosion, such as is found in the general base-level of a region, we have here to do with a slowly, delicately, and elaborately changing equilibrium of river action, accompanied by a corresponding change in river slope. For example, a large river in a mountain valley may reach grade in the early maturity of its region. It will then flow with a rushing current on a rapidly sloping bed of cobblestones, and may stand hundreds or even thousands of feet above base-level. In the old age of the region the same river will flow with a sluggish current on a nearly level bed of sand and silt through a peneplain, only a few tens or scores of feet above base-level.

This is a point that is not generally enough recognized. It is too often implied — in the absence of explicit statement to the contrary — that when a river is once balanced between erosion and deposition its slope thenceforward remains constant. The beginner would gather this understanding of the question from several of the definitions of "base-level" above quoted, but such is evidently not the case. When a stream is first graded, its channel is not level, and it has not reached the base of its erosive work. In virtue of the continual, though slow, variations of stream volume and load through the normal cycle, the balanced condition of any stream can be maintained only by an equally continuous, though small, change of river slope, whereby capacity to do work, and work to be done, shall always be kept equal. It might at first be thought that changes of this kind would be perceptible, and that there would be occasional departures of a river from the graded condition ; but such is not the case, because the change in the value of any variable in a unit of time is only by a quantity of the second order, by a differential of its total value. Once graded, a river will never depart perceptibly from the graded condition as long as the normal advance of the cycle is undisturbed. The slope of a river must necessarily be steeper on the first attainment of grade in early maturity, when an abundant load is received from the steep valley sides and the active headwaters, than in late old age, when the valley sides have been worn down almost level, and when the even headwater streams are weak and sluggish. Hence, just as a graded river has slopes of varying declivities in its different parts at any one time, so the slope at any one part of the river must vary at different times in the successive stages of the cycle.

Not only so ; it is eminently possible that the slope of a graded stream may have to be increased for a time after it has been first attained, for there is no necessity that the load should cease increasing just when its value has risen to equality with that which the stream can transport. There is much probability that, after grade is reached in a normal, undisturbed cycle, a river may have for a time to aggrade its valley floor until the time of maximum load is reached ; and only after the maximum gives way to a decrease of load can there be a beginning of that very slow and long-continued decrease of river slope which continues through late maturity and old age. Furthermore, if at any time in the cycle a change of climate should occur, new slopes would have to be developed by the streams in order to bring about a new balance between erosion and transportation under the new relation of load and volume. If, for example, the changes were from humid to arid conditions, all the valley floors would have to be steepened by aggradation. If from arid to humid, the graded valley floors would be sharply trenched, and in time reduced to lower slopes. There can be little doubt that under an increased rainfall the "base-level" described in southeastern California by Fairbanks would be sharply dissected, quite independent of any elevation of the region. I have already discussed certain aspects of this problem (*c*, 377).

The clearest account that I have found of the normal variation of the graded slope is in the paper by Johnson already cited. He says that the graded slope "continually alters its inclination. There is a slow departure from equilibrium, and there is closely following readjustment toward recovery of it." The graded slope passes through its "transformations with a slowness comparable to that of mountain wear. . . . It keeps pace with the slow growth of the débris mass following upon mountain lowering." But if a stream be deprived of the greater part of its load by some abnormal changes, it "would at once attack its former slope of equilibrium, and rapidly, though at a progressively slowing rate, lower it. On the other hand, its load largely increased, the stream would rapidly build up the slope. In either case, however, it would come to a stand at a new grade of equilibrium" (621).

The same author attaches much importance to the effect of climatic changes on graded river slopes. When describing the dissection of the High plains, he says :

It is not necessary, in order to account for change in behavior of the traversing streams, to appeal to deformation. A sufficient cause may be looked for in change of climate. There is record of erosion, with reversal to deposition and rebuilding, and reversal again finally to erosion, and there is reason for believing that this series of interruptions of the gradation cycle was an effect of climatic oscillation rather than of earth movement (628).

This is by far the most striking actual example of varying graded slopes on record, — an example that is easily defined in terms of changing grade, but not in terms of changing base-level. It is much more satisfactory to describe the High plains in terms of stronger or fainter graded slopes than to consider them "near base-level," as has been done in spite of their standing at altitudes of four thousand feet and more.

The conception of grade must therefore include the conception of different and changing slopes in large and small streams, in mature and old streams, in streams dissecting weak and strong rocks, in streams of arid and humid regions. The conception is of the greatest value as a supplement to the simpler idea of base-level ; but it is so intricate that it cannot be fully apprehended until the whole course of the cycle is patiently worked through. Yet a still further extension of the conception remains to be considered.

Base-Levels are of only Two Kinds, General (Permanent) and Local (Temporary); Grade includes not only the Balanced Condition of Large and Small, Mature and Old Water Streams, but that of All Kinds of Waste Streams as well. A final reason for giving different names to the limiting base of sub-aërial erosion and to the balanced condition of the mature and old streams that are working with respect to the limiting base is found in the essential identity of conditions in graded water streams and in graded waste streams, and in the strong unlikeness between the attitude of a base-level surface as defined in any of the above citations and the slopes often assumed by graded waste streams. These are points to which the geologists and geographers of the older schools gave little or no attention ; indeed, it is only about fifty years since some of the leaders of our science taught that rounded hills could not be formed by sub-aërial erosion and that they must be the work of the sea. It is now well understood, however, that slopes covered with soil of local or up-hill derivation are really "drained" by an association of many graded waste streams, whose behavior closely resembles that of graded water streams.

The first development of the balanced or graded condition in waste streams usually takes place on the outcrops of the weaker rocks that are exposed on freshly cut valley sides. Here graded waste slopes are locally developed ; the adjoining waste streams form a sheet or cloak of waste which creeps slowly down the slope, while untamed ledges of harder rocks are still kept bare by the removal of waste from their surface as fast as it is formed. These represent the falls and rapids of water streams, because the waste from above the ledges passes over them quickly ; while the graded waste-covered slopes represent the graded reaches of water streams, where the movement is more regular and leisurely. The less resistant of the bare ledges are the first to retreat under cover, permitting the grades below and above to unite in a single continuous slope, and so on, until all ledges are concealed under a graded sheet of waste, and the sharp, vigorous forms of youth and early maturity merge into the subdued and tamed forms of passing maturity and approaching old age. During the progress of this change there may be abundant examples of captures of one group of waste streams by the leading members of another group, especially in regions of tilted strata, thus increasing the resemblance of waste streams and water streams, until one is tempted to regard the difference between them as one of degree rather than of kind.

As maturity passes into old age, all the elevations are worn lower and lower and the graded cloak of waste covers more and more of the surface. As the later stages of the cycle are approached, the whole region, monadnocks excepted, is reduced to moderate relief, and bare ledges are rarely seen. On the faintly sloping forms of advanced old age the graded sheet of waste covers the entire surface between the water streams. Everywhere gently waste-covered slopes lead from the low arched divides to the streams. The surface soil, greatly refined in texture by long exposure to the weather in its deliberate journey, slowly creeps and washes to the streams, and the relief is reduced to smaller and smaller measures. The condition of grade, at first developed in the lower course of the larger rivers, next in their branches and headwaters, then on the valley sides and over the hills, has thus been extended all over the region. The organization that at maturity characterized the water streams has come in old age to characterize the streams and sheets of waste all over the land surface. From the beginning to the end of this process there is steady progress without break or interruption through the normal cycle. There is an essential unity of development through the whole of it. It is very desirable that this unity should be expressed in the terms employed in the description of land sculpture and land form, and that the balanced condition of water streams and waste streams alike should be expressed by such a term as "grade," rather than that an artificial distinction between them should be introduced by speaking of the balanced rivers as defining a "base-level," while balanced waste streams are given some other name by which their close affinity to graded water stream is concealed.

An old land surface, sheeted over with a graded soil cover, is a peneplain of erosion or of gradation; it passes slowly into a plain of gradation. It is almost the realization of that imaginary base-level surface described by Powell as "inclining slightly in all its parts toward the lower end of the principal streams draining the area through which the level is supposed to extend, or having the inclination of its parts varied in direction as determined by tributary streams"; but this imaginary surface is elusive and intangible, because of the impossibility of defining the stage of stream development when it should be introduced, and the length of graded stream course that it should follow; while, on the other hand, the graded land surface is a reality whose gradual development and slow change is one of its essential characteristics.

Until the imaginary surface is thus realized, it is hardly worth while to attempt to conceive it, for as far as the control of erosive processes is concerned, that is better exercised (as has been stated already) by the visible skeleton of the surface that is seen in graded streams than by the surface itself. It is always with reference to the graded course of the main river that the side streams are graded; it is with reference to all the graded streams that the slopes of the interfluves are graded. These relations of branch to trunk and of side slopes to streams are of the very greatest importance and must be considered with the utmost care; but the imaginary surface passing from river to river under the hills of the interfluves has relatively little importance as a control of the processes of erosion. With every extension headwards along the graded channels of branching streams, the surface becomes more warped and wrinkled, more difficult to conceive, more likely to differ as conceived by different minds. It must be not only irregularly warped when first defined, but it must vary slowly in form and slope. Just as no limit can be set to the headward part of the graded main stream or to the number of graded branch streams to be taken as guides for the imaginary warped base-level, so no limit can be set between the graded stream courses and the graded waste slopes of their head or along their sides. The imaginary surface should, if conceived at all, follow the lead of *all* the graded lines and surfaces as fast as they are developed; it should be extended as they are extended, modified as they are modified. But if this be agreed to, part of the imaginary surface becomes a real surface, and the rest may be neglected until it also is realized.

Just as every reach in a stream is graded with respect to the next downstream barrier or local base-level, so every waste slope is graded with respect to the ledge or cliff at its lower margin; the lowest reach, ending at the river mouth, is graded with reference to the general base-level or the ocean; the lowest graded slope of a valley side is graded with reference to the stream (or flood plain) in the valley bottom. Again, every bare ledge on a mountain side will, in time, be graded (or consumed) by the headward growth of the graded slope next below it, just as every ledge of rocks that makes a fall or rapid at the head of a reach will, in time, be obliterated by the upstream extension of the graded reach. (In both cases, when the time of extinction of the ledge is attained, the waste slope and the stream reach will probably have been worn somewhat farther into the land mass, assuming a somewhat fainter declivity — that is, coming closer to base-level — than was the case while the ledge still existed.)

The close similarity, the real homology between the two classes of streams, makes it all the clearer that "base-level" is not a good term to apply to either. It is not desirable to say that a hillside ledge is "base-leveled" when it is worn back so far that it disappears under the slope of the growing sheet of waste; yet it is certainly desirable to indicate by the use of an appropriate terminology that the disappearance of the ledge has been accomplished by changes of the same kind as those which have caused the obliteration of falls and rapids in rivers. Hence it seems desirable to say that every ledge, in valley side or stream bed, will in time be graded — not base-leveled — with respect to the attitude assumed at that future time by the graded — not base-leveled — reach or slope next below it.

It is, perhaps, on account of the elusive character of the imaginary warped surface that its definition is sometimes couched in indefinite language. In the original definition, Powell said:

I take some liberty in using the term "level" in this connection, as the action of a stream in wearing its channel ceases, for all practical purposes, before its bed has quite reached the level of the lower end of the stream. What I have called the base-level would, in fact, be an imaginary surface, inclining slightly (*a*, 204).

In a later paper he said again:

It will be understood that the land plain which is brought down to the level of the sea has its margin on the seashore, and that it extends back from the shore a distance which may be miles or hundreds of miles. As it stretches back, its surface rises slightly. The whole plain is not brought down absolutely to the level of the sea, but only nearly to that level (*b*, 34, 35).

Salisbury states that "no definite degree of slope can be fixed upon as marking a base-level." Geikie defines base-level as "a level not much above that of the sea." Brigham writes:

The great river first cuts its bed close to the sea-level, and we say that a portion of the valley is reduced to base-level. It lacks a little of it, but the difference is so small that we neglect it.

These qualified statements are apparently the result of attempting to define a surface in terms of its variable feature, slope, instead of in terms of its constant feature, balance of activities. Whatever slope is agreed upon must change to a fainter slope if more time is allowed; but the balance, once struck, is always maintained as long as the cycle endures. Another cause of difficulty in definition seems to have arisen from giving the same name to a variable and to its limit. Both the imaginary warped surface and the actual peneplain are essentially variables; their

variations are similar and systematic; they both approach, but
never reach, the limiting base of sub-aërial erosion. The latter is
essentially a constant, accurately definable from the beginning,
and remaining unchanged while the variable surfaces approach
it. It may be defined as the limit of either of these variables in
a strictly mathematical fashion. The base-level is the level base
toward which the land surface constantly approaches in accordance
with the laws of degradation, but which it can never reach.

Plains and Peneplains. The names for surfaces of ultimate
and penultimate sub-aërial erosion deserve brief consideration.
My own preference, prejudiced, perhaps, by a share that I have
had in making up names, would be to avoid "base-level" as a
technical name for any geographical form, to use "plain" spar-
ingly for surfaces of erosion, because of the rare occurrence of
complete or ultimate planation; and usually to employ "peneplain" as the name for the penultimate form developed in a cycle
of erosion. It was in order to avoid the implication of complete
erosion, and the objections that such an implication aroused, that
the term "peneplain" was suggested thirteen years ago. This
word gradually came into use with quotation marks and an explanatory footnote. The footnote disappeared first, and now the
quotation marks are frequently omitted, as if the word had gained
an established position, although among writers in Great Britain
the need of the term is still so little felt that it is generally mentioned as an American invention when used at all, instead of
being fully adopted, like "delta" and "atoll," without explanation
or acknowledgment.

There seems to be to-day less hesitation regarding the acceptance of the idea of far-advanced sub-aërial degradation than there
was fifteen years ago, — witness the use of "plain of erosion" by
Hobbs (137) as a name for the worn-down surface, now uplifted
and dissected, in the uplands of Connecticut; nevertheless it still
seems desirable to speak of such surfaces as peneplains in the
absence of proof that they were actually reduced to plains. The
alternatives for peneplain are as follows :

Powell contrasts "gradation or true plains" with "diastrophic
plains" (plateaus), the former being produced by gradation, a
"process accomplished through the agency of water," and the

latter by the uplifting of the earth's crust. This use of "gradation" is a natural complement of the use of "grade" in the sense
advocated in this essay. Gradation plains are then treated under
four heads: "sea plains," "lake plains," "stream plains," and
"flood plains." Of the first class it is said:

Whenever in any region the process of slow upheaval comes to an end,
and such district is still subject to degradation by rains and streams, the
process of reduction goes on until the surface is brought down to the level
of the sea. . . . The sea-level plain is permanent in the absence of dias-
trophism. . . . Low lands with surfaces more inclined, and with more
swiftly running streams, are still called "plains," though they are not fully
brought down to base-level; sometimes they are called "peneplains"
(*b*, 34, 35).

"Sea plain" has not come into general use, perhaps because
of possible confusion with "sea-cut plains," "or plains of marine
denudation." The following extract gives an example of the
employment of the term with double meaning by Hughes, in
describing the uplands of western Yorkshire:

It is to both of the agencies above mentioned [marine and sub-aërial
erosion], acting simultaneously throughout long ages, that we must refer
the tremendous results that we have forced upon our attention. . . . We
will refer to these great plateaus by the shorter term "sea plain," to distinguish them from the river plains or bed plains (131).

Dryer uses the phrase "graded plain" in a somewhat different
sense. The reduction of the border of a land area to a submarine
plain by sea action, while the rest of the land surface is reduced
to base-level by sub-aërial processes, would result in the production of a "graded plain, lying partly above and partly below
sea-level" (234). No example of this kind of plain is mentioned.
"Gradation plain" is used by Adams for a locally developed
peneplain between residual ridges (508).

The terminology employed by Hayes departs somewhat from
that in use with other writers. He says:

The processes which tend to produce a base-level plain are embraced
under the term "gradation." This includes aggradation and degradation. . . .
A "base-leveled surface" is any land surface, however small, which has been
brought approximately to a base-level, either general or local, by the processes
of gradation. When such a surface has considerable extent it becomes
a "base-level plain." . . . The term "base-level peneplain," or simply

"peneplain," is applied to a surface of which a greater or less proportion has been reduced to the condition of a base-level plain, but which contains also some unreduced residual areas (21, 22).

It seems to me that it is going too far to say that "a base-leveled surface is any land surface, however small, which has been brought approximately to a base-level, either general or local." It would follow from this definition that, inasmuch as every point in a continuously graded river is a local base-level for every other point farther upstream, the upper stretches of the flood plain or broad valley floor of a large river would be called a base-leveled surface, in spite of their standing several hundreds, or even thousands, of feet above the general base-level. The valley plain of the Platte, for example, attains altitudes of more than three thousand feet, and cannot be fitly described as a base-level plain, unless base-level is taken to mean a sloping surface. It may be more appropriately called a graded valley plain, or a graded valley floor, for these terms do not contain any implication that the surface is either low or level.

Another objection to the above use of "base-leveled surface" is that it arbitrarily separates graded valley floors and graded hillsides, whose analogies with respect to the processes of gradation ought to be exhibited rather than concealed in a systematic terminology. It can hardly be supposed that any one would to-day call a waste-covered hillside a "base-leveled surface," although it has every characteristic with respect to the processes of gradation that is possessed by a graded valley floor. A third objection to this use of "base-leveled surface" would be found when applying it to the High plains of eastern Colorado and western Kansas, which, according to the explanation offered by Johnson and cited above, were produced by aggradation during a time of less rainfall than at present. Here an extended surface was, as Hayes might phrase it, "brought approximately to a base-level, either general or local, by the processes of gradation," and yet it was actually built up hundreds of feet above the preëxistent and the present valleys, and thousands of feet above the general base-level, although there is no indication of any discontinuity in the graded surface between the High plains and the mouths of their aggrading rivers. The High plains are better called aggraded river-made plains, or "fluviatile plains"; and in this respect they resemble the great plains of northern India.

The Geographical Cycle. The period of time during which an uplifted land mass undergoes its transformations by the processes of land sculpture, ending in a low, featureless plain, has been called a geographical cycle, or, as Lawson phrases it, a "geomorphic cycle" (253). Hayes writes: "The term 'gradation period' is employed for the entire time during which the base-level remains in one position; that is, the interval between two elevations of the earth's surface of sufficient magnitude to produce a marked change in the position of sea-level" (22); but on later pages he uses the phrase "cycles of gradation," or simply "cycles," instead of "gradation periods." It matters little which of these terms is used, but it would certainly be an advantage that only one should be retained to express the single idea here considered.

Denudation and Degradation. It seems worth while to call attention in this connection to the desirability of a more careful discrimination than is customary between the terms "denudation" and "degradation." "Denudation" might be used advisedly as the name of those active processes, chiefly operative in the youth and maturity of a cycle, by which rock structures are laid bare, literally denuded, because their waste is removed as fast as it is formed. "Degradation," on the other hand, is more appropriately associated with those leisurely processes, characteristic of the later stages of the cycle, in which a graded slope is reduced to fainter and fainter declivity, although maintaining its graded condition all the while. Aggradation is naturally the opposite of degradation, and implies the deposition of rock waste by transporting agencies, the built-up surface being always kept essentially at grade. Thus defined, denudation would accompany the early work of downward corrasion by streams, and the longer-lasting work of valley widening by weathering and washing. It would be systematically transmuted into degradation as the processes that operate on the various lines of down-slope streaming attained the graded condition; the large rivers first, the smaller branch streams later; the headwater streamlets and the hillside waste streams later still. Retreating cliffs and summit ledges, the last strongholds of denudation, would pass into the phase of degradation when they are reduced under the graded waste cover in the stage of subdued relief, characteristic of late maturity and early old age ; and thenceforward all further erosion would be by degradation alone.

Conclusion. It may seem at first reading that this essay is concerned with words rather than with facts ; but such is not my intention. My object has been primarily to secure a just and accurate recognition of facts, and only secondarily to attach words to the facts as convenient handles by which to bring the facts forward. It is a fact of large import that the wearing down of land masses proceeds in an orderly manner, involving the disclosure of bare rock ledges (denudation) in the earlier stages of the cycle of erosion, and the concealment of all ledges under a graded sheet of waste in the later stages of the cycle (degradation). It is a fact of much delicacy that streams tend to assume a balanced condition as to corrasion and transportation ; that after once attaining this condition they preserve it as long as their work continues without disturbance ; but that the slope of their graded courses must vary systematically through the stages of maturity and old age, as well as through changes of climate. It is a fact of great value in geographical description that the balanced condition of water streams is imitated so closely by that of waste streams that one set of terms applies to both kinds of streams.

There can be no question that the adoption of a suitable term as the name for a fact is a great aid to the general recognition of the fact itself. It is largely on this account, as well as in the interests of a precise terminology, that I have here written out a series of notes that have been gathered during the past two years, and of which some account was given at the meeting of the Geological Society of America in Washington, in December, 1899.

It is admittedly difficult always to use terms in a manner that is perfectly consistent with their definitions. It is rarely possible to limit terms to a single meaning. It is probable that in this attempt to reduce our terminology to greater simplicity and better order than now prevails, I have laid myself open to criticism on the very grounds that are objected to in the course of this essay.

Further discussion may therefore be advisedly directed to a settlement of open questions. It is certainly open to consideration whether "denudation" and "degradation" should be limited as above suggested; but the advisability of holding "base-level" and "grade" to the meanings here indicated seems to be much less open to difference of opinion. The future meanings of these words will depend much less on the preference of the older geologists and geographers of to-day than on that of their younger successors. I therefore urge those who are now taking up the use of such terms as "base-level" and "grade," "denudation" and "degradation," to consider carefully the meaning to be adopted for them.

REFERENCES

Adams, G. I. "Physiography of the Arkansas Valley Region" (abstract). *Science*, XI (1900), 508.

Brigham, A. P. A Text-Book of Geology. New York, Appleton, 1901.

Campbell, M. C. "Drainage Modifications and their Interpretation." *Jour. Geol.*, IV (1896), 567–587, 657–678.

Cowles, H. C. "Physiographic Ecology of Chicago and Vicinity." *Botan. Gazette*, XXXI (1901), 73–108, 145–182.

Darton, N. H. "Outline of Cenozoic History of a Portion of the Middle Atlantic Slope." *Jour. Geol.*, II (1894), 568–587.

Dausse, M. F. B. "Note sur un Principe Important et Nouveau d'Hydraulique." *C. R. Acad. Sciences* (Paris), XLIV (1857), 756–766.

Davis, W. M. (*a*) "Geographic Methods in Geologic Investigation." *Nat. Geog. Mag.*, I (1889), 11–26.

(*b*) "Physical Geography in the University." *Jour. Geol.*, II (1894), 66–100.

(*c*) "A Speculation in Topographical Climatology." *Am. Meteorol. Jour.*, XII (1896), 372–381.

(*d*) "An Excursion to the Grand Cañon of the Colorado." *Bull. Museum Comp. Zoöl., Harvard College*, XXXIII (1901), 107–201.

Davis, W. M., and Wood, Jr., J. W. "The Geographic Development of Northern New Jersey." *Proc. Boston Soc. Nat. Hist.*, XXIV (1889), 365–423.

Diller, J. S. "Tertiary Revolution in the Topography of the Pacific Coast." *U. S. Geol. Surv., XIV Ann. Rep.*, Pt. II (1894), 397–434.

Dryer, C. R. Lessons in Physical Geography. New York, American Book Co., 1901.

Dutton, C. E. "Tertiary History of the Grand Cañon District." *U. S. Geol. Surv., Mon. II* (1882).

Fairbanks, H. W.   " Notes on the Geology of Eastern California."   *Am. Geol.*, XVII (1896), 63–74.

Gannett, H.   " Physiographic Types."   *U. S. Geol. Surv., Topog. Atlas U. S.*, Folio 1, 1896 ; Folio 2, 1900.

Geikie, J.   Earth Sculpture or the Origin of Land-Forms.   London, Murray, 1898.

Gilbert, G. K.   (*a*) " The Colorado Plateau Province as a Field for Geological Study.   *Am. Jour. Sci.*, XII (1876), 16–24, 85–103.

(*b*) Report on the Geology of the Henry Mountains.   *U. S. Geog. and Geol. Surv., Rocky Mountain Region.*   1877.

(*c*) "The Underground Water of the Arkansas Valley in Eastern Colorado."   *U. S. Geol. Surv., XVII Ann. Rep.*, Pt. II (1896), 551–601.

Greenwood, G.   Rain and Rivers.   London, Longmans, 1857.

Hayes, C. W.   " Physiography of the Chattanooga District in Tennessee, Georgia, and Alabama."   *U. S. Geol. Surv., XIX Ann. Rep.*, Pt. II (1899), 1–58.

Hill, R. T.   " The Geological History of the Isthmus of Panama and Portions of Costa Rica."   *Bull. Museum Comp. Zoöl., Harvard College,* XXVIII (1898), 151–285.

Hobbs, W. H.   " The Newark System of Pomperaug Valley, Connecticut."   *U. S. Geol. Surv., XXI Ann. Rep.*, Pt. III (1901), 7–162.

Hughes, T. McK.   " Ingleborough : Part I, Physical Geography."   *Proc. Yorkshire Geol. and Polytech. Soc.*, XIV (1901), 125–150.

Johnson, W. D.   " The High Plains and their Utilization."   *U. S. Geol. Surv., XXI Ann. Rep.*, Pt. IV (1901), 601–741.

Keith, A.   " Geology of the Catoctin Belt."   *U. S. Geol. Surv., XIV Ann. Rep.*, Pt. II (1894), 285–395.

Kümmel, H. B.   " Some Rivers of Connecticut."   *Jour. Geol.*, I (1893), 371–393.

Lawson, A. C.   " The Geomorphogeny of the Coast of Northern California."   *Bull. Dept. Geol., Univ. Cal.*, I (1894), 241–271.

McGee, W. J.   (*a*) " The Geology of the Head of Chesapeake Bay."   *U. S. Geol. Surv., VII Ann. Rep.* (1888), 537–646.

(*b*) " The Pleistocene History of Northeastern Iowa."   *U. S. Geol. Surv., XI Ann. Rep.* (1891), 189–577.

Marr, J. E.   The Scientific Study of Scenery.   London, Methuen, 1900.

Mill, H. R.   The International Geography.   London, Newnes, 1899.

Oldham, R. D.   " On the Law that governs the Action of Flowing Streams."   *Quart. Jour. Geol. Soc.*, XLIV (1888), 733–738.

Philippson, A.   "Ein Beitrag zur Erosionstheorie."   *Petermanns Mittheilungen*, XXXII (1886), 67–79.

Powell, J. W.   (*a*) Exploration of the Colorado River of the West and its Tributaries.   Washington, 1875.

(*b*) " Physiographic Processes "; " Physiographic Features."   *Nat. Geog. Mon.* (1895), 1–32, 33–64.   New York, American Book Co.

Rice, W. N., editor of Revised Text-Book of Geology, by James D. Dana. New York, American Book Co., 1897.

Russell, I. C.   Rivers of North America.   New York, Putnam, 1898.

Salisbury, R. D.   (a) "Surface Geology."   *Geol. Surv. New Jersey, Ann. Rep. State Geol. for 1892–1893*, 35–246.

(b) "The Physical Geography of New Jersey."   *Geol. Surv. New Jersey, Final Report*, IV (1898).

Scott, W. B.   An Introduction to Geology.   New York, Macmillan, 1897.

Tarr, R. S.   Elementary Physical Geography.   New York, Macmillan, 1895.

Van Hise, C. R.   "A Central Wisconsin Base-Level."   *Science*, IV (1896), 57–59.

Willis, B.   (a) "The Northern Appalachians."   *Nat. Geog. Mon.* (1895), 169–202.   New York, American Book Co.

(b) "Paleozoic Appalachia."   *Geol. Surv. Maryland*, IV (1900), 23–93.

Winslow, A.   "Lead and Zinc Deposits."   *Geol. Surv. Missouri*, VI (1894).

XIX

THE RIVERS AND VALLEYS OF PENNSYLVANIA

In Faltensystemen von sehr hohem Alter wurde die ursprüngliche Anordnung der Langenthäler durch das Ueberhandnehmen der transversalen Erosionsfurchen oft ganz und gar verwischt. — Löwl, *Petermanns Mittheilungen*, XXVIII (1882), 411.

I. INTRODUCTORY

Plan of Work here Proposed. No one now regards a river and its valley as ready-made features of the earth's surface. All are convinced that rivers have come to be what they are by slow processes of natural development, in which every peculiarity of river course and valley form has its appropriate cause. Being fully persuaded of the gradual and systematic evolution of topographical forms, it is now desired, in studying the rivers and valleys of Pennsylvania, to seek the causes of the location of the streams in their present courses; to go back, if possible, to the early date when central Pennsylvania was first raised above the sea, and trace the development of the several river systems then implanted upon it from their ancient beginning to the present time.

The existing topography and drainage system of the state will first be briefly described. We must next inquire into the geological structure of the region, follow at least in a general way the deformations and changes of attitude and altitude that it has suffered, and consider the amount of denudation that has been accomplished on its surface. We must at the same time bear in mind the natural history of rivers, their morphology and development; we must recognize the varying activities of a river in its youth and old age, the adjustments of its adolescence and maturity, and the revival of its decrepit powers when the land that it drains is elevated and it enters a new cycle of life. Finally, we shall attempt to follow out the development of the rivers of Pennsylvania by applying the general principles of river history to the special case of Pennsylvania structure.

General Description of the Topography of Pennsylvania. The strongly marked topographical districts of Pennsylvania can hardly be better described than by quoting the account given over a century ago by Lewis Evans, of Philadelphia, in his "Analysis of a Map of the Middle British Colonies in America" (1755), which is as valuable from its appreciative perception as it is interesting from its early date. The following paragraphs are selected from his early pages:

The land southwestward of Hudson's River is more regularly divided and into a greater number of stages than the other. The first object worthy of regard in this part is a rief or vein of rocks of the talky or isinglassy kind, some two or three or half a dozen miles broad; rising generally some small matter higher than the adjoining land; and extending from New York city southwesterly by the lower falls of Delaware, Schuylkill, Susquehanna, Gun-Powder, Patapsco, Potomack, Rapahannock, James River, and Ronoak. This was the antient maritime boundary of America and forms a very regular curve. The land between this rief and the sea and from the Navesink hills southwest . . . may be denominated the Lower Plains, and consists of soil washt down from above and sand accumulated from the ocean. Where these plains are not penetrated by rivers, they are a white sea-sand, about twenty feet deep and perfectly barren, as no mixture of soil helps to enrich them. But the borders of the rivers, which descend from the uplands, are rendered fertile by the soil washt down with the floods and mixt with the sands gathered from the sea. The substratum of sea-mud, shells and other foreign subjects is a perfect confirmation of this supposition. And hence it is that for forty or fifty miles inland and all the way from the Navesinks to Cape Florida, all is a perfect barren where the wash from the uplands has not enriched the borders of the rivers; or some ponds and defiles have not furnished proper support for the growth of white cedars. . . .

From this rief of rocks, over which all the rivers fall, to that chain of broken hills, called the South mountain, there is the distance of fifty, sixty, or seventy miles of very uneven ground, rising sensibly as you advance further inland, and may be denominated the Upland. This consists of veins of different kinds of soil and substrata some scores of miles in length; and in some places overlaid with little ridges and chains of hills. The declivity of the whole gives great rapidity to the streams; and our violent gusts of rain have washt it all into gullies, and carried down the soil to enrich the borders of the rivers in the Lower Plains. These inequalities render half the country not easily capable of culture, and impoverishes it, where torn up by the plow, by daily washing away the richer mould that covers the surface.

The South mountain is not in ridges like the Endless mountains, but in small, broken, steep, stoney hills; nor does it run with so much regularity. In some places it gradually degenerates to nothing, not to appear again for some miles, and in others it spreads several miles in breadth. Between South mountain and the hither chain of the Endless mountains (often for distinction called the North mountain, and in some places the Kittatinni and Pequélin), there is a valley of pretty even good land, some eight, ten, or twenty miles wide, and is the most considerable quantity of valuable land that the English are possest of; and runs through New Jersey, Pensilvania, Mariland and Virginia. It has yet obtained no general name, but may properly enough be called Piemont, from its situation. Besides conveniences always attending good land, this valley is everywhere enriched with Limestone.

The Endless mountains, so called from a translation of the Indian name bearing that signification, come next in order. They are not confusedly scattered and in lofty peaks overtopping one another, but stretch in long uniform ridges scarce half a mile perpendicular in any place above the intermediate vallies. Their name is expressive of their extent, though no doubt not in a literal sense. . . . The mountains are almost all so many ridges with even tops and nearly of a height. To look from these hills into the lower lands is but, as it were, into an ocean of woods, swelled and deprest here and there by little inequalities, not to be distinguished one part from another any more than the waves of the real ocean. The uniformity of these mountains, though debarring us of an advantage in this respect, makes some amends in another. They are very regular in their courses, and confine the creeks and rivers that run between; and if we know where the gaps are that let through these streams, we are not at a loss to lay down their most considerable inflections. . . .

To the northwestward of the Endless mountains is a country of vast extent, and in a manner as high as the mountains themselves. To look at the abrupt termination of it, near the sea level, as is the case on the west side of Hudson's River below Albany, it looks as a vast high mountain; for the Kaats Kills, though of more lofty stature than any other mountains in these parts of America, are but the continuation of the Plains on the top, and the cliffs of them in the front they present towards Kinderhook. These Upper Plains are of extraordinary rich level land, and extend from the Mohocks River through the country of the Confederates.[1] Their termination northward is at a little distance from Lake Ontario; but what is westward is not known, for those most extensive plains of Ohio are part of them.

These several districts recognized by Evans may be summarized as the coastal plain of nearly horizontal Cretaceous and later beds, just entering the southeastern corner of Pennsylvania; the marginal upland of contorted schists of disputed age; the South mountain belt of ancient and much disturbed crystalline rocks, commonly called Archæan; a space between these two traversed

[1] Referring to the league of Indian tribes, so called.

by the sandstone lowland of the Newark formation[1]; the great Appalachian valley of crowded Cambrian limestones and slates; the region of the even-crested, linear, Paleozoic ridges, bounded by Kittatinny, or Blue mountain, on the southeast and by Allegheny mountain on the northwest, this being the area with which we are here most concerned; and finally the Allegheny plateau, consisting of nearly horizontal Devonian and Carboniferous beds, and embracing all the western part of the state. The whole region presents the most emphatic expression not only of its structure, but also of the more recent cycles of development through which it has passed.

The Drainage of Pennsylvania. The greater part of the Allegheny plateau is drained westward into the Ohio, and with this we shall have little to do. The remainder of the plateau drainage reaches the Atlantic by two rivers, the Delaware and the Susquehanna, of which the latter is the more special object of our study. The North and West branches of the Susquehanna rise in the plateau, which they traverse in deep valleys; thence they enter the district of the central ranges, where they unite and flow in broad lowlands among the even-crested ridges. The Juniata brings the drainage of the Broad Top region to the main stream just before their confluent current cuts across the marginal Blue mountain. The rock-rimmed basins of the anthracite region are drained by small branches of the Susquehanna northward and westward, and by the Schuylkill and Lehigh to the south and east. The Delaware, which traverses the plateau between the anthracite region and the Catskill mountain front, together with the Lehigh, the Schuylkill, the little Swatara, and the Susquehanna, cut the Blue mountain by fine water gaps, and cross the great limestone valley. The Lehigh then turns eastward and joins the Delaware, and the Swatara turns westward to the Susquehanna; but the Delaware, Schuylkill, and Susquehanna all continue across South mountain and the Newark belt, and into the low plateau of schists beyond. The Schuylkill unites with the Delaware near Philadelphia, just below the inner margin of

[1] Russell has recommended the revival of this term, proposed many years ago by Redfield, as a non-committal name for the "new red sandstones" of our Atlantic slope, commonly called Triassic.

the coastal plain ; the Delaware and the Susquehanna continue in their deflected estuaries to the sea. All of these rivers and many of their side streams are at present sunk in small valleys of moderate depth and width, below the general surface of the lowlands, and are more or less complicated with terrace gravels.

Previous Studies of Appalachian Drainage. There have been no special studies of the history of the rivers of Pennsylvania in the light of what is now known of river development. A few recent essays of rather general character as far as our rivers are concerned, may be mentioned.

Peschel examined our rivers chiefly by means of general maps, with little regard to the structure and complicated history of the region. He concluded that the several transverse rivers which break through the mountains, namely the Delaware, Susquehanna, and Potomac, are guided by fractures anterior to the origin of the rivers (442). There does not seem to be sufficient evidence to support this obsolescent view, for most of the water gaps are located independently of fractures ; nor can Peschel's method of river study be trusted as leading to safe conclusions.

Tietze regards our transverse valleys as antecedent (600); but this was only a general suggestion, for his examination of the structure and development of the region is too brief to establish this and exclude other views.

Löwl questions the conclusion reached by Tietze, and ascribes the transverse gaps to the backward or headwater erosion of external streams, a process which he has done much to bring into its present important position, and which for him replaces the persistence of antecedent streams of other authors (*a*, 405 ; *b*).

A brief article that I wrote in comment on Löwl's first essay several years ago now seems to me insufficient in its method (*a*). It exaggerated the importance of antecedent streams ; it took no sufficient account of the several cycles of erosion through which the region has certainly passed ; and it neglected due consideration of the readjustment of initial immature stream courses during more advanced river life. Since then, a few words in Löwl's essay have come to have more and more significance to me ; he says that in mountain systems of very great age the original arrangement of the longitudinal valleys often becomes entirely confused by means of their conquest by transverse erosion gaps. This suggestion has been so profitable to me that I have placed the original sentence at the beginning of this paper. Its thesis is the essential element of my present study.

Philippson refers to the above-mentioned authors and gives a brief account of the arrangement of drainage areas within our Appalachians, but briefly dismisses the subject (149). His essay contains a serviceable bibliography.

If these several earlier essays have not reached any precise conclusion, it may perhaps be because the details of the geological structure and development of Pennsylvania have not been sufficiently examined. Indeed, unless the reader has already become familiar with the geological maps and reports of the Pennsylvania surveys, and is somewhat acquainted with its geography, I shall hardly hope to make my case clear to him. The volumes that should be most carefully studied are, first, the always inspiring classic, "Coal and its Topography" (1856), by Lesley, in which the immediate relation of our topography to the underlying structure is so finely described; the Geological Map of Pennsylvania (1856), the result of the labors of the first survey of the state; and the Geological Atlas of Counties, Volume X of the second survey (1885). Besides these, the ponderous volumes of the final report of the first survey and numerous reports on separate counties by the second survey should be examined, as they contain many accounts of the topography, although saying very little about its development. If, in addition to all this, the reader has seen the central district of the state and marveled at its even-crested, straight, and zigzag ridges, and walked through its narrow water gaps into the inclosed coves that they drain, he may then still better follow the considerations here presented.

II. OUTLINE OF THE GEOLOGICAL HISTORY OF THE REGION

Conditions of Formation. The region in which the Susquehanna and the neighboring rivers are now located is built in chief part of marine sediments derived in Paleozoic time from a large land area to the southeast, whose northwest coast line probably crossed Pennsylvania somewhere in the southeastern part of the state, doubtless varying its position, however, by many miles as the sea advanced and receded in accordance with the changes in the relative altitudes of the land and water surfaces, such as have been discussed by Newberry and Claypole. The sediments thus accumulated are of enormous thickness, measuring twenty or thirty thousand feet from their crystalline foundation to the uppermost layer now remaining. The whole mass is essentially conformable in the central part of the state. Some of the formations are resistant, and these have determined the position of our ridges; others are weaker, and are chosen as the sites of valleys and lowlands. The first are the Oneida and Medina sandstones, — which will be here generally referred to under the latter name alone, — the Pocono sandstone, and the Pottsville conglomerate; to these may be added the fundamental crystalline mass on which the whole series of bedded formations was deposited, and the basal sandstone that is generally associated with it. Wherever we now see these harder rocks, they rise above the surrounding lowland surface. On the other hand, the weaker beds are the Cambrian limestones (Trenton) and slates (Hudson river), all the Silurian except the Medina above named, the whole of the Devonian, — in which, however, there are two hard beds of subordinate value, the Oriskany sandstone and a Chemung sandstone and conglomerate, that form low and broken ridges over the softer ground on either side of them, — and the Carboniferous (Mauch Chunk) red shales and some of the weaker sandstones (Coal Measures).

Former Extension of Strata to the Southeast. We are not much concerned with the conditions under which this great series of beds was formed; but, as will appear later, it is important for us to recognize that the present southeastern margin of the beds is not by any means their original margin in that direction. It is probable that the whole mass of deposits, with greater or less variations of thickness, extended at least twenty miles southeast of Blue mountain, and that many of the beds extended much farther. The reason for this conclusion is a simple one. The several resistant beds above mentioned consist of quartz sand and pebbles that cannot be derived from the underlying beds of limestones and shales; their only known source lay in the crystalline rocks of the Paleozoic land to the southeast. South mountain may possibly have made part of this Paleozoic land; but it seems more probable that it was land only during the earlier Archæan age, and that it was submerged and buried in Cambrian time and not again brought to the light of day until it had been crushed into many local anticlines (Lesley), whose crests were uncovered by Permian and later erosion. The occurrence of Cambrian limestone on either side of South mountain, taken with its compound anticlinal structure, makes it likely that Medina time found this crystalline area entirely covered by the Cambrian beds; Medina sands must therefore have come from still farther to the southeast. A similar argument applies to the source of the Pocono and Pottsville beds. The measure of twenty miles as the former southeastern extension of the Paleozoic formations therefore seems to be a moderate one for the average of the whole series; perhaps forty would be nearer the truth.

Cambro-Silurian and Permian Deformations. This great series of once horizontal beds is now wonderfully distorted; but the distortions follow a general rule of trending northeast and southwest, and of diminishing in intensity from southeast to northwest. It is well known that in the Hudson valley a considerable disturbance occurred between Cambrian and Silurian time, for there the Medina lies unconformably on the Hudson river shales. It seems likely, for reasons that will be briefly given later on, that the same disturbance extended into Pennsylvania and farther southwest, but that it affected only the southeastern corner of the state; and that the unconformities in evidence of it, which are preserved in the Hudson valley, are here lost by subsequent erosion. Waste of the ancient land and its Cambro-Silurian annex still continued and furnished vast beds of sandstone and sandy shales to the remaining marine area, until at last the subsiding Paleozoic basin was filled up and the coal marshes extended broadly across it. At this time we may picture the drainage of the southeastern land area wandering rather slowly across the great Carboniferous plains to the still submerged basin far to the west: a condition of things that is not imperfectly represented, although in a somewhat more advanced stage, by the existing drainage of the mountains of the Carolinas across the more modern coastal plain to the Atlantic.

This condition was interrupted by the great Permian deformation that gave rise to the main ranges of the Appalachians in Pennsylvania, Virginia, and Tennessee. The Permian name seems appropriate here, for while the deformation may have begun at an earlier date, and may have continued into Triassic time, its culmination seems to have been within Permian limits. It was characterized by a resistless force of compression, exerted in a southeast-northwest line, in obedience to which the whole series of Paleozoic beds, even twenty or more thousand feet in thickness, was crowded gradually into great and small folds, trending northeast and southwest. The subjacent Archæan terrane doubtless shared more or less in the disturbance; for example, South mountain is described by Lesley as "not one mountain, but a system of mountains separated by valleys. It is, geologically considered, a system of anticlinals with troughs between. . . . It appears that the South mountain range ends eastward [in Cumberland and York counties] in a hand with five [anticlinal] fingers" (6).

It may be concluded with fair probability that the folds began to rise in the southeast, where they are crowded closest together, some of them having begun here while coal marshes were still forming farther west; and that the last folds to be begun were the fainter ones on the plateau, now seen in Negro mountain and Chestnut and Laurel ridges. In consequence of the inequalities in the force of compression or in the resistance of the yielding mass, the folds do not continue indefinitely with horizontal axes, but vary in height, rising or falling away in great variety. Several adjacent folds often follow some general control in this respect, their axes rising and falling together. It is to an unequal yielding of this kind that we owe the location of the anthracite synclinal basins in eastern Pennsylvania, the Coal Measures being now worn away from the prolongation of the synclines, which rise in either direction.

Perm-Triassic Denudation. During and for a long time after this period of mountain growth the destructive processes of erosion wasted the land and lowered its surface. An enormous amount of material was thus swept away and laid down in some unknown ocean bed. We shall speak of this as the Perm-Triassic period of erosion. A measure of its vast accomplishment is seen when we find that the Newark formation, which is generally correlated with Triassic or Jurassic time, lies unconformably on the eroded surface of Cambrian and Archæan rocks in the southeastern part of the state, where we have concluded that the Paleozoic series once existed; where the strata must have risen in a great mountain mass as a result of the Appalachian deformations; and whence they must therefore have been denuded before the deposition of the Newark beds. Not only so; the moderate sinuosity of the southeastern or under boundary of the Newark formation indicates clearly enough that the surface on which that portion of the formation lies is one of no great relief or inequality; and such a surface can be carved out of an elevated land only after long-continued denudation, by which topographical development is carried beyond the time of its greatest strength or maturity into the fainter expression of old age. This is a matter of some importance in our study of the development of the rivers of Pennsylvania; and it also constitutes a good part of the evidence already referred to as indicating that there must have been some earlier deformations of importance in the southeastern part of the state; for it is hardly conceivable that the great Paleozoic mass could have been so deeply worn off of the Newark belt between the making of the last of the coal beds and the first of the Newark. It seems more in accordance with the facts here recounted and with the teachings of geological history in general to suppose, as we have here, that something of the present deformation of the ancient rocks underlying the Newark beds was given at an early date, such as that of the Green mountain growth; and that a certain amount of the erosion of the folded beds was thus made possible in middle Paleozoic time; then again at some later date, as Permian, a second period of mountain growth arrived, and further folding was effected, and after this came deeper erosion, thus dividing the destructive work that was done into several parts, instead of crowding it all into the post-Carboniferous time ordinarily assigned to it. It is indeed not impossible that an important share of what we have called the Permian deformation was, as above suggested, accomplished in the southeastern part of the state while the coal beds were yet forming in the west; many grains of sand in the sandstones of the Coal Measures may have had several temporary halts in other sandstone beds between the time of their first erosion from the Archæan rocks and the much later time when they found the resting place that they now occupy.

Newark Deposition. After the great Paleozoic and Perm-Triassic erosions thus indicated, when the southeastern area of ancient mountains had been well worn down and the Permian folds of the central districts had acquired a well-developed drainage, there appeared an opportunity for local deposition in the slow depression of a northeast-southwest belt of the deeply wasted land, across the southeastern part of the state; and into this trough-like depression the waste from the adjacent areas on either side was carried, building the Newark formation. This may be referred to as the Newark or Trias-Jurassic period of deposition. The volume of this formation is unknown, as its thickness and original area are still undetermined; but it is pretty surely of many thousand feet in vertical measure, and its original area may have been easily a fifth or a quarter in excess of its present area, if not more than that. So great a local accumulation seems to indicate that while the belt of deposition was sinking, the adjacent areas were rising, in order to furnish a continual supply of material; the occurrence of heavy conglomerates along the margins of the Newark formation confirms this supposition, and the heavy breccias near Reading indicate the occurrence of a strong topography and a strong transporting agent to the northwest of this part of the Newark belt. It will be necessary, when the development of the ancestors of our present rivers is taken up, to consider the effects of the depression that determined the locus of Newark deposition and of the adjacent elevation that maintained a supply of material.

Jurassic Tilting. Newark deposition was stopped by a gradual reversal of the conditions that introduced it. The depression of the Newark belt was after a time reversed into elevation, accompanied by a peculiar tilting, and again the waste of the region was carried away to some unknown resting place. This disturbance, which may be regarded as a revival of the Permian activity, culminated in Jurassic, or at least in post-Newark time, and resulted in the production of the singular monoclinal attitude of the formation; and as far as I can correlate it with the accompanying change in the underlying structures, it involved there an over-pushing of the closed folds of the Archæan and Paleozoic rocks. This is illustrated in Figs. 12 and 13, in which the original and disturbed attitudes of the Newark and the

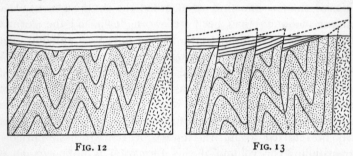

FIG. 12   FIG. 13

underlying formations are roughly shown, the over-pushing of the fundamental folds causing the monoclinal and probably faulted structure in the overlying beds. (See *Am. Jour. Sci.*, XXXII (1886), 342; and *U. S. Geol. Surv., VII Ann. Rep.* (1888), 486.) If this be true, we might suspect that the unsymmetrical attitude of the Appalachian folds, noted by Rogers as a characteristic of the range, is a feature that was intensified, if not originated, in Jurassic and not in Permian time.

It is not to be supposed that the Jurassic deformation was limited to the area of the Newark beds; it may have extended some way on either side; but it presumably faded out at no great distance, for it has not been detected in the history of the Atlantic and Mississippi regions remote from the Newark belt. In the district of the central folds of Pennsylvania, with which we are particularly concerned, this deformation was probably expressed in a further folding and over-pushing of the already partly folded beds, with rapidly decreasing effect to the northwest; and perhaps also by slip faults, which at the surface of the ground nearly followed the bedding planes ; but this is evidently hypothetical to a high degree. The essential point for our subsequent consideration is that the Jurassic deformation was probably accompanied by a moderate elevation, for it allowed the erosion of the Newark beds and of laterally adjacent areas as well.

Jura-Cretaceous Denudation. In consequence of this elevation, a new cycle of erosion was entered upon, which I shall call the Jura-Cretaceous cycle. It allowed the accomplishment of a vast work, which ended in the production of a general lowland of denudation, a wide area of faint relief, whose elevated remnants are now to be seen in the even ridge crests that so strongly characterize the central district, as well as in certain other even uplands, now etched by the erosion of a later cycle of destructive work. I shall not take space here for the deliberate statement of the argument leading to this end, but its elements are as follows : the extraordinarily persistent accordance among the crest-line altitudes of many Medina and Carboniferous ridges in the central district ; the generally corresponding elevation of the western plateau surface, itself a surface of erosion, but now trenched by relatively deep and narrow valleys ; the generally uniform and consistent altitude of the uplands in the crystalline highlands of northern New Jersey and in the South mountains of Pennsylvania ; and the extension of the same general surface, descending slowly eastward, over the even crest lines of the Newark trap ridges. Besides the evidence of less continental elevation thus deduced from the topography, it may be noted that a lower stand of the land in Cretaceous time than now is indicated by the erosion that the Cretaceous beds have suffered in consequence of the elevation that followed their deposition. The Cretaceous transgression in the western states doubtless bears on the problem also. Finally, it may be fairly urged that it is more accordant with what is known about old mountains in general to suppose that their mass has stood at different altitudes with respect to base-level during their long period of denudation than to suppose that they have held one altitude through all the time since their deformation.

It is natural enough that the former maintenance of some lower altitude than the present should have expression in the form of the country, if not now extinguished by subsequent erosion. It is simply the reverse of this statement that leads us to the above-stated conclusion. We may be sure that the long-maintained period of relative quiet was of great importance in allowing time for the mature adjustment of the rivers of the region, and hence due account must be taken of it in a later section. I say relative quiet, for there were certainly subordinate oscillations of greater or less value; McGee has detected records of one of these about the beginning of Cretaceous time, but its effects are not now known to be of geographical value; that is, they do not now manifest themselves in the form of the present surface of the land, but only in the manner of deposition and ancient erosion of certain deposits (*b*). Another subordinate oscillation in the sense of a moderate depression seems to have extended through middle and later Cretaceous time, resulting in an inland transgression of the sea and the deposit of the Cretaceous formation unconformably on the previous land surface for a considerable distance beyond the present margin of the formation. This is important as affecting our rivers. Although these oscillations were of considerable geological value, I do not think that for the present purposes they call for any primary division of the Jura-Cretaceous cycle; for as the result of this long period of denudation we find but a single record in the great lowland of erosion above described, a record of prime importance in the geographical development of our region that will often be referred to. The surface of faint relief then completed may be called the Cretaceous base-level lowland. It may be pictured as a low, undulating plain of wide extent, with a portion of its Atlantic margin submerged and covered over with a relatively thin marine deposit of sands, marls, and clays.

Tertiary Elevation and Denudation. This broad lowland is a lowland no longer. It has been raised over the greater part of its area into a highland, with an elevation of from one to three thousand feet, sloping gently eastward and descending under the Atlantic level near the present margin of the Cretaceous formation. The elevation seems to have taken place early in Tertiary time, and will be referred to as of that date. Opportunity was then given for the revival of the previously exhausted forces of denudation, and as a consequence we now see the formerly even surface of the plain greatly roughened by the incision of deep valleys and the opening of broad lowlands on its softer rocks. Only the harder rocks retain indications of the even surface which once stretched continuously across the whole area. The best indication of the average altitude at which the mass stood through the greater part of post-Cretaceous time is to be found on the weak shales of the Newark formation in New Jersey and Pennsylvania, and on the weak Cambrian limestones of the great Kittatinny valley; for both of these areas have been actually almost base-leveled again in the Tertiary cycle. They will be referred to as the Tertiary base-level lowlands ; and the valleys corresponding to them, cut in the harder rocks, as well as the rolling lowlands between the ridges of the central district of Pennsylvania will be regarded as of the same date. Whatever variations of level occurred in this cycle of development do not seem to have left marks of importance on the inland surface, though they may have had greater significance near the coast.

Later Changes of Level. Again at the close of Tertiary time, there was an elevation of moderate amount, and to this may be referred the trenches that are so distinctly cut across the Tertiary base-level lowland by the larger rivers, as well as the lateral shallower channels of the smaller streams. This will be called the Quaternary cycle ; and for the present no further mention of the oscillations known to have occurred in this division of time need be considered ; the reader may find careful discussion of them in the paper by McGee, above referred to. It is proper that I should add that the suggestion of base-leveling both of the crest lines and of the lowlands, which I have found so profitable in this and other work, is due largely to personal conference with Messrs. Gilbert and McGee of the Geological Survey ; but it is not desired to make them in any way responsible for the statements here given.

Illustrations of Pennsylvanian Topography. A few sketches made during a recent recess trip with several students through

Pennsylvania may be introduced in this connection. The first (Fig. 14) is a view from Jenny Jump mountain, on the northwestern side of the New Jersey highlands, looking northwest across the Kittatinny valley lowland to Blue, or Kittatinny, mountain, where it is cut at the Delaware Water Gap. The

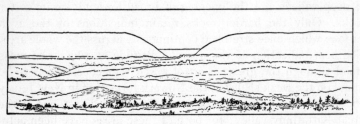

FIG. 14

extraordinarily level crest of the mountain preserves record of the Cretaceous base-level lowland; since the elevation of this ancient lowland, its softer rocks have, as it were, been etched out, leaving the harder ones in relief; thus the present valley lowland is to be explained. In consequence of the still later elevation of less amount, the Delaware has cut a trench in the present lowland which is partly seen to the left in the sketch. Fig. 15 is a general view of the Lehigh plateau and cañon, looking south from Bald mountain just above Penn Haven Junction.

FIG. 15

Blue mountain is the most distant crest, seen for a little space. The ridges near and above Mauch Chunk form the other outlines, all rising to an astonishingly even altitude, in spite of their great diversity of structure. Before the existing valleys were excavated, the upland surface must have been an even plain, — the Cretaceous base-level lowland elevated into a plateau. The valleys cut into the plateau during the Tertiary cycle are narrow here because the rocks are mostly hard. The steep slopes of the cañon-like valley of the Lehigh and the even crests of the ridges manifestly belong to different cycles of development. Figs. 16 and 17 are gaps, cut in Black Log and Shade mountains

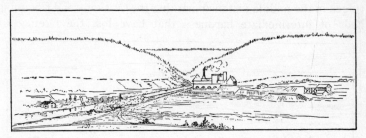

FIG. 16

by a small upper branch stream of the Juniata in southeastern Huntingdon county. The stream traverses a breached anticlinal of Medina sandstone, of which these mountains are the lateral members. A long, narrow valley is opened on the axial Trenton limestone between the two. The gaps are not opposite to each other, and therefore in looking through either gap from the outer country the even crest of the further ridge is seen beyond the axial valley. The gap in Black Log mountain (Fig. 16) is

FIG. 17

located on a small fracture, but in this respect it is unlike most of its fellows. (See *Second Geol. Surv. Pa.*, Report T_3, 19.) The striking similarity of the two views illustrates the uniformity that so strongly characterizes the Medina ridges of the central district. Fig. 18 is in good part an ideal view, based on sketches on the upper Susquehanna, and designed to present a typical illustration of the more significant features of the region. It shows the even crest lines of a high Medina or Pocono ridge in the background, retaining the form given to it in the Cretaceous cycle; the even lowlands in the foreground, opened on the weaker Siluro-Devonian rocks in the Tertiary cycle; and the uneven ridges in the middle distance marking the Oriskany and Chemung beds of intermediate hardness that have lost the Cretaceous

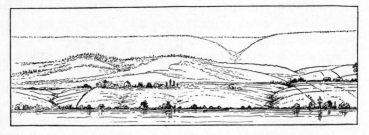

FIG. 18

level and yet have not been reduced to the Tertiary lowland. The Susquehanna flows distinctly below the lowland plain, and the small side streams run in narrow trenches of late Tertiary and Quaternary date.

If this interpretation is accepted, and the Permian mountains are seen to have been once greatly reduced and at a later time worn out, while the ridges of to-day are merely the relief left by the etching of Tertiary valleys in a Cretaceous base-level lowland, then we may well conclude with Powell that "mountains cannot remain long as mountains; they are ephemeral topographic forms" (*b*, 196).

III. GENERAL CONCEPTION OF THE HISTORY OF A RIVER

The Complete Cycle of River Life: Youth, Adolescence, Maturity, and Old Age. The general outline of an ideal river's history may now be considered, preparatory to examining the special history of the rivers of Pennsylvania as controlled by the geological events just narrated.

Rivers are so long-lived and survive with more or less modification so many changes in the attitude and even in the structure of the land, that the best way of entering on their discussion seems to be to examine the development of an ideal river of simple history, and from the general features thus discovered, it may then be possible to unravel the complex sequence of events that lead to the present condition of actual rivers of complicated history.

A river that is established on a new land may be called an original river. It must at first be of the kind known as a consequent river, for it has no ancestor from which to be derived. Examples of simple original rivers may be seen in young plains, of which southern New Jersey furnishes a fair illustration. Examples of essentially original rivers may be seen also in regions of recent and rapid displacement, such as the Jura or the broken country of southern Idaho, where the directly consequent character of the drainage leads us to conclude that, if any rivers occupied these regions before their recent deformation, they were so completely extinguished by the newly made slopes that we see nothing of them now.

Once established, an original river advances through its long life, manifesting certain peculiarities of youth, maturity, and old age, by which its successive stages of growth may be recognized without much difficulty. For the sake of simplicity, let us suppose the land mass, on which an original river has begun its work, stands perfectly still after its first elevation or deformation, and so remains until the river has completed its task of carrying away all the mass of rocks that rise above its base-level. The lapse of time will be called a cycle in the life of a river. A complete cycle is a long measure of time in regions of great elevation or of hard rocks; but whether or not any river ever passed through a single cycle of life without interruption we need not now inquire. Our purpose is only to learn what changes it would experience if it did thus develop steadily from infancy to old age without disturbance.

In its infancy the river drains its basin imperfectly, for it is then embarrassed by the original inequalities of the surface, and lakes collect in all the depressions. At such time the ratio of evaporation to rainfall is relatively large, and the ratio of transported land waste to rainfall is small. The channels followed by the streams that compose the river as a whole are narrow and shallow, and their number is small compared to that which will be developed at a later stage. The divides by which the side streams are separated are poorly marked, and in level countries are surfaces of considerable area and not lines at all. It is only in the later maturity of a system that the divides are reduced to lines by the consumption of the softer rocks on either side. The difference between constructional forms and these forms that are due to the action of denuding forces is in a general way so easily.recognized that immaturity and maturity of a drainage area can be readily discriminated. In the truly infantile drainage system of the Red River of the North, the interstream areas are so absolutely flat that water collects on them in wet weather, not having either original structural slope or subsequently developed denuded slope to lead it to the streams. On the almost equally young lava blocks of southern Oregon, the well-marked slopes are as yet hardly channeled by the flow of rain down them, and the depressions among the tilted blocks are still undrained, unfilled basins.

As the river becomes adolescent, its channels are deepened and all the larger ones descend close to base-level. If local contrasts of hardness allow a quick deepening of the downstream part of the channel, while the part next upstream resists erosion, a cascade or waterfall results ; but, like the lakes of earlier youth, it is evanescent and endures but a small part of the whole cycle of growth ; but the falls on the small headwater streams of a large river may last into its maturity, just as there are young twigs on the branches of a large tree. With the deepening of the channels, there comes an increase in the number of gulleys on the slopes of the channel ; the gulleys grow into ravines and these into side valleys, joining their master streams at right angles (La Noë and Margerie). With their continued development the maturity of the system is reached ; it is marked by an almost complete acquisition of every part of the original constructional surface by erosion under the guidance of the streams, so that every drop of rain that falls finds a way prepared to lead it to a stream and then to the ocean, its goal. The lakes of initial imperfection have long since disappeared ; the waterfalls of adolescence have been worn back, unless on the still young headwaters. With the increase of the number of side streams, ramifying into all parts of the drainage basin, there is a proportionate increase in the surface of the valley slopes, and with this comes an increase in the rate of waste under atmospheric forces ; hence it is at maturity that the river receives and carries the greatest load ; indeed, the increase may be carried so far that the lower trunk stream, of gentle slope in its early maturity, is unable to carry the load brought to it by the upper branches, and therefore resorts to the temporary expedient of laying it aside in a flood plain. The level of the flood plain is sometimes built up faster than the small side streams of the lower course can fill their valleys, and hence they are converted for a little distance above their mouths into shallow lakes. The growth of the flood plain also results in carrying the point of junction of tributaries farther and farther downstream, and at last in turning lateral streams aside from the main stream, sometimes forcing them to follow independent courses to the sea (Lombardini). But although thus separated from the main trunk, it would be no more rational to regard such streams as independent rivers than it would be to regard the branch of an old tree, now fallen to the ground in the decay of advancing age, as an independent plant ; both are detached portions of a single individual, from which they have been separated in the normal processes of growth and decay.

In the later and quieter old age of a river system, the waste of the land is yielded more slowly by reason of the diminishing slopes of the valley sides ; then the headwater streams deliver less detritus to the main channel, which, thus relieved, turns to its postponed task of carrying its former excess of load to the sea, and cuts terraces in its flood plain, preparatory to sweeping it away. It does not always find the buried channel again, and perhaps settling down on a low spur a little to one side of its old line, produces a rapid or a low fall on the lower slope of such an obstruction (Penck). Such courses may be called locally superimposed.

It is only during maturity and for a time before and afterwards that the three divisions of a river, commonly recognized, appear most distinctly ; the torrent portion being the still young headwater branches, growing by gnawing backwards at their sources ; the valley portion proper, where longer time of work has enabled the valley to obtain a greater depth and width ; and the lower flood-plain portion, where the temporary deposition of the excess of load is made until the activity of middle life is past.

" Maturity " seems to be a proper term to apply to this long-enduring stage ; for as in organic forms, where the term first came into use, it here also signifies the highest development of all functions between a youth of endeavor towards better work and an old age of relinquishment of fullest powers. It is the mature river in which the rainfall is best led away to the sea, and which carries with it the greatest load of land waste ; it is at maturity that the regular descent and steady flow of the river is best developed, being the least delayed in lakes and least over-hurried in impetuous falls.

Maturity past, and the power of the river is on the decay. The relief of the land diminishes, for the streams no longer deepen their valleys, although the hill-tops are degraded ; and with the general loss of elevation, there is a failure of rainfall to a certain extent ; for it is well known that up to certain considerable altitudes rainfall increases with height. A hyeto-graphic and a hypsometric map of a country for this reason show a marked correspondence. The slopes of the headwaters decrease and the valley sides widen so far that the land waste descends from them more slowly than before. Later, what with failure of rainfall and decrease of slope, there is perhaps a return to the early imperfection of drainage, and the number of side streams diminishes as branches fall from a dying tree. The flood plains of maturity are carried down to the sea, and at last the river settles down to an old age of well-earned rest with gentle flow and light load, little work remaining to be done. The great task that the river entered upon is completed.

Mutual Adjustment of River Courses. In certain structures, chiefly those of mountainous disorder on which the streams are at first high above base-level, there is a process of adjustment extremely characteristic of quiet river development, by which the down-hill courses that were chosen in early life, and as we may say unadvisedly and with the heedlessness and little fore-sight of youth, are given up for others better fitted for the work of the mature river system. A change of this kind happens when the young stream, taking the lowest line for its guide, happens to flow on a hard bed at a considerable height above base-level, while its branches on one side or the other have opened channels on softer beds ; a part of the main channel may then be deserted by the withdrawal of its upper waters to a lower course by way of a side stream. The change to better adjustment also happens when the initial course of the main stream is much longer than a course that may be offered to its upper portion by the backward gnawing of an adjacent stream (Löwl, Penck). Sometimes the lateral cutting or plana-tion that characterizes the main trunk of a mature river gives it possession of an adjacent smaller stream whose bed is at a higher level (Gilbert). A general account of these processes may be found in Philippson's serviceable "Studien über Wasserscheiden" (Leipzig, 1886). This whole matter is of much importance and deserves deliberate examination. It should be remembered that changes in river courses of the kind now referred to are un-connected with any external disturbance of the river basin, and are purely normal spontaneous acts during advancing development. Two examples, pertinent to our special study, will be considered.

Let *AB* (Fig. 19) be a stream whose initial consequent course led it down the gently sloping axial trough of a syncline. The constructional surface of the syncline is shown by contours. Let the succession of beds to be discovered by erosion be indicated in a section, laid in proper position on the several diagrams, but revolved into the horizontal plane, the harder beds being dotted and the base-level standing at *OO*. Small side streams will soon be developed on the slopes of the syncline in positions deter-mined by cross-fractures or more often by what we call accident ; the action of streams in similar synclines on the outside of the inclosing anticlines will be omitted for the sake of simplicity. In time the side streams will cut through the harder upper bed *M* and enter the softer bed *N*, on which longitudinal channels, indicated by hachures, will be extended along the strike (Fig. 20) (La Noë and Margerie). Let these be called "subsequent" streams. Consider two side streams of this kind, *C* and *D*, heading against each other at *E*, one joining the main stream lower down the axis of the syncline than the other. The headwaters of C will rob the headwaters of D, because the deepening of the channel of D is retarded by its having to join the main stream at a point where the hard bed in the axis of the fold holds the main channel well above base-level. The notch cut by D will then be changed from a water gap to a wind gap, and the upper portion of D will find exit through the notch cut by C, as in Fig. 21. As other subsequent headwaters make capture of C, the greater depth to which the lateral valley is cut on the soft rock causes a slow migration of the divides in the abandoned gaps towards the main stream, and before long the upper part of the main stream itself will be led out of the synclinal axis to follow the monoclinal valley at one side for a distance (Fig. 22), until the axis can be rejoined through the gap where the axial

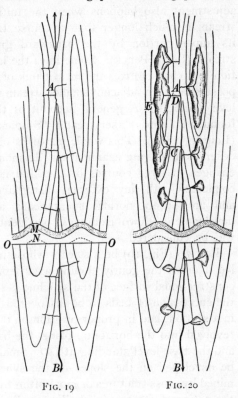

FIG. 19   FIG. 20

portion of the controlling hard bed is near or at base-level. The upper part of the synclinal trough will then be attacked by under-cutting on the slope of the quickly deepened channels of the lateral streams, and the hard bed will be worn away in the higher part of the axis before it is consumed in the lower part. The location of the successful lateral stream on one or the other side of the syncline may be determined by the dip of

the beds, gaps being cut quicker on steep than on gentle dips.
If another hard bed is encountered below the soft one, the process will be repeated ; and the mature arrangement of the streams
will be as in Fig. 23 (on a smaller scale than the preceding),
running obliquely off the axis of the fold where a hard bed of
the syncline rises above base-level, and returning to the axis

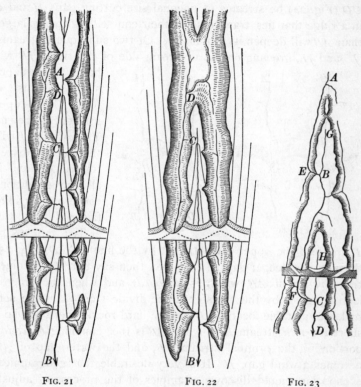

FIG. 21   FIG. 22   FIG. 23

where the hard bed is below or at base-level ; a monoclinal
stream wandering gradually from the axis along the strike of
the soft bed *AE*, by which the side valley is located, and returning abruptly to the axis by a cataclinal [1] stream in a transverse

[1] See the terminology suggested by Powell, Exploration of the Colorado River
of the West (1875), 160. This terminology is applicable only to the most detailed
study of our rivers, by reason of their crossing so many folds and changing so
often from longitudinal to transverse courses.

gap *EB* in the next higher hard bed, and there rejoining the diminished representative or survivor of the original axial or synclinal stream *GB*.

Terminology of Rivers changed by Adjustment. A special terminology is needed for easy reference to the several parts of the streams concerned in such an adjustment. Let *AB* and *CD* (Fig. 24) be streams of unequal size cutting gaps *H* and *G* in a ridge that lies transverse to their course. *CD* being larger than *AB* will deepen its gap faster. Of two subsequent streams, *JE* and *JF*, growing on the upstream side of the ridge, *JE* will

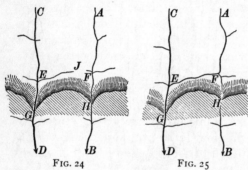

FIG. 24   FIG. 25

have the steeper slope, because it joins the deeper master stream. The divide *J* will therefore be driven toward *AB*, and if all the conditions concerned conspire favorably, *JE* will at last tap *AB* at *F*, and lead the upper part, *AF*, out by the line *FEGD* (Fig. 25) through the deeper gap *G*. We may then say that *JE* becomes the *divertor* of *AF*, which is *diverted;* and when the process is completed, by the transfer of the divide from *J*, on the soft rocks, to a stable location, *H*, on the hard rocks, there will be a short *inverted* stream *HF*; while *HB* is the remaining *beheaded* portion of the original stream *AB*, and the water gap of *AB* becomes a wind gap, *H*. It is very desirable that geographical exploration should discover examples of the process of adjustment in its several stages. The preparatory stage is easily recognized by the difference in the size of the two main streams, the difference in the depth of their gaps, and the unsymmetrical position of the divide *J*. The very brief stage of transition gives us the rare examples of bifurcating streams. For a short time after capture of the diverted stream by the divertor, the new divide will lie between *F* and *H*, in an unstable position, the duration of this time depending on the energy of the process of capture.

The consequences resulting from readjustments of this kind, by which their recent occurrence can be detected, are : a relatively sudden increase of volume of the divertor and hence a rapid deepening of the course of the diverting stream *FE*, and of the diverted *AF*, near the point of capture ; small side streams of these two being unable to keep pace with this change will join their masters in local rapids, which work upstream gradually and fade away (Löwl, Penck, McGee). The expanded portion *ED* of the larger stream *CD*, already of faint slope, may be locally overcome for a time with the increase of detritus that will be thus delivered to it at the entrance *E* of the divertor ; while the beheaded stream *HB* will find itself embarrassed to live up to the habits of its large valley (Heim). Geographical exploration with these matters in mind offers opportunity for the most attractive discoveries.

Examples of Adjustment. Another case is roughly figured in the next three diagrams (Figs. 26, 27, 28). Two adjacent synclinal streams, *EA* and *HB*, join a transverse master stream, *C*, but the synclines are of different forms ; the surface axis of one, *EA*, stands at some altitude above base-level until it nearly reaches the place of the transverse stream ; while the axis of the other, *HB*, descends near base-level at a considerable distance from the transverse stream. As lateral valleys *E* and *D* are opened on the anticline between the synclines by a process similar to that already described, the divide separating them will shift towards the stream of fainter slope, that is, towards the syncline *EA*, whose axis holds its hard beds above base-level ; and in time the upper part of the main stream will be withdrawn from this syncline to follow an easier course by crossing to the other, as in Fig. 27. If the elevation of the synclinal axis *AES* take the shape of a long, flat arch, descending at the farther end into a synclinal lake basin, *S*, whose outlet is along the arching axis *SA*, then the mature arrangement of stream courses will lead the lake outlet away from the axis by some gap in the nearer ascending part of the arch where the controlling hard bed falls near to base-level, as at *F* (Fig. 28), and will take it by some subsequent course, *FD*, across the lowland that is opened on the soft beds between the synclines, and carry it into the lower syncline *HB*, at *D*, where the hard beds descend below base-level.

The variety of adjustments following the general principle here indicated is infinite. Changes of greater or less value are thus introduced in the initial drainage areas, until, after attaining an attitude of equilibrium, further change is arrested, or if occurring,

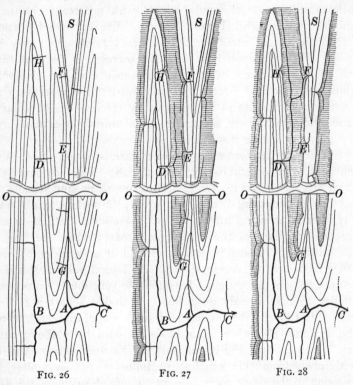

Fig. 26   Fig. 27   Fig. 28

is relatively insignificant. It should be noticed that the new stream courses thus chosen are not named by any of the terms now current to express the relation of stream and land history; they are neither consequent, antecedent, nor superimposed. The stream is truly still an original stream, although no longer young; but its channel is not in all parts strictly consequent on the initial constructional form of the land that it drains. Streams thus rearranged may therefore be named original streams of mature adjustment.

It should be clearly recognized that the process of adjustment is a very slow one, unless measured in the extremely long units of a river's life. It progresses no faster than the weathering away of the slopes of a divide, and here as a rule weathering is deliberate to say the least, unless accelerated by a fortunate combination of favoring conditions. Among these conditions, great altitude of the mass exposed to erosion stands first, and deep channeling of streams below the surface — that is, the adolescent stage of drainage development — stands second. The opportunity for the lateral migration of a divide will depend on the inequality of the slopes on its two sides, and here the most important factors are length of the two opposite stream courses from the water parting to the common base-level of the two, and inequality of structure by which one stream may have an easy course and the other a hard one. It is manifest that all these conditions for active shifting of divides are best united in young and high mountain ranges, and hence it is that river adjustments have been found and studied more in the Alps than elsewhere.

Revival of Rivers by Elevation and Drowning by Depression. I make no contention that any river in the world ever passed through a simple uninterrupted cycle of the orderly kind here described; but by examining many rivers, some young and some old, I do not doubt that this portrayal of the ideal would be found to be fairly correct if opportunity were offered for its development. The intention of the sketch is simply to prepare the way for the better understanding of our actual rivers of more complicated history.

At the close or at any time during the passage of an initial cycle such as the one just considered, the drainage area of a river system may be bodily elevated. The river is then turned back to a new youth and enters a new cycle of development. This is an extremely common occurrence with rivers, whose life is so long that they commonly outlive the duration of a quiescent stage in the history of the land. Such rivers may be called revived. Examples may be given in which streams are now in their second or third period of revival, the elevations that separate their cycles following so soon that but little work was accomplished in the quiescent intervals.

The antithesis of this is the effect of depression, by which the lower course may be drowned, flooded, or fjorded. This change is, if slow, favorable to the development of flood plains in the lower course ; but it is not essential to their production. If the change is more rapid, open estuaries are formed, to be transformed to delta lowlands later on.

Opportunity for New Adjustments with Revival. One of the most common effects of the revival of a river by general elevation is a new adjustment of its course to a greater or less extent, as a result of the new relation of base-level to the hard and soft beds on which the streams had adjusted themselves in the previous cycle. Synclinal mountains are most easily explained as results of drainage changes of this kind (*Science*, December 21, 1888).

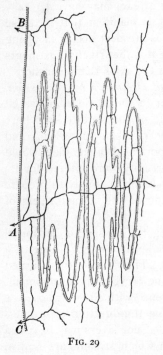

FIG. 29

Streams thus rearranged may be said to be adjusted through elevation or revival. It is to be hoped that, as our study advances, single names of brief and appropriate form may replace these paraphrases ; but at present it seems advisable to keep the desired idea before the mind by a descriptive phrase, even at the sacrifice of brevity. A significant example may be described.

Let it be supposed that an originally consequent river system has lived into advanced maturity on a surface whose structure is, like that of Pennsylvania, composed of closely adjacent anticlinal and synclinal folds with rising and falling axes, and that a series of particularly resistant beds composes the upper members of the folded mass. The master stream *A* (Fig. 29) at maturity still resides where the original folds were lowest, but the side streams have departed more or less from the axes of the synclinals that they first followed, in accordance with the principles of adjustment presented above. The relief of the surface is moderate, except around the synclinal troughs, where the rising margins of the hard beds still appear as ridges of more or less prominence. The minute hachures in Fig. 29 are drawn on the outcrop side of these ridges. Now suppose a general elevation of the region, lifting the synclinal troughs of the hard beds up to base-level or even somewhat above it. The deepening of the revived master stream will be greatly retarded by reason of its having to cross so many outcrops of the hard beds, and thus excellent opportunity will be given for readjustment by the growth of some diverting stream, _B_, whose beginning on adjacent softer rocks was already made in the previous cycle. This will capture the main river at some upstream point, and draw it nearly all away from its hard path across the synclinal troughs to an easier path across the lowlands that had been opened on the underlying softer beds, leaving only a small beheaded remnant in the lower course. The final rearrangement may be indicated in Fig. 30. It should be noted that every capture of branches of the initial main stream made by the diverting stream adds to its ability for further encroachments, for with increase of volume the channel

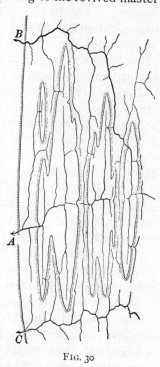

Fig. 30

is deepened and a flatter slope is assumed, and the whole process of pushing away the divides is thereby accelerated. In general it may be said that the larger the stream and the less its elevation above base-level, the less likely is it to be diverted, for with large volume and small elevation it will early cut down its channel so close to base-level that no other stream can offer it a better course to the sea; it may also be said that, as a rule, of two equal streams, the headwaters of the one having a longer or a harder course will be diverted by a branch of the stream on the shorter or easier course. Every case must therefore be examined for itself before the kind of rearrangement that may be expected or that may have already taken place can be discovered.

Antecedent and Superimposed Rivers. It not infrequently happens that the surface, on which a drainage system is more or less fully developed, suffers deformation by tilting, folding, or faulting. Then, in accordance with the rate of disturbance, and dependent on the size and slope of the streams and the resistance of the rocks, the streams will be more or less rearranged, some of the larger ones persisting in their courses and cutting their channels down almost as fast as the mass below them is raised and offered to their action. It is manifest that streams of large volume and considerable slope are the ones most likely to persevere in this way, while small streams and larger ones of moderate slope may be turned from their former courses to new courses consequent on the new constructional form of the land. Hence, after a disturbance we may expect to find the smaller streams of the former cycle pretty completely destroyed, while some of the larger ones may still persist; these would then be called antecedent streams in accordance with the nomenclature introduced by Powell (*a*, 153, 163–166). A fuller acquaintance with the development of our rivers will probably give us examples of river systems of all degrees of extinction or persistence at times of disturbance.

Since Powell introduced the idea of antecedent valleys and Tietze, Medlicott, and others showed the validity of the explanation in other regions than the one for which it was first proposed, it has found much acceptance. Löwl's objection to it does not seem to me to be nearly so well founded as his suggestion of an additional method of river development by means of backward headwater erosion and subsequent capture of other streams, as already described. And yet I cannot help thinking that the explanation of transverse valleys as antecedent courses savors of the Gordian method of explaining a difficult matter. The case of the Green river, to which Powell first gave this explanation, seems well supported; the examples given by Medlicott in the Himalayas are as good; but still it does not seem advisable to explain all transverse streams in this way, merely because they are transverse. Perhaps one reason why the explanation has become so popular is that it furnishes an escape from the old catastrophic idea that fractures control the location of valleys, and is at the same time fully accordant with the ideas of the uniformitarian school that have become current in this half of our century. But when it is remembered that most of the streams of a region are extinguished at the time of mountain growth, that only a few of the larger ones can survive, and that there are other ways in which transverse streams may originate (Hilber), it is evident that the possibility of any given transverse stream being antecedent must be regarded only as a suggestion, until some independent evidence is introduced in its favor. This may be difficult to find, but it certainly must be searched for; if not then forthcoming, the best conclusion may be to leave the case open until the evidence appears. Certainly, if we find a river course that is accordant in its location with the complicated results of other methods of origin, then the burden of proof may be said to lie with those who would maintain that an antecedent origin would locate the river in so specialized a manner. Even if a river persist for a time in an antecedent course, this may not prevent its being afterwards affected by the various adjustments and revivals that have been explained above; rivers so distinctly antecedent as the Green and the Sutlej may hereafter be more or less affected by processes of adjustment, which they are not yet old enough to experience. Hence, in mountains as old as the Appalachians the courses of the present rivers need not coincide with the location of the pre-Permian rivers, even if the latter persisted in their courses through the growth of the Permian folding; subsequent elevations and adjustments to hard beds, at first buried and unseen, may have greatly displaced them, in accordance with Löwl's principle.

When the deeper channeling of a stream discovers an unconformable subjacent terrane, the streams persist, at least for a time, in the courses that were determined in the overlying mass; they are then called superimposed (Powell), inherited (Shaler), or epigenetic (Richthofen). Such streams are particularly liable to readjustment by transfer of channels from courses that lead them over hard beds to others on which the hard beds are avoided; for the first choice of channels, when the unconformable cover was still present, was made without any knowledge of the buried rock structure or of the difficulties in which the streams would be involved when they encountered it. The examples of falls produced when streams terrace their flood plains and run on buried spurs has already been referred to as superimposed; and the rivers of Minnesota now disclosing half-buried ledges here and there may be instanced as illustrating the transition stage between simple consequent courses, determined by the form of the drift sheet on which their flow began, and the fully inconsequent courses that will be developed there in the future.

Simple, Compound, Composite, and Complex Rivers. We have thus far considered an ideal river. It now seems advisable to introduce a few terms with which to indicate concisely certain well-marked peculiarities in the history of actual rivers.

An original river has already been defined as one which first takes possession of a land area, or which replaces a completely extinguished river on a surface of rapid deformation.

A river may be simple if its drainage area is of practically one kind of structure and of one age, like the rivers of southern New Jersey. Such rivers are generally small. It may be composite when drainage areas of different structure are included in the basin of a single stream. This is the usual case.

A compound river is one which is of different ages in its different parts, as certain rivers of North Carolina which have old headwaters rising in the mountains and young, lower courses traversing the coastal plain.

A river is complex when it has entered a second or later cycle of development; the headwaters of a compound river are therefore complex, while the lower course may be simple in its first cycle. The degree of complexity measures the number of cycles that the river has entered.

When the study of rivers is thus attempted, its necessary complications may at first seem so great as to render it of no value; but in answer to this I believe that it may be fairly urged that, although complicated, the results are true to nature, and if so, we can have no ground of complaint against them. Moreover, while it is desirable to reduce the study of the development of rivers to its simplest form in order to make it available for instruction and investigation, it must be remembered that this cannot be done by neglecting to investigate the whole truth in the hope of avoiding too great complexity, but that simplicity can be reached safely only through fullness of knowledge, if at all.

It is with these points in mind that I have attempted to decipher the history of the rivers of Pennsylvania. We find in the Susquehanna, which drains a great area in the central part of the state, an example of a river which is at once composite, compound, and highly complex. It drains districts of diverse structure; it traverses districts of different ages; and it is at present in its fourth or fifth degree of complexity, its fourth or fifth cycle of development at least. In unraveling its history and searching out the earlier courses of streams which may have long since been abandoned in the processes of mature adjustment, it will be seen that the size of the present streams is not always a measure of their previous importance, and to this we may ascribe the difficulty that attends the attempt to decipher a river's history from general maps of its stream lines. Nothing but a detailed examination of geological structure and history suffices to detect facts and conditions that are essential to the understanding of the result.

If the postulates that I shall use seem unsound and the arguments seem overdrawn, error may at least be avoided by not holding fast to the conclusions that are presented, for they are presented only tentatively. I do not feel by any means absolutely persuaded of the correctness of the results, but at the same time deem them worth giving out for discussion. The whole investigation was undertaken as an experiment to see where it might lead, and with the hope that it might lead at least to a serious study of our river problems.

IV. THE DEVELOPMENT OF THE RIVERS OF PENNSYLVANIA

Means of Distinguishing between Antecedent and Adjusted Consequent Rivers. The outline of the geological history of Pennsylvania given above affords means of dividing the long progress of the development of our rivers into the several cycles which make up their complete life. We must go far back into the past and imagine ancient streams flowing down from the Archæan land towards the Paleozoic sea, gaining length by addition to their lower portions as the land grew with the building on of successive mountain ranges; for example, if there were a Cambro-Silurian deformation, a continuation of the Green mountains into Pennsylvania, we suppose that the preëxistent streams must in some manner have found their way westward to the new coast line; and from the date of this mountain growth it is apparent that any streams then born must have advanced far in their history before the greater Appalachian disturbance began. At the beginning of the latter, as of the former, there must have been streams running from the land into the sea, and at times of temporary elevation of the broad sand flats of the coal measures such streams must have had considerable additions to their lower length, rising in long-growing Archæan highlands or mountains, snow-capped and drained by glaciers for all we can say to the contrary, descending across the Green mountain belt, by that time worn to moderate relief in the far-advanced stage of its topographical development, and finally flowing across the coal-measure lowlands of recent appearance. It was across the lower courses of such rivers that the Appalachian folds were formed, and the first step in our problem consists in deciding, if possible, whether the streams held their courses after the antecedent fashion, or whether they were thrown into new courses by the growing folds, so that a new drainage system would be formed. Possibly both conditions prevailed, the larger streams holding their courses little disturbed, and the smaller ones disappearing, to be replaced by others as the slopes of the growing surface should demand. It is not easy to make choice in this matter. To decide that the larger streams persisted and are still to be seen in the greater rivers of to-day, only reversed in direction of flow, is certainly a simple method of treating the problem, but unless some independent reasons are found for this choice, it savors of assumption. Moreover, it is difficult to believe that any streams, even if antecedent and more or less persistent for a time during the mountain growth, could preserve till now their pre-Appalachian courses through all the varying conditions presented by the alternations of hard and soft rocks through which they have had to cut, and at all the different altitudes above base-level in which they have stood. A better means of deciding the question will be to admit provisionally the occurrence of a completely original system of consequent drainage, located in perfect accord with the slopes of the growing mountains; to study out the changes of stream courses that would result from later disturbances and from the mutual adjustments of the several members of such a system in the different cycles of its history; and finally to compare the courses thus deduced with those now seen. If there be no accord, either the method is wrong or the streams are not consequent but of some other origin, such as antecedent; if the accord between deduction and fact be well marked, varying only where no definite location can be given to the deduced streams, but agreeing where they can be located more precisely, then it seems to me that the best conclusion is distinctly in favor of the correctness of the deductions. For it is not likely, even if it be possible, that antecedent streams should have accidentally taken, before the mountains were formed, just such locations as would have resulted from the subsequent growth of the mountains and from the complex changes in the initial river courses due to later adjustments. I shall therefore follow the deductive method thus indicated and attempt to trace out the history of a completely original, consequent system of drainage accordant with the growth of the central mountain district.

In doing this, it is first necessary to restore the constructional topography of the region; that is, the form that the surface would have had if no erosion had accompanied the deformation. This involves certain postulates which must be clearly conceived if any measure of confidence is to be gained in the results based upon them.

Postulates of the Argument. In the first place, I assume an essential constancy in the thickness of the Paleozoic sediments over the entire area in question. This is warranted here because the known variations of thickness are relatively of a second order, and will not affect the distribution of high and low ground as produced by the intense Permian folding. The reasons for maintaining that the whole series had a considerable extension southeast of the present margin of the Medina sandstone have already been presented.

In the second place, I shall assume that the dips and folds of the beds now exposed at the surface of the ground may be projected upwards into the air in order to restore the form of the eroded beds. This is certainly inadmissible in detail, for it cannot be assumed that the folded slates and limestones of the Nittany valley, for instance, give any close indication of the form that the coal measures would have taken, had they extended over this district, unworn. But, in a general way, the Nittany massif was a complex arch in the coal measures as well as in the Cambrian beds; for our purpose and in view of the moderate relief of the existing topography it suffices to say that wherever the lower rocks are now revealed in anticlinal structure, there was a great upfolding and elevation of the original surface; and wherever the higher rocks are still preserved, there was a relatively small elevation.

In the third place, I assume that by reconstructing from the completed folds the form which the country would have had if unworn, we gain a sufficiently definite picture of the form through which it actually passed at the time of initial and progressive folding. The difference between the form of the folds completely restored and the form that the surface actually reached is rather one of degree than of kind; the two must correspond in the general distribution of high and low ground, and this is the chief consideration in our problem. When we remember how accurately water finds its level, it will be clearer that what is needed in the discussion is the location of the regions that were relatively raised and lowered, as we shall then have marked out the general course of the consequent water ways and the trend of the intervening constructional ridges.

Accepting these postulates, it may be said, in brief, that the outlines of the formations as at present exposed are in effect so many contour lines of the old constructional surface, on which the Permian rivers took their consequent courses. Where the Trenton limestone is now seen, the greatest amount of overlying strata must have been removed; hence the outline of the Trenton formation is our highest contour line. Where the Helderberg limestone appears, there has been a less amount of material removed; hence the Helderberg outcrop is a contour of less elevation. Where the coal beds are still preserved, there has been least wasting, and these beds therefore mark the lowest contour of the early surface. It is manifest that this method assumes that the present outcrops are on a level surface; this is not true, for the ridges through the state rise a thousand feet more or less over the intervening valley lowlands, and yet the existing relief does not count for much in discussing the enormous relief of the Permian surface that must have been measured in tens of thousands of feet at the time of its greatest strength.

Constructional Permian Topography and Consequent Drainage. A rough restoration of the early constructional topography is given in Fig. 31 for the central part of the state, the closest shading being the area of the Trenton limestone, indicating the highest ground, or, better, the places of greatest elevation, while the Carboniferous area is unshaded, indicating the early lowlands. The prevalence of northeast and southwest trends was then even more pronounced than now. Several of the stronger elements of form deserve names for convenient reference. Thus we have the great Kittatinny, or Cumberland highland, *CC*, on the southeast, backed by the older mountains of Cambrian and Archæan rocks, falling by the Kittatinny slope to the synclinal lowland troughs of the central district. In this lower ground lay the synclinal troughs of the eastern coal regions, and the more local Broad Top basin, *BT*, on the southwest, then better than now deserving the name of basins. Beyond the corrugated area that connected the coal basins rose the great Nittany highland, *N*, and its southwest extension in the Bedford range, with the less conspicuous Kishicoquilas highland, *K*, in the foreground. Beyond all stretched the great Allegheny lowland plains. The names thus suggested are compounded of the local names of to-day and the morphological names of Permian time.

What would be the drainage of such a country? Deductively we are led to believe that it consisted of numerous streams, as marked in full lines on the figure, following synclinal axes until

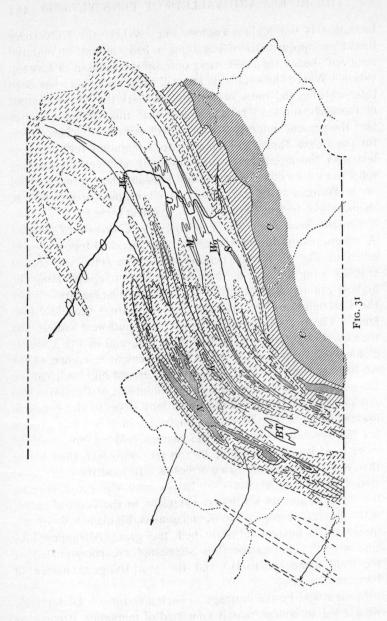

FIG. 31

some master streams led them across the intervening anticlinal ridges at the lowest points of their crests and away into the open country to the northwest. All the inclosed basins would hold lakes, overflowing at the lowest part of the rim. The general discharge of the whole system would be to the northwest. Here again we must resort to special names for the easy indication of these well-marked features of the ancient and now apparently lost drainage system. The master stream of the region is the great Anthracite river, carrying the overflow of the Anthracite lakes off to the northwest, and there perhaps turning along one of the faintly marked synclines of the plateau and joining the original Ohio, which was thus confirmed in its previous location across the Carboniferous marshes. The synclinal streams that entered the Anthracite lakes from the southwest (Fig. 31) may be named, beginning on the south, the Swatara (*S*), the Wiconisco (*Wo*), the Tuscarora-Mahanoy (*M*), the Juniata-Catawissa (*C*), and the Wyoming (*Wy*). One of these, probably the fourth, led the overflow from the Broad Top lake into the Catawissa lake on the middle Anthracite river. The Nittany highland formed a strong divide between the central and northwestern rivers, and on its outer slope there must have been streams descending to the Allegheny lowlands; and some of these may be regarded as the lower courses of Carboniferous rivers that once rose in the Archæan mountains, now beheaded by the growth of mountain ranges across their middle.

The Jura Mountains Homologous with the Permian Alleghenies. However willing one may be to grant the former existence of such a drainage system as the above, an example of a similar one still in existence would be acceptable as a witness to the possibilities of the past. Therefore we turn for a moment to the Jura mountains, always compared to the Appalachians on account of the regular series of folds by which the two are characterized. But while the initial topography is long lost in our old mountains, it is still clearly perceptible in the young Jura, where the anticlines are still ridges and the longitudinal streams still follow the synclinal troughs; while the transverse streams cross from one synclinal valley to another at points where the intervening anticlinal arches are lowest. We could hardly ask for better illustration of the deductive drainage system of our early Appalachians than is here presented.

Development and Adjustment of the Permian Drainage. The problem is now before us. Can the normal sequence of changes in the regular course of river development, aided by the post-Permian deformations and elevations, evolve the existing rivers out of the ancient ones?

In order to note the degree of comparison that exists between the two, several of the larger rivers of to-day are dotted on the figure. The points of agreement are indeed few and small. Perhaps the most important ones are that the Broad Top region is drained by a stream, the Juniata, which for a short distance follows near the course predicted for it; and that the Nittany district, then a highland, is still a well-marked divide, although now a lowland. But there is no Anthracite river, and the region of the ancient coal-basin lakes is now avoided by large streams; conversely, a great river — the Susquehanna — appears where no consequent river ran in Permian time, and the early synclinal streams frequently turn from the structural troughs to valleys located on the structural arches.

Lateral Water Gaps near the Apex of Synclinal Ridges. One of the most frequent discrepancies between the hypothetical and actual streams is that the latter never follow the axis of a descending syncline along its whole length, as the original streams must have done, but depart for a time from the axis and then return to it, notching the ridge formed on any hard bed at the side, instead of at the apex, of its curve across the axis of the syncline. There is not a single case in the state of a stream cutting a gap at the apex of such a synclinal curve, but there are perhaps hundreds of cases where the streams notch the curve to one side of the apex. This, however, is precisely the arrangement attained by spontaneous adjustment from an initial axial course, as indicated in Fig. 23. The gaps may be located on small transverse faults, but as a rule they seem to have no such guidance. It is true that most of our streams now run out of and not into the synclinal basins, but a reason for this will be found later; for the present we look only at the location of the streams, not at their direction of flow. As far as this illustration goes, it gives evidence that the smaller streams at least possess certain peculiarities that could not be derived from persistence in a previous accidental location, but which would necessarily be derived from a process of adjustment following the original establishment of strictly consequent streams. Hence the hypothesis that these smaller streams were long ago consequent on the Permian folding receives confirmation; but this says nothing as to the origin of the larger rivers, which might at the same time be antecedent.

Departure of the Juniata from the Juniata-Catawissa Syncline. It may next be noted that the drainage of the Broad Top region does not follow a single syncline to the Anthracite region, as it should have in the initial stage of the consequent Permian drainage, but soon turns aside from the syncline in which it starts and runs across country to the Susquehanna. It is true that in its upper course the Juniata departs from the Broad Top region by one of the two synclines that were indicated as the probable line of discharge of the ancient Broad Top lake in our restoration of the constructional topography of the state; there does not appear to be any significant difference between the summit altitudes of the Tuscarora-Mahanoy and the Juniata-Catawissa synclinal axes, and hence the choice must have been made for reasons that cannot be detected; or it may be that the syncline lying more to the northwest was raised last, and for this reason was taken as the line of overflow. The beginning of the river is therefore not discordant with the hypothesis of consequent drainage, but the southward departure from the Catawissa syncline at Lewistown remains to be explained. It seems to me that some reason for the departure may be found by likening it to the case already given in Figs. 26–28. The several synclines with which the Juniata is concerned have precisely the relative attitudes that are there discussed. The Juniata-Catawissa syncline has parallel sides for many miles about its middle, and hence must have long maintained the initial Juniata well above base-level over all this distance; the progress of cutting down a channel through all the hard Carboniferous sandstones for so great a distance along the axis must have been exceedingly slow. But the synclines next south, the Tuscarora-Mahanoy and the

Wiconisco, plunge to the northeast more rapidly, as the rapid divergence of their margins demonstrates, and must for this reason have carried the hard sandstones below base-level in a shorter distance and on a steeper slope than in the Catawissa syncline. The further southwestward extension of the Pocono sandstone ridges in the southern than in the northern syncline gives further illustration of this peculiarity of form. Lateral capture of the Juniata by a branch of the initial Tuscarora, and of the latter by a branch of the Wiconisco, therefore seems possible, and the accordance of the facts with so highly specialized an arrangement is certainly again indicative of the correctness of the hypothesis of consequent drainage, and this time in a larger stream than before. At first sight it appears that an easier lateral capture might have been made by some of the streams flowing from the outer slope of the Nittany highland ; but this becomes improbable when it is perceived that the heavy Medina sandstone would here have to be worn through, as well as the repeated arches of the Carboniferous beds in the many high folds of the Seven mountains. Again, as far as present appearances go, we can give no sufficient reason to explain why possession of the headwaters of the Juniata was not gained by some subsequent stream of its own, such as G (Fig. 28), instead of by a side stream of the river in the neighboring syncline ; but it may be admitted, on the other hand, that as far as we can estimate the chances for conquest, there was nothing distinctly in favor of one or the other of the side streams concerned ; and as long as the problem is solved indifferently in favor of one or the other, we may accept the lead of the facts and say that some control not now apparent determined that the diversion should be, as drawn, through D and not through G. The detailed location of the Juniata in its middle course below Lewistown will be considered in a later section.

Avoidance of the Broad Top Basin by the Juniata Headwaters. Another highly characteristic change that the Juniata has suffered is revealed by examining the adjustments that would have taken place in the general topography of the Broad Top district during the Perm-Triassic cycle of erosion. When the basin BT (Fig. 32) was first outlined, centripetal streams descended its slopes from all sides, and their waters accumulated as a lake in the center, overflowing to the east into the subordinate basin A, in the Juniata syncline alongside of the larger basin, and thence escaping northeast. In due time the breaching of the slopes opened the softer Devonian rocks beneath, and peripheral low-lands were opened on them. The process by which the Juniata departed from its original axial location, J (Fig. 32), to a parallel course on the southeastern side of the syncline, J (Fig. 33), has been described (Fig. 28). The subsequent changes are manifest. Some lateral branch of the Juniata, like N (Fig. 33), would work its way around the northern end of the Broad Top canoe on

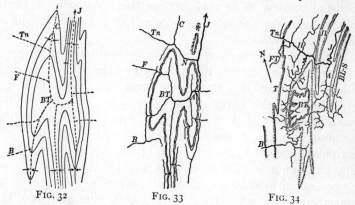

FIG. 32   FIG. 33   FIG. 34

the soft, underlying rocks and capture the axial stream, C, that came from the depression between Nittany and Kishicoquillas highlands; thus reënforced, capture would be made of a radial stream from the west, Tn, the existing Tyrone branch of the Juniata; in a later stage the other streams of the western side of the basin would be acquired, their divertor constituting the Little Juniata of to-day; and the end would be when the original Juniata, A (Fig. 32), that once issued from the subordinate syn-clinal as a large stream, had lost all its western tributaries, and was but a shrunken, beheaded remnant of a river, now seen in Aughwick creek, A (Fig. 34). In the meantime the former lake basin was fast becoming a synclinal mountain of diminishing perimeter. The only really mysterious courses of the present streams are where the Little Juniata runs in and out of the western border of the Broad Top synclinal, and where the Frankstown (*FT*) branch of the Juniata maintains its independent gap across Tussey's mountain (Medina), although diverted to the Tyrone, or main Juniata (*Tn*), by Warrior's ridge (Oriskany) just below. At the time of the early predatory growth of the initial divertor *N*, its course lay by the very conditions of its growth on only the weakest rocks; but after this little stream had grown to a good-sized river, further rising of the land, probably in the time of the Jurassic elevation, allowed the river to sink its channel to a greater depth, and in doing so it encountered the hard Medina anticline of Jack's mountain; here it has since persisted because, as we may suppose, there has been no stream able to divert the course of so large a river from its crossing of a single hard anticlinal.

The doubt that one must feel as to the possibility of the processes just outlined arises, if I may gauge it by my own feeling, rather from incredulity than from direct objections. It seems incredible that the waste of the valley slopes should allow the backward growth of *N* at such a rate as to enable it to capture the heads of *C*, *Tn*, *F*, and so on, before they had cut their beds down close enough to the base-level of the time to be safe from capture. But it is difficult to urge explicit objections against the process or to show its quantitative insufficiency. It must be remembered that when these adjustments were going on, the region was one of great altitude, its rocks then had the same strong contrasts of strength and weakness that are so apparent in the present relief of the surface, and the streams concerned were of moderate size; less than now, for at the time the Tyrone, Frankstown, and Bedford head branches of the Juniata had not acquired drainage west of the great Nittany-Bedford anticlinal axis, but were supplied only by the rainfall on its eastern slope, and all these conditions conspired to favor the adjustment. Finally, while apparently extraordinary and difficult of demonstration, the explanation if applicable at all certainly gives rational correlation to a number of peculiar and special stream courses in the upper Juniata district that are meaningless under any other theory that has come to my notice. It is chiefly for this reason that I am inclined to accept the explanation.

Reversal of Larger Rivers to Southeast Courses. Our large rivers at present flow to the southeast, not to the northwest. It is difficult to find any precise date for this reversal of flow from the initial hypothetical direction, but it may be suggested that it occurred about the time of the Triassic depression of the Newark belt. We have been persuaded that much time elapsed between the Permian folding and the Newark deposition, even under the most liberal allowance for pre-Permian erosion in the Newark belt; hence when the depression began, the rivers must have had but moderate northwestward declivity. The depression and submergence of the broad Newark belt may at this time have broken the continuity of the streams that once flowed across it. The headwater streams from the ancient Archæan country maintained their courses to the depression; the lower portions of the rivers may also have gone on as before; but the middle courses were perhaps turned from the central part of the state back to the Newark belt. No other cause gives so good an explanation of the southeastward flow of our rivers as this. The only test that I have been able to devise for the suggestion is one that is derived from the relation that exists between the location of the Newark belt along the Atlantic slope and the course of the neighboring transverse rivers. In Pennsylvania, where the belt reaches somewhat beyond the northwestern margin of the crystalline rocks in South mountain, the streams are reversed, as above stated; but in the Carolinas, where the Newark belt lies far to the east of the boundary between the Cambrian and crystalline rocks, the Tennessee streams persevere in what we suppose to have been their original direction of flow. This may be interpreted as meaning that in the latter region the Newark depression was not felt distinctly enough, if at all, within the Allegheny belt to reverse the flow of the streams, while in the former region it was nearer to these streams and determined a change in their courses. The original Anthracite river ran to the northwest, but its middle course was afterwards turned to the southeast.

I am free to allow that this has the appearance of heaping hypothesis on hypothesis; but in no other way does the analysis of the history of our streams seem possible, and the success of the experiment can be judged only after making it. At the same time I am constrained to admit that this is, to my own view, the least satisfactory of the suggestions here presented. It may be correct, but there seems to be no sufficient exclusion of other possibilities. For example, it must not be overlooked that if the Anthracite river ran southeast during Newark deposition, the formation of the Newark northwestward monocline by the Jurassic tilting would have had a tendency to turn the river back again to its northwest flow. But as the drainage of the region is still southeastward, I am tempted to think that the Jurassic tilting was not here strong enough to reverse the flow of so strong and mature a river as the Anthracite had by that time come to be ; and that the elevation that accompanied the tilting was not so powerful in reversing the river to a northwest course as the previous depression of the Newark basin had been in turning it to the southeast. If the Anthracite did continue to flow to the southeast, it may be added that the down-cutting of its upper branches was greatly retarded by the decrease of slope in its lower course when the monocline was formed.

The only other method of reversing the original northwestward flow of the streams that I have imagined is by capture of their headwaters by Atlantic rivers. This seems to me less effective than the method just considered ; but they are not mutually exclusive, and the actual result may be the sum of the two processes. The outline of the idea is as follows : The long-continued supply of sedimentary material from the Archæan land on the southeast implies that it was as continually elevated. But there came a time when there is no record of further supply of material, and when we may therefore suppose the elevation was no longer maintained. From that time onward, the Archæan range must have dwindled away, what with the encroachment of the Atlantic on its eastern shore and the general action of denuding forces on its surface. The Newark depression was an effective aid to the same end, as has been stated above, and for a moderate distance westward of the depressed belt, the former direction of the streams must certainly have been reversed ; but the question remains whether this reversal extended as far as the Wyoming basin, and whether the subsequent formation of the Newark monocline did not undo the effect of the Newark depression. It is manifest that as far as our limited knowledge goes, it is impossible to estimate these matters quantitatively, and hence the importance of looking for additional processes that may supplement the effect of the Newark depression and counteract the effect of the Newark uplift in changing the course of the rivers. Let it be supposed for the moment that at the end of the Jurassic uplift by which the Newark monocline was formed, the divide between the Ohio and the Atlantic drainage lay about the middle of the Newark belt. There was a long, gentle descent westward from this watershed and a shorter and hence steeper descent eastward. Under such conditions the divide must have been pushed westward, and as long as the rocks were so exposed as to open areas of weak sediments on which capture by the Atlantic streams could go on with relative rapidity, the westward migration of the divide would be important. For this reason it might be carried from the Newark belt as far as the present Allegheny front, beyond which further pushing would be slow, on account of the broad stretch of country there covered by hard horizontal beds.

The end of this is that, under any of the circumstances here detailed, there would be early in the Jurassic-Cretaceous cycle a distinct tendency to a westward migration of the Atlantic-Ohio divide ; it is the consequences of this that have now to be examined.

Capture of the Anthracite Headwaters by the Growing Susquehanna. Throughout the Perm-Triassic period of denudation, a great work was done in wearing down the original Alleghenies. Anticlines of hard sandstones were breached, and broad lowlands were opened on the softer rocks beneath. Little semblance of the early constructional topography remained when the period of Newark depression was brought to a close ; and all the while the headwater streams of the region were gnawing at the divides, seeking to develop the most perfect arrangement of water ways. Several adjustments have taken place, and the larger streams have been reversed in the direction of their flow ; but a more serious problem is found in the disappearance of the original master stream, the great Anthracite river, which must have at first led away the water from all the lateral synclinal streams. Being a large river, it could not have been easily diverted from its course unless it was greatly retarded in cutting down its channel by the presence of many beds of hard rocks on its way. The following considerations may perhaps throw some light on this obscure point.

It may be assumed that the whole group of mountains formed by the Permian deformation had been reduced to a moderate relief when the Newark deposition was stopped by the Jurassic elevation. The harder ribs of rocks doubtless remained as ridges projecting above the intervening lowlands, but the strength of relief that had been given by the constructional forces had been lost. The general distribution of residual elevations then remaining unsubdued is indicated in Fig. 35, in which the Crystalline, the Medina, and the two Carboniferous sandstone ridges are denoted by appropriate symbols. In restoring this phase of the surface form, when the country stood lower than now, I have reduced the anticlines from their present outlines and increased the synclines, the change of area being made greatest where the dips are least, and hence most apparent at the ends of the plunging anticlines and synclines. Some of the Medina anticlines of Perry and Juniata counties are not indicated because they were not then uncovered. The country between the residual ridges of Jurassic time was chiefly Cambrian limestone and Siluro-Devonian shales and soft sandstones. The moderate ridges developed on the Oriskany and Chemung sandstones are not represented. The drainage of this stage retained the original courses of the streams, except for the adjustments that have been described, but the great Anthracite river is drawn as if it had been controlled by the Newark depression and reversed in the direction of its flow, so that its former upper course on the Cambrian rocks was replaced by a superimposed Newark lower course. Fig. 35 therefore represents the streams for the most part still following near their synclinal axes, although departing from them where they have to enter a synclinal cove-mountain ridge; the headwaters of the Juniata avoid the mass of hard sandstones discovered in the bottom of old Broad Top lake, and flow around them to the north, and then by a cross-country

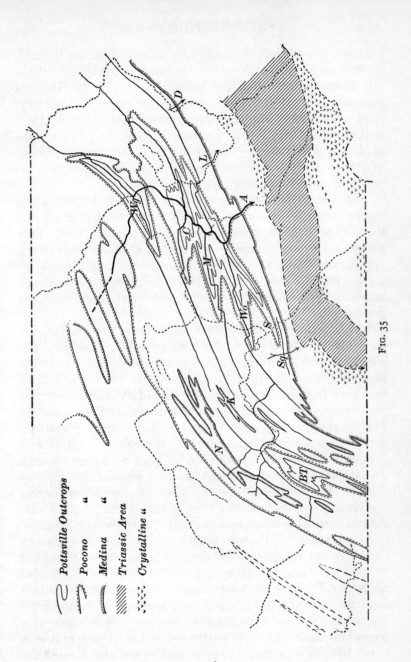

Pottsville Outcrops
" Pocono "
" Medina "
Triassic Area
Crystalline "

Fig. 35

course to the Wiconisco synclinal, as already described in detail. Several streams come from the northeast, entering the Anthracite district after the fashion generalized in Fig. 23. Three of the many streams that were developed on the great Kittatinny slope are located, with their direction of flow reversed; these are marked *Sq*, *L*, and *D*, and are intended to represent the ancestors of the existing Susquehanna, Lehigh, and Delaware. We have now to examine the opportunities offered to these small streams to increase their drainage areas.

The Jurassic elevation, by which the Newark deposition was stopped, restored to activity all the streams that had in the previous cycle sought and found a course close to base-level. They now all set to work again deepening their channels. But in this restoration of lost activity with reference to a new base-level, there came the best possible chance for numerous rearrangements of drainage areas by mutual adjustment, into which we must inquire.

I have already illustrated what seems to me to be the type of the conditions involved at this time in Figs. 29 and 30. The master stream *A*, traversing the synclines, corresponds to the reversed Anthracite river; the lowlands at the top are those that have been opened out on the Siluro-Devonian beds of the present Susquehanna middle course between the Pocono and the Medina ridges. The small stream *B*, that is gaining drainage area in these lowlands, corresponds to the embryo of the present Susquehanna, *Sq* (Fig. 35), this having been itself once a branch on the south side of the Swatara synclinal stream (Fig. 31), from which it was first turned by the change of slope accompanying the Newark depression; but it is located a little farther west than the actual Susquehanna, so as to avoid the two synclinal cove mountains of Pocono sandstone that the Susquehanna now traverses, for reasons to be stated below. This stream had to cross only one bed of hard rock, the outer wall of Medina sandstone, between the broad, inner lowlands of the relatively weak Siluro-Devonian rocks and the great valley lowlands on the still weaker Cambrian limestones. Step by step it must have pushed its headwater divide northward, and from time to time it would have thus captured a subsequent stream that crossed the lowlands eastward, and entered a Carboniferous syncline by one of the lateral gaps already described. With every such capture the power of the growing stream to capture others was increased. Fig. 29 represents a stage after the streams in the Swatara and Wiconisco synclines (the latter then having gained the Juniata) had been turned aside on their way to the Carboniferous basins. On the other hand, the Anthracite river, rising somewhere on the plains north of the Wyoming syncline and pursuing an irregular course from one coal basin to another, found an extremely difficult task in cutting down its channel across the numerous hard beds of the Carboniferous sandstones, so often repeated in the rolling folds of the coal fields. It is also important to remember that an aid to other conditions concerned in the diversion of the upper Anthracite is found in the decrease of slope that its lower course suffered in crossing the coal fields, if that area took any part in the deformation that produced the Newark monocline, — whichever theory prove true in regard to the origin of the southeastward flow of the rivers, — for loss of slope in the middle course, where the river had to cross many reefs of hard sandstone, would have been very effective in lengthening the time allowed for the diversion of the headwaters.

The question is, therefore, whether the retardation of down-cutting here experienced by the Anthracite was sufficient to allow the capture of its headwaters by the Susquehanna. There can be little doubt as to the correct quality of the process, but whether it was quantitatively sufficient is another matter. In the absence of any means of testing its sufficiency, may the result not be taken as the test? Is not the correspondence between deduction and fact close enough to prove the correctness of the deduction?

Present Outward Drainage of the Anthracite Basins. The Lehigh, like the Susquehanna, made an attempt to capture the headwaters of adjacent streams, but failed to acquire much territory from the Anthracite because the Carboniferous sandstones spread out between the two in a broad plateau of hard rocks, across which the divide made little movement. The plateau area that its upper branches drain is, I think, the conquest of a later cycle of growth. The Delaware had little success, except as against certain eastern synclinal branches of the Anthracite, for the same reason. The ancestor of the Swatara of to-day made little progress in extending its headwaters because its point of attack was against the repeated Carboniferous sandstones in the Swatara synclinal. One early stream alone found a favorable opportunity for conquest, and thus grew to be the master river, — the Susquehanna of to-day. The head of the Anthracite was carried away by this captor, and its beheaded lower portion remains in our Schuylkill. The Anthracite coal basins, formerly drained by the single master stream, have since been apportioned to the surrounding rivers. As the Siluro-Devonian lowlands were opened around the coal basins, especially on the north and west, the streams that formerly flowed into the basins were gradually inverted and flowed out of them, as they still do. The extent of the inversion seems to be in a general way proportionate to its opportunity. The most considerable conquests were made in the upper basins, where the Catawissa and Nescopec streams of to-day drain many square miles of wide valleys opened on the Mauch Chunk red shale between the Pocono and Pottsville sandstone ridges, the ancient middle waters of the Anthracite here being inverted to the Susquehanna tributaries, because the northern coal basins were degraded very slowly after the upper Anthracite had been diverted. The Schuylkill as the modern representative of the Anthracite retains only certain streams south of a medial divide between Nescopec and Blue mountains. The only considerable part of the old Anthracite river that still retains a course along the axis of a synclinal trough seems to be that part which follows the Wyoming basin ; none of the many other coal basins are now occupied by the large stream that originally followed them. The reason for this is manifestly to be found in the great depth of the Wyoming basin, whereby the axial portion of its hard sandstones are even now below base-level, and hence have never yet acted to throw the river from its axial course. Indeed, during the early cycle of denudation, this basin must have been changed from a deep lake to a lacustrine plain by the accumulation in it of waste from the surrounding highlands, and for a time the streams that entered it may have flowed in meandering courses across the ancient alluvial surface ; the lacustrine and alluvial condition may have been temporarily revived at the time of the Jurassic elevation. It is perhaps as an inheritance from a course thus locally superimposed that we may come to regard the deflection of the river at Nanticoke from the axis of the syncline to a narrow shale valley on its northern side before turning south again and leaving the basin altogether. But like certain other suggestions, this can only be regarded as an open hypothesis, to be tested by some better method of river analysis than we now possess; like several of the other explanations here offered, it is presented more as a possibility to be discussed than as a conclusion to be accepted.

I believe that it was during the earlier part of the great Jura-Cretaceous cycle of denudation that the Susquehanna thus became the master stream of the central district of the state. For the rest of the cycle, it was occupied in carrying off the waste and reducing the surface to a well-finished base-level lowland that characterized the end of Cretaceous time. From an active youth of conquest, the Susquehanna advanced into an old age of established boundaries; and in later times its area of drainage does not seem to have been greatly altered from that so long ago defined, except perhaps in the districts drained by the West and North Branch headwaters.

Homologies of the Susquehanna and Juniata. Looking at the change from the Anthracite to the Susquehanna in a broad way, one may perceive that it is an effect of the same order as the peripheral diversion of the Broad Top drainage, illustrated in Figs. 32, 33, and 34; another example of a similar change is seen in the lateral diversion of the Juniata above Lewistown and its rectilinear continuation in Aughwick creek, from their original axial location when they formed the initial Broad Top outlet. They have departed from the axis of their syncline to the softer beds on its southern side; *FE* of Fig. 27 has been diverted to *FD* of Fig. 28.

All of these examples are truly only special cases of the one already described, in which the Juniata left its original syncline for others to the south. The general case may be stated in a few words. A stream flowing along a syncline of hard beds (Carboniferous sandstones) develops side streams which breach the adjacent anticlines and open lowlands in the underlying softer beds (Devonian and Silurian). On these lowlands the headwaters of side streams from other synclines are encountered, and a contest ensues as to possession of the drainage territory. The divides are pushed away from those headwaters whose lower course leads them over the fewest hard barriers; this conquest goes on until the upper course of the initial main stream is diverted to a new and easier path than the one it chose in its youth in obedience to the first deformation of the region. Thus the Juniata now avoids the center and once deepest part of the old Broad Top lake, because in the general progress of erosion, lowlands on soft Devonian beds were opened all around the edge of the great mass of sandstones that held the lake; the original drainage across the lake, from its western slope to its outlet just south of the Jack's mountain anticline, has now taken an easier path along the Devonian beds to the west of the old lake basin, and is seen in the Little Juniata, flowing along the outer side of Terrace mountain and rounding the northern synclinal point where Terrace mountain joins Sideling hill. It then crosses Jack's mountain at a point where the hard Medina sandstones of the mountain were still buried at the time of the choice of this channel. In the same way the drainage of the subordinate basin, through which the main lake discharged eastward, is now not along the axis of the Juniata-Catawissa syncline, but on the softer beds along one side of it; and along the southern side, because the easier escape that was provided for it lay on that side, namely, via the Tuscarora and Wiconisco synclines, as already described. The much broader change from the Anthracite to the Susquehanna was only another form of the same process. Taking a transverse view of the whole system of central folds, it is perceived that their axes descend into the Anthracite district from the east and rise westward therefrom; it is as if the whole region had received a slight transverse folding, and the transverse axis of depression thus formed defined the initial course of the first master stream. But this master stream deserted its original course on the transverse axis of depression because a lateral course across lowlands on softer beds was opened by its side streams; and in the contest on these lowlands with an external stream, the Susquehanna, the upper portion of the Anthracite was diverted from the hard rocks that had appeared on the transverse axis. The distance of diversion from the axial to the lateral course in this case was great because of the gentle quality of the transverse folding; or, better said, because of the gentle dips of the axes of the longitudinal folds. This appearance of systematic rearrangement in the several river courses where none was expected is, to my mind, a strong argument in favor of the originally consequent location of the rivers and their later mutual adjustment. It may perhaps be conceived that antecedent streams might imitate one another roughly in the attitude that they prophetically chose with regard to folds subsequently formed, but no reason has been suggested for the imitation being carried to so remarkable and definite a degree as that here outlined.

Superimposition of the Susquehanna on Two Synclinal Ridges. There is, however, one apparently venturesome postulate that may have been already noted as such by the reader; unless it can be reasonably accounted for and shown to be a natural result of the long sequence of changes here considered, it will seriously militate against the validity of the whole argument. The present course of the middle Susquehanna leads it through the apical curves of two Pocono synclinal ridges, which were disregarded in the statement given above. It was then assumed that the embryonic Susquehanna gained possession of the Siluro-Devonian lowland drainage by gnawing out a course to the west of these synclinal points; for it is not to be thought of that any conquest of the headwaters of the Anthracite river could have been made by the Susquehanna if it had had to gnaw out the existing four traverses of the Pocono sandstones before securing the drainage of the lowlands above them. The backward progress of the Susquehanna could not in that case have been nearly fast enough to reach the Anthracite before the latter had sunk its channel to a safe depth. It is therefore important to justify the assumption as to the more westerly location of the embryonic Susquehanna, and afterwards to explain how it should have since then been transferred to its present course. A short-cut through all this roundabout method is open to those who adopt

in the beginning the theory that the Susquehanna was an antecedent river; but as I have said at the outset of this inquiry, it
seems to me that such a method is not freer from assumption,
even though shorter than the one here adopted; and it has the
demerit of not considering all the curious details that follow the
examination of consequent and adjusted courses.

The sufficient reason for the assumption that the embryonic
Susquehanna lay farther west than the present one in the neighborhood of the Pocono synclinals is simply that — in the absence
of any antecedent stream — it must have lain there. The whole
explanation of the development of the Siluro-Devonian lowlands
between the Pocono and Medina ridges depends simply on their
being weathered out where the rocks are weak enough to waste
faster than the inclosing harder ridges through which the streams
escape. In this process the streams exercise no control whatever
over the direction in which their headwaters shall grow; they
leave this entirely to the structure of the district that they drain.
It thus appears that, under the postulate as to the initial location
of the Susquehanna as one of the many streams descending the
great slope of the Kittatinny (Cumberland) highland into the
Swatara syncline, its course being reversed from northward to
southward by the Newark depression, we are required to suppose
that its headwater (northward) growth at the time of the Jurassic
elevation must have been on the Siluro-Devonian beds, so as to
avoid the harder rocks on either side. Many streams competed
for the distinction of becoming the master, and that one gained
its ambition whose initial location gave it the best subsequent
opportunity. It remains then to consider the means by which
the course of the conquering Susquehanna may have been subsequently changed from the lowlands on to the two Pocono
synclines that it now traverses. Some departure from its early
location may have been due to eastward planation in its advanced
age, when it had large volume and gentle slope and was therefore swinging and cutting laterally in its lower course. This
may have had a share in the result, but there is another process
that seems to me more effective.

In the latter part of the Jura-Cretaceous cycle the whole
country hereabout suffered a moderate depression, by which the

Atlantic transgressed many miles inland from its former shore-line, across the lowlands of erosion that had been developed on the littoral belt. Such a depression must have had a distinct effect on the lower courses of the larger rivers, which, having already cut their channels down close to base-level and opened their valleys wide on the softer rocks, were then "estuaried," or at least so far checked as to build wide flood plains over their lower stretches. Indeed, the flood plains may have been begun at an earlier date, and have been confirmed and extended in the later time of depression. Is it possible that in the latest stage of this process the almost base-leveled remnants of Blue mountain and the Pocono ridges could have been buried under the flood plain in the neighborhood of the river?

If this be admitted, it is then natural for the river to depart from the line of its buried channel and cross the buried ridges on which it might settle down as a superimposed river in the next cycle of elevation. It is difficult to decide such general questions as these ; and it may be difficult for the reader to gain much con-fidence in the efficacy of the processes suggested ; but there are certain features in the side streams of the Susquehanna that lend some color of probability to the explanation as offered.

Admit, for the moment, that the aged Susquehanna, in the later part of the Jura-Cretaceous cycle, did change its channel somewhat by cutting to one side, or by planation, as it is called. Admit, also, that in the natural progress of its growth it had built a broad flood plain over the Siluro-Devonian lowlands, and that the depth of this deposit was increased by the formation of an estuarine delta upon it when the country sank at the time of the mid-Cretaceous transgression of the sea. It is manifest that one of the consequences of all this might be the peculiar course of the river that is to be explained, namely, its superimposition on the two Pocono synclinal ridges in the next cycle of its history, after the Tertiary elevation had given it opportunity to rediscover them. It remains to inquire what other consequences should follow from the same conditions, and from these to devise tests of the hypothesis.

Evidence of Superimposition in the Susquehanna Tributaries. One of the peculiarities of flood-plained rivers is that the lateral streams shift their points of union with the main stream farther and farther down the valley, as Lombardini has shown in the case of the Po. If the Susquehanna were heavily flood-plained at the close of the Jura-Cretaceous cycle, some of its tributaries should manifest signs of this kind of deflection from their structural courses along the strike of the rocks. Side streams that once joined the main stream on the line of some of the softer northeast-southwest beds, leaving the stronger beds as faint hills on either side, must have forgotten such control after it was base-leveled and buried; as the flood plain grew, they properly took more and more distinctly downward-deflected courses, and these deflections should be maintained in subsequent cycles as superimposed courses independent of structural guidance. Such I believe to be the fact. The downstream deflection is so distinctly a peculiarity of a number of tributaries that join the Susquehanna on the west side that it cannot be ascribed to accident, but must be referred to some systematic cause. Examples of deflection are found in Penn's creek, Middle creek, and North Mahantango creek in Snyder county; West Mahantango, between the latter and Juniata county; and in the Juniata and Little Juniata rivers of Perry county. On the other side of the Susquehanna the examples are not so distinct, but the following may be mentioned: Delaware and Warrior runs, Chillisquaque creek and Little Shamokin creek, all in Northumberland county. It may be remarked that it does not seem impossible that the reason for the more distinct deflection of the western streams may be that the Susquehanna is at present east of its old course, and hence towards the eastern margin of its flood plain, as, indeed, its position on the Pocono synclinals implies. A reason for the final location of the superimposed river on the eastern side of the old flood plain may perhaps be found in the eastward tilting that is known to have accompanied the elevation of the Cretaceous lowland.

It follows from the foregoing that the present lower course of the Susquehanna must also be of superimposed origin, for the flood plain of the middle course must have extended downstream to its delta, and there have become confluent with the sheet of Cretaceous sediments that covered all the southeastern lowland, over which the sea had transgressed. McGee has already pointed out indications of superimposed stream courses in the south-eastern part of the state (*a*), but I am not sure that he would regard them as of the date here referred to.

The theory of the location of the Susquehanna on the Pocono synclinal ridges, therefore, stands as follows : The general position of the river indicates that it has been located by some process of slow self-adjusting development, and that it is not a persistent antecedent river ; and yet there is no reason to think that it could have been brought into its present special position by any process of shifting divides. The processes that have been suggested to account for its special location, as departing slightly from a location due to slow adjustments following an ancient consequent origin, call for the occurrence of certain additional peculiarities in the courses of its tributary streams, entirely unforeseen and unnoticed until this point in the inquiry is reached ; and on looking at the map to see if they occur, they are found with perfect distinctness. The hypothesis of superimposition may therefore be regarded as having advanced beyond the stage of mere suggestion and as having gained some degree of confirmation from the correlations that it detects and explains. It only remains to ask if these correlations might have originated in any other way, and if the answer to this is in the negative, the case may be looked upon as having a fair measure of evidence in its favor. The remaining consideration may be taken up at once as the first point to be examined in the Tertiary cycle of development.

Events of the Tertiary Cycle. The elevation given to the region by which Cretaceous base-leveling was terminated, and which I have called the early Tertiary elevation, offered opportunity for the streams to deepen their channels once more. In doing so, certain adjustments of moderate amount occurred, which will be soon examined. As time went on, much denudation was effected, but no widespread base-leveling was reached, for the Cretaceous crest lines of the hard sandstone ridges still exist. The Tertiary cycle was an incomplete one. At its close, lowlands had been opened only on the weaker rocks between the hard beds. Is it not possible that the flood plaining of the Susquehanna and the downstream deflection of its branches took place in the closing stages of this cycle instead of at the end of the previous cycle? If so, the deflection might appear on the branches, but the main river would not be transferred to the Pocono ridges. This question may be safely answered in the negative; for the Tertiary lowland is by no means well enough base-leveled to permit such an event. The beds of intermediate resistance, the Oriskany and certain Chemung sandstones, had not been worn down to base-level at the close of the Tertiary cycle; they had, indeed, lost much of the height that they possessed at the close of the previous cycle, but they had not been reduced as low as the softer beds on either side. They were only reduced to ridges of moderate and unequal height over the general plain of the Siluro-Devonian low country, without great strength of relief but quite strong enough to call for obedience from the streams alongside of them. And yet, near Selin's grove, for example, in Snyder county, Penn's and Middle creeks depart most distinctly from the strike of the local rocks as they near the Susquehanna, and traverse certain well-marked ridges on their way to the main river. Such aberrant streams cannot be regarded as superimposed at the close of the incomplete Tertiary cycle; they cannot be explained by any process of spontaneous adjustment yet described, nor can they be regarded as vastly ancient streams of antecedent courses; I am therefore much tempted to consider them as of superimposed origin, inheriting their present courses from the flood-plain cover of the Susquehanna in the latest stage of the Jura-Cretaceous cycle. With this tentative conclusion in mind as to the final events of Jura-Cretaceous time, we may take up the more deliberate consideration of the work of the Tertiary cycle.

The chief work of the Tertiary cycle was merely the opening of the valley lowlands; little opportunity for river adjustment occurred except on a small scale. The most evident cases of adjustment have resulted in the change of water gaps into wind gaps, of which several examples can be given, the one best known being the Delaware Wind Gap between the Lehigh and Delaware Water Gaps in Blue mountain. The wind gap marks the unfinished notch of some stream that once crossed the ridge here and whose headwaters have since then been diverted, probably to the Lehigh.

The difficulty in the case is not at all how the stream that once flowed here was diverted, but how a stream that could be diverted in the Tertiary cycle could have escaped diversion at some earlier date. The relative rarity of wind gaps indicates that nearly all of the initial lateral streams, which may have crossed the ridges at an early epoch in the history of the rivers, have been beheaded in some cycle earlier than the Tertiary and their gaps thereafter obliterated. Why the Delaware Wind-Gap stream should have endured into a later cycle does not at present appear. Other wind gaps of apparently similar origin may be found in Blue mountain, west of the Schuylkill and east of the Susquehanna. It is noteworthy that if any small streams still persevere in their gaps across a hard ridge, they are not very close to any large river gap; hence it is only at the very headwaters of Conedogwinet creek, in the northern part of Franklin county, that any water is still drawn from the back of Blue mountain. Again, these small stream gaps do not lie between large river gaps and wind gaps, but wind gaps lie between the gaps of large rivers and those of small streams that are not yet diverted. Excellent illustration of this is found on the "Piedmont sheet" of the contoured maps issued by the United States Geological Survey. The sheet covers part of Maryland and West Virginia, near where the North Branch of the Potomac comes out of the plateau and crosses New Creek mountain. Eleven miles south of the Potomac gap there is a deep wind gap; but farther on, at twenty, twenty-five, and twenty-nine miles from the river gap, are three fine water gaps occupied by small streams. This example merely shows how many important points in the history of our rivers will be made clear when the country is properly portrayed on contoured maps.

A few lines may be given to the general absence of gaps in Blue mountain in Pennsylvania. When the initial consequent drainage was established, many streams must have been located on the northward slope of the great Cumberland highland, *CC* (Fig. 31); they must have gullied the slope to great depths and carried away great volumes of the weak Cambrian beds that lay deep within the hard outer casings of the mass. Minor adjustments served to diminish the number of these streams, but the more effective cause of their present rarity lay in the natural selection of certain of them to become large streams; the smaller ones were generally beheaded by these. The only examples of streams that still cross this ridge with their initial Permian direction of flow to the northwest are found in two southern branches of Tuscarora creek at the southern point of Juniata county; and these survive because of their obscure location among the many Medina ridges of that district, where they were not easily accessible to capture by other streams.

Tertiary Adjustment of the Juniata on the Medina Anticlines. The lower course of the Juniata presents several examples of adjustment referable to the last part of the Jura-Cretaceous cycle and to the Tertiary cycle. The explanation offered for the escape of this river from its initial syncline did not show any reason for its peculiar position with respect to the several Medina anticlines that it now borders, because at the time when it was led across country to the Wiconisco syncline, the hard Medina beds of these anticlines were not discovered. It is therefore hardly to be thought that the location of the Juniata in the Narrows below Lewistown, between Blue Ridge and Shade mountains, and its avoidance of Tuscarora mountain, could have been defined at that early date. But all these Medina anticlines rise more or less above the Cretaceous base-level, and must have had some effect on the position taken by the river about the middle of that cycle when its channel sank upon them. Blue Ridge and Black Log anticlines rise highest. The first location of the cross-country stream that led the early Juniata away from its initial syncline probably traversed the Blue Ridge and Black Log anticlines while they were yet buried; but its channel cutting was much retarded on encountering them, and some branch stream working around from the lower side of the obstructions may have diverted the river to an easier path. The only path of the kind is the narrow one between the overlapping anticlines of Blue Ridge and Shade mountains, and there the Juniata now flows. If another elevation should occur in the future, it might happen that the slow deepening of the channel in the hard Medina beds which now floor the Narrows would allow Middle creek of Snyder county to tap the Juniata at Lewistown and lead it by direct course past Middleburgh to the Susquehanna; thus it would return to the path of its youth.

The location of the Juniata at the end of Tuscarora mountain is again so definite that it can hardly be referred to a time when the mountain had not been revealed. The most likely position of the original cross-country stream which brought the Juniata into the Wiconisco syncline was somewhere on the line of the existing mountain, and assuming it to have been there, we must question how it has been displaced. The process seems to have been of the same kind as that just given; the retardation of channel cutting in the late Cretaceous cycle, when the Medina beds of Tuscarora anticline were discovered, allowed a branch from the lower part of the river to work around the end of the mountain and lead the river out that way. The occurrence of a shallow depression across the summit of the otherwise remarkably even crest of Tuscarora mountain suggests that this diversion was not finally accomplished until shortly after the Tertiary elevation of the country; but at whatever date the adjustment occurred, it is natural that it should pass around the eastern end of the mountain and not around the western end, where the course would have been much longer and, therefore, not successfully to be taken by a diverting stream.

While the quality of these processes appears satisfactory, I am not satisfied as to the sufficiency of their quantity. If diversion was successfully practiced at the crossing of the Tuscarora anticline, why not also at the crossing of Jack's mountain anticline, on which the river still perseveres? It is difficult here to decide how much confidence may be placed in the explanation, because of its giving reason for the location of certain streams, and how much doubt must be cast upon it because it seems impossible and is not of universal application.

Migration of the Atlantic-Ohio Divide. There are certain shifted courses which cannot be definitely referred to any particular cycle, and which may therefore be mentioned now. Among the greatest are those by which the divide between the Atlantic and the Ohio streams has been changed from its initial position on the great constructional Nittany highland and Bedford range. There was probably no significant change until after the Newark depression, for the branches of the Anthracite river could not have begun to push the divide westward till after the eastward flow of the river was determined; until then, there does not seem to have been any marked advantage possessed by the eastward streams over the westward. But with the eastward escape of the Anthracite, it probably found a shorter course to the sea and one that led it over alternately soft and hard rocks, instead of the longer course followed by the Ohio streams over continuous sandstones. The advantage given by the greater extent of soft beds is indicated by the great breadth of the existing valleys in the central district compared with the less breadth of those in the plateau to the west. Consider the effect of this advantage at the time of the Jurassic elevation. As the streams on the eastern slope of the Nittany divide had the shortest and steepest courses to the sea, they deepened their valleys faster than those on the west and acquired drainage area from them; hence we find reason for the drainage of the entire Nittany and Bedford district by the Atlantic streams at present. Various branches of what are now the Allegheny and Monongahela originally rose on the western slope of the dividing range. These probably reached much farther east in pre-Permian time, but had their headwaters turned another way by the growth of the great anticlinal divide; but the smaller anticlines of Laurel ridge and Negro mountain farther west do not seem to have been strong enough to form a divide, for the rivers still traverse them. Now, as the headwaters of the Juniata breached the eastern slope of the Nittany-Bedford range and pushed the divide westward, they at last gained possession of the Siluro-Devonian monocline on its western slope; but beyond this it has not been possible for them yet to go. As the streams cut down deeper and encountered the Medina anticline near the core of the ridge, they sawed a passage through it; the Cambrian beds were discovered below and a valley was opened on them as the Medina cover wore away. The most important point about this is that we find in it an adequate explanation of the opposite location of water gaps in pairs, such as characterize the branches of the Juniata, below Tyrone, and again below Bedford. This opposite location has been held to indicate an antecedent origin of the river that passes through the gaps, while gaps formed by self-developed streams are not thought to present such correspondence (Hilber). Yet this special case of paired gaps in the opposite walls of a breached anticline is manifestly a direct sequence of the development of the Juniata headwaters. The settling down of the main Juniata on Jack's mountain anticline below Huntingdon is another case of the same kind, in which the relatively low anticlinal crest is as yet not widely breached; the gaps below Bedford stand apart, as the crest is there higher, and hence wider opened; and the gaps below Tyrone are separated by some ten or twelve miles.

When the headwater streams captured the drainage of the Siluro-Devonian monocline on the western side of the ancient dividing anticline, they developed subsequent rectangular branches growing like a well-trained grapevine. Most of this valley has been acquired by the West Branch of the Susquehanna, probably because it traversed the Medina beds less often than the Juniata. For the same reason it may be, the West Branch has captured a considerable area of plateau drainage that must have once belonged to the Ohio, while the Juniata has none of it; but if so, the capture must have been before the Tertiary cycle, for since that time the ability of the West Branch and of the Juniata as regards such capture appears about alike. On the other hand, Castleman's river, a branch of the Monongahela, still retains the drainage of a small bit of the Siluro-Devonian monocline, at the southern border of the state, where the Juniata headwaters had the least opportunity to capture it; but the change here is probably only retarded, not prevented entirely; the Juniata will some day push the divide even here back to the Allegheny Front, the frontal bluff of the plateau.

Other Examples of Adjustments. Other examples of small adjustments are found around the Wyoming basin (Fig. 36). Originally all these streams ran centripetally down the inclosing slopes, and in such locations they must have cut gullies and breaches in the hard Carboniferous beds and opened low back country on the weaker Devonians. Some of the existing streams still do so, and these are precisely the ones that are not easily reached by divertors. The Susquehanna in its course outside of the basin has sent out branches that have beheaded all the centripetal streams within reach; where the same river enters the basin, the centripetal streams have been shortened if not completely beheaded. A branch of the Delaware has captured the heads of some of the streams near the eastern end of the basin. Elsewhere, the centripetal streams still exist of good length. The contrast between the persistence of some of the centripetal streams here and their peripheral diversion around Broad Top is a consequence of the difference of altitude of the

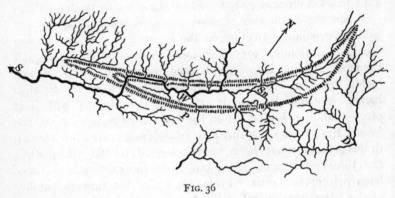

FIG. 36

old lake bottoms in the two cases. It is not to be doubted that we shall become acquainted with many examples of this kind as our intimacy with rivers increases.

Events of the Quaternary Cycle. The brief quaternary cycle does not offer many examples of the kind that we have considered, and all that are found are of small dimensions. The only capturing stream that need be mentioned has lately been described as a " river pirate" (Davis, *b*); but its conquest is only a Schleswig-Holstein affair compared to the Goth- and Hun-like depredations of the greater streams in earlier cycles.

The character of the streams and their valleys as they now exist is strikingly dependent in many ways on the relation of the incipient quaternary cycle to the longer cycles of the past. No lakes occur, exception being made only of the relatively small ponds due to drift obstruction within the glaciated area. Waterfalls are found only at the headwaters of small streams in the plateau district, exception again being made only for certain cases of larger streams that have been thrown from their pre-glacial courses by drift barriers, and which are now in a very immature state on their new lines of flow. The small valleys of this cycle are shallow and narrow, always of a size strictly proportional to the volume of the stream and the hardness of the inclosing rocks, exception being made only in the case of post-glacial gorges whose streams have been displaced from their pre-glacial channels. The terraces that are seen, especially on the streams that flow in or from the glaciated district, are merely a temporary and subordinate complication of the general development of the valleys. In the region that has been here considered, the streams have been seldom much displaced from their pre-glacial channels; but in the northwestern part of the state, where the drift in the valleys seems to be heavier, more serious disturbance of pre-glacial courses is reported. The facts here referred to in regard to lakes, falls, gorges, terraces, and displaced streams are to be found in the various volumes of the Second Geological Survey of the State (especially Carll, Reports I_3, I_4; White, Reports G_5, G_6; Lewis, Report Z); in regard to the terraces and the estuarine deflections of the Delaware and Susquehanna, reference should be made also to McGee's studies (*b*, *c*).

Doubtful Cases. It is hardly necessary to state that there are many facts for which no satisfactory explanation is found under the theory of adjustments that we have been considering. Some will certainly include the location of the Susquehanna on the points of the Pocono synclines under this category; all must feel that such a location savors of an antecedent origin. The same is true of the examples of the alignment of water gaps found on certain streams; for example, the four gaps cut in the two pairs of Pocono and Pottsville outcrops at the west end of the Wyoming syncline, and the three gaps where the Little Schuylkill crosses the coal basin at Tamaqua; the opposite gaps in pairs at Tyrone and Bedford have already been sufficiently explained. The location of the upper North Branch of the Susquehanna is also unrelated to processes of adjustment as far as I can see them, and the great area of plateau drainage that is now possessed by the West Branch, is certainly difficult to understand as the result of conquest. The two independent gaps in Tussey's mountain, maintained by the Juniata and its Frankstown branch below Tyrone, are curious, especially in view of the apparent diversion of the branch to the main stream on the upper side of Warrior's ridge (Oriskany), just east of Tussey's mountain.

Complicated History of our Actual Rivers. If this theory of the history of our rivers is correct, it follows that any one river as it now exists is of so complicated an origin that its development cannot become a matter of general study and must unhappily remain only a subject for special investigation for some time to come. It was my hope on beginning this essay to find some teachable sequence of facts that would serve to relieve the usual routine of statistical and descriptive geography, but this is not the result that has been attained. The history of the Susquehanna, the Juniata, or the Schuylkill is too involved with complex changes, if not enshrouded in mystery, to become intelligible to any but advanced students; only the simplest cases of river development can be introduced into the narrow limits of ordinary instruction. The single course of an ancient stream is now broken into several independent parts; witness the disjointing and diversion of the original Juniata, which, as I have supposed, once extended from Broad Top lake to the Catawissa basin. Now the upper part of the stream, representing the early Broad Top outlet, is reduced to small volume in Aughwick creek; the continuation of the stream to Lewistown is first set to one side of its original axial location and is then diverted to another syncline; the beheaded portion now represented by Middle creek is diverted from its course to the Catawissa basin by the Susquehanna; perhaps the Catawissa of the present day represents the reversed course of the lower Juniata where it joined the Anthracite. This unserviceably complicated statement is not much simplified if, instead of beginning with an original stream and searching out its present disjointed parts, we trace the composition of a single existing stream from its once independent parts. The Juniata of to-day consists of headwaters acquired from Ohio streams; the lake in which the river once gathered its upper branches is now drained, and the lake bottom has become a mountain top; the streams flow around the margin of the lake, not across its basin; a short course towards Lewistown nearly coincides with the original location of the stream, but to confound this with a precise agreement is to lose the true significance of river history; the lower course is the product of diversion at least at two epochs and certainly in several places; and where the river now joins the Susquehanna, it is suspected of having a superimposed course unlike any of the rest of the stream. This is too complicated, even if it should ever be demonstrated to be wholly true, to serve as material for ordinary study; but as long as it has a savor of truth, and as long as we are ignorant of the whole history of our rivers, through which alone their present features can be rightfully understood, we must continue to search after the natural processes of their development as carefully and thoroughly as the biologist searches for the links missing from his scheme of classification.

Provisional Conclusion. It is in view of these doubts and complications that I feel that the history of our rivers is not yet settled; but yet the numerous accordances of actual and deductive locations appear so definite and in some cases so remarkable that they cannot be neglected, as they must be if we should adhere to the antecedent origin of the river courses.

The method adopted on an early page therefore seems to be justified. The provisional system of ancient consequent drainage, illustrated in Fig. 31, does appear to be sufficiently related to the streams of to-day to warrant the belief that most of our rivers took their first courses between the primitive folds of our mountains, and that from that distant time to the present the changes they have suffered are due to their own interaction, — to their own mutual adjustment more than to any other cause. The Susquehanna, Schuylkill, Lehigh, and Delaware are compound, composite, and highly complex rivers, of repeated mature adjustment. The middle Susquehanna and its branches and the upper portions of the Schuylkill and Lehigh are descendants of original Permian rivers consequent on the constructional topography of that time; Newark depression reversed the flow of some of the transverse streams, and the spontaneous changes or adjustments from immature to mature courses in the several cycles of development are so numerous and extensive that, as Löwl truly says, the initial drainage has almost disappeared. The larger westward-flowing streams of the plateau are of earlier, Carboniferous birth, and have suffered little subsequent change beyond a loss of headwaters. The lower courses of the Atlantic rivers are younger, having been much shifted from their Permian or pre-Permian courses by Newark and Cretaceous superimposition, as well as by recent downward deformation of the surface in their existing estuaries. No recognizable remnant of rivers antecedent to the Permian deformation are found in the central part of the state; and with the exception of parts of the upper Schuylkill and of the Susquehanna near Wilkesbarre, there are no large survivors of Permian consequent streams in the ordinary meaning of the term "consequent." The shifting of courses in the progress of mature adjustment has had more to do with determining the actual location of our rivers and streams than any other process.

REFERENCES

Davis, W. M. (a) "Origin of Cross-Valleys." *Science*, I (1883), 325.

  (b) *Science*, XIII (1889), 108.

Hilber, V. *Petermanns Mittheilungen*, XXXV (1889), 13.

Lesley, J. P. *Proc. Am. Phil. Soc.*, XIII (1873), 6.

Löwl, F. (a) *Petermanns Mittheilungen*, XXVIII (1882), 405.

  (b) Über Thalbildung. Prag. 1884.

McGee, W. J. (a) *Am. Jour. Sci.*, XXXV (1888), 121, 134.

  (b) Ibid., 367, 448.

  (c) *U. S. Geol. Surv., VII Ann. Rep.* (1888), 545.

Peschel, O. F. Physische Erdkunde, II (1880), 442.

Philippson, A. Studien über Wasserscheiden, 149. Leipzig, 1886.

Powell, J. W. (a) Exploration of the Colorado River of the West, 153, 163–166. 1875.

  (b) Geology of the Uinta Mountains, 196. 1876.

Tietze, E. *Jahrbuch Geol. Reichsanstalt*, XXVIII (1878), 600.

XX

THE RIVERS OF NORTHERN NEW JERSEY
WITH NOTES ON THE CLASSIFICATION
OF RIVERS IN GENERAL

Northern New Jersey is drained by several streams which rise in the Archæan highlands, flow southeastward across the central Triassic plain, and reach the sea near the inland margin of the Cretaceous formation.

What kinds of rivers are these? Such a question can hardly be answered until we have examined rivers in many parts of the world, gaining material for a general history of rivers by induction from as large a variety of examples as possible; and until we have deduced from our generalizations a series of critical features sufficient to serve for the detection of rivers of different kinds wherever found.

The generalizations here referred to may be presented in the form of a classification, following the ideas of Powell, Gilbert, Heim, Löwl, and others, as follows:

Consequent Rivers. Those that have in their birth, at the time of their original establishment on the country which they drain, selected courses in accordance with the constructional slopes of the surface; for example, the Red River of the North and such of its branches as flow on the even surface of the lacustrine plain of Lake Agassiz; the several streams that drain the broken lava blocks of southern Oregon; certain streams and rivers of the Jura that drain the synclinal troughs of those mountains. Consequent streams may be divided into definite and indefinite groups. Definite consequent streams are those that follow well-defined constructional channels, such as the axial line of a synclinal trough, or the lowest point of an anticlinal arch between two synclinal basins; they are defined in location as well as in direction. Indefinite consequent streams are those that flow down constructional slopes, such as the flanks of an anticline, but whose precise location depends on those minor inequalities of surface that we term "accidental"; they are defined in direction but not in location, and they are as a rule branches of definite consequent streams.

Antecedent Rivers. Those that during and for a time after a disturbance of their drainage area maintain the courses that they had taken before the disturbance. In Powell's original definition of this class of rivers, he said that the valleys of the Uinta mountains are occupied by "drainage that was established antecedent to the corrugation or displacement of the beds by faulting or folding" (*a*, 163). No limit is set to the amount of corrugation or displacement or to the strength of the faulting or folding. It therefore seems advisable to consider what variations there may be from the strongly marked antecedent type; one extreme being in those cases where the displacement was a minimum and the perseverance of the streams a maximum, the other where the displacement was a maximum and the successful perseverance of the streams a minimum, or zero. The simplest examples of antecedent rivers are therefore found in regions that have been broadly elevated with the gentlest changes of slope, so as to enter a new cycle of topographical development, all the streams retaining their previous courses, but gaining ability to deepen their former channels down to the new base-level; such streams may be called "revived." Examples of revived streams are very common; nearly all the streams of the highlands of New Jersey are of this kind; all the streams of central and western Pennsylvania seem to belong in the same class. From these simple and common examples we shall some day, when our knowledge of rivers is better developed, be able to form a complete series leading to what is generally understood as the typical antecedent river, which has outlived deformation as well as elevation without suffering either deflection or ponding. Large rivers of strong slope, well inclosed in steep-sided valleys, or, in other words, vigorous adolescent rivers, have the best opportunity to persist across a belt of rising or writhing country, because a great deformation would be required to throw them from their courses. Small streams or large ones of faint slope in an open low country are more easily deflected. From the typical antecedent river the series may be continued by examples in which even the larger streams are less or more ponded or deflected by the deformation, until at the end of the series there is a complete extinction of the antecedent drainage and the establishment of an entirely original consequent drainage. The perfectly typical antecedent river, in the middle of this series, is certainly of rare occurrence, and is perhaps unknown.

Superimposed Rivers. Consequent streams, whose course is taken on a relatively thin, unconformably overlying mass, for a time preserve their initial courses, even though they may be quite out of accord with the underlying structures on which they have descended. Such streams were first recognized by Marvine, and afterwards named "superimposed," "inherited," or "epigenetic" by various authors. A full collection of examples of this class should begin with streams that depart from true consequent courses only locally, where they have discovered a small portion of the underlying formation, like the Merrimac at Manchester and other water-power towns of New Hampshire, where the stream has sunk upon rocky ledges beneath the surface drift and sands ; or like the Mississippi and other rivers in Minnesota which have in places cut through the drift sheet to the underlying crystallines. The series would conclude with streams that have stripped off the cover on which they were consequent, and have thus become superimposed on the underlying formation in their whole length.

There is a curious intermediate type of drainage lately recognized by McGee in the southern states, a superimposed drainage that is not inconsequent upon the buried surface beneath the unconformably overlying surface layer. It occurs in regions where a well-marked drainage had been established ; a brief submergence then allowed the deposition of a relatively thin mask of sediments ; an elevation brought the masked surface up again, and as it rose, the streams took possession of lines essentially identical with the courses of their ancestors, because the mask of newer deposits had not extinguished the antecedent topography. McGee proposes to call such streams "resurrected."

Subsequent Rivers. Rivers of all classes as a rule develop during their adolescence and more mature growth certain "subsequent" branches that were not in any way represented in the early youth of the system. Thus the indefinite members of the consequent drainage of the Jura mountains have developed subsequent streams on soft beds of monoclinal and anticlinal structures, where there could not possibly have been any consequent drainage lines at the birth of this system, unless we admit the supposed fracturing of the anticlinal crests, which seem unnecessary, to say the least. Even in the simplest style of drainage, growing on a level surface, many of the branches must be "subsequent," or as McGee has called them in such cases, "autogenetic."

Adjusted Rivers. Rivers of all classes are subject to spontaneous rearrangement or adjustment of their courses to a greater or less extent, in accordance with the weaker structural lines. This results from the migration of divides and the consequent abstraction or capture of one stream by another. The capture is generally made by the headward development of some subsequent branch. But after this kind of change has advanced to a certain extent, the divides become stable, and further change ceases. The rivers may then be said to be maturely adjusted. Under certain conditions, chiefly great initial altitude of surface, and great diversity of structure, that is, in mountainous regions, the changes arising from adjustments of this spontaneous kind are very great, so that the courses of a river's middle age may have very little resemblance to those of its youth, as Löwl has pointed out and as I have tried to show in the case of the Pennsylvania rivers. It may be difficult to recognize in such cases whether the youthful courses of a river system were consequent, antecedent, or superimposed. Adjustments of this kind were not discussed by Powell, although he makes brief mention of what I have called subsequent streams. The first appreciation that I gained of river adjustments came from the writings of Löwl; but I have since found that the general principles governing their opportunity were stated by Gilbert in his monograph on the "Henry Mountains of Utah" (141, 149), and by Heim in his "Mechanismus der Gebirgsbildung" (*i*, 272, etc.; *ii*, 79, 320).

Where do the rivers of northern New Jersey stand in this general scheme of river classification? We must again postpone the answer to the question while reviewing the history of the general geographical development of the region.

Topography of Northern New Jersey. The topography of northern New Jersey may be briefly described as made up of valleys and lowlands that have been etched in the now elevated surface of what may be called the Schooley peneplain on the Cretaceous base-level. The topographical atlas of New Jersey should be constantly referred to, in order to follow such a statement as this; but in order that the reader may, without undue difficulty, apprehend the meaning of my descriptions and recognize the various localities yet to be named without the trouble of searching for them on the maps of the atlas, I have attempted to draw a generalized bird's-eye view of northern New Jersey (Fig. 37) as it would be seen by an observer about seventy miles vertically above the center of southern New Jersey. The meridians are vertical, and east and west lines are horizontal, but oblique azimuths are foreshortened. The result is hardly more than a geographical caricature, and I publish it in part to experiment upon the usefulness of so imperfect an effort. An active imagination may perceive the long, even crest line of Kittatinny mountain on the northwest, rising beyond the rolling floor of the Kittatinny valley, as the great Allegheny limestone lowland is here called; then come the highland plateaus, of accordant altitude one with another, but without the mesa-like margin that my pen has not known how to avoid indicating. The central plain lies in the foreground, diversified by the various trap ridges that rise above its surface; First and Second mountains of the double Watchung crescent near the highlands; Sourland mountain in the southwest; and Rocky Hill, the southwestern reappearance of the Palisade's intrusive trap sheet, lying a little nearer to us. The central plain is also diversified by the fall line, a slight but rather distinct break in its surface from Trenton (*Tr.*) on the Delaware to a little below New Brunswick (*NB*) on the Raritan. The important drainage lines are: the Delaware, forming the western boundary of the state, trenching Kittatinny mountain at the Water Gap, cutting a deep transverse valley through the highlands where it receives longitudinal branches, and a shallower trench across the Kittatinny lowland and the central plain;

the Raritan, whose north and south branches head in the highlands, while the Millstone joins it from south of the fall line, cutting through Rocky Hill near Princeton (*Pr.*) on the way; and the Pequannock-Passaic, rising in the highlands, gathering tributaries in the low basin behind the Watchung ridges, and escaping to the front country as a single stream, the Passaic, through deep gaps at Paterson. The terminal moraine, marking the furthest advance of the second glacial invasion of post-Tertiary time, is indicated by an irregular dotted bank crossing the state, from the Narrows of New York bay, which it defines, on the east, passing over Second mountain by the gap at Summit (*S*), rising midway in the highlands over Schooley mountain, and traversed by the Delaware at Belvidere (*B*).

The Schooley peneplain is indicated by the crest and summit altitudes of Kittatinny mountain, the highland plateaus, and the trap ridges. This peneplain once lay low and essentially horizontal, the practically completed work of the processes of denudation acting on a previously high land through a long period of time; it is now lifted and tilted so that its inland portion rises to the height of the highlands, which are its remnants, while its seaward portion descends slowly beneath a cover of unconformable Cretaceous beds, southeast of the fall line, and thus hidden sinks gently beneath the Atlantic shore. The cover of Cretaceous sediments was laid on the southeastern part of the old peneplain during a moderate submergence of its seaward portion, before the elevation and tilting above mentioned (Fig. 38). Much of the cover has been worn away since the time of elevation (Figs. 39–42), which gave opportunity for the opening of deep valleys on the soft limestones and slates among the hard crystalline rocks of the highlands; and for the production of the broad Kittatinny valley lowland or peneplain on the wide belt of limestones beyond the highlands; and, furthermore, for the development of a broad base-leveled plain on the weak Triassic shales and sandstones where the old peneplain has been almost entirely destroyed. The Cretaceous cover remains only near the coast, where it stood too low to be attacked while the valleys and lowlands just described were carved out. An interesting peculiarity in the relation between the newer base-leveled

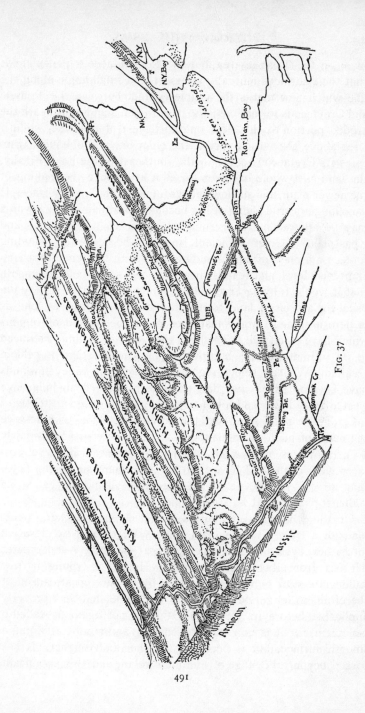

FIG. 37

plain on the Triassic area and the old Cretaceous peneplain is that their surfaces mutually intersect at a small angle along the line which now marks the visible contact between the Triassic and Cretaceous formations: the newer plain standing beneath the eroded portion of the older one northwest of this line, while it rises above the buried part of the older one and obliquely truncates its Cretaceous cover to the southeast of the line. Finally, the land as a whole has been raised a little since the making of the newer plain, and shallow valleys interrupt its broad surface. It is no longer a true plain; it has become a pastplain. A few words may be allowed me concerning these terms, "peneplain" and "pastplain." Given sufficient time for the action of denuding forces on a mass of land standing fixed with reference to a constant base-level, and it must be worn down so low and so smooth that it would fully deserve the name of plain. But it is very unusual for a mass of land to maintain a fixed position as long as is here assumed. Many instances might be quoted of regions which have stood still so long that their surface is almost reduced to its ultimate form; but the truly ultimate stage is seldom reached. We can select regions in which the valley lowlands have become broad and flat, the intermediate doab hills have wasted away lower and lower until they are reduced to forms of insignificant relief; and yet the surface still does not deserve the name of plain as unqualifiedly as do those young lands newly born from seas or lakes in which their geometrically level surfaces were formed. I have therefore elsewhere suggested (430) that an old region, nearly base-leveled, should be called an "almost-plain," that is, a peneplain.

On the other hand, an old base-leveled region, either a peneplain or a truly ultimate plain, will, when thrown by elevation into a new cycle of development, depart by greater and greater degrees from its simple featureless form, as young narrow valleys are sunk beneath its surface by its revived streams. It therefore no longer fully deserves the name that was properly applicable before its elevation. It must not again be called a peneplain, for it is now not approaching and almost attaining a smooth surface, but is becoming rougher and rougher. It has passed beyond the stage of minimum relief, and this significant fact deserves implication, at least, in a name. I would therefore call such a region a pastplain. The area of the weak Triassic shales was, until its late elevation, as good an example of an ultimate base-leveled plain as any that I have found; but now it is a pastplain, as any one may see while traveling across it on the train; its doabs are broad and continuous and its valleys are relatively narrow and shallow. The Kittatinny lowland is intersected by streams whose valleys sink below its generally even, gently rolling surface, but it was never so smooth as the Triassic plain. It was only a peneplain, and it is now a roughened peneplain. Perhaps the more adventurous terminologist will call it a past-peneplain, but I dare not venture quite so far as that. When the highlands were lowlands, their surface well deserved the name of peneplain, but they were lifted so long ago into so high a position that they are now cut into a complicated mass of rugged uplands. They no longer deserve the name of peneplain; and if in preceding paragraphs I have referred to them as constituting an old peneplain, it is because no satisfactory name has yet been applied to the particular stage of development of plains and plateaus in which they now stand.

The topography of northern New Jersey is therefore, like its structure, polygenetic. It exhibits very clearly a series of forms developed under three different geographical cycles, and closer search will doubtless discover forms belonging to yet other cycles, less complete and of briefer duration than these three. There is the tilted and deeply eroded peneplain of the highlands, whose initial form may be called the Schooley peneplain, from the distinct exhibition of one of its remnants on Schooley's mountain; this was the product of Jurassic and Cretaceous denudation. There is the younger central base-leveled plain, developed during Tertiary time, or thereabouts, on the weaker Triassic and Cretaceous beds; and the associated valleys of the same age that have been sunk into the weakest rocks of the highlands. There are the shallow valleys in the central plain, of the latest post-Tertiary cycle, requiring the name of this region to be changed from plain, as it was lately, to pastplain, as it is now. The first cycle, in which the Schooley peneplain was produced, witnessed the accomplishment of a great work;

it included in its later part, besides various other oscillations, the sub-cycle when the seaward or southeastern part of the peneplain was gently submerged and buried to a slight depth under Cretaceous deposits. The second cycle was shorter, being a time sufficient to base-level the softer beds, but not seriously to consume the harder parts of the preëxisting surface. We are still in the third cycle, of which but a small part has elapsed. The question with which this essay opened may now be taken up.

Revived and Superimposed Streams in New Jersey. The streams and rivers of northern New Jersey may be examined with the intention of classifying them according to their conditions of origin, to their degree of complexity as indicated by the number of geographical cycles through which they have lived, and to the advance made toward their mature adjustment.

The Musconetcong may be taken as the type of the highland streams. It flows southwestward along a narrow limestone valley between crystalline plateaus on either side, entering the Delaware a little below Easton, Pennsylvania (*E*, Fig. 37). It drains a country that has been enormously denuded, and during the Jura-Cretaceous cycle of this deep denudation there must have been time for it and its fellows to become thoroughly adjusted to the structure of the region; it must be chiefly for this reason that it flows so closely along the weak limestone belt and has its divides close by on the adjoining harder crystallines (*M*, Fig. 38). Whatever its origin, it has lost every initial feature that was discordant with the deep structures that it discovered beneath the initial surface; it is maturely adjusted to its environment. It endured to an old age during the base-leveling of the Schooley peneplain, and is now a "revived" stream, in at least its second cycle of work. Most of the other streams of the highlands and the country farther inland are also of this well-adjusted, revived kind. The streams of the Kittatinny valley lowland show not only the first revival of the kind just described, but also a second revival, in consequence of the recent uplift that has introduced the third cycle of development, this not being so clearly manifested in the highlands, where the rocks are harder and the valleys of the second cycle are narrower.

Look now at the drainage of the crescentic Watchung mountains; the curved edges of two great, warped lava flows of the
Triassic belt. The noteworthy feature of this district is that
the small streams in the southern part of the crescent rise on the
back slope of the inner mountain and cut gaps in both mountains in order to reach the outer part of the central plain. If
these streams were descended directly or by revival from ancestors, antecedent to or consequent upon the monoclinal tilting of
the Triassic formation, they could not possibly, in the long time
and deep denudation that the region has endured, have maintained, down to the present time, courses so little adjusted to

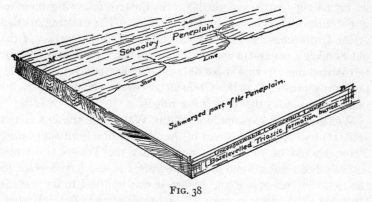

FIG. 38

the structure of their basins. In so long a time as has elapsed
since the tilting of the Triassic formation, the divides would
have taken their places on the crest of the trap ridges and not
behind the crest on the back slope. They cannot be subsequent
streams, for such could not have pushed their sources headwards
through a hard trap ridge. Subsequent streams are developed
in accordance with structural details, not in violation of them.
Their courses must have been taken *not long ago*, else they must
surely have lost their heads back of the Second mountain; some
piratical, subsequent branch of a larger transverse stream, like
the Passaic, would have beheaded them.

The only method now known by which these several doubly
transverse streams could have been established in the not too
distant past is by superimposition from the Cretaceous cover

that was laid upon the old Schooley peneplain. It has already been stated that when the highlands and this region together had been nearly base-leveled, the coastal portion of the resulting peneplain was submerged and buried by an unconformable cover of waste derived from the non-submerged portion; hence, when the whole area was lifted to something like its present height, a new system of consequent streams was born on the revealed sea-bottom. Since then, time enough may have passed to allow the streams to sink their channels through the unconformable cover and strip it off, and thus superimpose themselves on the Triassic rocks below; we should therefore find them, in so far as they have not yet been readjusted, following inconsequent, discordant courses under formation. The existing overlap of the Cretaceous beds on the still buried Triassic portion of the old Schooley peneplain makes it evident that such an origin for the Watchung streams is possible; but it has not yet been independently proved that the Cretaceous cover ever reached so far inland as to cross the Watchung ridges.

Want of other explanation for the Watchung streams is not satisfactory evidence in favor of the explanation here suggested. There should be external evidence that the Triassic area has actually been submerged and buried after it was base-leveled to the Schooley peneplain and before it was uplifted to its present altitude; other streams as well as the ones thus far indicated, should bear signs of superimposition; and if adjustment of the superimposed courses has begun, it should be systematically carried farthest near the largest streams. I shall not here state more than in brief form the sufficient evidence that can be quoted in favor of the first and second requisites. Suffice it to say, that the overlap of the Cretaceous beds (which contain practically no Triassic fragments) on the beveled Triassic strata at Amboy and elsewhere indicates submergence after base-leveling; and that the pebbles, sands, and marls of the Cretaceous series point clearly to the highlands as their source. The submergence must therefore have reached inland across the Triassic formation at least to the margin of the crystalline rocks. Some shore-line cutting must have been done at the margin of the highlands during Cretaceous time, but the generally rolling surface of the old peneplain leads me to ascribe its origin chiefly to sub-aërial wasting. Moreover, the North Branch of the Raritan, between Mendham and Peapack (* Fig. 37) and the Lockatong (*L*), a small branch of the Delaware, on the West Hunterdon sandstone plateau, give striking indications of superimposition in the discordance of their courses with the weaker structural lines of their basins, so unlike the thoroughly adjusted course of the Musconetcong and its fellows, the Pohatcong, the Lopatcong, and others.

Growth of Subsequent Streams. The third requisite of the proof of the inland extension of the Cretaceous and the resulting superimposed origin of the Watchung streams may be stated

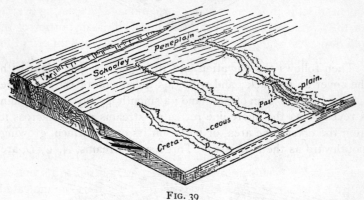

FIG. 39

in detail, as being more in the line of this essay: has the adjustment that accompanies superimposition systematically advanced farther near the large streams than near the small ones? The character of this adjustment should be first examined deductively. Given a series of streams of different volumes, flowing southeastward, in the direction of the present dip of the remnant of the Cretaceous cover, over the former inland extension of this superposed formation, how will these streams react on one another when they sink their channels into the underlying Triassic formation?

The conditions during the formation of the cover of Cretaceous beds are illustrated in Fig. 38, where the Triassic portion of the peneplain is submerged and the shore-line of the

transgressing ocean has reached the margin of the crystalline
rocks. The waste from the crystallines is spread out as a series
of gravels, sands, and marls on the base-leveled Triassic area.

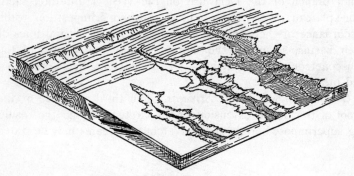

FIG. 40

Then follows the elevation and tilting of the peneplain with
the cover on its back; and with this regression of the sea there
is an equivalent gain of new land; a smooth, gently sloping plain
is revealed as the shore-line retreats; streams run out across it
from the crystalline area, or begin on its open surface, growing
mouthward as the land rises. Three such streams, *A*, *C*, *D*, are

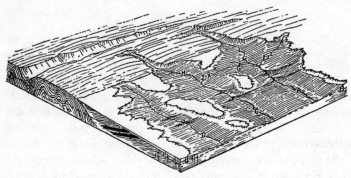

FIG. 41

shown in Fig. 39; their opportunity for deep valley cutting is
indicated by the depth of the new base-level, *BL*, below the general surface of the country. While these streams are deepening
their channels in the Cretaceous cover, which is unshaded with

marginal contour lines in the figures, their subsequent autogenetic branches are irregularly disposed, because there is no
lateral variation of structure to guide them; but after a time the

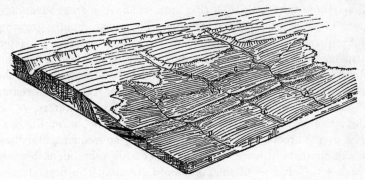

FIG. 42

base-leveled surface of the buried Triassic beds is reached, as is
shown by linear shading in the valley bottoms of Figs. 40–43.
The growth of the subsequent branches then developed will be
along the strike of the Triassic softer beds, that is, about square
to the course of the three transverse streams under consideration. The most rapid growth will be found on the branches

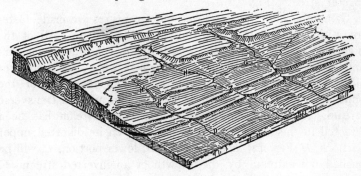

FIG. 43

of the largest stream, *A*, because it will most quickly cut down
its channel close to the base-level of the time and thus provide
steep, sloping valley sides, from which the subsequent branches
cut backwards most energetically. In due time the main streams

discover the particularly resistant transverse lava sheets in the underlying formation, and then the subsequent branches of the largest transverse stream on the upstream side of the obstructions, for example, F and G (Fig. 40), will have a great advantage over those of the smaller streams. The most rapidly growing subsequent branch, G (Fig. 41), of the largest transverse master stream, A, may grow headwards so fast as to push away the divide, X, which separates it from the head of the opposing subsequent branch, J, of the next adjacent smaller transverse stream, C, and thus finally to capture and divert the headwaters, H, of the smaller transverse stream to the larger one, as in Fig. 42. The divide creeps while the two opposing subsequent branches are in contest; it leaps when the successful subsequent branch reaches the channel of the conquered stream. The first stream captured in this way must necessarily be the nearest to the large stream. The diversion of the considerable volume of headwaters, H, to the channel of the small subsequent branch, G, causes it to deepen its channel rapidly; the same effect is perceptible in H for a distance above its point of capture and diversion; the increased load of sediment thus given to G will be in great part dropped in a fan delta, where it enters the flat valley of the master stream (Fig. 42).

Gaining strength by conquest, other captures are made, faster for a time, but with decreasing slowness as the head of the diverting subsequent branch recedes from the original master; and at last, equilibrium may be gained when the headwater slope of the diverting branch is no greater than that of the opposing subsequent branch of the next uncaptured transverse stream. After the capture of a transverse stream has been effected in this way, the divide, Y, between its diverted upper portions, H (Fig. 42), and its beheaded lower portion, C, will be pushed downstream by the growth of an inverted stream, V. This goes on until the equilibrium is attained, and further shifting is prevented on reaching the hard, transverse lava sheets, Z (Fig. 43); here the divide is maturely established. In the case of a system of transverse streams, C, D, etc. (Fig. 43), successively captured by the subsequent branch of a single master, the divides, Z, Y', between the inverted (V, V') and beheaded (C, D)

portions of the captured streams will for a time present different stages of approach to establishment. The divide on the line of that one of the original streams, C, that is nearest to the master stream, A, may reach a final stable position, Z; while on the next stream, farther away from the master, the beheaded portion, D, may still retain a short piece above the gap in the upper lava sheet, not yet secured by the inverted stream, V', and a third stream, farther away still from the master (not shown in Fig. 43), might remain uncaptured and independent.

It is by such tests as these that we may hope to recognize the occurrence of partial adjustment in the streams of the Watchung crescent as a result of their superimposition on the Triassic formation from its former Cretaceous cover. The greater the degree of complexity in the tests proposed, the more confidence we shall have in the theory when the tests successfully meet the facts. Hence the reason for deductively carrying out the theoretical conditions to their extremest consequences in order to increase the complexity of the tests that are to be confronted with the facts. This, as a matter of method, seems to be of great practical importance in any attempt to decipher the past progress of geographical development.

The admirable contoured topographical maps of New Jersey, issued by the Geological Survey of that State under the leadership of the late Professor George H. Cook, afforded means of applying the deductive tests above outlined without the necessity of plodding over all the country concerned; but however good the maps are, it is hardly necessary to say that they can be interpreted with a better appreciation of the facts that they represent after an excursion on the ground has given the student some personal acquaintance with it. This I have tried to gain on various occasions, maps in hand.

Atlas sheet number six, including the central red-sandstone area and the five-mile-to-an-inch geological map of the state, presents in the clearest manner the facts of form and structure involved in our problem; and to my mind the correspondence between theory and fact is very striking. The Pequannock-Passaic is the master transverse stream of the region; its pre-eminence was probably due in the beginning to its gathering, from the unsubmerged highlands, a greater amount of drainage than belonged to any other stream that ran southeastward down the gentle slope of the newly revealed Cretaceous cover. It was at that time a compound, composite river : compound, because it drained areas of different ages ; composite, because these areas were of different structures. Existing examples of compound, composite rivers are seen in the Catawba, the Yadkin-Pedee, the Cape Fear, and the Neuse rivers of North Carolina, which all rise on the inland crystalline area and traverse the coastal quaternary plain before reaching the sea. But unlike these, there must have been, when the old submerged land rose with the Cretaceous cover on its back, numerous small streams whose drainage area lay entirely within the Cretaceous plain. These were simple streams, flowing over a structure of one kind and one age. Their modern homologues are seen in the Maurice, the Great and Little Egg Harbor, and the Wading rivers of southern New Jersey, and I suppose also in various relatively short streams of North Carolina, such as the Lumber, Great Cohera, and Mocassin.

It cannot be supposed that the original Pequannock-Passaic possessed the large southern branch, which I shall call the upper Passaic, by which Great Swamp is now drained ; for had this been the case, the divides between the branches of the upper Passaic and the heads of the small streams that now still cross both of the trap ridges must long ago have been driven to a stable position on the crest line of the inner ridge. It should be recognized that the present roundabout drainage of the Great Swamp is a post-glacial feature, determined by the morainic barrier that crosses the basin from Summit, *S*, to Morristown, *M* ; the pre-glacial drainage of the southern part of the inner crescent was undoubtedly of a simpler and more direct pattern. The upper Passaic member of the Pequannock-Passaic system must be regarded as a branch of subsequent development, guided by some of the softer Triassic beds when they were reached beneath the Cretaceous cover, and very successful in capturing and diverting other transverse streams that were smaller than its master. For some distance on either side from the Pequannock-Passaic gap in the trap ridges at Paterson, the existing streams are perfectly adjusted to the Triassic structure; that is, the ridges are persistent divides, and the lateral subsequent branches of the master flow along the strike of the softer shales and sandstones, except where lately thrown off their courses by glacial drift barriers. This I interpret as meaning that the Pequannock-Passaic master stream hereabouts made so early a capture of adjacent superimposed streams that all traces of their initial discordant courses have been obliterated by the development of structurally accordant subsequent streams.

The Watchung ridges extend only about eight miles northward of the Paterson gaps, but reach thirty miles southwestward. It is therefore chiefly in the latter direction that we may expect to find examples of incomplete adjustment following superimposition and capture. At Milburn there is a deep gap in First mountain, and opposite this, at Summit S (Fig. 37), a partly drift-filled gap in Second mountain; this I am disposed to regard as the former outlet of the Rockaway-Rahway river, which on account of its considerable size was not captured by the Passaic until it had cut its passage across the trap sheets almost to a safe depth. The diverted upper portion — the Rockaway — now joins the Passaic, its crooked course from the highlands via Boonton (Bn) being a post-glacial irregularity; the beheaded lower portion — the Rahway — heads on the ridge of Second mountain, retains the pair of subsequent streams between the two ridges, and flows in diminished volume to the sea, the divide between the two portions being in its mature stable position on Second mountain.

South of the Milburn gap there are three streams that maintain water gaps in First mountain, and five head branches of these three streams rise behind the crest of Second mountain. These must be interpreted as remnants of streams that once rose further inland and whose upper courses have been captured by the victorious upper Passaic; but it is noteworthy that here, at the greatest distance from the gap of the master stream at Paterson, the divides between the diverted and beheaded portions of these southern streams should lie in unstable positions back of the crest line of Second mountain. This is exactly what the hypothesis of a superimposed origin for these streams would require; and if the complexity of accordance between deduction and fact here presented be duly considered, I believe new confidence may be gained in the hypothesis of superimposition, already rendered likely from other evidence.

The rectangular courses of the streams that cross First and Second mountains southwest of Milburn do not militate against their initial obliquely superimposed courses; for, as Gilbert has shown, oblique courses across tilted beds, alternately hard and soft, will gradually shift until they follow rectangular courses along the strike of the soft beds and square across the strike of the hard beds. Middle Brook, at the southern bend of First mountain, near Bound Brook (*BB*), presents the peculiarity of branching east and west while on the trap sheet of the mountain. This may be due to a retention here, where the dip is moderate, of an initially superimposed bifurcation, or to guidance by fractures at this point where the course of the mountain changes rather abruptly; the facts at hand do not serve to make choice between these alternatives.

Green River in the Uinta Mountains. The lesson of greatest importance in this study lies, to my mind, in the gradual development of accordant subsequent streams in a region where the unchanged superimposed drainage would show no such accordance. Similar adjustment of subsequent streams to structural features may characterize drainage systems that were originally antecedent; and with this principle in mind I have recently read over with renewed interest Powell's classic study of the Green river where it crosses the Uinta mountains (*a*, 152–166). (See also the geological map in the "Geology of the Uinta Mountains.") The Green river and the smaller streams of its lateral cañons and valleys are all regarded as antecedent. Let us examine the arguments on which this conclusion rests.

The Green river itself rises many miles north of the Uinta range, traverses a relatively low basin before reaching the flank of the mountains, and then instead of turning away, it boldly enters the great uplift and trenches it from side to side in a profound cañon, flowing out to the southwest on its way to the Colorado. There is relatively low ground at the eastern end of the range, several thousand feet lower than the summits of the range on either side of the Green river cañon, and many thousand feet lower than the restored crest of the great uplift; but the river does not follow this open roundabout course. Powell says that the river cut through, instead of running around, the great obstruction, because it " had the right of way; . . . it was running ere the mountains were formed." Had the mountain fold been formed suddenly, it would have turned the river around it to the east; " but the emergence of the fold above the general surface of the country was little or no faster than the progress of the corrasion of the channel. . . . The river preserved its level, but the mountains were lifted up. . . . The river was the saw which cut the mountains in two " (*a*, 152, 153). If this interpretation is correct, the Green river would be the type of a perfect antecedent stream, but it appears to me that the case is probably overstated in that respect. Perhaps it would have been more deliberately stated in a later volume if Powell's intention of describing more fully the three chief kinds of drainage of the region had been carried out (*b*, v). Not having seen the region, my comments may have little value; but the context of Powell's report, the description of the immense series of lacustrine beds, over a mile thick, north of the mountains, and the eastward deflection of the river where it traverses the mountains, all seem to me to indicate that the Green was by no means continuously successful in maintaining its antecedent course across the uplift. It is by no means a typical antecedent river. The great series of lacustrine beds upstream from the cañon, with conglomerates where they rest on the northern flank of the mountains, are fully recognized in the report, and must mean that the upper portion of the river was for a time shut back, or ponded. During part of this time there may have been no overflow across the growing mountains, for the lower lacustrine beds contain fossils indicative of brackish water (*b*, 84, Chap. III, by C. A. White). The intermittent growth of the mountains and the repeated return of lacustrine conditions, with gradually freshening water, is indicated by the strong unconformities that occur at various points in the lacustrine beds, and by the change in the fossil fauna. It must be conceded from this that the upper portion of Green river was repeatedly ponded back by mountain growth across its middle course; we therefore have not now any close indication of its pre-lacustrine course above the mountains ; the ancient, or pre-Uinta, upper portion of the river was extinguished by the lacustrine sediments, and to that extent the Green river departs from the perfect antecedent type.

In the second place, if the original Green river existed upon the upper surface of the beds that were at a subsequent date raised to form the Uinta uplift, it does not appear to be clearly proved that its course at that early time was closely coincident with its present course in the mountainous area. The first deformations of the mountain growth may have temporarily interrupted its flow, as is made likely by the lacustrine deposits already referred to ; and when the rise in the level of the waters of the lake overtook the uplift, probably at a time of slower mountain growth than that which first formed the lake, the point of overflow may have been many miles to one side of its previous drowned-out course. The moderate elevation of the eastern end of the range, where it connects with the Yampa plateau, may possibly have then been a little higher than a point farther west, where the overflow was consequently located. This is perhaps hardly as probable as the postulates involved in arguing a truly antecedent course for the river ; but its impossibility is not as strictly proved as would be necessary before a definite conclusion as to the continuous persistence of an antecedent river could be finally accepted. Such continuity of action must be rare and should be rigorously demonstrated if possible.

It must, moreover, be remembered that Emmons is of the opinion that the Colorado river is not antecedent at all, but is superimposed on the eastern portion of the Uinta range from a course that it had chosen upon a sheet of horizontal sediments — the Wyoming conglomerate — which he supposes once stretched unconformably all over the previously deeply eroded surface of the uplifted range, where the cañon is now cut. He quotes facts of two kinds in evidence of this : first, the remnants of the Wyoming conglomerate still lie on ridges as high as those that inclose the river cañons ; second, the Green and certain of its branches possess tortuous courses, out of accord with the structure of the range. It might be added that the wide, open valley of Brown's park in the middle of the range is best explained as the product of a pre-Wyoming cycle of erosion by rivers that were extinguished when the Wyoming beds were laid over the mountains. The strongest objection to Emmons's conclusion seems to be the great amount of erosion that it requires; erosion sufficient not only to remove the Wyoming conglomerate from nearly all its former overlap on the Uinta range, where it had buried and extinguished a pre-Wyoming drainage, but also to carry away a vast extension of the formation at the same height, north of the range. It may be best to conclude that both antecedent and superimposed processes must be called on; for one must hesitate before admitting that the Wyoming beds stretched all across the country north and east of the Uinta range up to the height at which the remnants are now found on the range; it seems more likely that some part of the height of these remnants is due to a relatively local elevation. As far as this is the case, it gives reason for regarding the Green as an antecedent river; that is, antecedent to the local elevation of the Wyoming beds, but long posterior to the elevation of the Uinta range; but as the river now flows — according to Emmons's theory — on beds lying unconformably below those on which its course was chosen, it is for this reason to be classed as superimposed.

The Green river, therefore, certainly departs from the type of an antecedent stream; the departure is distinct in its repeated ponding, whereby its upper course was broadly and indeterminately shifted from its original location; and is at least possible, if not probable, in its defeat at the line of uplift and subsequent superimposition on a new line of overflow. The mountains wrenched the saw that afterwards cut them in two.

A study of the Jura drainage, of which a fuller account may be given at some future time, has led to the provisional conclusion that many of its streams show a combination of consequent and antecedent characteristics. They appear to be consequent on the early stages of the deformation, but antecedent to its later growth, and for this kind of a stream I have no satisfactory name to suggest at present.

Heim has shown that the Reuss and the adjacent smaller transverse streams of northern Switzerland near Lucerne are in part persistent across a series of folds, and in part slightly shifted from one course to another and ponded in Lake Lucerne; but unless the other ranges of the Alps rise hereafter faster than they have heretofore, the geologist of the future will reasonably regard the more mature Reuss as an essentially successful antecedent river.

The Sutlej and other rivers that escape from the inner valleys of the Himalaya by deep gaps in the outer ranges are described by Medlicott as antecedent to the elevation of the ranges through which they flow, their antecedent origin being argued from the delta-like structure of the upturned beds in the outer gorges, as if the rivers were now cutting down the deformed deltas of an earlier time; but the heavy gravel and sand deposits in their upper valleys indicate that they were nearly, if not quite, ponded for a time during the deformation.

Rivers seem to have the habit of cutting down their upturned deltas. Bonney refers to several such examples among the rivers that flow northward from the Alps and transect particularly thick portions of the upturned marginal conglomerates and sandstones, which he regards as the deltas formed by the same rivers at an earlier time, when the mountain folding had not extended outward as far as it does now from the axis of the Alps. I have suspected that the same kind of evidence might be used to indicate that the Delaware above Trenton, between Pennsylvania and New Jersey, is in part even of pre-Triassic origin, for where it now enters the Triassic belt there is a particularly heavy and coarse sandstone, sometimes conglomeratic. Being a large stream, it might persist in an anaclinal course through the northwestward monocline formed by the Jurassic uplift of the Triassic beds, although the smaller streams of the region were then probably extinguished, to be replaced by a new system consequent upon the new order of things.

Large rivers, more or less persistent in the face of opposing disturbance, therefore appear to be generally recognized; but it is noticeable that those quoted from the Himalaya and the Alps presumably occupied, at the time of disturbance, well-inclosed valleys, from which it would have been difficult for them to escape backwards or laterally; and that, even if successful in the end, they for a time suffered defeat or ponding of greater or less extent and duration. There is no evidence that the Green river was well inclosed immediately north of the Uinta mountains at the time of their first elevation; hence the likelihood of its temporary ponding or inclosure is increased.

It is stated by Powell that not only the Green but even the smaller streams of the Uintas are of origin antecedent to the mountains. He writes:

> The explanation of the cañons of Green river will assist us in understanding the origin of the lateral valleys and cañons. The streams were there before the mountains were made; that is, the streams carved out the valleys and left the mountains. The direction of the streams is indisputable evidence that the elevation of the fold was so slow as not to divert the streams, although the total amount of elevation was many thousands of feet. Had the fold been lifted more rapidly than the principal streams could have cut their channels, Green river would have been turned about it, and all the smaller streams and water ways would have been cataclinal (*a*, 162).

This appears to me an unproved conclusion, and the evidence of it needs careful attention. It appears that there are several streams which descend from the crest of the mountains towards the flanks, but instead of running all the way out to the margin of the fold, they turn along the strike of a monoclinal valley, and thus reach the main river by a short cut. Such streams are cataclinal for a time, then monoclinal. It is in reference to these that it is said, "the streams were there before the mountains were made"; and again, "the drainage was established antecedent to the corrugation or displacement of the beds by faulting and folding" (*a*, 163). In approaching this conclusion Powell says that these streams cannot be consequent, for

> valleys consequent upon the corrugation, which was one of the conditions of the origin of the Uinta mountains, could not have taken the direction observed in this system; they would have all been cataclinal, as they ran down from the mountains, and turned into synclinal valleys at the foot, forming a very different system from that which now obtains (*a*, 166).

Nor can the streams be superimposed, for the "later sedimentary beds, both to the north and south, were found not to have been continuous over the mountain system, but to have been deposited in waters whose shores were limited by the lower reaches of the range" (a, 166). Therefore the discordant streams must be antecedent.

It appears to me that the possibility of error in this argument lies in the omission of all consideration of the migration of divides and the resulting adjustment of stream courses to deep internal structure; but at the time of the exploration of the Colorado river, this important process in the development of rivers was not understood. It now seems only natural that the original, consequent, cataclinal streams, flowing down the slopes of the range from crest to flanks, should have permitted the opening of subsequent monoclinal branches on the soft beds that they discovered; and that the shifting of divides in these monoclinal valleys should have led to the capture of several cataclinal streams by that particular one of the subsequent branches that grew out from the master stream, the Green river itself. Thus it must happen that the streams " which head near the summit of the range and running down the flank turn into the Green river are, in their upper courses, cataclinal, and when they turn to follow the strike of the rocks into Green river, are monoclinal" (a, 161), this being a normal result of river work in cutting down the thousands of feet of rocks of various hardnesses here concerned. The smaller streams of the Uinta range are therefore certainly not of necessity antecedent to the Uinta uplift; the probability is that they were originally purely consequent, and that at present they are nicely adjusted to the structures that they have discovered.

I have learned so much from the doctrine of base-leveling, as presented in Major Powell's writings, that I shall hope to profit by the lesson of the Uinta drainage as well; that is, the possibility that an apparently sound conclusion may be overturned when new processes that bear upon it are discovered. It is here said that the drainage of the Watchung crescent in New Jersey is an example of partial adjustment following a superimposed origin; hence the necessity of watching closely for the discovery of new principles in the history of river work that may call for a revision of this conclusion.

Anaclinal and Reversed Rivers in New Jersey. There are two other examples of peculiar accidents in the history of rivers in

New Jersey to which I wish to call attention ; both of them are in the latest cycle of the development of the state, that is, in the cycle which has changed the central region from its even base-leveled lowland surface to the pastplain as we now see it. Like the uplift of the Schooley (highland) peneplain, the uplift of the central plain, in passing from the second to the third cycle, was not uniform throughout, but was greater in one place than in another. In the neighborhood of the lower Raritan river a distinct though gentle slope to the northwest is apparent in the unconsumed surface of the pastplain ; but this strong river runs southeastward against the slope ; it is an anaclinal stream. The tilting of the pastplain is moderate, and its rocks are weak ; the river is large and strong ; its anaclinal course is therefore best explained by regarding it as a mild example of an antecedent stream. But Ambrose's brook, a small stream to one side of the Raritan, flows northwest with the gentle slope that was given to the pastplain ; it is therefore not a survivor from the previous cycle, but is a new stream consequent on the slight deformation by which the latest cycle here considered was ushered in. Manalapan and Assanpink are apparently of the same kind (see Fig. 37).

The Millstone river appears to be intermediate as respects origin between the Raritan river and Ambrose's brook. It appears still to lie for the most part in the channel that it occupied before the elevation and tilting of the base-leveled central plain, but the tilting of the plain seems to have reversed its direction of flow. It rises near the center of the state and flows northwestward till it joins the Raritan near Somerville, and on the way it crosses from the thrown or depressed to the heaved or elevated side of the fall line, and passes through a deep gap in the trap ridge of Rocky hill, back of Princeton. I believe there is no other Atlantic river which runs against the fall line in this way, and it is certainly at first sight remarkable that a stream of moderate size like the Millstone should have held its own against a displacement that sufficed to deflect great rivers like the Delaware and the Susquehanna from their courses.

The Millstone appears to have been a stream of the normal kind in the previous cycle before the tilting of the central plain, when it probably ran southeastward with its fellows and carried off its share of waste in the base-leveling process of that time. No other supposition than this seems consistent with the general history of the region. It was during that cycle that the deep gap was cut in the Rocky hill trap ridge. Then came the deformation of the base-leveled plain, the relatively recent elevation and gentle tilting that have permitted the streams to carve it into a pastplain, and with this, the dislocation along the fall line. The inclination of the interstream surfaces of the pastplain leaves no doubt that it was tilted to the northwest, and to this tilting we must ascribe the present direction of the Millstone flow. But why did not the accompanying dislocation on the fall line throw this moderate-sized stream off its track and divert it southwestward to the Delaware at Trenton, or northeastward to the Raritan below New Brunswick? The effect of the dislocation appears with considerable distinctness along a line from Trenton towards Amboy, in the less altitude of the general surface of the pastplain to the southeast than to the northwest of the line, the difference of altitude of the two parts being about a hundred feet. The persistence of the Millstone against such a dislocation seems to require that we should postulate a slower and smaller movement here than that which deflected the Delaware.

The reversed course of the Millstone cannot be regarded as an example of inversion following a capture of its ancient northern headwaters by a branch of the Raritan; for in such a case surely the inversion could not have progressed farther south than the hard trap ridge of Rocky hill, where a stable divide would have been formed; nor can the Millstone be regarded as an original stream, first developed and consequent upon the deformation of the central plain, for in that case it should consist of two separate parts: one part running from the actual head of the river to the fall line, where it would turn southwest and cross the faint flat divide that separates it from the Delaware; the other part beginning by Princeton, north of the fall line, and running thence north to the Raritan. The continuity of these two parts in the actual Millstone seems to be explicable only by regarding the river as the upper portion of a single larger river that had reached an old age in the previous cycle; it was then broken in two at the head of the present river where the greatest elevation of the central plain occurred, and thus had its former headwaters reversed from the southeast to a northwest direction of flow across and against the fall-line break by the tilting of the plain. Only in this way can the deep gap in Rocky hill be explained. The river is thus consequent on the tilting of the plain, and yet antecedent to the accompanying faulting. It cannot be called an original stream, for it had an ancestor in its very channel. It is not a purely consequent stream, for it runs against the heaved side of a fault. It is not a strictly antecedent stream, for it flows in a direction determined by a disturbance that occurred late in its life. It is too exceptional a stream to have a generic name. We cannot expect to find many others like it.

The result that has been of the greatest interest to me in these studies is the discovery of well-recorded and peculiar histories in the commonplace, small-sized rivers of our Atlantic slope. We have looked for some years to the West as the region where river history should be illustrated, because it was there that the pioneers in this branch of study taught us the lessons on which our further work must depend. But home study as well as distant travel has its rewards, and with the progress of good topographical work on this side of the country we confidently await much instruction from a close acquaintance with the curious histories of many of our rivers which we know now only by name.

REFERENCES

Davis, W. M. *Am. Jour. Sci.*, XXXVII (1889), 430.

Emmons, S. F. Fortieth Parallel Survey, II (1877), 194, 205, 206.

Powell, J. W. (*a*) Exploration of the Colorado River of the West. 1875.

   (*b*) Geology of the Uinta Mountains. 1876.

XXI

RIVER TERRACES IN NEW ENGLAND

I. GENERAL STATEMENT

Theories of River Terraces. The terraces carved by streams
in the washed drift of our valleys have been frequently studied
and described since the beginnings of geological investigation
in New England. In nearly all cases more attention has been
given to terrace pattern as seen in vertical cross section than as

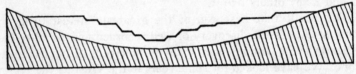

FIG. 44

presented in horizontal plan. The cross section is usually represented as in Fig. 44, in which the depth of the rock-floored valley
is made greater than that of the new valley carved in the drift
filling. A notable feature of such terrace sections is that the
open space measured across the valley between the scarps of
the low-level terraces is narrower than that between the scarps

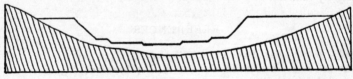

FIG. 45

of the high-level terraces; and this fact has frequently given
rise to the supposition that the volume of our streams to-day is
less than that of the streams by which the high-level terraces
were carved. It will, however, be shown from what follows that
the characteristic cross section of a terraced valley in which the

river has not yet reached rock bottom exhibits few stepping terraces, and is fairly represented by Fig. 45 ; while if stepping terraces are present, a characteristic section on which the most

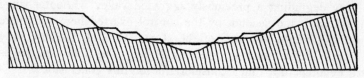

FIG. 46

significant points for a mile or more up and down the valley are projected, would show that the base of many of the terraces is determined for short distances (ten to fifty feet) by a rock ledge, as in Fig. 46, or, better, in Fig. 47. This factor in the development of terraces was first recognized, as far as my reading has

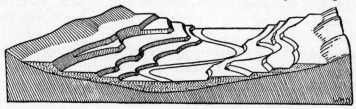

FIG. 47

gone, by Hugh Miller (the younger), whose view will be presented in abstract on a later page.

Although the controlling ledges occupy a very small fraction of the terrace length, they are of dominant importance, and there can be little doubt that the finest flights of stepping

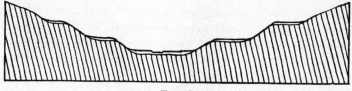

FIG. 48

terraces in New England are to be thus explained. Terraces of the kind shown in Fig. 48 are different from those here studied, as will be more fully stated in the next section.

When the terrace pattern is considered in plan as well as in cross section, it appears that our terraces may be accounted for, first, by the behavior of a meandering and swinging stream, slowly degrading a previously aggraded valley without change in volume; and second, by the control exerted here and there over the lateral swinging of the stream through the discovery of rock ledges, as suggested by Miller. The following pages are devoted to a fuller consideration of this conclusion.

II. PRELIMINARY INQUIRY

Various Kinds of Terraces. For the sake of clearness it is desirable to exclude at the outset all kinds of terraces other than those here studied. The terraces that occupy so many of our valleys are known as river terraces, drift terraces, or alluvial terraces. They have as to origin nothing in common with the terraces of sea-shores, such as occur on the coastal slopes of Cuba, or with the lake-shore terraces so well developed in the basins of Bonneville and Lahontan. They bear little resemblance to structural rock benches, such as break the slopes of valley sides in dissected plateaus, as in West Virginia, or on a still larger scale in the Colorado cañon. They have little likeness to the silt and gravel-covered rock terraces formed when a graded river, revived by uplift, cuts a new valley in its former valley floor, as along the gorge of the Rhine on its way through the Schiefergebirge of western Germany.

Our New England drift terraces have a flat and nearly level upper surface or plain, limited backwards by rising ground and forwards by falling ground, and to that extent they resemble the terraces of all the classes above mentioned, but they have certain well-marked features of their own. They are evidently the river-carved remnants of a body of stratified clays, sands, or gravels that once occupied in larger volume than to-day the rock-floored valleys of still earlier origin. Their upper surface, the terrace plain or floor, slopes with the fall of the stream by which their scarped face or front has been eroded; and in this they differ from sea-shore and lake-shore terraces and from structural rock benches, none of which have any particular relation to the slope of neighboring streams. They consist of unconsolidated, stratified drift; if a ledge appears in any part of a drift terrace, it is manifestly an accidental element, although, as will be shown, it may exert a controlling influence on the pattern of the terrace front; in this our drift terraces differ from the structural rock benches of valley sides in dissected plateaus, and from the rock terraces that represent the former valley floors of revived rivers, both of which consist essentially of rock, even though the latter may bear a veneer of river drift on their surface, as in Fig. 48. Moreover, drift terraces are, in nearly all cases, developed with much more irregularity of pattern than is the case with the terraces of other kinds. A single drift terrace — unless it be the highest one of a series — is seldom traceable many miles along a valley side; its length may be only a few hundred yards. Terraces of other kinds are usually much more persistent.

Furthermore, our drift terraces differ from other terraces in the place that they occupy in the geographical cycle. They are not products of normal erosion during an undisturbed stillstand of a land mass, but are the consequence of some relatively short-lived episode during which a greater or less departure is made from the normal progress of a cycle. The terraces of New England occupy well-opened rock-floored valleys of earlier origin, and thus imply the previous attainment of maturity in the cycle which witnessed the development of our hills and valleys. The glacial period witnessed certain modifications of the pre-glacial valleys and closed with the accumulation of abundant drift in them, as well as with certain changes of level by which the rivers were prompted to wash the valley drift away. Post-glacial time has allowed the rivers to enter well upon this task; yet, even when the task has been completed, the normal cycle of erosion in New England will not have advanced far beyond its pre-glacial phase, — so brief are the glacial and terrace episodes compared to the time required for base-leveling a region of resistant rocks.

Systematically considered, river terraces may be best associated with the forms assumed by the waste of the land on the way to the sea. Flood plains and alluvial fans are representative examples of the form assumed by land waste while it is stopping on its way down a valley. Terraces are examples of the forms assumed by waste that still remains in its stopping place after part of its volume has been swept forward again.

Terrace Patterns. Before entering upon the consideration of the process of terracing it will be well to examine briefly the more characteristic elements of terrace pattern, especially as seen in horizontal plan. The plain or floor of a drift terrace frequently presents a rapid variation in width, usually terminating in points at its upstream and downstream ends, as in Fig. 49. The borders are prevailingly formed of curves of greater or less length,

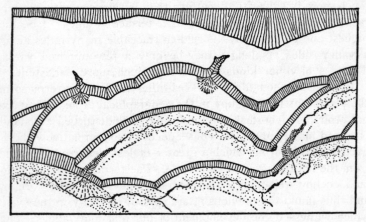

FIG. 49

but of tolerably uniform radius, concave to the stream and frequently uniting in cusps. When several cusps are grouped, one back of the other, so as to form a strong salient, they may be called a terrace spur. Convex borders fronting the stream occur but rarely. The highest plain of a flight of terraces backs against the ascending slopes of the older valley side and accepts their outline as its border, as in Fig. 49; while each lower terrace, as well as the existing flood plain,—the "intervale," or "interval" of New Englanders,—backs against the scarp of the next higher terrace; thus the intermediate members of a flight of terrace steps possess similar but not necessarily parallel outlines, front and back; the cusps between the curves all point towards the stream. The back border of a terrace is frequently followed by a marshy channel from which the terracing stream has been withdrawn by a short-cut, or cut-off (as is more fully considered below), before the channel was filled ; terrace plains thus characterized may slope gently away from the axis of the valley towards their back border, and if they are of moderate breadth, the backward slope may be a relatively conspicuous feature, as in the lower terrace in the middle of Fig. 49. Terraces of this kind were called " glacis terraces " by Hitchcock (58). They are of very common occurrence, and serve to show that the sudden withdrawal of the terracing stream from a roundabout channel to a more direct course has not been unusual.

The scarp of a terrace connects the front border of the plain above with the back border of the plain below. Its sloping surface therefore presents a succession of curved reëntrants, separated by salients of greater or less acuteness. It is well known that the curved terrace fronts have been carved by the successive encroachments of a curved stream which once swung against their base, and that the stream has swung laterally at least as many times as there are terraces ; but the behavior of the swinging stream has seldom been traced in detail.

Although the plain and the descending scarp at its front are usually taken together as bounding a terrace, these two surfaces are not genetically connected in river terraces as they are in constructional lake-shore or delta terraces. River terraces being of destructional origin, it is the ascending scarp at the back of a terrace that should be associated with the plain beneath and in front of it. The line along the reëntrant edge between the plain and the ascending slope at its back is the most significant of all terrace lines. The front line of a terrace plain is of less significance, for it is determined merely by the slipping of the sands and clays down to the line of the under-cut scarp at the back of the next lower terrace ; the front line of a terrace plain is therefore of value only in so far as it represents the back line of the next terrace beneath.

Terrace scarps are steepest where the cutting stream has most recently swung against their base. In a series of stepping terraces, the youngest and steepest scarps are at the bottom of the flight ; but when all the terraces of intermediate levels are destroyed by a chance lateral swing of the stream so that it under-cuts even the highest terrace plain, then the whole descent from highest to lowest level may be fresh-cut with sharp edges at top and bottom. In older terraces the scarps weather to a gentler slope, and the edges are rounded off. A convex slope of erosion is thus formed above and a concave slope of deposition below. The older the terrace, the greater is the part of its front occupied by rounded slopes, and the gentler is the slope of the shortened tangent between them. At the same time, the salients or cusps between the reëntrants of the scarps, as seen in plan, lose their original sharpness of definition and become blunt and dulled. There has been no attempt to show details of this kind in the accompanying diagrams.

Gulches are often worn in terrace fronts by wet-weather streams, and fans are spread on the terrace plain below. The abandoned stream channels at the back border of a plain are usually taken as guides for surface drainage, whose gathered waters dissect the plain where it is cut off by the next lower terrace. A rather systematic drainage pattern is thus devel-oped, as in Fig. 49.

The several theories by which terraces have been explained may now be reviewed.

Terraces carved by Streams of Diminishing Volume. The primi-tive explanation of terraces is that the whole space between the upper terrace scarps represents the channel of a huge river by which the valley was once drained, and that successive diminu-tions of volume to that of the present river are indicated by the decrease of breadth between the terraces in descending order. Although this view has sometimes received distinguished advo-cacy, it has never gained general acceptance among geologists or geographers. It has, however, been very generally supposed that the present rivers are much smaller than they were when they began the work of terracing; hence it is desirable to consider the special features that should appear if a decrease in stream volume had actually taken place.

The best indication of the volume of the stream by which a terrace has been carved is afforded by the curvature of its frontal scarp. If the scarps of the low-level terraces have a radius and an arc of curvature similar to these elements in the existing river meanders, and significantly smaller than in the high-level scarps, while curves at intermediate levels show intermediate values, a diminution of stream volume may be fairly inferred. If the radius and arc of curvature are of about the same measure in the three cases, no change in stream volume is indicated.

On the other hand, if a stream were charged with abundant and coarse load in the last stages of its aggrading action, as seems to have been frequently the case in New England, its slope must have been relatively strong; and a graded river with a heavy load on a strong slope does not develop curves of as small radius as it would when subsequently flowing with the same volume but with a finer load on a gentler slope; hence a large radius of curvature in the uppermost terraces should not alone be taken as an indication of large volume; large arc of curvature should also be found before large volume is inferred. It is for this reason that some of the uppermost terraces of the Connecticut and the Westfield rivers, whose scarps seem to sweep in curves of greater radius than do those of the low-level terraces, cannot alone give assurance of a former greater volume for their rivers.

It is, however, rendered very probable by what is known of the later stages of the glacial period that many of our streams had greater volume then than now. The most effective cause for greater volume was the constraint of the ice sheet, whereby the drainage from the basins of north-flowing rivers was turned over the divides into the valleys of south-flowing rivers. This may have been the case while the ice still covered the northern basins, their waters (as far as they had any) then running as sub-glacial streams, which may have been forced to ascend slopes and cross divides. Effective constraint may also have been provided after the ice had at least in part withdrawn from the northern basins but when it remained in sufficient force to obstruct their normal outlets, thus forming lakes whose overflow ran across a pass in the divide to some southern valley. Another cause for increased volume of our south-flowing rivers was the importation into their basins of a considerable snowfall that was received on the ice sheet over some northern basin. A fourth cause for increased volume of our rivers lies in a possibly greater precipitation during the later stages of the glacial period than at present. A fifth cause lies in a relatively rapid melting of the retreating ice sheet. It is eminently possible that these various causes may have contributed effectively to an increase in river volume while the New England valleys were aggrading with drift; but it does not follow that volumes decidedly larger than those of to-day were continued into the period of terracing.

Except where direct evidence is given by curvature and arc of high-level terrace scarps, a formerly greater volume of the terracing streams should be regarded only as a possible, not as an actual, occurrence. It is especially desirable that large bulk and coarse texture of terrace deposits should not be too readily accepted as evidence of former greater volume of streams; for bulk of deposits is a function of time as well as of rate of action, and texture is a function of slope as well as of stream volume and velocity. Hence until time and slope are shown to have been insufficient to account for bulk and texture of deposits, it is not compulsory to account for them by greater stream volume.

Even if decrease of volume has been of general occurrence during the period of terracing, it has nevertheless not been in control of terrace development; for if it had been, stepping terraces should be much more abundant than they are to-day. As a matter of fact, the diagrams by which terraced valleys are ordinarily represented, give an exaggerated idea of the prevalence and perfection of these graceful forms. It is rare to find a long flight of stepping terraces on both sides of a valley; it is rare to find a flight of terraces continued for any long distance along a valley side; when more than three or four low steps are to be counted, it is usually only for a moderate fraction of a mile that they persist. A large part of the length of our terraced valleys is bordered by a few terraces of strong scarps, or by a high terrace with one or two lower ones beneath it; and it is not uncommon to find at least one side of a valley inclosed by a single scarp in which the whole descent is made at once from the highest terrace plain to the lowest. If terracing had been due to a general decrease in the volume of our rivers, stepping terraces should be much more prevalent, and broad flood plains between the high scarps of a single terrace on each side of the valley should be much more rare than they are; and when the whole descent from high terrace to flood plain is made in a single scarp on one side of the valley, stepping terraces with broad treads should be well developed on the opposite side; but no such arrangement of terrace form can be said to prevail. Decrease of river volume must therefore be at most a subordinate cause of terracing, if, indeed, it is not as a rule a negligible factor in their production.

This conclusion seems to have been clearly in the mind of Adams, state geologist of Vermont, who, in 1846, wrote as follows:

The first stage in the process in which the terraces originated, the deposition of the materials, we have before referred to the older Pleistocene. The process of denudation must have next followed, when the rivers, cutting down their channels through the drift barriers, lowered them gradually above the barriers. Flowing through the level deposits of sand, they must have formed serpentine channels, as rivers do now in alluvial plains; consequently, by increasing the convexity of the bends, and then cutting them off, or wearing away their headlands and shifting their beds, they would be meanwhile removing the greater part of the materials thus disturbed. By this process the greater portion of the original plain must have been carried off, and it is not necessary to suppose that the distance between opposite terraces is any indication of greater magnitude of the river, but only of its shifting its channel (145, 146).

Terraces carved by Streams of Increasing Slope. When the basin of an aggrading river system is slightly tilted, it may be expected that those streams whose slopes are decreasing will aggrade their valleys more rapidly than before, unless their point of junction with a degrading stream may be lowered more than their headwaters are depressed by tilting; while those whose slopes are increasing will change their action from aggrading to degrading. It is well known that New England has suffered a differential elevation in post-glacial time. The post-glacial clays of Lake Champlain and southern Maine were deposited when the sea stood three hundred feet or more above its present level. The clays of the Connecticut valley in Massachusetts were, according to Emerson, deposited in lakes or bodies of slack water at or very close to the sea-level of their time, but the clays now reach elevations approaching two hundred feet. No post-glacial changes of level of such amounts are known to have taken place along the southern New England coast. Our south-flowing rivers have therefore been accelerated, while those flowing northward have been retarded; and to this differential tilting Shaler has ascribed the weak terracing by streams of the latter class in contrast to the active terracing by those of the former.

While it is thus made very probable that the erosion of valley drift was determined by the unequal elevation of New England in post-glacial time, it does not follow that individual terraces are in any close way related to this movement. Several cases must be here distinguished.

The northern uplift may have been accomplished in a single movement and so rapidly as to have revived the streams to an unusual activity of erosion, whereby they deepened their valleys quickly for a time, and did not begin to swing laterally, in the manner essential to terracing, until they had developed new grades of gentle declivity after the rapid uplift had ceased. In this case only a single high-level terrace and no intermediate terraces would be formed, and there would be but few low-level terraces.

A second supposition includes cases of repeated rapid uplifts separated by deliberate pauses, each of which would produce a result similar to that of the previous case. Here we should expect the river to have swung laterally at as many different levels as there had been pauses during the total uplift; and the flood plain formed during each pause would be of relatively persistent occurrence down the valley. But in order to protect the terrace remnants of the successive flood plains from being consumed by the river when it swings from side to side at lower levels, it is necessary to postulate that the movements of uplift should succeed each other at shorter and shorter intervals, so that the later-carved flood plains should be narrower than the earlier ones. The chief objection to this supposition is not so well directed against the postulate just mentioned as against the requirement of correlated levels in the terrace on the two sides of a valley. Such correlation is occasionally found, but it is by no means characteristic of our terraced valleys in general. The terrace levels are usually so discordant on the opposite sides of a valley that they cannot be considered the records of stillstands of the land between times of rapid uplift.

A third supposition considers an uplift so slow that the south-flowing rivers were never much accelerated; for during slow uplift the larger rivers might continue to swing actively from side to side, while all the time degrading the valley floor. In this case terraces might be cut at many different levels on opposite sides of the valley, according to the habit of the river in its lateral swinging.

The third supposition seems most appropriate to New England, for all of our valleys in which terraces are well developed, exhibit flood-plain remnants at many levels, high and low, and neither so few in number nor so accordant in relative altitude above the river as to imply that lateral swinging had occurred only during the quiet intervals between rapid uplifts. But it should be noted that this conclusion applies better to the valleys of good-sized streams or rivers than to those of small brooks; for the latter frequently show only faint terraces or no terraces at all, even though they are branches of rivers whose valleys are well terraced. This seems to mean that an uplift which was so slow that a good-sized river could easily keep pace with it by down-cutting, may have been too fast for such a result in the case of a small stream. While the able-bodied rivers may thus have been always effectively at grade, leisurely swinging from side to side and at the same time slowly wearing down their valley floors, the small streams may have been for much or all of this time above grade, and therefore unable to widen their little valleys, although actively engaged in deepening them. On the other hand, even the largest rivers have not been able to maintain a graded channel in the rock ledges upon which they have been here and there superposed by the drift cover. They are still actively cutting down such ledges, but they are not yet able to widen the rock notch that they are cutting, thus imitating the condition of their smallest branches, which have not yet been able to widen their little valleys even in clays and sands. Bowlder clay or till is of a resistance between the feebleness of stratified drift and the strength of rock ledges. If a mass of till is discovered, the stream may be successful in cutting down its channel to grade, and yet unsuccessful in opening a valley floor; and thus a bowlder-clay "shut in" may be produced between open

valley floors or "intervals" that have been eroded in weak stratified drift farther up and down stream. Little river, a mile southwest of Westfield, Massachusetts, offers examples of this kind.

The small changes made in rock ledges during the development of an extended series of river terraces serve to indicate
how short is the duration of the episode in which the alluvial
filling of a valley is terraced, in comparison with the time needed
for the erosion of the rock-bound valley itself, or still more with
a whole cycle of erosion, in which a mountain mass is reduced
to a plain of degradation.

While slow uplift is thus seen to be consistent with the production of many terraces, it is not consistent with their preservation, for it does not explain the diminution of the interscarp
space from the higher to the lower levels. Indeed, the present
rivers might tend to develop broader flood plains by strong lateral
swinging at the faint grades now assumed than they had developed at the stronger grades during the earlier stages of possibly
more active uplift and heavier load; and the broad, low flood
plains would necessitate the under-cutting of all or nearly all the
earlier high-level terraces by the present stream, and the concentration of nearly all the separate scarps in a single high-terrace
front, as in Fig. 45. Examples in which this condition has been
actually attained are to be found in the valleys of various rivers,
as will be more fully set forth in following pages. Single high-
scarped terraces are indeed so common as to warrant the conclusion that high-level and intermediate terraces would nearly
always be destroyed by the swinging of the river at a lower
level but for the occurrence of some special conditions by
which they are preserved.

Terraces carved by Streams of Diminishing Load. A graded
river may be caused to degrade as well by diminishing its load
as by increasing its slope, volume remaining constant. A diminution of load since the stage of glacial retreat is highly probable,
for not only the streams that issued from the ice sheet but those
also which washed the freshly exposed drift-covered land surface
were in all probability highly charged with detritus in late glacial
and early post-glacial time. Indeed, increase of load may have
been almost as potent a cause of filling the valleys with washed

drift as was the depressed attitude of the land in the north and the consequent enfeebled slope of the south-flowing rivers. As the ice disappeared and as the land surface was more or less covered with vegetation, the load of the streams should have been lessened, and they must thereupon have set to work to degrade the valleys that they had just before been aggrading, even if no change of slope had taken place. This process, if working alone, must have been very gradual, and might therefore have allowed plenty of time for lateral swinging and terrace carving. But, as before, no explanation is here found for the production of stepping terraces. On the contrary, when the diminution of load was further advanced, the rivers would degrade their valley floors more and more slowly, and the tendency would then be to destroy all the earlier terraces by broadening the flood plain to a maximum.

That the rate of degradation by our rivers was really slow is proved by the flights of stepping terraces here and there in different valleys; and that the normal tendency of the larger rivers is to destroy nearly all the earlier-made terraces by opening broad flood plains at low levels is proved by the frequent occurrence of high scarps descending from the highest terrace plain nearly or quite to the lowest. Hence it is for the preservation of high-level and intermediate terraces rather than for their production that a more efficient cause than any yet discussed is to be sought.

Preservation of Terraces by Rock Ledges. What is more natural than that a river, swinging from side to side as it slowly degrades its valley floor, shall here and there be restrained on coming against a ledge projecting from the sloping valley wall; and that the deeper the valley is excavated, the less breadth of free swinging can remain! This idea was first given explicit statement in Miller's paper on "River Terracing; its Methods and their Results," as illustrated by observations in Scotland. After a review of earlier writings, this author says:

The modern rivers . . . have struck rock at very variable depths. In hundreds of cases, after winding freely about, encountering only soft clays and the like, and constructing terraces of various kinds, they have here and there become rock-bound, and prevented from pursuing their work of terrace-building after their former manner, as well as from destroying the terraces they had already made (298). . . .

When . . . the rivers commenced to work upon shallow, wide-bottomed valleys, soft and yielding in their nature, except where crossed by bars of rock . . ., they proceeded to plane far and wide, traveling from breadth to breadth to an extent never now equaled. With banks nowadays eight or ten times as high, and rock-bound at perhaps ten times as many points, it is no wonder that the modern rivers should seem to have "run *in*" (299, 300).

Rock ledges, however, are not here given the importance they deserve. The reader will not surely gain from Miller's article a full measure of the value of ledges in determining the pattern of terraces, and of stepping terraces in particular. Hence a more detailed statement of the relation of ledges to terrace pattern and to terrace development seems desirable, especially with reference to the valleys of New England, where this explanation of terraces has not previously been applied.

It should be further noted that certain postulates of Miller's essay do not command entire assent. He states that "it is not allowable to have recourse to coast elevation, or climatic changes, or periodicity of any kind, without first proving that the terraces range in opposite pairs" (304, 305). This seems to be an unnecessary limitation of possibilities; for, as is here explained on page 540, a river that is impelled to gradual degradation by a slow rising or tilting of the land may produce unpaired terraces as it wanders to and fro across its valley floor. On another page Miller concludes that rivers "cannot but concentrate their channels as they excavate them, unless the amount of planation is out of all proportion to the rate of deepening" (300), and seems to imply in this statement that a large ratio of lateral erosion to degradation, such as is here assumed for our New England rivers, and further considered in later sections, is an improbable ratio. To this it may be answered that the occurrence of stepping terraces at one and another point in our larger valleys certainly justifies the assumed ratio by showing that lateral swinging should be measured in hundreds or thousands of feet at many successive stages of degradation, while the total degradation is usually to be measured in tens of feet and seldom exceeds one or two hundred feet. A possible reason for the difference of values given to this ratio may be that Miller's studies were

directed to the moderate-sized rivers of Scotland, while the best
terraced valleys in New England are those of large rivers like
the Connecticut and the Merrimac and their stronger branches;
and, as has been already pointed out, a large river may swing
actively during an uplift that gives a small river no time for
anything but down-cutting. These two items are, however, of
secondary importance in Miller's theory compared to rock ledges.

In reviewing various other essays of earlier dates several suggestive passages have been found, hinting at the importance of
rock ledges. Adams makes the following statement:

> If a terrace has been formed before the complete removal of the obstruc-
> tions in the channel [the context shows that these obstructions are " solid
> rock "], the same process must have been repeated within the new and nar-
> rower level of interval. We should thus have a second terrace. Repetitions
> of the process in cases where the obstructions were not entirely removed
> would occasion a greater number of terraces (146).

Something more explicit is found in Edward Hitchcock's "Surface Geology." In describing a middle section of the Connecticut
valley, where the terraces became famous from the writings of
this author, it is said that " the rock often projects through the
terraces" (18), but the service of the rock in protecting the overlying terrace from being cut back is not announced. Further on
a description is given of the basin of the Westfield river, where
the effect of ledges in determining the number and pattern of
the terraces is very striking; here it is briefly stated that " the
materials of which all these terraces are formed are clay, sand,
and gravel, though the red sandstone shows itself occasionally
near the river " (20). The secret is told in an account of the terraces of the Deerfield : " The river would encroach still farther
upon this hill, had it not struck a ledge of red sandstone, which
will at least retard its lateral erosion" (19); and again,

> the reason why those [terraces] on Pine hill remain, I find to be that they
> rest on a protuberant mass of red sandstone. On the west side of the hill
> . . . is an ancient bed of Deerfield river . . . which was prevented from
> making any further lateral encroachments by the underlying rock (20).

Yet in spite of the understanding thus shown of the importance
of ledges in these particular instances, the generality of the relation of ledges and terraces is not brought forward; and the above

instances of the local restraint exercised by ledges have never been quoted, so far as I can find, by any of the many readers of Hitchcock's well-known essay.

A fuller recognition of the part played by defending ledges is to be found in Emerson's "Geology of Old Hampshire County, Massachusetts." It is here said that the Connecticut river in the neighborhood of Holyoke "has now cut its bed deep in the sandstones and is thus prevented from oscillating" (730). A little farther down the valley "the river early became entangled in rock and has cut only vertically" (733). In the northern part of the state "the river everywhere cut down rapidly to rock and has not swung widely to east and west, but has been condemned from the beginning to rock-cutting" (733). "Across Chicopee there is a fine, low terrace bounded on the east by a high scarp of the high terrace, which everywhere shows till in great force beneath the sands of the old lake" (730; see also 627, 632). It should be noted, however, that these passages are chiefly concerned with the occurrence of trenches, floored with rock and lined on both banks with ledges. The part played by an isolated ledge of rock or by a bank of till in preventing the further swinging of the river and thus defending the terraces above it is not brought forward.

Origin of Terraces in New England. Three conclusions may now be stated in order that the reader may have in mind the end to which the preceding and following pages lead. First, a diminution of stream volume may have taken place during the terracing of our New England valleys, but it has not been essential to the production of the observed terraces. Second, the terracing rivers have slowly degraded their aggraded valleys while actively swinging from side to side, degradation probably being the result of the combined action of a slow northern uplift and a gradual decrease of load, and in spite of a probable decrease of volume. Third, the chance discovery of rock ledges by the swinging river is the chief cause of the systematic diminution of interscarp space and of the preservation of terraces, as seen in a typical section of stepping terraces.

A full statement of the process of terracing, therefore, involves a consideration, first, of the behavior of a free-swinging, slowly degrading river; and, second, of the constraint that may be imposed on such a river by the accidental encounter with previously buried ledges at various points in its course and at various stages in its history. This anticipatory statement may aid in the understanding of the following pages.

III. THE THEORY OF RIVER TERRACES

Plan of Statement. The previous paragraphs have given a general consideration of several theories of river terraces, with the result of deciding that one of them offers a much better explanation of observed facts than the others. It is now proposed to examine the successful theory with more care, first, by making a somewhat detailed study of such processes of river action as are involved in the theory; second, by deducing with some minuteness the various patterns of terraces that can be formed by these river processes. It will then be possible to make in Part IV a thorough test of the verity of the theory by confronting its deduced consequences with the facts determined by observation.

It should be understood that the deductive character of the succeeding paragraphs is more apparent than real. Many features of river work here presented as deductions were discovered by observation. It is true that an expectation of certain occurrences had been aroused by the deductive consideration of certain processes, but there has been so continual an interweaving of observation and theory during the growth of these pages that it is now rather difficult to determine the order in which the various items here recorded came to mind. It is therefore chiefly for the sake of a continuous presentation of the theory of river terraces that a largely deductive treatment is here adopted. When the whole theory has been apprehended, it is relatively easy to test its verity by observations pertinent to its different parts.

The other theories of terracing, regarded as unsuccessful in our preliminary inquiry, should be further considered before they are discarded; but inasmuch as the more they are examined the less competent they seem to explain the facts observable in the terraced valleys of New England, it does not seem worth while to give them more explicit consideration here.

Behavior of a Wandering River. The diagrams introduced in the following sections represent several successive stages in the process of slow degradation by a wandering river. The postulates as to river behavior on which the diagrams are based are (1) the degrading stream continually maintains an essentially graded condition ; (2) the lateral swinging of the meandering channel is very much faster (a hundredfold, for example) than the degradation of the valley floor ; (3) the breadth over which a free river (not constrained by ledges) tends to swing laterally ˴is greater than the breadth of the meander belt (the belt included by tangents to the meandering channel) ; (4) an individual meander tends to enlarge its radius and to work its way down the valley until it may be abandoned at season of high water for a short-cut across a flood-plain lobe, or at any season (but usually at high water) for a cut-off through the narrowing neck of a lobe. It is believed that abundant justification may be found for all these postulates, either in the observed behavior of a graded river or in the success with which they lead to an understanding of the peculiar patterns of our terraces. The several postulates may now be reviewed.

(1) If the change in the ratio of load to carrying power (volume and slope) proceed very slowly, a river may remain in an essentially graded condition all through the process of aggrading or of degrading its valley, and through the change from aggrading to degrading. It is true that the graded condition depends on a balance between load and carrying power, and it would at first sight appear that any change in either quantity would destroy the balance and throw the river out of grade. But if the change is only by a quantity of the second order, — that is, if either load, volume, or slope is changed only by a differential of its value in a unit of time, — adjustment to the new condition will follow so immediately that no failure of adjustment will be noticeable. A similar maintenance of an essentially graded condition obtains in the degradation of graded (waste-covered) hillsides as they pass from maturity to old age. It is, however, not likely that the very slow degradation of a valley floor which accompanies the advance from maturity to old age in a normal cycle of rock erosion will result in terraces, because the general

processes of weathering may lower the flood plain about as fast as the river sinks to a fainter and fainter slope. The rate of degradation of a terracing river in a drift-filled valley, resulting from a climatic change or from a land movement, may therefore be allowed a decidedly higher value than that of an aging river in a normal, undisturbed cycle.

(2) It is well understood that a graded stream may continue to work actively in wearing or building its banks laterally, however slowly such a stream aggrades or degrades its valley floor.

(3) There are abundant examples of rivers whose lateral oscillation or swinging carries them from side to side of a flood plain that is much wider than their meander belt. The Mississippi is a noted case of this kind. Its meander belt is six or eight miles wide in a flood plain whose inclosing bluffs are from twenty to sixty miles apart. A similar relation may be seen in many meadow flood plains, drained by small brooks.

(4) The fourth postulate involves a principle of river action which may be familiar to hydrographers, but which is, nevertheless, not commonly stated. Imagine a stream in a broad flood plain passing from a straight stretch or tangent to a well-defined curve. On the tangent AB (Fig. 50), the thread of fastest current might, as far as local control is concerned, lie along the middle of the channel, or indifferently on one side or other of the middle line. On entering the curve the fastest current is gradually shifted, BC, towards the outer bank of the channel, and there flowing steadily all around the curve, CD, it determines the line of greatest depth. On passing from the curve the thread of fastest current is necessarily delivered to the next downstream tangent, DE, on the down-valley side of the channel, and only after flowing for a significant distance will the fastest current gain a path near mid-channel. If the curves or meanders are close set, so that one curve passes directly into the next one with no intervening tangent, then the thread of fastest current must, on passing the point of inflexion, enter the upstream end of the next curve near its inner or convex bank, and only gradually be displaced towards the outer bank as inertia has time to bring about its usual effect.

As a result of this systematic displacement of the fastest current from the mid-channel line, the bank that it approaches will be worn away, while deposition will take place along the bank from which the fast current is withdrawn. The stream will therefore tend to wear away the bank on the outer side of its curves (but perhaps failing to begin this action just at the

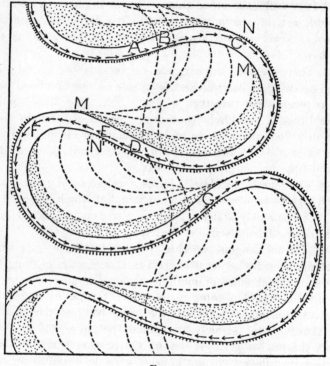

Fig. 50

beginning of the curves) and on the down-valley side of short tangents. The curves will thus increase in radius and arc and the meander belt will widen, while each meander will tend to move slowly down the valley. The flood plain must be scoured out for a certain stretch (NN') around the concave banks and along the up-valley side of every lobe, while a scroll of new flood plain (MM) is added around the end and on the down-valley side of the lobe.

All this may be easily recognized in the meanders of a meadow brook; and that it occurs even in the Mississippi is abundantly illustrated in the large-scale maps (three inches to a mile) published by the Mississippi River Commission (see especially sheets 36, 38, 39), where the lines of flood-plain growth pass around the end and along the down-valley side of each lobe, while they are cut across by the encroaching river on the up-valley side of the lobe, as indicated in Fig. 50. Still more definite proof of this feature in the behavior of a meandering river is found in the new edition (1900) of the Preliminary Map of the Mississippi (one inch to a mile), in which a red overprint indicates the new position of the channel, as determined some fifteen years after the previous survey (see especially sheets 14, 16, and 18).

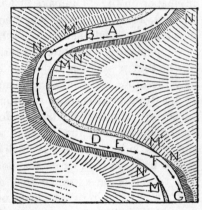

FIG. 51

The same down-valley shifting of the meanders is seen in the inclosed meanders of many rivers, typified in North Branch of the Susquehanna (Fig. 51). This fine river has incised its course beneath the uplands of northern Pennsylvania. The upland spurs that enter the river curves have been subjected on their up-valley sides to a persistent sweeping that is but little less effective than that by which the curved reëntrants between the spurs have been scoured out. The up-valley side of the spurs have strong bluffs, as different from their gentle down-valley slopes as are the high lateral bluffs that inclose the curves from the gentle terminal slopes of the spurs. It is noteworthy that in this case of a rock-walled valley, the down-valley shifting of the curves does not seem to have been more than fifteen or twenty times greater than the degrading of the river channel in the latest period of valley trenching; while in the case of terracing streams in drift-filled valleys, the first of these changes exceeds the second in a much higher degree. It may be further noted that the North Branch of the Susquehanna above Wilkesbarre seems for some time past to have ceased deepening its valley, for narrow double-curved scrolls of flood plain are now systematically added to the outer end and the down-valley side of the spurs, as may be especially well seen just above Tunkhannock, and as is indicated by the dotted areas *MM'*, opposite the under-cut bluffs *NN'* (Fig. 51).

Other examples of meandering valleys, exhibiting the systematic lateral growth and down-valley shifting of the meander curves, might be instanced; a few of them are mentioned in my paper on the "Drainage of Cuestas" (89). It is my hope to give at another time a fuller account of this phase of river development, and then to show how satisfactorily the stage of development may be stated in terms of the flood-plain pattern.

The four postulates above announced concerning river action may therefore be taken as well supported.

A natural limit is set to the dimensions of a growing meander curve on a flood plain by the formation of short-cuts across flood-plain lobes at time of high water, or of cut-offs when the narrowing neck of a lobe is finally worn through, a roundabout course being in both cases abandoned for a more direct one. It may therefore be expected that the abandoned channels, such as are preserved in ox-bow lakes on existing flood plains, and in swampy half-filled channels at the back border of many terraces, will on the average show a larger radius of curvature than the curves of the existing river; and the maps of the Mississippi give some support to this expectation. Emerson has pointed out (735) the tendency of our New England rivers and streams to form loops or ox-bows on the right of their general course, from which they return to a nearly direct course by short-cuts or cut-offs, only to begin again the work of right-handed loop-cutting. He states that the Connecticut near Northampton, Massachusetts, has seven deserted loops on the right (west) and none on the left; some of its tributaries have sharp bends and oxbows thirty times as numerous on the right as on the left of their course. It is naturally suggested that this asymmetry is the result of the deflective force arising from the earth's rotation.

Terminology of Wandering Rivers. The terms already introduced regarding rivers that wander about their flood plains may now be summarized and somewhat extended. The space inclosed between tangents drawn outside of the curves or meanders of the stream is the meander belt. This belt will widen while the meanders are normally wearing their outer bank; but on the occurrence of a short-cut across a flood-plain lobe or of a cut-off through the narrowing neck of a lobe, the belt will locally collapse. Here the river course becomes relatively direct for a time, only to develop serpentines again as new meanders are established. The progressive movement of the meanders down the valley will be called sweeping. Upstream and downstream will be used in their ordinary sense, but up-valley and down-valley will be substituted when it is desired to indicate a more general direction than that of the circuitous channel.

The lateral movement of the meander belt from one side of the valley floor to the other will be referred to as swinging. It is not always possible to distinguish between the true lateral swinging of the meander belt as a whole and the more local shifting of an irregularly sweeping meander. The compound movement of sweeping meanders in a swinging meander belt will be called wandering, this term being fully justified when it is noted that many unsystematic irregularities must be developed in a stream channel, whereby it will depart significantly from the simple and regular movements here considered. The whole breadth of the valley floor that may be worn down by the stream will be called the belt of wandering; this corresponds to many of our flood plains or "intervals."

In an ideal case, a regularly growing pattern of meander curves might be imagined slowly sweeping down a valley, the meander belt collapsing here and there, now and then, but growing again to its ordinary breadth as new curves are developed in the place of the old ones. At any point in the valley an endless procession of meanders would sweep past.

If it be now supposed that the wandering stream is slowly degrading its valley floor, each meander will sweep past a given point at a slightly lower level than that of its predecessor; and each time the meander belt swings across the valley from one side to the other and back again, it will return at a distinctly lower level than that at which it left. The flood plains formed at different stages of this leisurely process will differ in altitude, and all of them will be inclined gently down the valley. It is the remnants of these flood plains that form our terrace plains.

Ideal Terrace Patterns: Early Stage. Soon after the stage of degradation has been definitely established and the meandering stream begins to swing across the valley at a little lower level than before, a condition represented in Fig. 52 may be

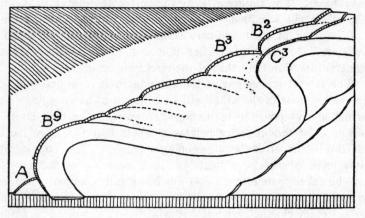

FIG. 52

reached. In this figure, as in a number that follow, it is supposed that the view is taken from a considerable height, looking northwest across the valley of a south-flowing river. The terrace plains are left blank in most of the diagrams. The western meander in the foreground of Fig. 52 is now scouring out a curve in a low concave terrace scarp (B), the ninth of its kind within the limits of the diagram. A small portion of a terrace (A), of slightly less height, is shown in the immediate foreground; it may represent the work of the preceding westward meander, while the next following westward meander is cutting out a deeper terrace (C), in the background. Terrace A may be taken as one of the first marks made by the degrading stream. Terrace B is of greater height than A because A has been under-cut and consumed in the production of B, except in the immediate foreground. Terrace C is as yet independent of B, and therefore shows a height to be measured only by the few inches or feet of depth to which one sweeping meander cuts below the plain of its predecessor. The curves and cusps of terrace B result from a vacillation of the meander during its down-valley progress; a rather sharp cusp being left between B^2 and B^3, while the curves from B^3 to B^9 have arcs so small as to join in an early straight terrace front.

It may be noted that the small curves by which a nearly straight terrace front is usually formed are as a rule to be expected only towards the side of a valley, and less commonly on a terrace spur that advances into the valley. For example, in Fig. 53 the little curves A, C, D, E record so many positions of the meander apex, and will not now be destroyed until a later meander under-cuts them. Scarps of this kind may be called one-sweep scarps; and their cusps, one-sweep cusps. Several similar cusps are shown in Fig. 52. The longer curve $E E'$, cut by the advancing front

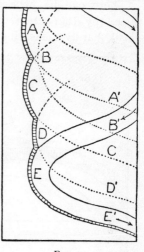

FIG. 53

of the meandering river, may be abandoned if the river is diverted by a short-cut to a new course, and if so, the advancing terrace spur will be smooth trimmed.

A terrace whose scarp has been almost evenly trimmed by the small vacillations of a down-sweeping meander will face the axis of the valley. A terrace whose scarp has been under-cut by the forward half of a down-sweeping meander will face obliquely up the valley, as in the foreground of Fig. 53. Inasmuch as the normal progress of meander-sweeping is down the valley, it would seem, at first thought, that no terrace scarps could be carved so as to face in that direction; but on second thought it will be seen that the lateral growth of a meander may cause part of the curve to grow up-valley faster than the meander is carried in the other direction by the normal down-valley sweeping of the meander system; and in this case a terrace scarp facing obliquely down-valley will be carved. An example of this kind is shown near the foreground of Fig. 54. It is manifest that the development of terraces facing down-valley will be favored wherever the down-valley sweeping of a group of meanders is for any reason checked while the enlargement of their curves is continued.

There can be little doubt that the height of terraces produced by the action of successive meanders would be very small, hardly measuring as many inches or quarter inches as

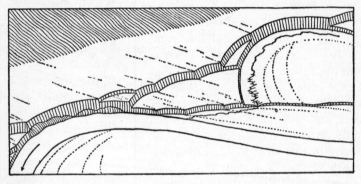

FIG. 54

actual terraces measure in feet. Let it therefore be now supposed that after a series of one-sweep scarps has been carved, the river swings away from the western side of its valley and for a time occupies itself in carving scarps on the eastern side. Many meanders will have swept down the valley during the eastward swing of the meander belt, each meander leaving its faint scar on the valley floor. When the river swings westward again, it will be working at a lower level than before, and as it then once more under-cuts the high plain, a distinct terrace with a scarp of ten or twenty feet will be formed. Terraces of distinctly different levels may therefore usually be taken to represent different swings of the meander belt; terraces that represent only the sweeps of successive meanders while the belt remains almost stationary must be so faint as to be hardly noticeable.

A cusp which results from the slightly vacillating forward sweep of a single meander, as B^6, B^7, etc. (Fig. 52), has already been called a one-sweep cusp. The terrace plain extending forward from the base of such a cusp will be a smoothly continuous surface on both sides of the apex. When the two parts of a terrace plain on either side of a cusp differ in height by a foot or two, they are probably the product of different (but not necessarily successive) meanders; and such a cusp may be called a two-sweep cusp, because the two levels probably represent different sweeps in the meander belt. When the difference in height is a number of feet, the cusp is probably a two-swing cusp, because the two levels are then best explained by different (but not necessarily successive) swings of the meander belt. Examples of the forms described above are frequently observed.

Ideal Terrace Pattern: Middle Stage. If the sweeping and swinging of the river continue until, as in Fig. 54, a fifth return of the meander belt to the western side of the valley is accomplished, a terrace pattern of some complication may result. Few and small remnants of the higher terrace plains are to be expected at this stage, for they have been repeatedly undercut and destroyed. Larger and more numerous remnants of the lower plains may be still preserved, for they have been less frequently attacked. A triangular portion of the third-swing plain is shown in the middle of the figure; on the right appears a still larger piece of the fourth-swing plain, from which the river was withdrawn by a short-cut across the flood plain (not shown in the figure), leaving an unfilled channel which now guides a small brook. The fifth westward swing of the river has, during the down-valley sweep of a single meander over the length of the diagram, under-cut and destroyed part of the fourth-swing plain on the right; it has destroyed all of the fourth-swing and part of the third-swing plain in the middle and all of the earlier plains toward the left, where the meander under-cuts the high scarp and recent landslips have occurred. The greater the number of swings, the smaller and rarer will be the remnants of the higher terrace plains, unless some special control is present to preserve them.

A special interest attaches to the form and arrangement of
the cusps that are produced by the chance intersection of the
curved terrace fronts. In the two-sweep or two-swing cusps,
two patterns may be produced, according as the higher scarp is
on the up-valley or down-valley side of the cusp, as in Figs.
55 and 56. The higher scarp is evidently the younger of the
two that unite in the cusp; it is continued in direction, but
with less height beyond the point of intersection. From the
appearance of a letter Y in the shaded scarps of the diagrams
forms of this kind may be called two-swing (or two-sweep)
cusps, with an upstream or a downstream Y-stem, as the case
may be. All the elements of such cusps are variable. The
location of the cusp is at the chance intersection of two lines

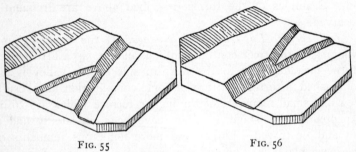

FIG. 55   FIG. 56

that have no particular relation to each other. The angle of the
Y may vary through a large range. The heights of the scarps
have no definite relation, except that the higher single scarp
must be the sum of the other two.

A series of one-sweep cusps may occur with some regularity
along a valley side, but two-sweep and two-swing cusps cannot
be expected to show so definite an arrangement, unless under the
control of something more systematic than the action of the wandering stream. In Fig. 54, for example, two series of one-sweep
cusps in the middle of the diagram stand in normal down-the-
valley order, but all the two-swing cusps are located indifferently
to one another. So on the left side of Fig. 49; but on the right
side of that figure, three one-sweep cusps on successive terraces
are placed in line, one forward of the other, as if in some way
systematically related or subject to some common control.

In view of these various ideal combinations, it is evidently desirable to analyze the special configurations that may be due to river action alone, in order to detect more surely the patterns that must be referred to some other cause.

A later-made one-sweep cusp may occasionally chance to stand in front of an earlier-made one-sweep cusp, as in the

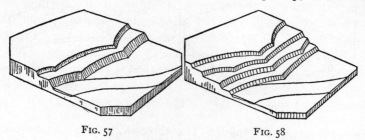

FIG. 57   FIG. 58

farther part of Fig. 57; but it is evidently out of the question that four cusps should gain a systematic position of this kind, as in the center of Fig. 58, without some common control. Whenever such arrangement is found, special examination should be made of it. Again, while a two-swing cusp is of common occurrence, a three-swing cusp (Fig. 59) must be rare, for it involves the intersection of three unrelated lines

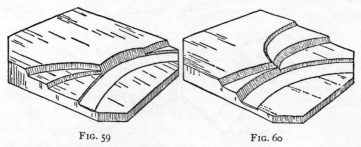

FIG. 59   FIG. 60

in a systematic manner; and a four-swing cusp (Fig. 60) is practically an impossible occurrence. True, a three-swing cusp must be produced at a certain stage of the change shown in Fig. 61, where a sweeping meander is under-cutting its scarp and thus pushing one two-swing cusp, *A*, towards another two-swing cusp, *B*; for at a certain stage in the under-cutting, *A* will be pushed into coincidence with B, thus forming a three-swing cusp. But it is very improbable that this temporary stage will be preserved. The under-cutting will continue and the temporary three-swing cusp will then be divided into two

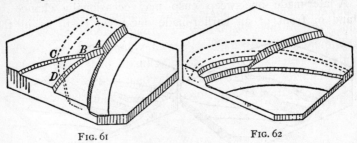

FIG. 61   FIG. 62

two-swing cusps, C and D. The three-swing cusp can be preserved only when, just at the moment of its formation, the stream is withdrawn by a short-cut or a cut-off, and such a coincidence must be of very rare occurrence. Withdrawals of the stream may, however, happen likely enough before or after the momentary stage of the three-swing cusp; and the various patterns thus producible are indicated by the full and broken lines in Figs. 61–64. The eight possible cases of this kind result from different combinations of the up-valley or down-valley half of a meander with two-swing cusps of upstream

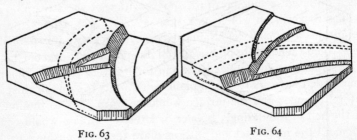

FIG. 63   FIG. 64

or downstream Y-stems. Evidently, then, no combination of unguided sweeping and swinging meanders will produce an orderly grouping of cusps such as is shown in Fig. 58.

Ideal Terrace Patterns : Late Stage. When the causes that determine the degradation of a valley floor weaken and disappear, the stream will repeatedly swing to and fro on about the same plane. Even the basal terraces of a series may then be almost completely swept away by the wandering river, as in Fig. 65, and the whole descent from the high-level terrace to the existing flood plain may be, for considerable distances along the valley side, united in a single strong escarpment. The conditions under which this result may be brought about are first, the attainment of nearly fixed values of volume and load, such as might be reached when a glacial climate had given way to a milder climate and the latter had become well established; second, the cessation of any slow uplift by which degradation had

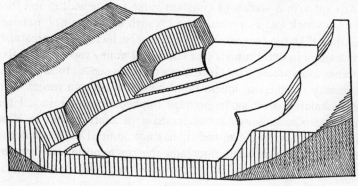

FIG. 65

been initiated or aided; third, superposition of the stream on a strong rock sill on which corrasion is very slow. Under these conditions a stream would almost cease to degrade its channel, and would then devote practically all its energy to lateral cutting. The stream would wander back and forth across its valley floor, unimpeded save by its flood-plain bank, until it came against a lateral terrace; and the terrace would be worn back to the limit of the belt of wandering. Sooner or later the stream would consume all the high-level and intermediate terraces, pushing back their united scarps into a single scarp, by which the highest terrace plain would then descend at once to the flood plain. Stepping terraces would no longer characterize this stage of valley development, but a few low terraces might remain not yet consumed here and there, as in Fig. 45.

Miller seems to suggest that an increase in the height of terrace scarps is in itself a cause for a decrease in interscarp space.

The restraint exercised by rock upon the modern rivers strengthens their natural tendency, of which sufficient account has not been made, to occupy narrower portions of valleys the more they deepen them. It has been too hastily concluded, because rivers now occupy narrow valleys flanked by terraces comparatively broad, that therefore they have vastly shrunk, — from dimensions, in fact, proportional to the greater breadth (299).

He then goes on with the statement already quoted regarding the "banks nowadays eight or ten times as high" as formerly. It thus seems to be implied that it is "natural" for the interscarp space of a stream of constant value to lose width; and that not only rock ledges restrain the breadth of the belt of wandering, but that the increase in height of the inclosing scarps also has a share in determining this feature of valley form. A similar opinion is expressed by Gilbert (133). This seems to me an unnecessary conclusion, unless rapid elevation up to a recent date be postulated also, as is perhaps implied by Miller in a later sentence. Certainly, so far as increase of scarp height in New England valleys is concerned, it has not sufficed to prevent the broadening of the valley floor and the consumption of terraces at higher levels, so long as the terraces consist only of clay, sand, and gravel.

It may be noted that if there had been a diminution of volume during the deepening of a drift-filled valley, the obliteration of stepping terraces would be delayed, but not prevented. It has already been explained that some diminution in stream volume is certainly probable. It may now be added that many valleys have, in spite of this very probable decrease of stream volume, already reached in one or another part of their length the late stage of terracing just described, in which all the descent from the highest terrace to the flood plain is concentrated in a single scarp, and that in many other parts of these valleys only a few basal terraces remain beneath the strong scarp of the high terrace. It thus becomes all the more probable that diminution of volume is not an important cause of the decrease in the breadth of the interscarp space, and that where stepping terraces occur, they must be in large part referred to some special and local cause. Such a cause is found in the presence of rock ledges, as suggested by Miller; and to that element of the problem we may now turn.

Defended Terrace Cusps: Early Stage. It has thus far been tacitly postulated that no buried ledges should be discovered by the wandering river. Such, indeed, is the condition usually assumed in the cross section of a series of typical terraces, as in Fig. 44. Let a new series of terraces now be developed, in which ledges shall here and there be discovered as the river degrades its valley floor to greater and greater depths. It is evident that the number of such ledges may vary greatly. They might be

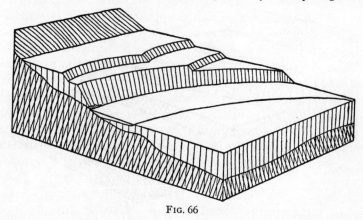

FIG. 66

numerous and frequently encountered by a terracing river in a narrow valley with rugged rock walls and bottom; they might be almost absent and hardly ever discovered in a broad valley that had been heavily aggraded. In all cases it is important to note that the slope of a ledge face will seldom be as steep as the average slope of a terrace front, which may be as much as 30° in freshly cut scarps.

As before, the river wanders about freely so long as it is working on unconsolidated sands and clays; and thus several low terraces may be formed in the manner already described. But when a ledge is encountered in the river bank, as at the left forward edge of Fig. 66, the rock is practically indestructible. The stream will in a comparatively short time swing away, after having altered its course more or less in a fruitless effort to wear back the obstacle. The ledge thus comes to determine a cusp in the terrace front. A salient of this kind may be called a defended cusp, in distinction from the accidental or free cusps described in the previous sections; the terrace behind it cannot be destroyed by the stream.

Following the colloquial style often adopted for field descriptions, a terrace of this kind is sometimes entered in my notes as a "can't-be," in contrast to the low "not-yet" terraces of Fig. 65.

It should be noted that the ledge here considered does not determine the depth to which the river may work; the rock is

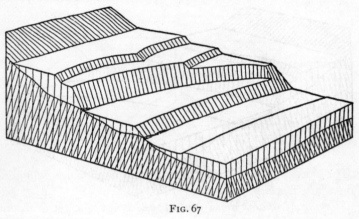

FIG. 67

exposed only in the river bank and enters but a little distance into the channel. The slope of the river and the depth to which it has cut at this or any other point in its course are assumed to be determined in all cases thus far detailed by the maintenance of an essentially graded channel with respect to some controlling base-level farther downstream; the sea at the river mouth, a larger river into which the smaller stream enters, or a broad sill of rock that stretches all across the channel, somewhere farther down the valley.

When the withdrawing stream swings back again at a lower level, as in Fig. 67, it cannot often under-cut and destroy all of the terrace on whose back border the first ledge rises, because, as has been noted, the slope of the ledge is seldom so steep as that of the terrace scarp. A second encounter with the ledge will usually be made before the swinging stream has entirely consumed the terrace of the previous swing. Every return of the swinging river against a sloping reef of rocks will thus be recorded by a little strip of terrace behind the defending ledges, and a flight of stepping terraces will necessarily be produced wherever a large group of ledges slopes under the valley drift into the belt of river action. The length of the ledge exposed at the back of each terrace may be but a few feet, but its effect will be prolonged by a trailing terrace, as it may be called, stretching hundreds or thousands of feet along the valley side. It is in this way that the best flights of stepping terraces are produced.

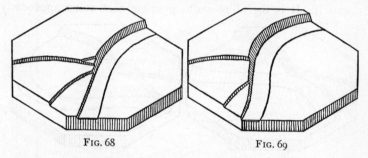

FIG. 68   FIG. 69

The special features of terraces associated with defending ledges are next to be examined.

Slipping Meanders and Blunt Cusps. It has not yet been possible to discover by observation how a down-sweeping meander will make its passage past a ledge, but it may be inferred from the forms of terraces found in various valleys that a stream has two methods of procedure in such an exigency. The first is considered in this section, and is illustrated in Figs. 68–71; the second is taken up in the next section, with Figs. 72–74.

Let it be supposed that the river in Fig. 68 is now making its fourth swing against the western side of its valley, and that a buried ledge lies a few hundred feet back of the group of free cusps in the middle of the diagram. The ledge is discovered in Fig. 69; it lies somewhat below the apex of a down-sweeping meander. Assuming that the meander curve is to remain practically unchanged, it can pass the ledge only by withdrawing somewhat towards the axis of the valley; it may thus, as it were, slip by the obstacle that stands immovable in its way. The stream is represented as having just slipped past the ledge in Fig. 70, and as having swept somewhat farther down the valley in Fig. 71. All records of the first and third swing of the river are now destroyed, so far as this part of the valley is concerned; the terrace front shows a high, defended, one-sweep cusp, a free two-sweep cusp with an upstream Y-stem, and a free one-sweep cusp.

The ledge at the base of the defended cusp may come to be more or less concealed by the sands that are washed down from the weathering scarp. In time it may be entirely covered, and its presence will then be known only if a roadcut or a boring reveals it. It is therefore quite possible that some apparently

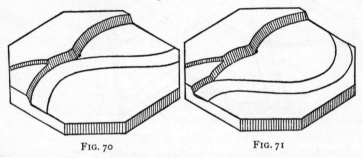

FIG. 70   FIG. 71

free cusps are really defended cusps, with their defending ledge ambushed beneath a thin cover of soil.

Compressed Meanders and Sharp Cusps. Let it now be supposed that the river in Fig. 69 is unable to slip past the ledge. The front of the curve is held fast; the apex of the curve bends outward and cuts a curved reentrant in the terrace front next upstream from the ledge, as in Fig. 72. The meanders farther upstream continue their advance, and the meander next to the ledge is therefore compressed to a relatively strong curvature, as in Fig. 73. The defended cusp is now sharpened. It may come to point somewhat up the valley. The compressed meander cannot slip by the ledge; there is no escape for the stream save by a short-cut across the narrowing flood-plain lobe at time of high water; thus the condition of Fig. 74 will in due time be developed. A rather sharp cusp, one of whose sides faces up the valley, will be produced, and the great concave scarp adjacent to it will have an abandoned channel at its base.

Terrace Fronts near Defended Cusps. The difference between the behavior of slipping and of compressed meanders may be inferred to depend on the position of the obstructing ledge with regard to the apex of the meander. If the ledge is discovered near the apex of the meander, the stream may slip past the obstacle, as in the example first given. If the ledge is

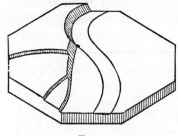

Fig. 72

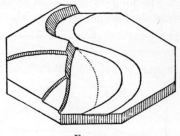

Fig. 73

encountered near the point of river inflexion, — that is, on the tangent between two meanders, — compression of the meander upstream from the obstacle is likely to result.

In both these cases the defended cusp is likely to be associated with several short curves and free blunt cusps for a little

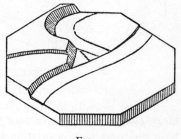

Fig. 74

distance down-valley, while a rather long reëntrant curve usually joins its up-valley side. The short curves and blunt cusps may be blended so as to produce a convex terrace front for a little distance down-valley from the ledge ; and this convex front will be separated from the long concave reëntrant by a more or less pronounced angle at the defended cusp. The reason of this may be easily understood from Fig. 75. The ledge was here first discovered by a down-sweeping meander, of whose first work only the short scarp *A* remains. The meander was then compressed so as to scour out a large concave reëntrant, and was withdrawn from the channel *B* at its base by a short-cut (outside of the diagram). A meander on the new course of the stream, swinging westward, trimmed off the terrace front in successive lines, *C, D, E*; but as this meander had no definite relation to the ledge, and as the general sweeping of its curve was down-valley, it did not trim the terrace front with any special regard to the down-valley side of the defending ledge. In brief, the tendency of a stream to sweep its meanders down-valley commonly results in trimming off the terrace front close to the up-valley side of a defending ledge, but it is only by chance that the terrace is worn

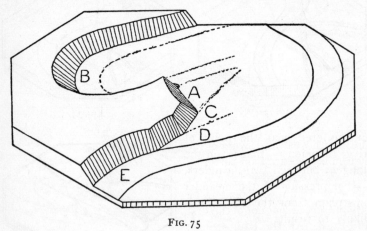

FIG. 75

away close on the down-valley side of the ledge. The pattern here deduced may be matched in many actual examples.

Defended Cusps : Later Stage. After a ledge has once been discovered by the swinging river, there is much probability that the forward reach of its under-slope will present an obstruction to the stream every time it swings again towards the valley side. For example, let the stream of Fig. 74 be supposed to have returned from a swing to the eastern side of its valley floor. It will now be at a lower level than before and will therefore be halted somewhat in advance of the defended cusp previously developed. Fig. 76 shows the blunt cusp of a slipping meander thus determined. Another swing out and back having been accomplished, Fig. 77 shows the work of a compressed meander (*A*), which for a time was held up-valley from a third exposure of the long-sloping ledge; but the stream was then withdrawn from its roundabout course by a short-cut, after which a sweeping meander wore out the three short curves (*B*) down-valley from the ledge; and still later, the next down-sweeping meander (*C*) trimmed off the terrace front close to the ledge preparatory to slipping past the obstacle and pushing still farther back the down-valley side of the terrace front. Another stage is shown in Fig. 78. Here

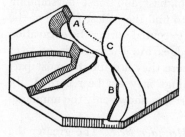

FIG. 76

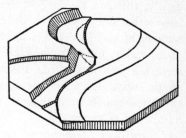

FIG. 77

the eighth westward swing of the stream is recorded (compare Fig. 68). Part of the plain formed by the second swing happens to be still preserved, but not of the first and third. All the later swings, fourth to eighth, are well indicated. A strongly compressed meander of the eighth swing has

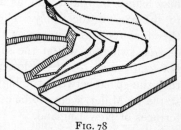

FIG. 78

trimmed off all the terraces a little distance up-valley from their ledges, and would have trimmed them still closer but for being withdrawn by a short-cut. A later meander of the same swing is less successfully wearing away the down-valley extension of the terraces.

It is evident that an infinite variety of terrace patterns may be expected in association with defending ledges, yet they must all conform to certain general laws of development.

If the ledge lies at a low level, the greater part of the terraces that have been cut at swings of higher level will have been destroyed before the ledge has a chance to defend them. If the ledge is of large size, rising nearly to the highest terrace level and standing forward in such a position that the stream may frequently swing against its buried slope, a whole flight of stepping terraces may be not only formed but preserved by it. Here the early terraces, unlike those of free-swinging rivers, are defended by ledges, and cannot be attacked by the later swings and sweeps of the stream. They are subject to destruction only by general weathering and washing of the valley sides. It is evidently, then, to the largest and highest and most outstanding ledges that one must go in order to find the fullest record of the number of swings that a river has executed during the excavation of its valley, for only on such ledges are the records of river terracing well preserved. Elsewhere they are for the most part swept away. Even here some swings may not be recorded. In short, the maximum number of terraces shows only the minimum number of river swings.

Diminished Swinging of the Meander Belt. The greater the depth to which the valley floor is degraded, the more frequently may ledges be found, and, as a rule, the nearer will they stand to the axis of the valley. The number of defended cusps will therefore tend to increase as the valley deepens. The breadth of free swinging will at the same time decrease, and the space between the scarps of the lower terraces will necessarily be less than the space between the higher terraces. This principle, first stated by Miller, seems to be essential in explaining the stepping terraces of New England.

It must frequently happen that ledges approach the axis of a valley more closely at one point than at another. The valley may be well beset with buried reefs for a fraction of a mile or more, and then may be relatively free from ledges for several miles up and down stream. Where the ledges are numerous, the valley will be narrowed and the terraces will be preserved in good number; but in the stretches that are comparatively free from ledges, or in which ledges are found only at low levels, the valley floor may be broadly opened, and but few of the many flood plains that the river there formed at various levels will be preserved. These open basins, often bordered by a single high-scarped terrace, have attracted less attention than they deserve in the discussion of terracing; and well-developed flights of terraces have been given an importance that their restricted occurrence hardly warrants.

Distribution of High-Scarp and Low-Scarp Terraces. Ledges may be gradually disclosed at various points up and down the valley, each one having an effect in cusp-making and terrace-keeping appropriate to its position with respect to the valley axis. The frequent swinging of the meander belt from side to side during the slow degradation of the valley floor requires that the discovery of every ledge lying well within the belt of wandering should be made soon after the stream has degraded the valley floor to the level of the ledge top. If the valley floor is deepened ten feet during a complete swing of the meander belt to and fro, it would be very unlikely that a ledge within the breadth of swinging should escape discovery until the valley floor was worn down twenty feet below the ledge summit. It would be impossible for the discovery to be postponed so long that the stream should first encounter the ledge fifty feet below its top, unless the ledge were situated rather far to one side of the valley axis, where it might not be encountered by the down-sweeping meanders every time the meander belt swung across the valley. The more likely case is that an actively swinging, slowly degrading stream will discover the upper part of every ledge lying well within the belt of wandering, and that thereafter the stream will frequently swing against the slope of the ledge at lower and lower levels as the valley floor is deepened; unless, indeed, another ledge, nearer the axis of the valley, and with a lower summit than the ledge already discovered in its neighborhood, prevents the river from swinging laterally so far as it had at higher levels.

This specialized conception of the terracing process leads to some reasonable deductions as to the distribution of high-scarp and low-scarp terraces. They are summarized in Fig. 79. A low-scarped terrace is formed near the western border of the belt of wandering shortly after degradation has begun (see further side of figure). After six swings the river discovers a ledge (also on the further side of the diagram) somewhat within the belt of wandering. Then all the terraces of earlier swings lying back of this ledge will be preserved. On every later westward swing the river is halted nearer and nearer to the axis of the valley. Thus a flight of stepping terraces is formed in connection with a series of defended cusps; but on account of the absence of ledges on the near side of the diagram and of the increased breadth of wandering as the later stage of terracing is approached, the river destroys all traces of the earlier terraces in the foreground, where the tenth swing produces a single scarp by which the highest plain descends to the river level. Then the eleventh and twelfth

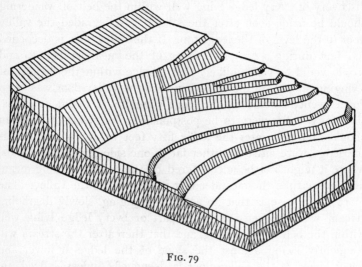

FIG. 79

swings are held off from the high scarp by a lower ledge on whose slope two low-scarped terraces are carved. It may therefore be concluded that low, undefended, high-level terraces of early swings are most likely to be preserved back of defended cusps of later swings; that the undefended terraces of early swings will probably be swept away in the production of a single high-scarped terrace wherever broad swinging at low levels is not prevented; and that when high scarps occur in a flight of stepping terraces they are more likely to be found at or near the top than near the bottom of the flight.

Effect of Rock Barriers. Superposition upon strong rock barriers has already been considered on preceding pages, in so far as it determines the separation of a valley into several compartments, in each of which the flood plain is thenceforward graded with respect to the next down-valley barrier. This is a very familiar condition in New England, as the water power in the falls or rapids on the down-valley side of the barriers has repeatedly determined the location of our manufacturing villages and cities. In the present section brief consideration is given to the effect of rock barriers in producing a fixed node, as Emerson has called it (736), in a stream that elsewhere vibrates freely as it meanders and swings on its flood plain. It is, however, not yet clear how a wandering stream will behave up and down valley from a fixed node. Several suppositions may be made.

First, the meanders will sweep down the meander belt, and the meander belt will swing to and fro across the valley,

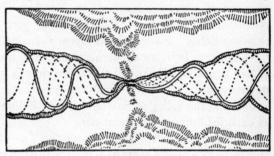

FIG. 80

but the amplitude of both movements will be decreased as the node is approached, and extinguished as it is reached. So far as my observations go, this condition is more appropriate down-valley than up-valley from a fixed node. Below the node slight curves may be formed; these may develop into normal meanders (Fig. 80; the river flows to the right), as they sweep away from the sill; but such development will probably be gradual, and hence the valley floor will widen gradually in that direction.

Second, the meanders may continue almost in full force as they approach the node from up the valley, merely changing in the lowest part of their course that leads directly to the sill. This might involve the introduction of a "kink" into the meander system, at the point where a change is made from the normal down-sweeping curve to the constrained course that leads to the ledge. That such a sharp bend is possible seems to be shown by certain peculiar forms in the meanders of the Theiss on the plain of Hungary, it being probable that bends of this kind result from the faster down-sweeping of some meanders than of others. The considerable breadth of flood plain often observed next upstream from a node supports this supposition.

Third, the fixed node may perhaps induce the formation of free nodes, evenly spaced from the ledge of superposition; then between the fixed node and the free nodes, the stream might vibrate as a stretched string vibrates when it is lightly "stopped" at a third or a quarter of its length. Symmetrical free terrace cusps would result from this process. So systematic a movement would seem to be possible only in rare cases, if at all; but the terraces of Chicopee river above Beecham Falls, a few miles northeast of Springfield, Massachusetts, give some support to this possibility. Further observation is needed in this direction.

When two barriers occur near together, leaving a free space of half a mile or so between them, the river is fixed at two nodes, but may vibrate between them. A remarkable case of this kind is found in the valley of Saxtons river at Bellows Falls, Vermont, as described on a subsequent page.

Relation of Terrace Patterns on the Two Sides of a Valley. It has been already pointed out as a matter generally accepted by many observers that the terraces on the two sides of a valley need not necessarily agree in number or in height. The relations of terrace patterns as seen in plan on the two sides of a valley have been less considered. It is desired here to indicate certain relations that seem to obtain in special cases.

When a group of defended cusps occurs in a valley of moderate breadth, the stream must have been repeatedly deflected across the valley by the defending ledges, so as often to impinge upon the opposite side of the valley in about the same place. Hence reëntrants of more than usual size may there be worn out, next up-valley from which a group of free cusps may thus come to stand about opposite the defended cusps. If the meander next above the ledge is somewhat compressed, the stream may strike more squarely across the valley and under-cut the down-valley side of a terrace with somewhat greater vigor than usual. The valley of the Westfield river, a mile or so upstream from Westfield, Massachusetts, offers some remarkable examples of this kind.

When a side stream enters the valley of a degrading main stream, it tends to push the main stream away, and thus causes it to wear out reëntrants opposite to the entrance of the side stream. Reacting from such reëntrants, the main stream will strike across the valley and scour out another group of reëntrants below the mouth of the side stream. When this transverse deflection of the main stream is confirmed by the occurrence of a guiding ledge, the reëntrants will be all the more persistently and repeatedly carved out. The Connecticut seems to show an example of double control by the Westfield and by ledges in the southern part of Springfield, Massachusetts; and the Westfield itself, two miles east of Westfield village, offers a similar example of double control.

Ratio of Sweeping, Swinging, and Degrading. The foregoing analyses of the process by which a graded and wandering river may degrade and terrace its valley suggests a method by which a quantitative determination may be made of the ratios of sweeping, swinging, and degrading. If numerous measures are taken of the difference of level between adjacent terraces in a certain section of a valley, it may be expected that two groups of minimum differences should be found; the group of smaller values representing the deepening of the valley floor in the interval between the down-valley sweeping of two successive meanders; the group of larger values representing the deepening between two successive swings of the meander belt.

If measures of this kind were taken in different sections of a valley system, it might be possible to determine from their variations whether an even regional uplift or a tilting were chiefly responsible for the activity of the river in carving its terraces, as the following considerations will show.

In the case of uniform uplift over a large area let it be assumed that the movement was räther quickly initiated, and then steadily continued until it rather rapidly weakened at its close. We should then expect that the terrace scarp marking the interval between two lateral swings of the meander belt would be of greatest measure and relatively constant in the lower course of the main river; but the slow initiation of the uplift might possibly be recorded by a few low terraces at the top of the series; the slow close of the uplift and the very slow degradation of the valley floor in later time might be recorded by a few terraces of lower and lower scarps at the base of the series. If any terrace in the lower course of the river could be followed up the valley, it would assume a relatively higher and higher position in the series ; for when the river had, in its lower course, worn down its valley floor to a low grade at the close of the period of uplift, there would still be a considerable amount of degradation permitted to the middle and upper part of the river. As a result, the very low terraces at the base of the series near the river mouth might gain a higher rank and a greater scarp height farther upstream. If the terraces could be followed up to the headwaters of the river system, they would become narrower and finally disappear in single-scarped V-shaped valleys. So far as they could be recognized, the upper members of a headwater series might correspond in date to the basal members near the river mouth ; while the basal members of a headwater series would decrease in scarp height as they were traced down-valley, until they at last merged in the even flood plain of the middle or lower river course. So many are the irregularities of drift terraces that there has not to my knowledge been any systematic attempt to discover the facts by which these deductions might be confirmed.

In the case of a tilting, with fulcrum at the river mouth and at right angles to the general river course, the maximum height of two-swing terrace scarps would be found somewhere near the middle course of the river, and the scarp height would thence decrease down-valley and up-valley. It seems that in such a terrace system as that of the Connecticut it may be possible to apply this test and thus gain from the dimensions of the terraces a direct proof as to the kind of movement by which the work of terracing was initiated, as well as a confirmation of the evidence already in hand regarding the nature of post-glacial movement in the New England province.

Relation of the Preceding Deductions to the Observations described in the Following Sections. The facts presented in the following sections are chiefly details of structure and form, directly observable ; changes of form are occasionally noted, but these are of relatively small measure. All these details are but the present members of a long series of facts, every one of which might have been recorded, had observers been living to witness them; and then the origin of terraces would be fully understood. But the earlier members of the series are hopelessly lost to observation from being prehistoric. In their unavoidable absence theory attempts to supply a series of conditions, pictured by the reasonably guided imagination, which shall imitate the series of past facts, and thus, as it were, call them to life, bring them into the field of vision. The success of the theory is not to be measured so much by the apparent reasonableness of its fundamental suppositions, or by the definiteness with which various imaginary consequences may be deduced from it, as by the accuracy with which the observable members of the deduced consequences imitate the facts of actual occurrence. The greater the number of peculiar categories of observed facts, the greater the probable correctness of a theory whose deduced consequences can match all of them. Hence the importance of minute observation and careful generalization on the one hand, and of accurate and detailed deduction on the other. Hence also the importance of carefully distinguishing these unlike processes in order that their results may be systematically confronted in an unprejudiced comparison. The elaboration of the deductions in the preceding sections therefore seems to be as necessary a part of the study of terraces as is the accumulation of observations for presentation in the following sections.

The theory of terracing has here been presented before the observations of terraces are detailed, because it is the theory with its deduced consequences and not the facts that are on trial. Furthermore, it is only after the presentation of the theory that the pertinent facts can be conveniently selected from among many others and that their bearing can be clearly appreciated. True, the attempt might be made independent of any theory to observe all facts thoroughly and to record them minutely, in the hope of including every item that could be asked for in the testing of whatever theory should afterwards be invented; but under this method of work items of minor importance are confused with those of major importance, and their recital becomes so long that the beginning is forgotten before the end is reached. As a matter of fact, observational study of this kind is notoriously incomplete. Indeed, the terrace problem, like many others, gives striking illustration of the difficulty, if not the impossibility, of really seeing all the essential facts when only the eyes of the observer are trusted; and it illustrates at the same time the critical power that is given to observation when it is directed towards significant points instead of being allowed to wander in the vain hope of finding all the facts before theorizing is begun. For example, if it is not already manifest from the deductions of the preceding paragraphs that the terrace spurs formed of grouped cusps and the outcropping ledges that are associated with them are of particular significance, no doubt will remain on this point when the observations detailed in the following paragraphs are reviewed; yet in all that has thus far been written on this subject in New England, no description of grouped cusps is to be found, and no recognition of the significance and the generality of the relation between ledges and cusps is recorded. It is as if it had been thought that all parts of a terrace are equally significant; that when ledges appear at the terrace base they are of no particular importance. Even the citations made above from the writings of Edward Hitchcock do not show that that careful observer thought the ledges he described were of any more than local importance; and certainly no later observer has been led by Hitchcock's essay to understand the control that ledges exercise in determining terrace pattern and terrace preservation. Yet after apprehending this control and discovering the suggestive relation that must obtain between ledges and cusps, the observer no longer strays over his field; he directs his steps and secures in the least possible time the greatest possible results.

Largely deductive as the preceding portion of this essay is in its present form, the reader should not suppose that it was prepared independently of observation. The actual progress through the problem has involved repeated alternations of external and internal work; the collection of observations and the induction of generalizations on the one hand, and on the other hand the invention of hypotheses, the deduction of their consequences, the confrontation of deductions with generalizations, the evaluation of agreements, and the repeated revision of the whole process. It is not profitable to expose the personal history of a study all through these stages, for the convenience of the reader is best served by a careful separation of its two phases ; and to the second of these we may now turn in Part IV with no more delay than is required for the citation of the following pertinent extract from Playfair's " Illustrations of the Huttonian Theory of the Earth." After pointing out that to wait for the completion of discoveries in other sciences before theorizing in geology "would not be caution, but timidity, and an excess of prudence fatal to all philosophical inquiry," this lucid writer of a century ago proceeds as follows :

The truth, indeed, is, that in physical inquiries the work of theory and observation must go hand in hand, and ought to be carried on at the same time, more especially if the matter is very complicated, for there the clue of theory is necessary to direct the observer. Though a man may begin to observe without any hypothesis, he cannot continue long without seeing some general conclusion arise ; and to this nascent theory it is his business to attend, because, by seeking either to verify or to disprove it, he is led to new experiments or new observations. He is also led to the very experiments and observations that are of the greatest importance, namely, to those *instantiae crucis*, which are the *criteria* that naturally present themselves for the trial of every hypothesis. He is conducted to the places where the transitions of nature are most perceptible, and where the absence of former, or the presence of new circumstances, excludes the action of imaginary causes. By this correction of his first opinion, a new approximation is made to the truth ; and by the repetition of the same process, certainty is finally obtained. Thus theory and observation mutually assist one another ; and the spirit of system, against which there are so many and such just complaints, appears, nevertheless, as the animating principle of inductive investigation. The business of sound philosophy is not to extinguish this spirit, but to restrain and direct its efforts " (524, 525).

IV. OBSERVATIONS OF RIVER TERRACES IN NEW ENGLAND

Valley of the Westfield River, Massachusetts : Eastern Section. This branch of the Connecticut rises among the hard-rock Berkshire hills of western Massachusetts, the round remnants of the uplifted and dissected Cretaceous peneplain of the Appalachian province, and thence flows eastward part way across the broad valley lowland that has been excavated in the weaker Triassic formation during later Tertiary time. Between the eastern base of the crystalline uplands and the ridge formed on the main sheet of extrusive trap within the Triassic area, the stream has excavated a fine series of terraces in the unconsolidated drift deposits that have been so abundantly spread over the Triassic lowland by the Connecticut and its tributaries.

The village of Westfield lies near the middle of this terrace system and serves to mark the separation of its unlike eastern and western divisions. In the eastern division, Westfield river, reinforced by Little river, a branch which leaves the hills two miles south of the main stream, has opened a broad basin at an elevation of about 140 feet. The basin floor is nearly everywhere inclosed by the strong scarp of a single high terrace whose plain stands at altitudes of 240 to 280 feet. The plain is not of simple origin. On the southeast its surface is rolling, as if consisting of morainic and kame-like deposits. On the north it is smooth and its sands are fine enough to have been raised in occasional dunes; here the plain falls off southwestward to the valley of Powdermill brook in a series of lobes, whose intermediate depressions are too large to have been excavated by local drainage : hence it is probable that this part of the plain is a delta front in one of the areas of deposition described by Emerson (650–653). South of the main basin the smoother part of the high plain (Poverty plains) is regarded by Diller (265) as an extension of the plain on the north, the originally continuous surface having been formed by the flooded Connecticut. Westward up the Westfield valley the high plain ascends towards the hills and is of much coarser materials than elsewhere; this part seems to have been capped by the local outwash from the high ground during the period of aggradation. As the coarse upper gravels lie on fine sands and silts, this high plain is probably, like the one on the north, a delta surface, built up in standing water.

The strong scarps *B* (Fig. 82), by which the high drift plains descend to the main low-level basin, everywhere present concave reëntrants, whose curves unite in cusps — usually two-sweep cusps — of greater or less acuteness; and this shows that the streams have repeatedly swung against the terrace scarp, under-cutting it and pushing it back, after the present grade had been essentially reached. The curved reëntrants are of somewhat larger radius on the north than on the south, as if they had been scoured by the Westfield and Little rivers, respectively. With the significant exception of certain points on the east and west, to be described below, all these cusps, at least twenty-four in number, are free, undefended by ledges. We have, therefore, here an example of a vigorous stream with a good-sized branch working in a broad deposit of loose drift, and free to sweep, swing, and wander over a large area. A late stage of terracing has been reached, for the wide plain is nearly or quite reduced to grade with respect to a relatively permanent local base-level in the trap-ridge notch on the east. The detention of further degradation by the trap barrier is a factor of importance; for many recent swings of the streams must have, on this account, tended to destroy earlier terraces by reducing them all to one level, instead of tending to make new ones at lower levels. Whatever flood plains may have been produced during the excavation of the present basin floor, the streams have now so well taken advantage of their opportunity for lateral corrasion or "sapping" that terraces at high and intermediate levels are nearly everywhere obliterated, and even the low terraces are as a rule destroyed by the broad swinging of the streams at their present grade.

Westfield river is at present nowhere working against the base of the high terrace on the north; its actual course lies about half a mile to the south of the scarp, but several of its former courses along the terrace base are clearly revealed in a series of shallow, swampy troughs, the remains of channels from which escape seems to have been effected by repeated short-cuts or cut-offs. The river is now engaged at several points in grading down to modern flood-plain level a broad and low terrace, parts of which are not yet destroyed.

Little river was, in 1901, sweeping against its high terrace on the south at two points a little east of the New Haven and Northampton Railroad. Here the usual cover of vegetation has been removed from the scarp, the sands are under-cut, and the face of the scarp is sliding intermittently into the stream. Small sand dunes are formed at the top of the sliding bank by the northwest winds which sweep the sand up from below. It is evident that, by a repetition of sweeping and swinging of this kind, the high terrace has been worn back to its present outline.

Where the rivers have withdrawn from the high-scarped terrace, flat fans have been formed at the outlet of the minor lateral valleys of small brooks, or beneath little gullies of wet-weather wash. The fan of Powdermill brook, for example, forms a low barrier, X (Fig. 82), across a deserted channel of Westfield river, and thus determines a swampy depression just northeast of Westfield station. The further course of the brook follows the marshy deserted channels of Westfield river at the base of the scarp for over a mile.

It would be difficult to find better illustrations of the deductions presented on page 545 than are offered by this beautiful basin. The two chief streams, far from exhibiting any incapacity to open their valley floors, have now widened them to a greater breadth than ever before. Whatever decrease of capacity may be due to decrease of stream volume and of stream slope, and whatever increase of work may be due to the more active wash of side streams on account of gain in height of valley sides, the main streams are certainly more competent to corrade laterally now than they have ever been, and there is every probability that they will in the future continue to widen their basin still further by intermittent attacks on its border until restrained by defending ledges or by the hand of man. Indeed, so nearly complete is the obliteration of all terraces above the level of the present basin floor, one might be tempted to conclude that the Westfield and Little rivers never produced any extended series of flood plains in this division of their course at higher levels than those of modern times, until an examination of the western division of the Westfield terraces proves that flood plains must have been produced at various levels in the eastern division as well as elsewhere

Evidently then, as far as this example goes, it affords no evidence that the production and preservation of terraces is due to any incompetence arising from decrease in the volume or from other changes in the habits of our New England streams. Terrace preservation must be due to some control external to the streams; and of this we find immediate proof on looking at the eastern and western inclosure of the broad basin just described.

The basin is inclosed on the east by the approach of a defended spur, *A* (Fig. 81), on the north towards a free spur, *B*, on the south, beyond which a subordinate basin, *C*, is again opened. The defended spur carries a terrace plain at a height of two hundred feet, and the highest plain rises farther north by

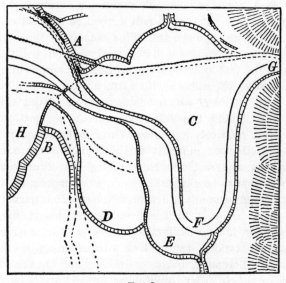

FIG. 81

a faded scarp of gentle slope. Sandstone ledges are abundant along the western base of the spur; they are unusually steep, in part because of the eastward dip of the strata, and in part because of a certain amount of under-cutting by the Westfield when it ran beneath them. The eastern side of the spur is not trimmed close to the defending ledges, but illustrates the unsymmetrical relations shown in Fig. 74. Widely as the river has swung from side to side in the basin farther west, it was here strongly constrained. Not only so; Westfield river has been somewhat impelled northward by the entrance of Little river from the south (west of the area shown in Fig. 81) ; and it is probably in part at least on this account that the basin has been so well broadened northward ; yet on every sweep or swing against the sandstone reef the river was not only restrained from further northward conquest at that point, but was deflected obliquely southward across the valley. It is very probable that the excavation of the subordinate basin C is due to this cause, for it is opened farther to the south than to the north. Three strong southward loops of the river, D, E, F (including the present one), are here recorded, and it can hardly be by chance that the river has thus repeatedly turned southward on its way to the fixed node G in the trap-ridge notch.

Nearly opposite to this well-defended spur, but a little farther westward, the free spur B, rising to the full height of the drift plain, separates the subordinate eastern basin C, and that part of the main basin H which has been scoured out chiefly by Little river. Unlike the defended spur on the north, the free spur is not a relatively permanent feature of the valley ; it will be removed without difficulty if Little river takes a fancy to trim away its western base. Nevertheless, its occurrence to-day does not appear to be altogether a matter of chance, for it seems to illustrate the systematic features described on page 558.

The main basin is inclosed on the northwest by a well-defended spur, known as Prospect Hill, A, (Fig. 82), just west of Westfield station ; this will be further described with the terraces of the western division of the valley. On the southeast Little river is held from swinging at present levels by superposition on a transverse sandstone ledge, to which brief reference will be made farther on. The contrast between the openness of the main basin, excavated where the streams have not been restrained by ledges, and the narrowness of the entering valleys where ledges have been encountered, is most striking.

Western Section. The western division of the Westfield terraces, occupying the valley for about four miles from Westfield village to the base of the hills, is of greater interest than the eastern, inasmuch as it preserves the records of river work at many levels between the highest and the lowest plains. I have prepared a somewhat detailed account of it for publication

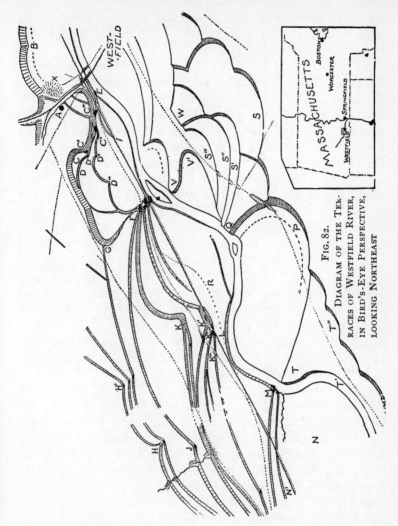

FIG. 82. DIAGRAM OF THE TER-
RACES OF WESTFIELD RIVER,
IN BIRD'S-EYE PERSPECTIVE,
LOOKING NORTHEAST

in the *American Journal of Science*, and hence shall here refer only
to such features as confirm the deductions of earlier paragraphs.

The chief features of this interesting locality are shown in a
bird's-eye view in Fig. 82, as if looking northeast from a height
of several thousand feet above the left front corner of the
diagram. The Boston and Albany Railroad runs through the

view for a distance of about a mile and a half; the foreground scale is larger than that for the background; heights are exaggerated; outcropping ledges are black.

From Westfield to a small rural settlement known as Pochassic Street, two miles to the west, many small ledges are exposed, and many stepping terraces occur along the northern side of the valley. Few ledges are seen on the southern side, and there the valley is generally bordered by a strong upper terrace with a few low terraces beneath it. On the northern side there are four groups of defended terrace cusps, forming what may be called the Pochassic (just to the left of Fig. 82), Perry's (K), Brown's (F), and Prospect spurs (A), while curved reëntrants have been excavated between the spurs where ledges are rare or wanting. The reëntrants show that the river has everywhere attempted to widen its valley, while the terraces on the defended spurs show that the widening has been locally prevented by the outcropping ledges. Wherever free cusps occur they exhibit the patterns deduced as of common occurrence on page 543. None of the combinations there deduced as rare are found. The cusps are usually more closely trimmed on the up-valley than on the down-valley side. It would be difficult to imagine a more complete confirmation of Miller's theory than is here presented.

Special mention may be made of a few features. Just east of Pochassic Street a series of at least nine terraces, H to M, may be counted. They range in height from eight to fifteen feet, and thus suggest a rough measure for the amount of valley deepening during a swing of the river southward across the valley and back again. This maximum number is evidently dependent on the numerous ledges here discovered at all levels from highest to lowest. Although no other part of the valley shows so many terraces, it must be concluded that flood plains, continuous with the remnants here preserved, were made far up and down the valley; and hence that the river was essentially at grade during the whole process of valley degradation. Two terraces at the top of this flight, in the reëntrant east of Pochassic Street, exhibit minor reëntrants of small radius and large arc near H and H', comparable to the curves of the present river, thus indicating that no significant change of volume has occurred since the work of terracing began. A broad terrace plain stretches back of Perry's spur, K, and four low terraces rise above it to higher levels, showing that four northward swings were here executed. The fifth terrace (counting from the top of the series) runs forward to Perry's spur, because the highest ledge of that spur was discovered when the river was making its fifth northward swing. It is worth noting that several defending ledges in this spur would be unseen but for road and railroad cuts. The fourth terrace swings forward in a long sweeping curve to the apex of Brown's spur, F, because the summit ledge was there found by the fourth northward swing. Only two distinct terraces occur on the high plain back of Prospect spur, A, because the ledges in that spur rise still higher than in Brown's spur. In a word, the river has always shown a capacity for broad swinging until it became hampered in its movements by coming upon previously buried spurs. Brown's spur is peculiar in being closely trimmed on the down-valley side as well as on the up-valley side. Prospect spur has a terraced reëntrant, C, scoured out at mid-height with small radius and large arc, far back on its up-valley side; that is, a meander of the river has there been twice compressed against defending ledges, after the style of Fig. 73. Elsewhere the meanders seem to have slipped past the defending ledges, after the style of Figs. 68–71.

The terraces on the south side of the valley are in several cases determined indirectly by the ledges on the north side. This is most distinctly the case where the river formerly swept forward from the lowest and farthest forward of the Pochassic ledges M, and consequently cut out one of the deepest reëntrants on the south side of the valley P. A single scarp now descends from the high-level plain into this strong recess. Similar but less manifest relations are suspected elsewhere; thus K', K'', K''' on the north may correspond with S', S'', S''' on the south. Conversely, a number of low-level terraces remain on the south side of the valley south of Brown's spur, perhaps because the repeated northward swings of the river into the largest northward reëntrant, that between Brown's and Prospect spurs, have not required their removal. The numerous free cusps here found exhibit the features already deduced as of common occurrence. It is intended to make a close measurement of the slopes of these terrace plains in the hope of correlating the now separate remnants of single flood plains, and thus tracing the history of the terracing process in some detail.

Little River. A few words may be said about Little river, although the southern side of its valley has not been closely studied. The valley of this stream is divided into three sections by two barriers of sandstone, next upstream from which are considerable bodies of till. The till has been cut down to grade with the sandstone barriers, but the valley in the till is held to a small width, practically without terraces. Relatively few terraces are found even where the valley is bordered by stratified drift. In explanation of this it should be noted that Little river is smaller than the Westfield, and that a small stream must be hurried in attempting to keep pace with the degrading action of its master. Hence the smaller stream will have little opportunity for lateral swinging and terracing so long as it runs through loose drift to a more actively degrading master stream. There are two conditions under which opportunity for lateral swinging will be presented to the smaller stream. First, when the master stream has effectively ceased degrading its valley. This is now the case with the Westfield, because it has cut down upon a hard-rock barrier in the trap-ridge notch; and it is probably for this reason that the lower section of Little river has swung so broadly and opened the extensive valley floor already described as forming the southern part of the open basin east of Westfield. Naturally enough, then, the inclosure of the broad valley floor on the south, where Little river is alone responsible for the form of its border, is nearly everywhere a single high-scarp terrace with numerous one-sweep or two-sweep cusps. In other words, Little river is swinging on its present flood plain more broadly than it has at any earlier time during the process of degradation. Second, whenever the smaller stream becomes superposed upon a rock barrier, its work in the next upstream stretch proceeds at its own rate, entirely independent of that of the master stream. Hence the valley floor in such a stretch tends to widen and thus to under-cut all the narrower flood plains formed in earlier stages of degradation. This is the case with both the second and third sections of the Little river valley. It has a well-opened valley floor usually inclosed by single terrace scarps that rise to the full height of the upper plain, so far as I have followed them. The simple scarps have well-developed reëntrants and cusps, showing an active lateral swinging of the stream at present grade, but not giving indication of an equivalent swinging at any higher flood-plain level, and hence not giving support to the opinion that the river is to-day of an enfeebled constitution.

Valley of Saxtons River, Vermont. Saxtons river enters the Connecticut from the west at Bellows Falls, Vermont, and shows a beautiful variety of terrace forms for some three miles above its mouth. Figs. 83 and 84, separated by an unrepre-sented interval of about half a mile, give rough illustration of these features. Careful survey would undoubtedly show that the sketch maps need many changes in details, but it is be-lieved that the relative positions of terraces, with their free and defended cusps, are shown with sufficient accuracy for the purposes of the present discussion. The chief points here illustrated are as follows :

Western Section. In the upstream or western section, (Fig. 83), there are numerous ledges, but none of them have acted as local base-levels. The present valley floor is graded with respect to a heavy rock barrier a little east of the limit of Fig. 83, and at the western border of Fig. 84. In the three strong ledges M, Q, R (Fig. 83), on the north side of the valley, the rocks are schists, with strong dip to the northeast, and hence with bold outcrops to the southwest. The stream has swung against the steep face of these ledges, sweeping them practically free from drift on the up-valley side down to modern flood-plain level, but fine flights of stepping terraces are preserved on the down-valley side of each ledge, where the trailing remnants of successive flood plains have been defended from stream attack. At least ten different terrace levels can be counted adjoining ledge M. The third and fourth levels from the top are pleas-antly shaded by a pine grove, and are used as a picnic ground, access to which is conveniently given by an electric railroad on the valley floor. Some of these terraces may have been carved by a small stream that here enters from the north, but in any case they have all been developed with respect to graded flood plains of the main stream. Their vertical interval ranges from five to ten feet, which may be taken here, as in other cases, to represent the amount of deepening that the valley floor suffered between two northward swings of the stream. The value of the ledges is most manifest; they defended the upper terraces from being consumed when the lower terraces were cut by the returning stream.

Ledges Q and R present similar features in flights of eight and six steps, respectively. The river is to-day swinging vigorously against the base of ledge M. The modern flood plain reaches the base of Q and R and is opened northward between M and Q in a space that seems to be comparatively free from ledges. The ledges here outcropping on a low terrace at N and O seem to have served the double purpose of stopping the northward swinging of the main stream and of limiting the east and west swinging of the side stream at that level. I have not closely examined the terraces up-valley from M, but at least one of the blunt cusps there seems,

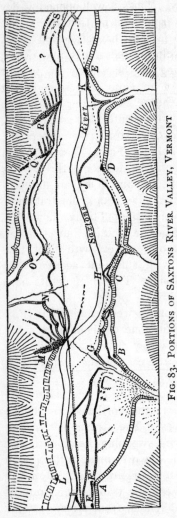

FIG. 83. PORTIONS OF SAXTONS RIVER VALLEY, VERMONT
(Scale, about four inches to a mile)

when seen from the terrace on the opposite side of the valley, to be defended by a ledge at present flood-plain level. Down-valley from *R* the valley side is heavily wooded for quarter of a mile. Then it closes in as numerous ledges and bowlders make their appearance about *S*, near the main road bridge.

Low-scarp terraces are wanting at high levels on the south side of the valley. The upper plain descends by a single strong scarp, twenty feet or more in height. It presents a number of

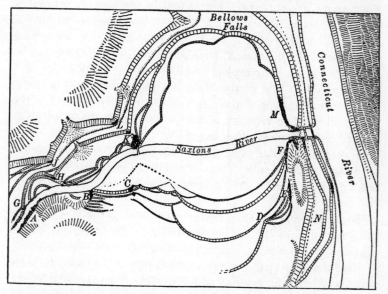

FIG. 84. PORTIONS OF SAXTONS RIVER VALLEY, VERMONT

(Scale, about four inches to a mile)

sweeping reëntrants between the defended cusps *A, B, C, D,* and *E.* The *A–B* reëntrant is floored by a rather uneven plain in which several indistinct terraces have been cut on what seems to be at least in part a mass of till, for large bowlders are seen thereabout; and this plain is cut off in front by two terraces, whose blunt cusps from *F* to *G* appear to be in part determined by ledges, in part by bowlders. The small tributary stream that crosses this reëntrant from the south has formed a fan on the high terrace plain and again on the floor of the reëntrant, but it is now dissecting the fans. No *B–C* reëntrant has been carved out, perhaps because till was there discovered. Several ledges were encountered at lower levels between *G* and *H*, against all of which the stream has swung most faithfully. The valley floor would surely be wider to-day had these ledges not existed. A fine reëntrant was swept out between the defended cusps *C* and *D* when the river ran at a height about ten feet over the modern flood plain, and another effort was here made to widen the valley floor at its present level; but as ledges are now discovered at *H* and *J*, farther forward than *C* and *D*, the lower reëntrant has not quite consumed all of the earlier flood plain. A low terrace, caught on ledges *J* and *K*, stands in front of the reëntrant between *D* and *E*. The projection of the strong but low cusp at *J* as compared to that of the blunt but high cusp at *D* is one of the best illustrations of the effect of ledges that is found in this little valley. The river must have slipped past the ledge at *D*, as well as past most other defending ledges hereabouts; but a compressed meander must have been caught for a time on the ledge at *J*. Down-valley from *E* a modern swing of the stream has under-cut all the earlier terraces, and a full-height scarp is the result.

These terraces are even better than those of the Westfield for purposes of field illustration, inasmuch as defended cusps here occur in abundance on both sides of the valley. The narrowing of the interscarp space, as the valley floor was degraded to lower and lower levels, is manifestly due to the presence of the ledges. That the river was continuously acting as a graded but degrading stream is sufficiently proved by the fine flight of stepping terraces at *M*. That the preservation of the successive terraces is not due to any shrinking of the stream from its first intention as to valley widening is proved by the vigor with which it has opened the modern flood plain to as great a width as the numerous ledges permit.

It was on seeing, in October, 1900, the relation of the defended cusp of the little terrace at *F* to the corresponding defended cusp of the next higher terrace a little farther back at *A*, that the value of ledges in determining terrace pattern and in preserving the upper terraces from later attacks of the stream first came to my mind. The manner in which this explanatory idea first took shape was as good an example of the sudden invention or birth of theory as I have ever experienced, for the theory was essentially complete at the moment of its first conscious appearance ; since then it has only been confirmed by finding that it had already been born to Miller, and by deducing its more minute consequences as presented in Part III of this essay in order to confront them with numerous examples of actual terrace forms, some of which are described on these pages.

Eastern Section. The lower stretch of Saxtons river (Fig. 84) gives beautiful illustration of terraces produced by a stream that has oscillated between two fixed nodes. At the upper node the stream is narrowly held by ledges at A and G. A little farther upstream is a rocky gorge with cascades, from which the stream is diverted for water power. The lower valley becomes somewhat more open as the space widens between the ledges B, C, on the south, and J-H, L-K, on the north. The small reëntrants between these ledges nearly everywhere bear the marks of having been energetically swept back as far as possible by the stream at various levels during the erosion of the valley. The stream has swung northward at least nine times on the J-H group of ledges, and southward at least seven times on the B group, where till seems to supplement the restraint of rock.

On leaving the cascade and the rapids below it, the stream has graded its course with respect to the eastern rock node between M and F-E; none of the ledges encountered on the way have had other effect than in limiting the breadth to which the successive flood plains have been opened during the degradation of the valley. That the degradation was gradual, giving the stream abundant time for broad swinging and wandering, right and left, is abundantly proved by the terrace remnants of flood plains at various levels.

Passing the narrows at C, L-K, there is a broad stretch comparatively free from ledges, until the heavy ridge of rock, M, F-E, is encountered close to the junction of Saxtons river with the Connecticut. The ridge is now cut through by a narrow gorge, with falls on the downstream side where the road and railroad bridges cross the stream ; whether this gorge is entirely the work of post-glacial time, I cannot say.

An oval plain, known as the Basin farm, has been opened between the upper and lower narrows, its smooth fields uniting with the curving terrace scarps in a most graceful and pleasing landscape. The Basin plain probably had twice as great an area at the level of its mid-height terraces as it now has at the level of the modern flood plain; but this reduction of area is not to be wondered at, in view of the increasing constriction imposed upon the swinging stream by the mutual approach of the ledges C and K as lower and lower levels were reached.

A few special features deserve mention. A southward deflection of the stream from ledge K and an increasing southward meander of the stream in consequence of this deflection, with a southward swinging of such a meander, has probably been responsible for some of the large reëntrants on the south side of the basin; but it is not yet apparent why the reëntrants on the north should have been repeatedly worn farther from the line between the nodes than on the south. The various combinations of two-sweep cusps in the group of nine stepping terraces next down-valley from ledge C is in every respect confirmatory of the deductions (p. 544). It is notable that remnants of terraces at intermediate heights form little recesses in the cusps of later origin, as might have been expected. The terraces in the wooded slope south of C have not been traced out; but a little farther east four low-scarped terraces rise at D above the plain that forms the top of the nine-step flight, thus making a series of thirteen steps. Curiously enough, these four upper terraces, forming the upper members of the longest flight that I have yet counted, swing northeastward from what seems to be a free cusp, thus apparently imitating conditions similar to those of Figs. 58 and 60. No ledge is visible in the front of this group, but as the scarp of the ninth terrace, here descending to the seventh, also bows a little forward directly in front of the apparently free cusp, I am much inclined to think that there is really some defense here, now masked by a slipping drift cover. A soil auger test is proposed to settle this doubt. A detailed map of this basin and its terraces would be well worth preparing.

The Connecticut below Bellows Falls, Vermont. The Connecticut river at Bellows Falls is superposed on a large body of rock,

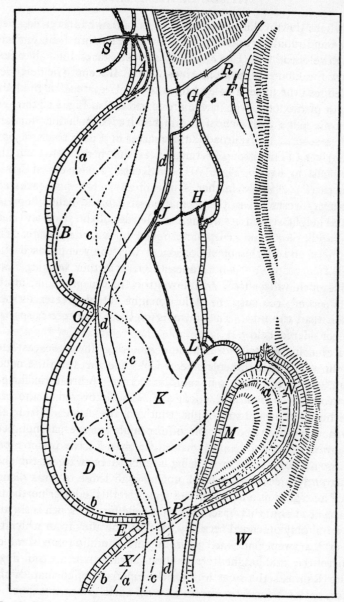

FIG. 85. THE CONNECTICUT TERRACES FROM BELLOWS FALLS TO WALPOLE

(Scale, about an inch and a half to a mile)

on whose down-valley side the river is narrowed in rushing cascades and rapids. A mile farther downstream three fine terraces are developed at *A* (Fig. 85), on the west side of the valley just below the mouth of Saxtons river, *S*, and all seem to be defended by ledges : the upper two by ledges of the large rock ridge at the mouth of Saxtons river (these are marked *N* in Fig. 84), the lowest by a ledge that stands several hundred feet farther forward and is seen in the railroad cut a quarter of a mile south of Saxtons river. (This group of terraces is shown as seen from the southeast in Fig. B, Plate VIII, of Russell's " Rivers of North America.") A little farther south the two lower terraces are cut away westward in the formation of a broad valley floor, *B*. A full-height scarp rises at the back border of the floor, and near its middle is a blunt cusp determined by a strong ledge. The southern end of this open section of the valley is inclosed by a high free cusp, *C*, at whose apex the river is now working. Another open valley floor, *D*, follows the free cusp and is limited by a second free cusp, *E*, of less height but of greater forward reach than the first. The meaning of these two free cusps will be considered below.

Returning to Bellows Falls and following down the east side of the valley past the entrance of Cold river, *R*, from the northeast, ledges are found to be more numerous. A broad mid-height terrace was opened until a ledge, *F*, was discovered in the base of the uppermost terrace just south of the Alstead road ; the farther southward extension of the high terrace has not been followed. The mid-height terrace, followed by the upper north-and-south road, was cut back by a much later swing of the river near present flood-plain level, until a high ledge, *G*, was discovered an eighth of a mile south of Cold river : the lower north-and-south road skirts its base. Nearly a mile farther south is a group of admirably defended terrace cusps, *H*, up-valley from which the river has swept out some vigorous curves, and on one of which, where the mid-height terrace first advances near the Fitchburg Railroad, the river was nearly superposed ; the rapids that occurred here for a time were abandoned as the river slipped off the northwest slope of the ledges. Near this point the lower terrace advances to the river bank on account of the farther forward reach of other ledges, J; one of them now outcrops in the river bank and thus insures the enduring protection of at least part of the low plain on which the railroad is here laid. It is thus evident that the meander belt of the river has here been constrained to take a more and more westward course as it cut deeper and deeper, and it is probably on this account that the first large western reëntrant below Saxtons river has been so thoroughly scoured out at a low level.

The lower eastern terrace is gradually cut back down-valley from the foremost defending ledge ; and a broad, low plain, K, is thus opened to a half-mile width, after which it narrows towards the bridge between Walpole (W) and Westminster (X). The mid-height terrace continues down-valley from the abandoned rapids, first showing an apparently free two-sweep cusp ; then a defended cusp, L, the defending ledge of the latter being disclosed in a shallow railroad cut at the base of the terrace ; after this the terrace is cut some distance back in a low-level reëntrant, inclosed by a scarp concave southward or down-valley. A little farther on an isolated hill, M, traversed by the main valley road and crowned by a mansion, is separated from the main slopes of the eastern side of the valley by a deep trench, N, of large sweeping curvature to the northeast, and for the most part apparently cut in till. The trench has a rather strong under-cut slope on the outer side of its curved course, and a gently terraced slope on its inner side. There can be no doubt that it marks a former path of the river around a lobate spur, and that the river was diverted from the trench at a comparatively modern, though unrecorded, date by wearing through the narrow neck of the spur at P, a little upstream from Walpole bridge. The second one, E, of the two free cusps above mentioned on the west of the river, is the unconsumed remnant of the neck of this spur, west of the cut-off ; the isolated hill, M, is the terminal part of the spur northeast of the cut-off. The following explanation of the relation between the two free cusps C, and E, may be suggested.

At an early stage of the time during which the river was making its great northeastward détour around the spur EM, its course may be represented by the curve a, a, a, a. The normal order of change in these curves would develop a later course *b, b, b, b,* thus opening out the two large westward reëntrants *B* and *D,* and leaving the free cusp *C* as yet unconsumed between them. Had this process been normally continued, the free cusp *C* would have been in time worn away by the down-valley sweeping of the first *b* meander ; but before this was accomplished, the cut-off occurred at *P.* Now it may be shown by a study of the detailed maps of the Mississippi River Commission that when a cut-off occurs, a systematic series of changes is initiated, and that these changes are extended upstream as well as downstream from the cut-off. The essence of the changes is such that the straightening of the course at the cut-off tends to straighten it elsewhere also, and that this tendency is most active near the cut-off and weakens with distance from it. Following this principle, the course *b, b, b, b* will be changed to *c, c, c, c* and to *d, d, d* (the present channel). The river will thereby be withdrawn from both of the westward reëntrants, around whose up-valley curves it was probably flowing when the cut-off took place. Thus the free cusp *C* will be left unconsumed for a time at least. It may perhaps be possible, by accumulating other examples of changes similar to this one, to give some degree of verity to the rather hazardous explanation here offered.

The Connecticut below Turners Falls, Massachusetts. My field notes here are hardly of sufficient detail to serve as the basis of a sketch map. Suffice it to say, that for several miles down the river from Turners Falls to the Fitchburg Railroad bridge in Montague there are numerous examples of defended terraces, fully confirming the principles already illustrated and suggesting some new ones, to which I hope to return in a later essay. But concerning a stretch of the river southward from this section, Emerson has written as follows :

The subsidence of the waters of the Connecticut lakes to the present Connecticut river was very rapid.... As a result, one goes down — through the whole length of the Montague Lake, which was well filled up in the flood time, except in its southern portion — by a great scarp to the series of erosion terraces of the modern river, the highest of which rise but a few feet above the level of the flood plain (725).

This conclusion as to the "very rapid" change of level by which the erosion of the present valley floor in the former drift filling was initiated, seems to be based entirely on the feature here noted, namely, the great scarp by which descent is made from the high drift plain to the low terraces of the modern river. The conclusion is so directly opposed to the one that I have reached in the course of the present study that it has been considered with some care. In the end I am led to doubt its validity for the following reasons :

First, the occurrence of the single great scarp does not necessarily prove that the river suddenly cut its channel down from the level of the "lakes" to about that of the modern flood plain. The single great scarp is here, as in other examples of the same kind, perfectly consistent with a leisurely degradation by the river, and with the production of numerous flood plains during the degradation, provided only that the modern swinging of the river has been greater than the swinging at higher levels, whereby all remnants of the earlier flood plains shall have been destroyed. It has been shown that this is habitual with a number of streams wherever they are free to swing in loose drift of fine texture ; and it appears from Emerson's description that such was the case with the Connecticut while it was sweeping away the fine silts of the Montague "lakes."

Second, the leisurely lateral swinging of Saxtons and Westfield rivers at high levels, as recorded by the upper members of the terrace flights in the valleys of those tributaries of the Connecticut, show that they were not hurried in the early stages of their work of degradation; yet hurried they must have been, had the master river suddenly intrenched itself in the weak drift filling of its aggraded valley. There are, to be sure, certain rock and till barriers between these terrace flights and the junction of their streams with the Connecticut, and such barriers might separate a quickly degrading trunk river from slowly degrading tributaries ; but it is believed that the barriers are too low to have been encountered until after the high-level terraces had been carved.

Third, there are certain points where the Connecticut itself exhibits stepping terraces at altitudes of at least eighty or more feet above its present level. The best of these are at East Deerfield, two miles south of Turners Falls, where the Fitchburg

Railroad crosses a group of terraces between the mouth of the Deerfield and the east-south bend of the Connecticut. Here an eastern profile from the high terrace south of the railroad station to the river crosses five terraces, the height of whose scarps I have estimated at 30, 25, 15, 18, and 35 feet (total, 123 feet). If the profile be taken northward from the high terrace, seven scarps are passed, including the descent from the lowest plain to the river, with heights estimated at 30, 25, 10, 5, 15, 10, and 15 feet (total, 110 feet). The locality of these terraces is openly connected with that of the high scarps in the Montague silts; and hence a leisurely process of degradation with repeated lateral swinging is probable there as well as here. The only essential difference between the two localities is that the terraces are for good reason preserved in East Deerfield, where the river has become increasingly constrained by successive discoveries of sandstone ledges, while they have been destroyed farther south, where the river has been free to swing at modern levels.

The Connecticut near Springfield, Massachusetts. There are few ledges exposed hereabouts and few stepping terraces. The high terrace that is nearly continuous on the east side of the valley from Springfield up to Chicopee is now swept by the river for a part of its length, and within this stretch a sandstone ledge is seen in the river bank. In the southern part of Springfield there are several ledges and some exposures of bowldery till, by which the opening of the valley to the east has been restrained, and a little farther south, by the mouth' of Pecowsic brook, a strong ledge deflects the river to the southwest.

No ledges are found in the terrace scarps on the western side of the valley hereabouts, although several rather well-formed cusps project forward towards the river: one at the grounds of the Country Club, another at the old meetinghouse north of West Springfield, and a third between West Springfield and the Agawam. The Westfield river enters the main valley in the reëntrant between the second and third cusps, while south of the third cusp the Connecticut has repeatedly scoured out reëntrants, from which it has been withdrawn by short-cuts or cut-offs. I am inclined to think that the Connecticut has been pushed eastward by the action of the Westfield; that it has therefore repeatedly swung westward from the Pecowsic ledges, and that the Agawam reëntrants are thus to be explained. If so, they fall into the same class with those of the Westfield in the reëntrant next west of the trap-ridge notch. The southernmost of the three free cusps on the west side of the Connecticut valley, below the entrance of the Westfield, would thus correspond with the free cusp on the south side of the Westfield, below the entrance of Little river. The other free cusps of the Connecticut may perhaps come to find an explanation in a process similar to that suggested for the free cusps between Bellows Falls and Westminster.

There is nothing in this stretch of the river to suggest a significant diminution of volume since terracing began. The frequent occurrence of high single scarps would, on the other hand, suggest that the river is to-day demanding a breadth of swinging as great as or greater than it ever did before.

The Merrimac between Concord and Manchester, New Hampshire. The Merrimac, near Concord, has opened a broad flood plain, on which a number of former meanders are now represented by oxbow lakes. On the east the plain is commonly bounded by a single high scarp, which the river is actively undercutting at one point. On the west there is a single high scarp bordering part of the plain north of the city; but a few ledges appear, and the scarp is divided into several terraces as the city is entered. Passing down the valley (southward) ledges appear more frequently, the breadth of the flood plain gradually decreases, and terraces appear in increasing numbers. The valley about Concord is one of the best examples for illustration of the capacity of an unconstrained river to open a broad flood plain inclosed by strong scarps, as typified in Figs. 45 and 65 ; while farther south the valley exhibits the complete control exercised upon a swinging river by the chance discovery of ledges during the progress of degradation. This process is shown to have been gradual by the preservation of flood-plain remnants at various heights, wherever ledges are present to defend their bases ; yet so complete is the destruction of the plains at intermediate levels just above Concord that one might there infer that the river had had no opportunity to swing laterally until the opening of the present flood plain was begun.

REFERENCES

Adams, C. B. *Second Annual Report on the Geology of the State of Vermont* (1846).

Davis, W. M. "The Drainage of Cuestas." *Proc. Geol. Assoc.* (London), XVI (1899), 75–93.

Diller, J. S. "Westfield during the Champlain Period." *Am. Jour. Sci.,* XIII (1877), 262–265.

Emerson, B. K. "Geology of Old Hampshire County, Massachusetts." *U. S. Geol. Surv., Mon. XXIX* (1898).

Gilbert, G. K. Report of the Geology of the Henry Mountains. Washington, 1877.

Hitchcock, E. "Illustrations of Surface Geology." *Smithsonian Contributions to Knowledge* (1857).

Miller, H. "River Terracing: its Methods and their Results." *Proc. Roy. Phys. Soc.* (Edinburgh), VII (1883), 263–305.

Playfair, J. Illustrations of the Huttonian Theory of the Earth (1802).

Shaler, N. S. "Fluviatile Swamps of New England." *Am. Jour. Sci.,* XXXIII (1887), 210–221.

XXII

THE SEINE, THE MEUSE, AND THE MOSELLE

The Three Rivers. The narrow basin of the Meuse lies between the widespreading branches of the Seine on the west and of the Moselle on the east. The slender trunk stream of the Meuse, with hardly a tributary on either side, is like one of those tall, closely trimmed poplars that the traveler often sees

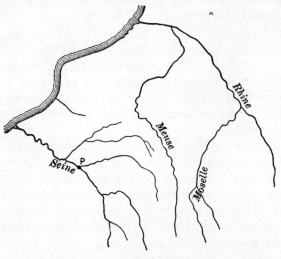

FIG. 86

along the national roads of France, and the comparison is not altogether inapt, for there is good reason to think that the Meuse has really been trimmed of certain branches which have been diverted to the basins of its larger neighbors. Its basin is, indeed, like the dwindling territory of a petty prince between the encroaching kingdoms of powerful rulers on either side. The evidence of this will appear when we examine the characteristics of the three rivers.

The Vigorous Meanders of the Seine. The Seine, after gathering in its upper branches both above and below Paris, pursues a strongly meandering course to the sea. Its lower valley is sunk with rather steep sides in a comparatively even upland, which itself is a surface of denudation. Although without complete proof on this point, I am led to suppose that this gently rolling upland is an uplifted peneplain, that is, a denuded region that was once reduced to a surface of moderate relief close to its controlling base-level and then raised by some gentle process of elevation to its present altitude. During the development of the peneplain the Seine, the master river of the region, must have attained an extremely faint grade, and at the same time have taken on the habit of swinging from side to side in comparatively regular curves or meanders such as are characteristic of rivers with gentle slope. With the uplift of the region the meandering river would proceed to incise its channel beneath the uplifted surface, and thus Ramsay accounted for its peculiar intrenched meanders many years ago. They seem to be features of old age retained in youth of the present cycle of denudation as an inheritance from an advanced stage of a preceding cycle.

In the second cycle of denudation, now in progress, the belt of country inclosed by lines tangent to the outer meander curves of the Seine seems to have broadened to greater width than it possessed before the uplift of the region occurred. The evidence of this is seen in the long sloping descent of each tongue of land which enters one of the river curves and from which the river seems to have receded, while the outer side of the swinging current under-cuts a bluff of steep descent from the upland, as if the river were pressing against it. The great curves around which the river swings fit in nearly all cases close to the bluff on their outer side. It is an able-bodied river, a river of a robust habit of life.

The Case of the Ste. Austreberte. Not far below the city of Rouen and precisely at the small town of Duclair, on the north bank of the Seine, there is an interesting little occurrence strongly confirmatory of the invigorated habit of the swinging river. Duclair is situated on the outer side of a large north-turning

meander. Into this north-turning meander descends a long sloping spur from the upland south of the river; east and west of
Duclair similar long sloping spurs descend from the northern

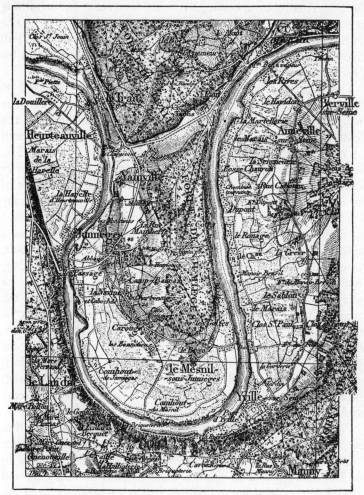

FIG. 87. VALLEY OF THE SEINE, NEAR DUCLAIR

upland into the adjacent south-turning meanders. On looking
closely at the map of the country or, still better, on looking
over the region itself from the top of the bluff at the back of

the town, it is seen that the western of the two northern spurs is obliquely cut across by a narrow, dry, flat-bottomed valley, which is just in continuation of the course of a little stream known as the Ste. Austreberte, coming from the northeast and mouthing in the Seine at Duclair. The dry valley was evidently at one time followed by the lower course of this stream, and it is still followed by the highway and the railway, for which it serves for a short-cut on their way down the Seine (Fig. 87).

The question then arises, Why has the stream deserted so well-prepared a path? The answer is not far to seek. The change evidently occurred because the Duclair meander of the Seine pushed its inclosing bluff farther and farther north until the river cut through the ridge that separated it from the Ste. Austreberte and thus tempted that stream to desert its lower course. This little fact, taken in connection with the slopes of the dove-tailing spurs, fully justifies the opinion that the Seine is a most vigorous river, not only competent to swing around the curves of its former meanders, but demanding an increased radius for every curve, and thus widening its meander belt. Here and there, it is true, the swinging course of the river departs somewhat irregularly from the round curves of its valley, as if the river had shrunk away somewhat from the strong curves which it once followed. This may perhaps be explained as the result of the diminishing velocity of the river, now that it has cut its new valley deep below the adjacent upland and close to the controlling base-level, but the irregularities are exceptional and they need not be further considered. As a whole, the river may be regarded as an able-bodied stream turning vigorously from curve to curve on its way to the sea.

The Robust Habit of the Moselle. Let us next glance at the lower course of the Moselle. Passing below its upper branching course and following it below Trèves through the highlands to the Rhine, we find here again a most serpentine valley incised beneath the general upland of the region. Ascending from the valley bottom, which the traveler ordinarily follows, to the level of the inclosing upland, it is even more manifest here than in northwestern France that we have to do with an uplifted and well-dissected peneplain. The surrounding region is one in which the rocks are greatly deformed, possessing all the characteristics of mountain structure, but few of the characteristics of mountain height. Indeed, the upland between Trèves and the Rhine is one of the best examples of an uplifted peneplain that I have seen. The gently rolling surface shows little regard for the great diversity in the attitude of its rocks. Here and there it is still surmounted by low, linear eminences, such as the Idarwald and the Soonwald, following the strike of resistant quartzites. These I would call "monadnocks," taking the name from a typical residual mountain which surmounts the uplifted peneplain of New England in southwestern New Hampshire.

But how has the Moselle come to follow a meandering valley deeply incised in the peneplain? It is manifest, from what is now known concerning the geological development of land surfaces, that during the later stages of the denudation of the middle Rhine highlands the streams of the region must have flowed idly along meandering courses with gentle slope in channels little below the surrounding surface ; but at present the streams, and especially the master rivers of the region, have deeply incised courses inclosed by steep-sided valleys. Clearly, then, the region has been uplifted since the denudation of the peneplain and is now well entered in a second cycle of denudation. The meanders developed in the later stages of the previous cycle of denudation are inherited in the early stage of the present cycle.

It is worth noting, however, that there seems to have been a pause during the general elevation of the region, for the valley of the Moselle may be described as a narrow, meandering trench cut in a wide-open, flat-bottomed trough, the trough being sunk well beneath the general surface of the adjacent upland. The same sequence of forms may be clearly recognized in the valley of the Rhine, particularly in the neighborhood of Bacharach, where the old river alluvium still lies on the floor of the uplifted trough, although the existing river trench is sunk several hundred feet beneath it. It must therefore be concluded from the relation of the upland, the trough, and the trench that the uplift of the region to its present height was accomplished in two movements, and that a longer interval of comparative rest followed the first movement than has yet elapsed since the second; but it must also be understood that the time that has elapsed from the first of these movements to the present day is very short compared to the long cycle of denudation during which the ancient mountains of the region were worn down to the general surface of the peneplain.

The meanders which the Moselle now follows in its serpentine trench are therefore to be regarded as the inheritance of a meandering habit that it acquired on the floor of the trough, but here, as in the case of the Seine, the present width of the meander belt is somewhat greater than the width of the former belt, judging from the difference in the slopes of the interior spurs and the steep bluffs opposite them on the outer side of the river curves. The Moselle, like the Seine, swings around its curves with a robust, full-bodied action, nowhere hesitating to make the circuit with strong pressure on its outside bank.

The Two Cut-offs above Berncastel. At several points the spurs from the upland have very narrow necks through which the valley railway passes in short-cut tunnels. Although I have not found any example of the diversion of a side stream by the lateral growth of the river meanders, yet such a change is imminent just above Pünderich, where the ridge between the Moselle and the Alfbach is reduced to a very narrow measure. But it does appear that just above Berncastel the Moselle has played upon itself the same trick that the Seine has played upon the Ste. Austreberte. The Moselle at this point has an exceptionally straight course, but to the right and left of it rise two isolated hills, inclosed by troughs of horseshoe shape whose outer slopes rise to the general uplands. From the study of the maps at home I had come to the opinion that these troughs represented former meanders of the river, now abandoned in favor of the more direct intermediate course, and an inspection of the district on the ground has confirmed this belief. (See Fig. 88.)

Nothing can be more satisfactory than the agreement shown between the features of these abandoned meanders and of the meanders still occupied by the river farther down the trench. The radius of curvature is essentially the same in the several cases. The slopes on the outsides of the troughs have the

FIG. 88. VALLEY OF THE MOSELLE, NEAR BERNCASTEL

characteristic, bluff-like descent from the upland. The isolated hills are the ends of interlocking spurs, now dissevered from the uplands by the cross-cut of the river; the ends of these hills that project into the horseshoe troughs have the comparatively gentle descent of the spurs that are elsewhere found projecting into the actual meanders. Not only so; the eastern branch of the southern horseshoe is just opposite and in line with the western branch of the northern horseshoe. There can be no doubt that the vigorous Moselle has here so earnestly swung against its outer bank that it has actually shortened its own course by cutting through the narrow necks of the intervening spurs. Perhaps I am giving too much emphasis to this occurrence. It is not a great rarity, for similarly abandoned river meanders are not infrequent in other plateaus. They are known in the plateau of Würtemberg, where it is trenched by the Neckar at Lauffen and just above, and in the plateau of western Pennsylvania, trenched by the Ohio and its branches. It is not, however, the mere occurrence of these cut-off meanders, but rather the lesson that they teach, that deserves emphasis. They all indicate strong river action. The Moselle must therefore be regarded as an able-bodied, vigorous river, like the Seine.

The Staggering Meuse. Let us now look at the Meuse. From some distance above Commercy, downstream as far as Verdun and beyond, this river, like the others, follows a well-defined meandering valley, incised beneath uplands on either side. As before, the slope of the bluffs on the outer side of the valley curves is comparatively steep, while the slope of the spurs on the inner side of the curves is relatively gentle. Just above Commercy, near Sorcy-sur-Meuse, one of the spurs is almost cut through and is now connected with its upland by a very narrow and low neck, which alone separates the flood plain of the curving valley on either side. The railway and canal both save distance by cutting across the low neck. At Dun-sur-Meuse the neck of a former spur is entirely cut through. It now stands as an isolated hill surrounded on all sides by the flat valley floor.

It is manifest, then, that this valley was excavated by a river hardly less vigorous than those that cut the valleys of the Seine and the Moselle, but the vigorous river that was once here is now nowhere to be found. The floor of the valley is at present occupied for the most part by broad, green meadows, instead of by a free-swinging current of water, and the only

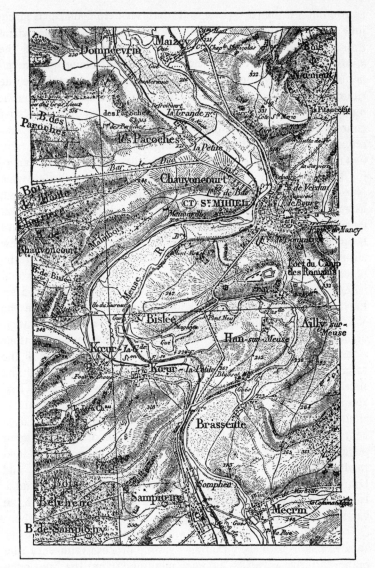

FIG. 89. VALLEY OF THE MEUSE, NEAR ST. MIHIEL

stream to be found is the little Meuse, wandering here and there on the broad meadows and staggering with most uncertain step around the valley curves. It wriggles from place to place, now touching this side of the valley, now that, swinging indifferently against the steep bluffs and gentle slopes of the spurs, sometimes even running for a short distance up the valley in its irregular path. Is it not then clear that since the time when this winding valley was made there has been a great diminution in the volume of water that follows it? No other conclusion seems admissible; and hence a reason for the loss of volume must be sought. (See Figs. 89 and 90.)

The loss of volume cannot be ascribed to any climatic change, for that should have affected the Seine and Moselle as well. May it then be ascribed to a change of the area drained, whereby the Seine and the Moselle gained the drainage area which the Meuse lost? If this were so, the Meuse would have become smaller and smaller, while the Seine and Moselle grew larger and larger. The dwindling Meuse would have lost the power of swinging boldly around its valley curves; it would have fallen into the present timid habit of staggering, after the fashion of other small streams, but at the same time the Seine and the Moselle would have been confirmed in their vigorous habit of swinging freely around the curves of their valleys. Is it possible, then, that the side branches of the Meuse have really been trimmed from the trunk river, and that the trimmed branches have been engrafted into the systems of the Seine and the Moselle?

The Migration of River Divides. The question thus raised leads to a consideration of the general problem of the shifting or migration of river divides, a subject that is of particular interest to the student of physical geography. At first sight one would be inclined to think that the crest line of a divide between adjacent river basins would merely waste lower and lower as it weathered away, without shifting laterally, and therefore without causing any change in the area of the adjacent drainage basins. It is probable, however, that this simple process is of very rare occurrence in nature. It is much more likely that the line of the divide will move more or less to one side or the other as it weathers away, on account of the unequal rate of wasting of its two slopes. The possible causes of unequal wasting are various.

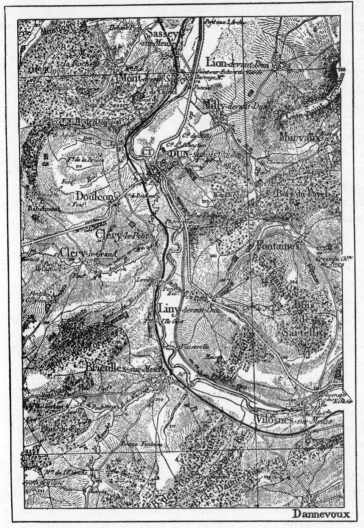

FIG. 90. VALLEY OF THE MEUSE, NEAR DUN-SUR-MEUSE

The declivity of the two slopes may differ, in which case the steep slope wastes faster than the other, and the divide is very slowly pushed toward the flatter slope. The rocks underlying the two slopes may be of different resistance; then the weaker one will, as a rule, waste away the faster, and the divide will gradually migrate toward the more resistant rocks. Again, the agencies of erosion may be of different activities on the two slopes; one slope may have a greater rainfall than the other, or may suffer a greater number of alterations from freezing to melting. Although the last is generally a subordinate cause, it probably contributes in a small way to the solution of the problem as a whole.

The shifting of the divide, as thus explained, is generally accomplished by a slow migration. In some cases, however, when the divide is pushed to the very side of a stream whose basin it inclosed, then a little further change diverts all the upper drainage of this stream into the encroaching basin, and with this change the divide makes a sudden leap around the upper waters of the diverted river, after which the slow migration may be resumed. The movement of a divide may therefore be described as alternately creeping and leaping.

Whether this process is of very general importance or not can hardly be decided at the present time, but there are certain regions in which its application is most illuminating to the studies of the physical geographer. Philippson has brought the subject to general attention in his "Studien über Wassercheiden," where a full account of what others have done up to 1885 may be found. Oldham has told how certain headwaters of the Indian rivers are pushing their divides through the innermost of the Himalayan ranges, and thus acquiring drainage area that formerly belonged to the interior streams of the elevated Tibetan plateau. This example is one of the best in which the process depends chiefly on the unequal declivity of the slopes on the two sides of the divide. Heim has described the depredations of the Maira in beheading the upper course of the Inn, thus accounting in a most beautiful manner for the little lakes at the head of the Engadine valley, where this contest is going on. The special map of the Ober-Engadine, published in 1889, on a scale of 1 : 50,000, by the Swiss topographical bureau, gives fine illustration of the significant features of river interaction in this region.

A remarkable case of river diversion occurs in the shift of the course of the Vistula from its former path down the valley now occupied by the Netze to a more northward course, by which it flows directly to the Baltic sea, the point of change being at the town of Bromberg. This is well illustrated on the Prussian topographical maps, and has been described in a general way by various writers on the geography of north Germany. Whether it was caused by the spontaneous interaction of streams competing for drainage area or not, I shall not at this distance venture to say, but shall hope to find a full explanation of the change in a forthcoming essay by Berendt. Jukes-Brown has described an interesting case in England, where the Trent captured the headwaters of the Wytham, and in a volume of the *Geographical Journal* of London I have attempted a more general treatment of the same region. Readers who wish to follow the subject into examples of greater intricacy may find some problematical examples in the rivers of Pennsylvania and northern New Jersey.

In the general discussion of this problem we should recognize two divisions : first, the processes by which it is accounted for, these having just been summarily described ; second, the topographical forms by which its occurrence may be recognized, distinction being made between examples occurring in the remote or the recent past and others likely to occur in the near or distant future. Illustration of the second division of the subject can best be given by describing the concrete case of the river Marne near Châlons, than which no better example has come to my notice anywhere in the world (see Fig. 92).

The Case of the Marne below Châlons. In the province of Champagne the Marne drains an extended interior lowland inclosed by a forested upland on the west. The lowland is the product of comparatively rapid erosion during late Tertiary time on weak upper Cretaceous strata. It is for the most part covered by extensive farms. The upland stands where the lower Tertiary strata have, during the same period of time, more successfully resisted erosion. As the dip of the strata is gently westward, the eastern margin of the upland is marked by a steep escarpment. The Marne gathers many branches from the lowland and escapes on its way to the sea by a deep valley cut through the upland. In this valley it receives two branches on the southern side, to which special attention should be given. The first is the Surmelin, whose head is found in the upland near its eastern precipitous margin ; but, curiously enough, although this stream of course diminishes toward its source near Montmort, the valley that it occupies maintains an almost constant width some six miles farther, nearly to the escarpment of the upland. The second branch is the Petit Morin. This, like the Marne, heads in the lowland east of the upland, and also, like the Marne, escapes by a deep and narrow valley through the upland. The lowland area that it drains is, however, very small, and for about ten miles from its head there is an extended marsh, known as the Marais de St. Gond, lying partly on the lowlands and partly in the entrance to the narrow valley in the upland.

In searching for a reason for this arrangement of the Marne and its two branches, it is important to notice that if the branches were prolonged eastward, they would both lead to streams, the Soude and the Somme (not to be confused with the river Somme in northwestern France), flowing for some distance on the lowland toward the heads of the branches, but then turning northward and entering the Marne directly.

The Beheading of the Surmelin and the Petit Morin. In explanation of all these facts let it be supposed that the two pairs, Soude-Surmelin and Somme-Morin, were once actually continuous streams at a time before the lowland was eroded on the weak rocks east of the upland, and let the verity of the supposition be tested by the likelihood of a natural, spontaneous change from that condition to the present (cf. Fig. 91).

When the paired streams flowed westward, they, like the Marne, must have run in the direction of the dip of the strata ; hence they may all be called *consequent* streams. They must all have passed from the weak Cretaceous strata to the resistant Tertiary strata. The Marne is much the largest of these three streams, and its valley must have been deepened rapidly, while the other valleys must have been deepened slowly. As the valleys were deepened they progressively widened, but the widening must have been much more rapid on the weak than on the resistant strata ; and the deep valley of the Marne must have widened in the weaker strata much more rapidly than the neighboring shallow valleys of the Soude-Surmelin and the Somme-Morin.

Now the question arises, Will the divides between these three valleys shift in such a manner as to alter the assumed original arrangement to the actual arrangement? Undoubtedly they would, and for the following reasons:

The valley of the Marne being deeper than that of the Soude-Surmelin, the divide between the two would be pushed away from the larger and toward the smaller streams, and eventually the upper course of the Soude-Surmelin would be diverted by a

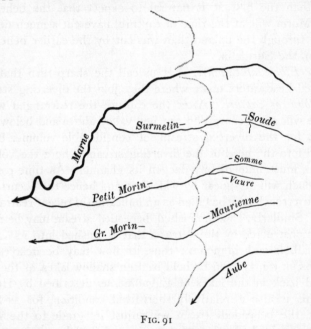

FIG. 91

growing side branch of the Marne (the lower part of the Soude) and thus led to join that vigorous river, while the lower course of the Soude-Surmelin (the Surmelin) would remain as a diminished, beheaded river. The side branch of the Marne, which causes the diversion, belongs to the class of streams called *subsequent*. Let us next look at. the divide between the Soude-Surmelin and the Somme-Morin. At first, as these streams are of about equal volume, the divide between them would not be pushed significantly to one side or the other, but after the capture of the Soude by a branch of the Marne, the Soude would rapidly deepen its valley on the weak strata, and from that time forward the divide between the Soude and the Somme-Morin would be systematically pushed toward the latter. Eventually the upper waters of this stream would also be diverted to the Marne by the way of the lower Soude, leaving the lower waters (the Petit Morin) as another diminished, beheaded stream; but inasmuch as this second capture must occur at a much later date than the first, it is natural to expect that the beheaded Petit Morin will, at the time of capture, have cut a much deeper valley through the upland than was cut by the earlier beheaded stream, the Surmelin.

The Elbow of Capture. Let us call the sharp turn that the diverted headwaters make where they join the diverting stream *the elbow of capture.* After the capture the rearranged water course will cut a sharply intrenched valley above and below this elbow, for the diverted stream, of considerable volume, being turned into the head of the diverting stream, where the volume is zero, must immediately deepen its channel. As time passes, the trench will disappear by widening, and hence the occurrence of such a trench may be taken as an indication of recent rearrangement. Similarly, the diminished, beheaded stream may be more or less obstructed by the detritus that is washed into its valley by small, lateral branches; thus its flow may be delayed by swamps, or it may even be held back in shallow lakes, as the Inn is held back in the lakes of Engadine, as described by Heim; but this is also a relatively short-lived condition, for as time passes, the beheaded stream will adjust its grade to the work that its diminished volume has to do, and its lakes and swamps will disappear.

In nearly all cases further shortening is enforced upon the beheaded stream below the elbow of capture. It deepens its valley slowly, while the reënforced subsequent diverter deepens its valley with relative rapidity; hence the divide will be pushed away from the elbow of capture, and the beheaded stream will be progressively diminished. The distance of the source of the beheaded stream from the elbow of capture may therefore be generally taken as a measure of the remoteness of the time when the capture took place. It not infrequently happens that a small stream is developed, flowing into the elbow of capture from the neighborhood of the source of the beheaded stream, and progressively lengthening as the divide is pushed away and the beheaded stream is shortened. Let us call streams of this class *inverted* streams. They will manifestly be wanting at elbows of recent capture, but they may attain a length of several miles if the capture occurred long enough ago.

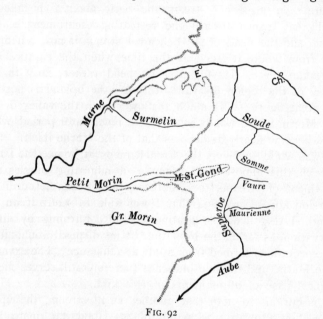

FIG. 92

Now look at the actual arrangement of the streams on the lowland west of Châlons and on the upland beyond the escarpment, while bearing these deductive criteria in mind. The Somme has lately been captured by the growth of a subsequent branch from near the elbow of the Soude ; for behold at the little village of Ecury-le-Repos a sharp elbow in the course of this stream and a narrow trench for a moderate distance above and below the elbow. The Petit Morin is evidently the lower course of the Somme. On account of its diminished volume, it is for the present unable to keep its valley clear of the detritus that is washed down from the steep valley sides in the upland, probably near Boissy and Le Thoult; hence the great marsh of St. Gond and its extensive deposits of peat about the head of the stream. The marshy head of the Petit Morin is still close to the elbow of capture at Ecury-le-Repos, and no obsequent stream is yet developed in this case. The change is clearly of recent date.

Look next at the Soude-Surmelin system. Here the capture occurred long ago; there is no sign of a gorge at the elbow of capture. An obsequent stream, the Berle, about four miles in length, has grown toward the retreating escarpment of the upland, and the head of the beheaded stream is now ten miles away from where it stood at the time when the capture had just taken place. Having lost its head rather early in the history of the region, its valley through the upland is not cut to a great depth; it is much shallower than the valley of the Petit Morin, which was beheaded at a much later period, when it had become nearly as deep as that of the Marne itself.

It was while studying the French maps at home that I first came on this almost ideal example of migrating divides and adjustment of streams to structures, but it was not until an excursion abroad in 1894 that I was able to study it on the ground. I then had the gratification of confirming by direct observation, as far as the brief time at my disposal would allow, the expectations formed from study at a distance. The example of the Marne and its side branches therefore still serves me as a typical case of adjustments of this kind.

It is curious to note that another small stream, the upper Vaure, flows toward the marsh of St. Gond, but instead of being diverted northward by the Soude to the Marne, it is diverted southward by the Superbe, a subsequent branch of the Aube. It seems also probable that this subsequent branch has diverted the Maurienne at Pleurs, and thus cut it off from the Grand Morin, whose head is, like that of the Surmelin, on the upland west of the escarpment.

It is manifest that the terminology here employed will be of service in simplifying the description of other examples of shifting divides and river adjustment if they possess the same systematic features as are here so well exhibited. That such is the case I can confirm from the study of several examples near the escarpment of the Swabian Alp in Würtemberg, where the headwaters of the Neckar are actively pushing away the divide that separates them from the northern tributaries of the upper Danube. Although the arrangement of parts is not the same as in the example near Châlons, yet the homologies of the two regions can clearly be made out. The same may be said of the rivers of central England, which are, as a rule, well adjusted to the valleys between the uplands of the oölite and the chalk.

Diversion of the Upper Moselle from the Meuse. After this long digression let us now return to the case of the Meuse and see whether indications can be found that any of its branches have been diverted to the basins of the Seine or of the Moselle. The first example to be mentioned is found in the neighborhood of Toul, and for simplicity of description I shall take the liberty of changing the names of the streams in this region in accordance with the diagram on the following page, the actual names being given in thin-lined letters, and the assumed names in heavy-lined letters. The case may then be briefly stated as follows: The Toul (upper Moselle) once flowed through a meandering valley and joined the Meuse at the little village of Pagny-sur-Meuse. The meandering valley trenches an upland of middle oölite strata, but in the course of time the Pompey, a branch of the Moselle, pushed away the divide at its head, tapped the Toul where the city of that name now stands, and diverted it from the Meuse to the Moselle. My attention was first called to this example by my kind friend, M. Emm. de Margerie, who was so good as to refer me to the writings of several French authors by whom it had been described more or less fully and to whose essays I thereupon referred either in the original or in some citation.

The first fact to note is that the abandoned valley between Toul and Pagny swings on large, curved meanders, after the fashion often assumed by the valleys of large rivers, but never imitated by valleys of small streams. It is true that the valleys of small streams may, in the course of time, become comparatively wide, but they can never develop systematically curving meanders of large radius with steep, sloping bluffs on the outside of the curves and long, sloping spurs on the inside of the curves. The form of the valley from Toul to Pagny, therefore, at once suggests not only that a stream once passed through it, but also that the stream was a large one.

In the second place, on looking more closely at the topographical details in the neighborhood of Toul, it is seen

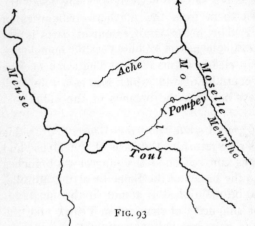

FIG. 93

that we have here a well-developed elbow of capture, — a sharp bend in the river course, independent of local rock structure. The Toul makes a sharp turn from the direction of its upper course and swings off along the course of the Pompey to the Moselle. The Pompey was once merely one of many small branches of the Moselle, of which the neighboring Ache may be taken as the type; but in consequence of adding the large volume of the Toul to the formerly small volume of the Pompey, the valley has been distinctly deepened both down and up stream from the elbow of capture below the former level of the

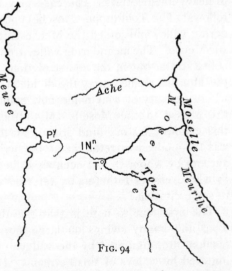

FIG. 94

streams, and now exhibits the steep-sided trench characteristic of recent captures. Not only the diverted Toul but several of its branches above the elbow of capture have intrenched themselves beneath the general level of the open valley plain of lower oölite strata on which they formerly flowed. On restoring the surface of this old valley floor by filling up the trenches which now dissect it, it may be seen to slope at such a grade as would lead it to the floor of the meandering valley on the way to the Meuse. Immediately after the diversion of the Toul we may imagine that only a small stream, the Pagny, fed by the drainage from the valley slopes, was left to follow the meandering valley to the Meuse. This would be the diminished, beheaded stream of our terminology. But in consequence of the development of the deep trench at the elbow of capture and the accompanying growth of the reversed stream, the Ingressin, the beheaded Pagny has been still farther shortened and is now not more than two and one-half miles in length. In this connection the following altitudes are significant :

Junction of the Meurthe and Moselle at Pompey, about 190 metres.
Elbow of capture, at Toul, 204 metres.
Old valley floor at elbow of capture, about 255 metres.
Divide between Ingressin and Pagny, 265 metres.
Junction of the Pagny and Meuse, 245 metres.

The Pagny and the Ingressin. Let me here turn a moment from the main subject to consider some special features of the meandering valley and its present occupants, the Pagny and the Ingressin. In the first place, midway in the valley, at the village of Foug, there is a little stream coming in from the Bois Romont on the north. The topographical details of the district give good reason for thinking that this little stream used to join the valley at Lay-St.-Remy on the next meander to the west, and thus we have here a repetition of an accident of the Ste. Austreberte type. When the vigorous Toul was running through this valley and widening its meander belt it must have pushed its swinging current so vigorously against the outer side of its curves that it cut through the ridge separating the Foug meander from the little stream on the north, and thus changed the mouth of its own tributary from a lower to an upper meander.

This may be added to the evidence indicating the former passage of a large river through the meandering valley.

Next as to the obsequent Ingressin, whose head is at least six miles from the elbow. The comparative narrowness of the trench both above and below the elbow of capture by Toul would not lead us to expect an obsequent stream of much length, and I therefore suggest the following explanation of the rather surprising length of the Ingressin. A little southwest of Foug is the narrowest part of the old valley, its narrowness here being due to the greater resistance of the middle oölite, which form the highland through which it is cut. From these steep slopes it appears that a significant amount of waste has crept down into the valley trough, obstructing it more or less and producing a swamp of small dimensions. The beheaded Pagny seems to have been unable to hold its course through this obstruction. It probably accumulated for a time in a shallow lake above the obstruction until, on overflowing into the gorge at the elbow, this part of its course reversed its direction of flow, and thus gave rise to a reversed stream, which is now called the Ingressin.

All this, however, only by way of suggestion. Further study of the geographical aspects of the country is necessary before this suggestion deserves acceptance. There need, however, be no doubt on the general problem concerning the diversion of the Toul from the Meuse to the Moselle, and to my mind the case would be perfectly satisfactory if no pebbles from the Vosges had ever been found in the valley of the Meuse below Pagny. The dimensions of the meandering valley, the systematic form of its bluffs and curves, the gorge above and below the elbow of capture at Toul, the relation of the old valley plain in which the gorge was cut to the floor of the meandering valley that leads through the upland, and the accident that happened to the little side stream at Foug, all combine into so systematic an arrangement of parts as to leave no doubt that an explanation which can account for them by a single and simple process is their true explanation.

The Diminished Meuse. Looking now again at the Meuse by Commercy we must recognize it as a river whose volume has been diminished by the diversion of an important tributary to another river system. Its volume having diminished, it is unable now to accommodate itself to the large curves of its valley and must, instead, advance in an uncertain course as it staggers along on the valley floor. Not only so; having lost volume, it seems unable to maintain so gentle a slope as it had assumed when its volume was larger, for its flood plain now has every appearance of having filled up the former valley trough to a moderate depth. It therefore gives us an illustration of a river which has changed its action from degrading its slope when its volume was large to aggrading its slope now that its volume is small.

What the Meuse has lost the Moselle has gained, and the considerable addition that the Toul has given to its volume has undoubtedly confirmed its habit of swinging boldly around the meanders of its lower valley, even to the point of cutting almost or quite through the necks of its meander spurs.

The Aire and the Bar. Let us next look at the case of the Aire. This stream was once an affluent of the Meuse on the western side of its basin, but it has been diverted to swell the volume of the Seine. The elbow of capture in this case lies about two miles east of Grand Pré. The Aire coming from the southeast here makes a sharp turn westward through the ridge of lower Cretaceous strata that bears the forest of Argonne and thus joins the Aisne. In direct continuation of the course of the Aire an open valley leads to the Meuse a little below Sedan. The greater length of this valley is followed by a small stream, the Bar; but while the valley exhibits strong meanders of rather large radius, the Bar is nothing but a little brook that wriggles here and there, back and forth, on the valley floor. The slopes of the valley floor have the usual systematic arrangement, — steeper slopes on the outside of the curves, gentler slopes on the inside. A spur that enters one of the meanders from the upland on the west, covered by the Boisle Queue near St. Aignan, has so narrow a neck that the canal leading from the Meuse to the Seine system has cut a trench through the neck instead of going around the spur. (See Fig. 95.)

FIG. 95. THE LOWER VALLEY OF THE BAR

The indications of the former greater volume of water in the stream that once swung boldly around the meanders of this valley are perfectly conclusive. But now the little Bar staggers about in the most random manner, quite unable to continue the widening of the meanders and the narrowing of the necks of the spurs by running systematically against the outer side of the valley curves. The meadow-like quality of the flat valley floor suggests that the Bar has aggraded its course since the greater volume of water was withdrawn at the Grand Pré elbow, thus repeating the features of the Meuse about Commercy. Following up the Bar, the breadth of the valley and the radius of its large meanders are slowly diminished for a long distance; but the little Bar, winding through the meadow floor, rapidly diminishes, and near Buzancy the meadow is left without more drainage than is given by such ditches as the farmers have cut here and there for the better drying of their flat, marshy fields. Passing farther to the southeast along the meandering valley, we soon find a small stream, successively called the Moulin, Briquenay, and Agron, flowing southward for seven miles in a trench cut along the valley trough to the elbow of capture above Grand Pré. This is now separated from the head of the Bar by a flat plain, and is there-

Fig. 96

fore a reversed stream, like the Ingressin already described.

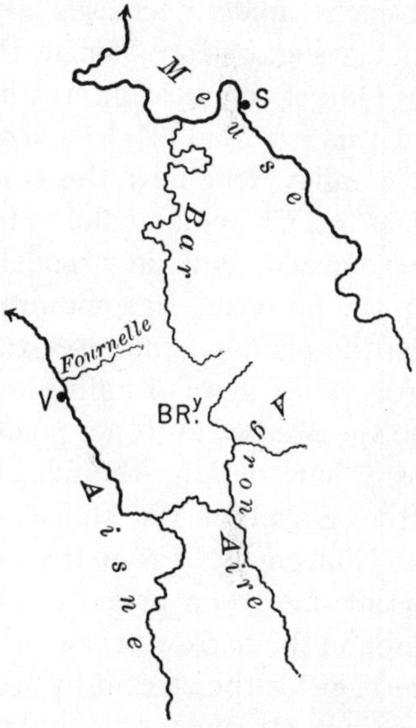

Whether the divide at present existing between the obsequent Briquenay-Agron and the beheaded Bar has been determined in this case by the accumulation of detritus washed in from the valley slopes, as it apparently was in the case of the Pagny, I cannot surely say; but there does not appear to be much disparity between the time required for the amount of widening that the gorge of the Aire has received at the elbow of capture and for the headward growth of the back-handed Briquenay-Agron. As in the case of the Toul (upper Moselle), so with the Aire; its old valley floor, occupied at a time when it still ran down the valley now occupied by the Bar, is easily recognized in the flat, terrace-like benches in either direction from the elbow of capture ; but these benches now overlook the widened trench of the diverted Aire and the narrower trench of the reversed Briquenay-Agron. A considerable depth is maintained by the trench of the Aire for some distance up the stream from the elbow of capture and, of course, also through the former valley floor of the diverter on the way to Aisne ; but on going up the reversed stream its trench rapidly decreases in depth, and near Buzancy it makes but a slight depression in the meadows.

One of the most interesting points of view for the appreciation of this example of river arrangement is on the flat fields of the old valley floor near the elbow of capture, just south of the village of Champigneulle. Here all the different parts are easily recognized, as if on a model made expressly for the explanation of the problem. In some pits dug here and there by the roadside on the plain one may see the old river gravels laid down by the Aire while it was running at this high level on its way northward to the Meuse. Another point of view no less instructive is offered after surmounting the hill by which the national road southward from Sedan, on the Meuse, crosses over to the valley of the Bar at Chevenges. From the summit and along the southward descent one has a beautiful view of the broad valley as it swings around the narrow-necked spur of the Bois le Queue, but he looks in vain for the stream by which the valley was cut. He fails to see any stream at all until descending to the valley floor, when the only occupant of the great, boldly swinging valley is found to be a little meadow brook.

Here, as before, it should be remembered that it is not the width of the valley that is essentially discordant with the size of the brook that now drains it ; for in the late maturity of the geographical development of a land surface even small streams have broad valleys. The discordance which proclaims that the valley is not the work of the existing stream is seen in the relative dimensions of their meanders. The valley swings regularly in curves of at least half a mile in radius, and maintains this habit of curvature with small diminution far up toward the elbow of capture and probably still farther south. The stream turns and twists in curves whose radius may often be less than a hundred feet. The following altitudes are instructive :

> Junction of Bar and Meuse, 153 metres.
> Divide in old valley trough between the beheaded Bar and the reversed Briquenay-Agron on the meadows west of Buzancy, 175 metres.
> Junction of the reversed Briquenay-Agron with the Aire, at elbow of capture, 130 metres.
> Floor of old Aire valley, at elbow of capture, 182 metres.
> Junction of Aire and Aisne, 113 metres.
> The advantage of depth thus gained by the Aire is about 50 metres.

It is worth noticing that if the Aire had not been diverted at Grand Pré, it would soon have been captured farther down its former valley at Brieulles-sur-Bar, for here the Fournelle, a branch of the Aisne, has almost cut through the forested ridge of Argonne, as the following heights show :

> Mouth of Fournelle in Aisne by Vouziers, 100 metres.
> Divide between head of Fournelle and Bar, near Noirval, 174 metres.
> Bar at Brieulles, 168 metres.

In comparing the case of the Toul (upper Moselle) and Aire, we see that these rivers are the diverted upper portions of branches that once belonged to the Meuse. The diverters (by which the Toul was given over to the Moselle and the Aire to the Aisne) may later be called the Pompey and the Grand Pré, respectively, the latter ultimately delivering its prize through the Marne to the Seine. The beheaded streams of the two are the Pagny and the Bar. The former is so insignificant that I have had to invent a name for it, finding no name for the stream but only the " Marais de Pagny " entered on the État-Major map of 1 : 80,000. The Bar is the best example that I have ever seen of a beheaded stream trying ineffectually to live up to the robust habits of its great predecessor.

The Diminished Meuse again. The loss suffered by the Meuse and the increase gained by the Seine through the diversion of the Aire are of no great moment, but as far as they go they serve to confirm each river in the habits that now characterize it, — the Meuse in staggering with uncertain steps around its valley curves, the Seine and the Moselle in swinging boldly around their curves and undermining the inclosing bluffs. It should be noted, however, that when a large tributary is diverted from a point high up on the trunk of a main river, the loss of volume that the change produces may be a large fraction of the total volume that once belonged to the main river, and hence that the loss may greatly affect the ability of the main river still to follow the swinging valley that it cut out when its volume was greater. On the other hand, when a tributary of relatively small volume is diverted from some point near the middle of the main river, the loss thus occasioned will be a comparatively small fraction of the trunk volume, and the change of habit thus produced will be correspondingly small. It is for this reason that the staggering of the Meuse near Commercy is so much more marked than between Sedan and Mézières. The loss of the Toul (upper Moselle) was a much more serious affair for the Meuse than the loss of the Aire.

Supplementary Problems. There are certain aspects of this problem that remain to be considered briefly. First, are there any other examples of branches diverted from the system of the Meuse to those of its neighbors on the west and east? Although I have been unable to find any direct signs of them on the map, there still does seem to be indication that other diversions have occurred. On looking at the Meuse above Pagny, it is there almost as much out of proportion to its valley as it is below Pagny. It is possible, therefore, that other headwater branches higher up than the upper Moselle have been diverted. Looking at the Aire, it appears that the present radius of the meanders is much smaller than the radius of the swinging valley that is followed by the little Bar, and from this it may be inferred that not only the existing Aire, but the drainage of a still larger basin once ran down the valley of the Bar. Perhaps the upper Ornain represents something of the additional volume that the Aire once possessed, but I cannot find direct indication that such is the fact. The maps on the scale of 1 : 80,000 seem hardly of sufficient detail to enable one to solve this phase of the problem by indoor study alone. The whole subject calls for extended study in the field, and a more interesting problem could hardly be selected for a summer's work.

Another subject to which no reference has yet been made is, nevertheless, of fundamental importance to the whole problem : Why is it that the Seine and the Moselle are waxing at the expense of the waning Meuse? Why do they possess an advantage while the intermediate stream is at a disadvantage? How could the Meuse ever have gained so large a drainage area as it once must have had, if at a later state of its history it was to be so closely shorn of its branches? This is too large a problem to enter far upon now, but it contains two elements that may be briefly stated. One is that many of the streams in the region of the Meuse are longitudinal streams, that is, they run chiefly along the strike of the weaker strata and their valleys have long ascending slopes on the eastern side and more abrupt slopes on the western side. The highlands reached by these slopes are determined by the outcrop of more resistant strata than those of the valleys which the streams have excavated. Longitudinal streams of this kind I have called *subsequent*, believing that they cannot have originated in immediate consequence of the original slopes of the land surface when it first arose above the sea, but that their opportunity came later when the wasting of the weak strata allowed the headward growth of streams along their strike, after the manner explained in connection with the adjustments of the Marne and its branches near Châlons. The Meuse and at least some of the branches that it once had therefore seem themselves to have been the result of depredations committed on the territory of some still earlier river or rivers, and if this is true, the sympathy that the present impoverished condition of the Meuse excites is not deserved.

However this may be, why is it that the Meuse has lately found so great difficulty in deepening its valley and thus saving its branches from capture by its neighbors? The chief cause of this difficulty must be looked for in the uplift of the Ardennes, across whose resistant rocks the lower Meuse has, during Tertiary time (perhaps only during later Tertiary time), been cutting its grand gorge. Like the highlands of the middle Rhine, the Ardennes consist of ancient and deformed rocks which have once been reduced to a peneplain of moderate relief drained by idle streams, but across which the Meuse is now actively cutting a deep transverse valley in consequence of the strong uplift of the region. While the peneplain was yet a lowland, the Meuse was comparatively safe from depredations, but during the elevation of the peneplain and thereafter, great difficulty must have been experienced in deepening the valley. The Moselle must also have had some difficulty in deepening its valley through the uplifted highlands of the middle Rhine, but the uplift there does not seem to have been so great as it was in the Ardennes, and thus the Seine and the Moselle seem to have gained an advantage over the unlucky river between their headwaters. It is, indeed, remarkable enough that the Meuse is still able to maintain its course across the uplifted Ardennes, and its success can only be explained by regarding it as an excellent example of an antecedent river. It has battled manfully to preserve its course, and in this it has been wonderfully successful, for the highlands of the Ardennes through which its deep gorge is cut, are now higher than the uplands in which its meandering valley is sunk for some distance above the Mézières. Yet although successful in holding its way through the revived mountains of the Ardennes, it has had to pay dearly for this success by the loss of its side branches. The hard rocks of the uplifted Ardennes form a sill that holds the upper Meuse at a relatively high level and allows the head branches of the Seine and Moselle to under-cut it on either side. Thus it is left as a waning river, still persevering bravely in its course, but much embarrassed by the diversion to its encroaching neighbors of certain tributaries from whom it had expected loyal assistance in its great task of cutting a way through all obstacles to the sea.

XXIII

THE SCULPTURE OF MOUNTAINS BY GLACIERS

The Present Condition of the Problem of Glacial Erosion. The problem of glacial erosion in mountains has in recent years been carried many steps towards its solution by means of a series of studies in which the forms of formerly glaciated and of never glaciated mountains have been systematically compared. It has thus come to be believed by a number of observers that the glacial erosion of piedmont lake basins must be extended to the over-deepening of the main mountain valleys far upstream from the lakes, and that the retrogressive glacial erosion of cirques carries with it the sapping and sharpening of the culminating ridges and peaks. The last-named effect is truly not the direct work of ice, but it is so closely dependent upon glacial erosion that it should be included in any discussion of the sculpture of mountains by glacial agencies, just as the wearing of slopes and ridges by the weather goes with the erosion of valley bottoms by rivers.

The observations and discussions that have led to a belief in strong glacial erosion are to be found in many different essays. Some of the earlier essays were based on almost intuitive insight ; as when Ramsay was led to advocate the glacial erosion of lake basins, Gastaldi to accept the glacial erosion of cirques, and Helland to announce the glacial erosion of fiords. Many of the later essays are more surely founded on comparative studies, such as those on over-deepened valleys in the Cascade mountains of Washington by Gannett, and in the Alps by Penck ; on the fiords of Alaska by Gilbert, and of New Zealand by Andrews ; on the cirques of the Sierra Nevada of California by Johnson, of the Carpathians by de Martonne, and of the Big Horns by Matthes ; and of the sharpened peaks of the Alps by Richter, and of Skye by Harker. There has thus been a great growth in the number of facts to be explained and a notable advance in the methods by which explanation is reached. It seems no exaggeration to say, in view of all this progress, that the sculpture of mountains by glaciers has been given that degree of extreme probability which we may fairly call demonstration. It should not, however, be overlooked that certain investigators still remain unconvinced, notably Heim and Kilian in the Alps, Bonney and Garwood in England, and Spencer and Fairchild in the United States.

Method of Discussion here Adopted. Most of those above named as believing in strong glacial erosion have not been led to their belief by an intimate study of the physics of glaciers or of the mechanics of glacial erosion, but by a study of the unlike forms that characterize glaciated and non-glaciated mountains, as has already been stated. Their line of thought seems to be essentially as follows : " It is difficult to determine whether the ancient glaciers did or did not significantly modify the mountains that they occupied, as long as we study only the structure and movement of existing glaciers. Let us therefore adopt another method. We will make two contrasted suppositions : glaciers cannot erode, and glaciers can erode ; we will consider the appropriate consequences of each supposition separately ; we will next confront these consequences with the facts of observation ; and then, according as one or the other group of consequences is verified by the facts, we shall be able to determine impartially which one of the suppositions is correct."

In such a problem as this it is evident that if glaciers cannot erode, we ought not to find any significant differences between the forms of glaciated and of non-glaciated mountains ; but if glaciers can erode, we ought to find in glaciated mountains a whole series of peculiar forms, and these forms ought to be appropriately related to the form and movement of glaciers. The essential steps in the application of this method may now be outlined.

The Forms of Normally Sculptured Mountains. The forms of non-glaciated, normally sculptured mountains are well known to exemplify Playfair's law as to the accordant junction of lateral and main streams and valleys. In mountains which have reached a sub-mature or a mature stage of normal carving, and in which lakes are therefore drained away and waterfalls are worn down to grade, except in small headwater streams, the law of decreasing slope from stream head to stream mouth will also obtain; and then the accordance that has been earlier developed at the junctions of main and side streams will be found to prevail even at the junctions of the innumerable headwater branches into which river systems are divided; and as each little head stream is followed up to its source, its steepening slope will be prolonged up the still steeper waste-covered slopes in the head and sides of the ravines which ascend to the mountain crests; but over the crests themselves there will be a decreasing convex slope. Examples of these normal forms which have come under my own observation are parts of the Apennines in northern Italy, the Cévennes in southeastern France, the Black mountains of North Carolina, some of the lower ranges in the Rocky mountains and farther west, and certain non-glaciated members of the Tian Shan system; to these might be added the outer ranges of the Himalayas at Simla and certain ranges in the Argentine Republic, except that, when these examples were seen, my attention had not been especially awakened to the points here considered. The perfection of stream organization thus exhibited, with its delicate interdependence of parts, should be regarded as one of the strongest witnesses to the truth of the principles of rational uniformitarianism.

An important extension of Playfair's law concerns the relation of stream channels to each other and to the valleys in whose floors they are eroded. The channels occupy a very small part of the cross section of the valleys, because water is a nimble fluid and its streams flow quickly in comparatively slender courses; furthermore, the very fact that the stream surfaces and the valley floors that border them meet in accordant level at the points of stream and valley junction necessitates the discordant junction of the channel beds whenever the confluent streams are of different size. The discordant junction of channel beds is not a conspicuous fact, because the streams in the comfortable climates of the older civilized countries usually fill their channels and hide their beds from immediate observation; but it is, nevertheless, a well-assured fact and a very important element in the present discussion.

Deductions from Theories. Now if glaciers have no erosive power, then maturely dissected mountains that have been glaciated should present no features significantly unlike those above described for mature non-glaciated mountains. But if glaciers have strong erosive power, special and significant features should be found in mountains where glaciers have had time enough to do their work. The most notable features of this kind that one would expect to find, may be stated as follows : A large part of the cross section of a glaciated valley would be included in the trough-like channel that was scoured out and occupied by the heavy, sluggish glacier ; the bed of such a trough would have rock steps and rock basins similar to those in the bed of a river channel, but appropriately of much greater size ; the sides or walls of such a trough would be comparatively even and parallel, like the sides or banks of a river channel ; the troughs of small side glaciers would necessarily be of much less depth than the troughs of large trunk glaciers, and hence the bed of a side trough would hang hundreds of feet over the bed of the trunk trough ; the valley sides above the trough would, in mountains of mature sculpture, be less steep than the trough walls themselves ; the heads of the glacial beds would be broad-floored cirques, because the heads of glaciers are broad and leaf-like instead of being divided minutely like the headwater streams of rivers ; the summits and ridges between cirques which head near each other would be sharpened into peaks and arêtes by atmospheric weathering, induced by the retrogressive glacial erosion of the ice in the cirques, and by the glacial widening of the troughs. Other features might be named, appropriate to glaciers of large or small size, or of short or long duration, but those here set forth are sufficient for a brief exposition.

Graphic Illustrations of Glacial Sculpture. The attempt is made in Figs. 97, 98, and 99 to present examples of the unlike features just described. The figures make no pretense of being drawn from actual mountains ; but they are in a way made up from various observations, sketches, and photographs, and in this respect correspond to the "deduced consequences" of the hypothesis that glaciers can erode, as announced in the preceding paragraph ; for the consequences are not simply abstract deductions; they have been tested at nearly every step by observation. The figures undoubtedly need many amendments; they are hard and crude, yet they have some value in making the preceding paragraph clearer than it would be without them. Moreover, the figures ambitiously attempt to exhibit the changes that a given mountain mass would suffer from a pre-glacial time of normal sculpture, through a pronounced glacial period, to a post-glacial time in which the work of the glacial period has as

FIG. 97. A NORMALLY ERODED MOUNTAIN MASS, NOT AFFECTED BY GLACIAL EROSION

yet been but little affected by the return of normal conditions; in this respect they are necessarily only ideal examples.

Fig. 97 shows the rounded, dome-like forms of a subdued mountain mass. The cliffs and ledges of an earlier stage of normal erosion have been worn away, and the waste cover has been very generally extended over the graded slopes that now reach from valley bottom to mountain top. This stage of mountain sculpture was chosen because it is so well represented in the Sawatch range of the Rocky mountains in Colorado in association with glacially sculptured forms, such as are illustrated in the later figures. Normally sculptured mountains of sharper form, like those of southern California, might have been taken, had I seen them otherwise than in photographs. The main valley is widely opened; its floor is well graded to a continuous slope; its stream has no lakes or falls, but swings smoothly along a somewhat sinuous course between the spurs that come down with moderate slope from the higher ridges. The side valleys branch in a delicate fashion upwards, splitting the spurs into many spurlets; but all the streams and valley floors unite in accordant fashion at their many points of junction. The spurs are round-shouldered forms, exhibiting very few outlines by which their elusive curves may be represented; indeed, as here drawn, they have an undue resemblance to the sprawling feet of some huge pachyderm. I believe that if mountains of this kind had been more familiar to those who have discussed the question of glacial sculpture in the Alps, a closer approach to agreement on the question of glacial erosion might have been reached ere now.

Fig. 98 is intended to represent the accomplished work of a heavy glacial system on the mountain mass of Fig. 97. The main glacier has gained room for its broad current by wearing off the ends of the spurs that formerly entered the main valley from either side; and it has gained room for its heavy and deep ice body by excavating the valley floor to a greater depth than it had in pre-glacial time. The side glacier which enters from the upper left corner of the figure is manifestly less deep than the main glacier; hence, while the ice surfaces of the main and side ice streams unite at accordant grade, the beds of their troughs or channels cannot unite in that even fashion; for when the troughs are once scoured out to a satisfactory depth for the two unequal ice streams, further change of trough depth will be small. The smaller branch glaciers in the main mountain mass have enlarged the branch valleys that they occupy, and retrogressive erosion at the heads of these glaciers has transformed the tapering valley heads of pre-glacial time into blunt-headed cirques. The slopes of the spurs and summits have been greatly steepened, and the ridges and peaks greatly sharpened, by the active weathering resulting from glacial under-cutting in the branch troughs and cirques. On the extreme right another mountain is shown in which two cirques have been excavated, not of sufficient size to transform the pre-glacial dome into a sharpened peak, yet large enough to have encroached on the spur that separated them, and thus to have transformed part of it into a serrate ridge. Mt. Elbert, the highest summit of the Rocky mountains within the United States, presents just this sort of a contrast to its slightly lower neighbor, La Plata peak, whose summit has been sharpened into Alpine form. If the glacial conditions here pictured should last long enough, it is not to be doubted that the mountains would in time be reduced to lower and gentler forms than are here presented in the toothed peaks and serrated spurs of the central mass; and eventually they might be worn down so low that the glaciers would slowly and spontaneously disappear, in consequence of the increasing mildness of climate thus produced, — such being Tyndall's suggestion for the Alps; but the very fact that strongly glaciated forms, with the associated peaks and arêtes, now characterize the ranges that were heavily glaciated in Pleistocene time, suffices to prove that the glaciers did not disappear because of their own action in wearing down the mountains, but because of some external control of climatic change.

Fig. 99 illustrates the appearance of the mountains and valleys after the glaciers of Fig. 98 have melted away. Now there is a superabundance of detail; the difficulty in drawing is to select the most significant outlines and to omit the rest. The forms that rose above the ice streams in Fig. 98 are here reproduced without essential change. The spurs on the left are unaltered in form, but are somewhat worn down from their appearance in Fig. 97. The forms that were buried under the ice streams of Fig. 98 are here disclosed to the light of day. The troughs of the smaller branch glaciers have ungraded floors, on which rock basins and rock steps alternate. The troughs of the large side glacier and of the main glacier are better smoothed. Alluvial fans are already accumulating on their sides, just as they are in the Alps and in other glaciated ranges. The fact of such accumulation suffices to prove a strong change from the conditions under which the troughs were excavated to the conditions in which they are now being filled up. The truncated spur ends now continue downwards in the over-steepened trough sides and curve at the base into the U-shaped trough floor. The junctions of the various glacial troughs, to which the name of valleys is of course ordinarily applied, are essentially discordant. The trough of the large side glacier hangs high above the floor of the main glacier trough; the troughs of the smaller branch glaciers hang over the trough of the large side glacier. If the main

FIG. 98. THE SAME MOUNTAIN MASS AS IN FIG. 97, STRONGLY AFFECTED BY GLACIERS WHICH STILL OCCUPY ITS VALLEYS

trough could be followed down to its end, a large basin should be shown, occupied by a lake, and inclosed by morainic walls. As time progresses, all these peculiar features will be changed to normal features. A beginning of such changes is seen in the little slits by which the mouths of the hanging valleys are already beginning to be cut down; in the filling of the lakelets in the rock basins of the smaller branch troughs; and in the rapid wasting of the sharpened ridges and peaks, by which they will in time be rounded again; but the small amount of work thus far accomplished proves that the time since the evacuation of the district by its glaciers is comparatively short.

It is manifest that if a vigorous glacial system should soon again come to occupy the mountainous area of Fig. 99, it would produce relatively small changes compared to those by which the forms of Fig. 97 have been altered to those of Figs. 98 and 99 ; for the glacier system of the second epoch would find the valley troughs so well adapted to its needs that there would be

FIG. 99. THE SAME MOUNTAIN MASS AS IN FIG. 98, SHORTLY AFTER THE GLACIERS HAVE MELTED FROM ITS VALLEYS

relatively small necessity of modifying them. The amount of sculpture effected in a first glacial epoch may therefore be reasonably estimated as of much greater volume than in a second glacial epoch.

Consequences of Theories confronted with Facts. When glaciated mountains are visited with the unlike consequences of the contrasted supposition above stated in mind, there can be little doubt whether glaciers are effective eroding agents or not. As far as the glaciated mountains of the world have been explored, it is found that they possess a large number of peculiar forms, which differ most strikingly from the forms due to the normal processes of erosion; it is further found that these peculiar forms are distributed with respect to one another in a most systematic and significant manner; and it is finally perceived that the peculiar forms are essentially similar to those above described and figured as producible by glaciers, under the supposition that glaciers have effective erosive power and that they have had time to use it. Thus the efficiency of glaciers in carving glaciated mountains is demonstrated by essentially the same method that has so thoroughly demonstrated the efficiency of the normal erosive agencies in carving non-glaciated mountains.

It can hardly be questioned that if, as Andrews has well pointed out, students of mountains had not come upon glaciated forms until after they had seen a good variety of normal forms, the exceptional quality of the needle peaks and the serrated ridges, of the rock basins and the rock steps, of the truncated spur ends and the over-steepened trough walls, of the hanging side valleys and the over-deepened main valleys, would have been sooner appreciated. But, as a matter of fact, the Alps and other strongly glaciated ranges have been taken as types of mountain form from a time when there was no question at all of glacial erosion; and as a consequence the exceptional quality of many Alpine forms has passed relatively unnoticed. The literature of the subject shows that the peculiar features which characterize glaciated mountains are not regarded as exceptional by observers whose experience has been gained chiefly in mountains like the Alps; yet, on the other hand, the peculiar features of glaciated mountains are very impressive when they are seen by one whose standard of normal mountain form has been established in non-glaciated mountains, and still more so when they are considered in view of the reasonable consequences of the supposition that glaciers can erode their valleys or can modify preëxistent normal valleys.

Examples of glaciated mountains known to me from my own experience to possess the peculiar features above mentioned are: the Highlands of Scotland, where hanging cirques (corries), trough valleys, and valley-floor lakes abound; the Alps, where all of the characteristic forms of glaciated mountains are strongly developed ; Norway, where the relation of hanging lateral valleys and over-deepened main valleys is persistent and convincing; various ranges of the Rocky mountains in the United States, where the contrast of glaciated and non-glaciated forms is very striking ; and some of the higher ranges in the Tian Shan. In several of these ranges the sharpness of the peaks and arêtes between neighboring cirques is in strong contrast to the more rounded summits where cirques are farther apart or absent. When we note the significant variation in the size of these glacial features from the isolated small cirques, such as Partsch has described in the low mountains of central Germany, to the great confluent cirques and deep trough valleys of the high Sierra Nevada, as described by Lawson ; when we recall their world-wide distribution, from the great fiord systems of Alaska, as set forth by Gilbert, to the only less impressive fiords of New Zealand, as pictured by Andrews ; and when we note the systematic relations of their several elements, as has been so fully presented for the various glacial systems of the Alps in the masterful monograph by Penck and Brückner, now approaching completion, the trustworthiness of these unanimous witnesses to glacial erosion is unimpeachable. It should not, however, be forgotten that glaciated mountains present certain smaller elements of form for which no satisfactory explanation has yet been offered ; it is because these elements are truly subordinate to the prevailing larger features that they are not given consideration here. It must also not be overlooked that the actual processes of glacial erosion are not yet fully understood; as to this important problem it will only be noted that while the plucking of large blocks must be important as long as the glacial bed is uneven, the scouring of ledges and the grinding of plucked blocks to fine waste must also be allowed great measure of effectiveness, because the coarse-textured moraines at the lower end of glaciated valleys are generally so small in comparison to the excavated spaces farther upstream.

Insufficiency of Arguments against Glacial Erosion. A brief consideration may be given as to the insufficiency of certain arguments advanced by those who do not believe that glaciers have any significant power to erode valleys.

It has been noted that the ice at the side or the lower end of glaciers, where its movement against the adjoining rock is open to observation, will flow around a ledge instead of removing it. The same may be said of water ; yet no one doubts that water, armed with rock waste, is an effective agent of erosion. It seems as if the essential element of abundant time were here neglected by the non-glacial erosionists ; for even if we accept the epigram that glaciers are to mountains what sandpaper is to furniture, it cannot be doubted that sandpaper would wear any piece of furniture down to nothing if it were used long enough and if the supply of cutting sand were continually renewed. And it must be remembered that we cannot measure the duration of the several epochs of the glacial period in various mountain ranges until we know the rate and the amount of glacial work. At present both these quantities are more or less uncertain ; it is therefore premature at present to conclude that glaciers cannot have done much work because they seem to work slowly.

It has been urged that once the loose material of pre-glacial weathering is scoured away, deeper glacial erosion is insignificant. This not only overlooks the possible long duration of a glacial epoch, whereby work of slow rate can reach a great amount; it also begs the whole question of the method of glacial erosion. There is much evidence from the detailed form of the cliffs and sills in glacial troughs that the plucking of joint blocks as well as the scouring of rock surfaces plays a large part in glacial erosion, and that this process goes on without any aid from weathering in the ordinary sense ; that plucking may exceed scouring in the earlier stages of the modification of normal valleys to glacial troughs, if, indeed, it is not still an important process even after the troughs have been worn fairly round and smooth. In the absence of all opportunity for direct observation of this process beneath the trunk of a heavy glacier, it may be better determined by a comparison of the forms of once-glaciated and never-glaciated mountains than in any other way.

It is often pointed out that the lower end of a glacier advances over loose deposits without removing them ; and to this may be added the unquestionable fact that broad and heavy sheets of till in the glaciated areas of Europe and North America lie upon unconsolidated gravels. To infer from these facts that glaciers cannot greatly erode their channels would be equivalent to inferring that a stream which descends from a mountain into a desert and lays down its detritus at its withering lower end cannot erode the valley through which its upper course descends ; or equivalent to inferring that the Ganges, which is spreading out a great delta among the distributaries near its mouth, cannot erode deep valleys in the mountains of its source. This argument cannot be accepted as valid until it is shown that the action of the small and vanishing lower end of a glacier may be fairly taken to represent the action of its heavy middle part. The contrasts between the bare rock surfaces of the Scandinavian or the Laurentian highland and the heavy drift deposits on the plains of northern Germany or the prairies of the upper Mississippi valley suffice to prove that glacial action, like river action, varies from place to place ; in both, erosion characterizes the upper and middle parts, and deposition characterizes the lower part. The glacial sculpture of mountains, as here set forth, is not in the least inconsistent with the glacial deposition of mountain waste on the piedmont lowlands.

It is sometimes said that rocky knobs, rising like those of Sion from a valley floor, and showing rough ledges on their down-valley side, contradict the idea of glacial erosion ; for it is urged that if glaciers erode, such knobs ought to be worn away. There are several unproved tacit postulates in this argument. It is silently assumed that the knobs in question retain approximately their pre-glacial form ; but it may well be that they are unconsumed remnants of greatly eroded masses, and the choice between these alternatives is precisely the matter at issue. It is silently assumed that glaciers would not, if their work were interrupted at any accidental stage, leave knobs on their channel beds ; yet no evidence is given to prove that the transformation of normal pre-glacial valleys into well-rounded glacial troughs is not a progressive work, which would show many signs of being unfinished if time enough had not been allowed for the finishing. It is silently assumed that the production of rough ledges on the down-valley side of a knob are not within the possibilities of glacial erosion ; but there is much evidence that a glacier may roughen one side of a rock mass by dragging or plucking away large blocks, while it smooths the other side by scouring down preëxistent irregularities.

Insufficiency of the Explanations of Special Forms without Glacial Erosion. Some of the explanations offered by non-glacial erosionists for those peculiar forms of glaciated mountains here ascribed to glacial erosion may now be presented.

Large lakes, such as those which are piedmont to the Alps, are explained by the warping or local depression of pre-glacial valleys with subordinate aid from morainic barriers. The argument presented by Wallace against this view seems to me conclusive. If the lake basins are formed by the warping or damming of essentially unmodified pre-glacial valleys, the lake water should invade numerous side valleys, and thus form lateral bays ; for the side valleys must have been, in pre-glacial time, worn down to accordant junction with their maturely wide-open main valleys. It is well known that the Alpine lakes are singularly deficient in lateral bays. To test the value of this evidence, let any never-glaciated mountain range be examined to see what sort of a lake would be formed by warping or damming one of the larger valleys at the mountain base. The contrast between such a lake and the Alpine lakes is most striking. But it should be carefully borne in mind that in the present explanation of piedmont lakes by glacial erosion, it is not only the lake basin, as Ramsay believed, but much of the valley depth and breadth within the mountains that has been worn out by ice action.

Cirques and the sharpened summit forms often associated with them have had so little close study, except by those who regard them as directly or indirectly of glacial origin, that they need not be further considered here.

Hanging lateral valleys, opening in the over-steepened walls of over-deepened main-valley troughs, have had several explanations. One of the most recent writers on this subject doubts whether hanging valleys are, after all, of so striking a character and of so peculiar a distribution as to constitute serious evidence for glacial erosion ; he suggests that, for those which do exist, some peculiar and sufficient, though now unknown, explanation will probably be found, without having recourse to anything so extravagant as the deepening of the main-valley trough by ice action. This is simply a series of skeptical assumptions and vague suggestions that need not be answered until they are made more specific.

Another writer, recognizing the hanging attitude of lateral valleys as characteristic of Alpine valley systems, suggests that the lateral valleys were occupied and protected from erosion by glaciers, while the main valley was deepened by normal river erosion. One objection to this is its extreme improbability ; for a series of independent glaciers could not agree to hold their ends at the mouths of the lateral valleys for a time long enough for the main valley to be deepened by hundreds, and widened by thousands, of feet below their level. Another objection, lately pointed out by Penck, is that hanging laterals occur not only where both trunk and lateral valleys were glaciated, but also in certain parts of the Alps where only the main valley was glaciated ; in the latter case, the protection of the lateral valleys against erosion by the presence of lateral glaciers cannot be assumed.

A third explanation is to the effect that lateral valleys will be left "hanging," if the region in which they occur be tilted so as to steepen the slope of the main river but not of its branches. Apart from the sufficient objections that may be urged against this explanation, in view of the general principles of river action, it is pertinent and logical to ask that the possibility of such an origin for hanging lateral valleys should be tested in a region where tilting can be proved on independent grounds, and where glacial action has not taken place ; indeed, one might fairly expect that the advocates of this explanation would be the first to test it in a non-glaciated region before putting faith in it, but they do not seem to have done so. It might be tested in the southwestern slope of the central *massif* of France, or in the piedmont belt of the southeastern United States, where the revival of valley erosion by regional tilting cannot be doubted ; but no hanging lateral valleys occur there, although the main valleys are often of so moderate a width as to indicate that they have been exposed to erosion for a much shorter time than that which would be required by normal erosion in producing the wide main valleys above which the lateral valleys hang so con-spicuously in glaciated mountains. Hence, if a relatively short time has sufficed for the lateral streams to wear down their valley mouths as deep as the main valleys in these non-glaciated districts, a longer time should certainly have sufficed to bring about accordant junctions of lateral and main valleys in glaciated mountain ranges, on the supposition that normal erosion has alone been operative there. The fact that such accordant valley junctions do not prevail in glaciated ranges shows that the sup-position just stated is erroneous.

A fourth explanation remains to be mentioned, and this, in its relations to the whole question of land sculpture, seems to me the most peculiar of all. This explanation asserts that when local rains occur, they will contribute to the erosion of only certain of the lateral valleys, while the main valley will always receive some of the local rainfall, and hence will always suffer some erosion at such times ; therefore the main valley will be eroded faster than the laterals, which will consequently be left "hanging." This is tantamount to saying that hanging lateral valleys are normal features, to be expected in all moun-tain ranges as the result of the normal processes of erosion. Such a conclusion is contrary to experience and to the well-based principles of land sculpture. It gainsays Playfair's law, which is one of the best established generalizations in physio-graphic geology. It takes the Alps, a strongly glaciated range, as an example of normal mountain sculpture, and thus begs the very question in discussion. It is here characterized as the most peculiar of all the explanations offered for hanging valleys, because it goes so directly counter to observation in other than glaciated regions. It is, of course, not to be forgotten for a moment that a large trunk river may, in its youth, cut down its valley faster than the smaller side streams can cut down theirs, and thus introduce a hanging arrangement of lateral valleys with respect to the trunk valley ; but it must also not be for-gotten that as soon as the trunk river approaches grade, the further deepening of its valley is greatly retarded ; and that then, while the trunk river devotes its energy (apart from that of transportation) chiefly to widening its valley floor, the side streams overtake it and develop accordant junctions of lateral and trunk valleys. It needs but little observation in non-glaciated areas to see that the chapter of early youth, in which a trunk river may be deeper than the mouths of the lateral valleys, is very short; that this peculiar relation only appears when the contrast between the volumes of trunk river and side stream is great; and that in all examples of non-glaciated mountains and plateaus, an accordant relation of lateral and main valley floors obtains as soon as the main valleys acquire a significant breadth. The last point is of essential importance, because in all the examples of hanging lateral valleys of glaciated mountains yet described, the main valley is not a narrow cleft, in which hanging laterals would be normally appropriate, but a well-opened valley with respect to which hanging laterals are normally most inappropriate. In the Alps, the main valleys are half a mile, a mile, or over a mile in width. It is entirely out of the question to ascribe the over-deepening of these wide valleys to any normal process, independent of glacial action.

As to various other explanations of hanging valleys, they are essentially irrelevant. Sea cliffs, strongly under-cut by surf, may have valleys opening in their faces in hanging fashion; but this has no possible bearing on the hanging valleys of glaciated mountains. Faults may occasionally be found, recent enough in date to dislocate the valley floors that they traverse; but they should dislocate mountain flanks and ridges also. To suppose that the numerous hanging valleys of glaciated mountains are of this origin involves special conditions, at once so numerous and so improbable that to state them is to discredit them.

A Fallacy leading to a Quandary. In fine, it remains only to point out the two positions, on one or the other of which there is refuge for those conservatives who, on the ground of the apparent inefficiency of existing glaciers to erode their beds, hesitate to conclude that the piedmont lake basins, the over-deepened main valleys, the hanging side valleys, the valley-head cirques, and the sharpened peaks of glaciated mountains are the work, directly or indirectly, of ancient glaciers. The conservatives may, on the one hand, attempt to explain by normal erosive processes, as has just been suggested, the features which are here classed as peculiar ; but so long as the peculiar features are found only in glaciated mountains, and so long as normal processes are not shown to be capable of producing them, the offered explanations by normal processes must be doubted. On the other hand, the conservatives who hesitate to accept glacial erosion may suppose that in pre-glacial times some special agency or conspiracy of agencies, not now known, prophetically selected all those mountainous regions that were afterwards to be glaciated, worked upon them in essentially the manner that glaciers would work if they could, and then withdrew into obscure inactivity. But this is incredible, because the unknown agency or agencies could not possibly have been so circumspect as to produce only small cirques and short trough valleys in the high mountains of low latitudes and in the lower mountains of middle latitudes ; to produce, in the high mountains of middle latitudes and in the lower mountains of high latitudes, large cirques and long main-valley troughs, over which the side valleys open in the most significant hanging fashion ; and to produce in these valleys and their cirque heads a great number of rock basins in which lakes now stand. Either one of these refuges for the conservative is so uncomfortable a quandary that the road leading to it must be regarded as lying on fallacious ground.

It is thus both along direct and indirect lines of evidence that many observers have been led in recent years away from the supposition that glaciers cannot erode, and toward the supposition that glaciers can erode, even though the methods of glacial erosion are not yet fully understood. The sculpture of mountains by glaciers is indeed now proved by so many facts, widely and yet systematically distributed, that it savors of extreme conservatism any longer to deny the efficacy of glacial erosion.

XXIV

GLACIAL EROSION IN FRANCE, SWITZERLAND, AND NORWAY

Introduction. Many years ago I presented to the Boston Society of National History an essay on Glacial Erosion, in which my own observations were supplemented by a review of all that I could find written on the subject, in the hope of reaching some safe conclusion regarding what was then (as it is still) a mooted question. Although recognizing effective erosion to depths of "a moderate number of feet" where ice pressure was great and motion was rapid, in contrast to deposition where pressure and motion were reduced and where the amount of sub-glacial drift was excessive, I could not at that time find evidence to warrant the acceptance of great glacial erosion, such as was advocated by those who ascribed Alpine lakes and Norwegian fiords to this agency. In a retrospect from the present time, it seems as if one of the causes that led to my conservative position was the extreme exaggeration of some glacialists, who found in glacial erosion a destructive agency competent to accomplish any desired amount of denudation, — an opinion from which I recoiled too far. Since the publication of my previous essay I had gradually come to accept a greater and greater amount of glacial erosion in the regions of active ice motion; but in spite of this slow change of opinion, the maximum measure of destructive work that, up to last year, seemed to me attributable to glaciers was moderate; and it was therefore with great surprise that I then came upon certain facts in the Alps and in Norway which demanded wholesale glacial erosion for their explanation. The desire of some years past to revise and extend my former essay then came to be a duty, which it is the object of this paper to fulfill.

My former revision of the problem divided the arguments for glacial erosion under four headings : observations on existing glaciers and inferences from these observations; the amount and arrangement of glacial drift; the topography of glaciated regions; and the so-called argument from necessity, that is, the belief that glaciers must have done this and that because nothing else competent to the task could be found. It is not possible for me at present to review all the new material pertinent to the whole problem; attention can be given here chiefly to a few examples under the third heading.

A Glaciated Valley in Central France. It is evident that if it were possible to obtain a definite idea of the pre-glacial topography of a glaciated district, the amount of glacial work might be readily determined as the difference between the pre-glacial and the present form; independent evidence sufficing to prove that general denudation of the rocky crust in the brief post-glacial epoch had been inconsiderable. This method leads one to conclude that in general the topography of southern New England has not been strongly modified by glacial action; for we find here on the whole the same maturely dissected upland that prevails in regions of similar structure outside of the glacial boundary, the uplands being explained as parts of an uplifted peneplain of late Mesozoic date, and the valleys as the work of ordinary erosion in a part of Tertiary time; but this method of measuring glacial erosion by dating topographical forms had not been developed twenty years ago. Strong glacial erosion may, however, be expected in New England where ice motion was locally accelerated, as through the notches of the White mountains. Again, in the glaciated area of the Central Plateau of France I had the opportunity in January, 1899, of seeing a valley that had been locally modified to a determinate amount by a glacier that once descended northwest from the Cantal along the valley of the Rhue to the junction of the latter with the Dordogne. Outside of the glaciated area the valleys of the plateau — an uplifted and sub-maturely dissected peneplain, mostly of crystalline rocks — frequently follow incised meandering courses, in which the steep concave slopes are regularly opposed to the gentler convex slopes, the latter being spur-like projections of the uplands, advancing first from one side and then from the other side of the valley. Valleys of this kind are singularly systematic in form, as the result of the combined downward and outward cutting by their streams which, already winding or meandering when the erosion of the valleys began, have increased the width of their meander belt while they deepened their valleys. On entering the glaciated valley of the Rhue it is found that the regularly descending spurs characteristic of the non-glaciated valleys are represented by irregular knobs and mounds, scoured on their upstream side and plucked on the downstream side; and that the cliffs formed where the spurs are cut off, as in Fig. 100, are sometimes fully as strong as those which naturally stand on the opposite side of the valley. The spurs generally remain in sufficient strength to require the

FIG. 100. THE GLACIATED VALLEY OF THE RHUE

river to follow its pre-glacial serpentine course around them, but they are sometimes so far destroyed as to allow the river to take a shorter course through what was once the neck of a spur. But it should be noted that the short-cuts are sometimes narrow gorges incised in the half-consumed spurs; and in such cases the displacement of the Rhue from its former roundabout course is probably to be explained by constraint or obstruction by ice. The short-cuts here described are not for a moment to be confounded with the normal cut-offs through the narrowed necks of spurs, such as are so finely exhibited in the meandering valleys of the Meuse and the Moselle. The short courses are distinctly abnormal features, like the rugged knobs to which the once smooth-sloping spurs are now reduced.

It was thus possible in the valley of the Rhue to make a definite restoration of pre-glacial form, and to measure the change produced by glaciation. The change was of moderate amount, but it was highly significant of glacial action, for it showed that while a slender, fast-flowing stream of water might contentedly follow a serpentine course at the bottom of a meandering valley, the clumsy, slow-moving stream of ice could not easily adapt itself to so tortuous a path. The more or less complete obliteration of the spurs was the result of the effort of the ice stream to prepare for itself a smooth-sided trough of slight curvature; and if the rocks had been weaker, or if the ice had been heavier, or if the glacial period of the Cantal had lasted longer, this effort might have been so successful as to have destroyed all traces of the spurs. Fortunately, the change actually produced only modified the spurs, but did not entirely destroy them; and their rugged remnants are highly significant of what a glacier can do.

Rocky Knobs in Glaciated Areas. On thus generalizing the lesson of the Rhue, it is seen that just before the complete obliteration of the spurs, some of their remnant knobs may be isolated from the uplands whence these pre-glacial spurs descended. It is out of the question to regard the ruggedness of such knobs as an indication of small change from their preglacial form, as has been done by some observers. The ruggedness is really an indication of the manner in which a glacier reduces a larger mass to smaller dimensions, by plucking on the downstream side as well as by scouring on the upstream side. It is possible that knobs in other glaciated valleys than that of the Rhue may be of this origin; they should then be regarded not as standing almost unchanged and testifying to the incapacity of glacial erosion, but as surviving remnants of much larger masses, standing, like monadnocks above a peneplain, as monuments to the departed greater forms. The two knobs at Sion (Sitten) and the Maladeires, all detached from Mont d'Orge in the upper valley of the Rhone, the hills of Bellinzona in the valley of the Ticino, the rocks of Salzburg where the Salzach emerges from the Alps, and even the Borromeo islands in lake Maggiore, may perhaps be thus interpreted.

Rugged as these knobs may be on the downstream side, it would be an unreasonable contradiction of the conclusions based on observations of many kinds to maintain that their ruggedness was of pre-glacial origin.

The ice stream from the Cantal at one time expanded sufficiently to flood the uplands bordering the valley of the Rhue, where it produced changes of a most significant kind. The neighboring unglaciated uplands are of systematic form ; broad, smoothly arched masses rise, round-shouldered, between the narrow valleys that are incised beneath them ; the uplands are,

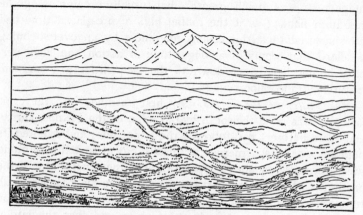

FIG. 101. GLACIATED KNOBS ON THE CENTRAL PLATEAU OF FRANCE

as a rule, deeply soil-covered, and bare ledges prevail only on the stronger slopes of the young valleys that have been eroded since the peneplain was raised to its present upland estate. But within the glaciated area near the Rhue the broadly rounded forms of the uplands are replaced by a succession of most irregular rocky knobs, from which the pre-glacial soils have been well scoured away, as in Fig. 101. This seems to be a form most appropriate to glacial action on a surface that had been weathered to variable depths in pre-glacial time. The ice action sufficed to rasp away the greater part of the weathered material and to grind down somewhat the underlying rock, often giving the knobs a rounded profile, but it did not nearly suffice to reduce the rocky surface to an even grade. The ice action seems here to have resembled that of a torrent which might sweep away the waste on a flood plain and lay bare and erode the rock ledges beneath, but whose duration was not sufficient to develop a graded floor appropriate to its current.

Another example of this kind seems to occur where the huge glacier of the Inn, escaping from its well-inclosed channel within the mountains, once spread forward in a great fan of ice over the foothills at the northern border of the Alps and crept out upon the piedmont plain. The glance that I had at this foothill district from a passing train gave me the impression that its ruggedness was much greater than usually obtains along the mountain flanks; as if the rolling hills of pre-glacial time had been scoured to an increasing roughness by an overwhelming ice flood that would, if a longer time of action had been permitted to it, have worn down all the inequalities to a smooth, maturely graded floor.

The Valley of the Ticino. My first entrance into the Alps last year was from the south by the valley of the Ticino. Thirty-one years before I had followed the same valley and admired its bold sides and its numerous waterfalls, but at that time nothing was noticed that seemed inappropriate to the general idea of the erosion of valleys by their rivers. Thirty years is a long enough time for one to learn something new even about valleys, and on my second visit it was fairly startling to find that the lateral valleys opened on the walls of the main valley of the Ticino five hundred feet or more above its floor, and that the side streams cascaded down the steep main-valley walls in which they have worn nothing more than narrow clefts of small depth. This set me wondering, not only as to the meaning of so peculiar an arrangement of valleys and streams, but also as to the reason why so peculiar an arrangement should not have sooner attracted attention as an exceptional characteristic of Alpine topography. Playfair long ago, when describing the relation of side valleys to their trunk, showed clearly that they had " such a nice adjustment of their declivities that none of them join the principal valley either on too high or too low a level; a circumstance which would be infinitely improbable if each of these vallies were not the work of the stream that flows in it " (102); yet the whole course of the passing century has hardly sufficed to make full application of this law. So much latitude is usually allowed in the relation of branch and trunk valleys that hundreds of observers, many of whom must have been cognizant of Playfair's law, have made no note of the extraordinary exceptions to it that prevail in the glaciated valleys of the Alps. Even the most pronounced advocates of glacial erosion, with a few exceptions to be noted below, have been silent regarding the remarkable failure of adjustment between the declivities of lateral and main glaciated valleys. Indeed, in reviewing the writings of those who have accepted a large measure of glacial erosion, one must be struck with the undue attention that they have given to lake basins and the relative inattention to valleys. This disproportion is probably to be explained as a result of the greater contrast that prevails between a river and a lake than between a river and its branch; it is perhaps for this reason that the attention of geologists and geographers has generally been directed to the origin of lakes rather than to the

FIG. 102. VAL D'OSOGNA, A HANGING LATERAL VALLEY OF THE TICINO

relation of branch and trunk streams, even when the former cascade from their lateral valleys into the main valley. That glacial erosionists made so little claim for the general deepening of glaciated valleys while they demanded a great deepening of those parts of valleys which have been scoured down to form lake basins has always seemed to me a difficulty in the way of accepting the demanded measure of lake-basin erosion; and this difficulty was supported by the well-attested observation that the side slopes of glaciated valleys manifest no marked or persistent increase of declivity in passing from above to below the limit of glaciation. If glaciers had scoured out deep lake basins, like those of Maggiore and Geneva, they ought to have significantly deepened the valleys upstream from the lakes; and if the valleys were thus significantly deepened, it seemed as if their slopes should be steeper below than above the limit of glacial action. The denial of the latter requisite seemed to me to carry with it the denial of the two preceding suppositions.

Features of Strongly Glaciated Valleys. It is true that the uppermost limit of glaciation, *QR* (Fig. 103), in Alpine valleys is not attended by a persistent change in the steepness of the

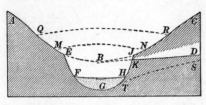

FIG. 103. SECTION OF A GLACIATED VALLEY

valley sides, *AE*, *CJ*; but on descending well within the glaciated valley, a very strong change may usually be found in the slope of the valley walls. The larger valleys, once occupied by heavy glaciers from the lofty, central snow fields, are characterized by basal cliffs, *EF*, *JH*, that rise several hundred or even a thousand feet above their broad floors, and thus inclose what may be called a bottom trough, *EFHJ*, half a mile or a mile wide. The bottom trough of the Ticino, as seen when one looks upstream towards Giornico, is a very striking feature. The basal cliffs are comparatively straight-walled; they have no sharp spurs advancing into the valley floor. The rock floor, *G* (Fig. 103), is buried by gravels, *FH*, to an unknown depth. It is only from the benches above the basal cliffs that the valley sides flare open with maturely inclined slopes; and it is at a moderate depth beneath the level of the benches at the top of these basal cliffs that the lateral valleys, *DK*, open on the walls of the main valley.

The bottom trough within the basal cliffs and beneath the lateral valleys seems to be of glacial origin. It is in the first place a characteristic feature of all the larger glaciated Alpine valleys, as I am assured by Professors Penck, Brückner, and

Richter, with whom this matter was carefully discussed one summer. The non-glaciated valleys manifest no such peculiar form. It is not simply that the terminal portion, *JBK*, of a lateral valley has been cut off by the glacial widening of the main valley floor; the main valley has been strongly deepened, as is assured by the relation of its floor, *FH*, to the prolongation of the floor of the lateral valley, *KB*. The first may be several hundred feet — indeed, in some valleys a good thousand feet — below the second. The lateral valleys must have once entered the main valley at grade, for the flaring sides of the main valley indicate maturity; the side slopes *AE*, *CJ* must have once met at *B*. Even the lateral valleys have an open V-section, proving that their streams had cut down to a graded slope, *DB*, that must have led them to an accordant junction with the main river. Nothing seems so competent as glacial erosion to explain the strong discordance of the existing valleys.

The lateral as well as the main valleys have been glaciated, but the former do not exhibit changes of form so distinctly as the latter; in the Ticino system the lateral valleys did not, as far as I saw them, seem to have been much affected by glaciation, a fact that may be attributed to the small size of their branch glaciers in contrast with the great volume of the trunk glacier. There is no sufficient evidence that the valley floor between the basal cliffs has been faulted down after the fashion of a *graben;* for although this origin is advocated by Rothpletz (237) for the Linththal, the evidence that he adduces for the limiting faults is not agreed to by Alpine geologists in general, and the persistent association of the bottom troughs with the crooked course of preëxistent, maturely open valleys involves special conditions of faulting that cannot be accepted without the strongest evidence.

It is not satisfactory to explain the bottom trough as having been worn out by normal trunk-river erosion, leaving the side streams, as it were, hanging or suspended above them, for to admit such an origin would be to go counter to all that has been learned regarding the systematic development of valleys. Here it is with regret that I must differ from the opinion of two eminent Swiss geologists, who explain the deepening of the main valleys by a revival in the erosive power of the rivers as a result of a regional uplift, while they regard the hanging lateral valleys as not yet accordantly deepened by their smaller streams. It is true that narrow trenches are cut in the floors of the hanging valleys, showing that their streams have made some response to the erosion of the bottom trough in the main valley, and if the bottom trough were a narrow cañon, this relation of trunk and branch streams might be considered normal; but if the breadth as well as the depth of the bottom trough had been acquired by normal river erosion, the side valleys should now, it seems to me, have been trenched much deeper than they are, to some such slope as *ST* (Fig. 103).

The opinions of Rütimeyer and Heim on this question are as follows: Rütimeyer gave an excellent account of hanging lateral valleys thirty years ago in his description of the valley of the Reuss (13–24). He recognized benches, or *Thalstufen*, on each side of the valley above the basal cliffs of the existing bottom trough, and regarded them as the remnants of a former, wide-open valley floor. Side valleys of moderate fall enter the main valley about at the level of the *Thalstufen*, and their waters then cascade down over the basal cliffs to the Reuss. Glacial erosion is dismissed as incompetent to erode the bottom trough; indeed, the time of glacial occupation of the valley is considered a period of rest — a sort of "pupa stage" — in its development. The discordance of main and lateral valleys is ascribed entirely to the differential erosion of their streams. Heim's views on this matter are to be found in his "Mechanismus der Gebirgsbildung" (*a*, 1, 282–301) and in an article "Ueber die Erosion im Gebiete der Reuss" (*b*). He recognizes that the bottom troughs have been excavated in the floors of preëxisting valleys, whose stream lines had been reduced to an even grade (profile of equilibrium, *Gleichgewichtslinie*) and whose lateral slopes had been maturely opened. The side streams must at that time have eroded their valleys deep enough to enter the main valley at accordant grade, as stated above. Since then it is concluded that an elevation of the region has caused a revival (*Neubelebung*) of the main river; and the present greater depth of the main valley is, according to Heim, merely the natural result of this revival, while the smaller side streams have not yet been able to deepen their valleys. The height of the *Thalstufen* or remnants of the former valley floor, seen in the benches above the basal cliffs of the bottom trough, is taken as a measure of the elevation that the mountain mass has suffered.

Apart from the improbability that the deepening of a bottom trough by a revived main river could truncate so many lateral valleys with so great nicety as is repeatedly the case, leaving their streams to cascade down in clefts but slightly incised in the main-valley walls, the following considerations lead me to reject the possibility of explaining the discordance between side and main streams by a normal revival of river action.

Relation of Trunk and Branch Valleys. The general accordance of maturely developed main and lateral valleys in non-glaciated regions, as recognized by Playfair, is to-day fully established by innumerable observations in many parts of the world. Truly, during the attainment of mature development it is possible that a large river may outstrip a small branch stream in the work of deepening its valley, but the discordance thus produced can prevail only during early youth; for as soon as the main river approaches grade, the further deepening of its valley is retarded, while at the same time the steepened descent of the lateral streams at their entrance into the main valley accelerates their erosive work. Hence, even if a large trunk river has for a time eroded its valley to a significant depth beneath the tributary valleys, this discordance cannot endure long in the history of the river. Examples of such normal discordance are to be found in non-glaciated regions only in the branch streams of rivers that occupy very narrow cañons; and even rivers in cañons sometimes receive their branches at accordant grade, as seems to be usually the case with the Colorado, if one may judge by photographs. The narrow, post-glacial gorges cut by active streams habitually receive their branches — when they receive any — from hanging side gorges; and an excellent example has long since been on record in the gorge of Cattaraugus Creek in western New York, where a branch, the Canaserowlie, falls into the main gorge from a side gorge of much less depth. Referring to this, Hall wrote: " In the more recently excavated channels we find the streams falling over the very edge of the cliff, having produced no perceptible recession in the margin of the fall" (380). But however appropriate a discordance of branch and trunk may be in early youth, it cannot endure long enough to be associated with maturely opened main valleys. It should be noted that discordance of side and main valleys may also be found where a large river has lately been turned to a new path, as in the normal progress of the capture of the upper course of one river by the headward gnawing of a branch of another river (see reference to Russell below), or in the new arrangements of drainage lines in a region from which a glacial sheet has lately withdrawn. Furthermore, the valleys of very small wet-weather streams are frequently discordant with the valley of a serpentine river, if they enter it from the upland that is under-cut by the concave bank of the river. But these cases cannot find application in the hanging valleys of the Alps. The hanging valleys that open on sea cliffs, such as those of Normandy, are of course quite another matter.

Over-deepened Main Valleys and Hanging Lateral Valleys. Now it is characteristic of the bottom troughs of the glaciated Alpine valleys that they are broad-floored; they cannot be described as cañons in any proper sense of that word; the walls are steep enough, but they are too far apart. If the existing breadth of the troughs had been acquired in the ordinary manner by the lateral swinging of the main stream and by the lateral weathering of the walls, the long time required for such a change would have amply sufficed for the lateral streams to cut down their valleys to grade with the main valley; and their persistent failure to do so indicates the action of something else than normal river work in the widening of the main valley. This is the very kernel of the problem.

If a main valley were excavated along a belt of weak rocks, the side valley might stand for some time at a considerable height above the main-valley floor. Certain hanging valleys in the Alps seem at first sight to belong to this class, but such is not really the case. For example, where the Linth flows into the Wallen See, the well-defined bottom troughs of the river and of the lake both pass obliquely through a syncline of strong lower Cretaceous limestone, which forms cliffs on their walls. Side streams drain the high synclinal areas; one such stream cascades from the west into the Linth trough back of the village of Näfels; another cascades from the north into the Wallen See near its western end. The first explanation for such falls is that they are normally held up on the resistant limestone; but it should be noted that the bottom troughs of the Linth and the Wallen See have been cut down and broadly opened in the same limestones. If the troughs were of normal river origin, the side streams, also, should have by this time trenched the limestones deeply instead of falling over the limestone cliffs at the very side of the larger troughs. In the Ticino valley where the side streams are most discordant, massive gneisses prevail; the structure is so nearly uniform over large areas that it affords no explanation of the strong discordance between side and main valleys.

It thus seems obligatory to conclude that the bottom troughs of the larger Alpine valleys were deepened and widened by ice action. This belief is permitted by the abundant signs of glacial erosion on the spurless basal cliffs, and required by the persistent association of over-deepened bottom troughs and discordant hanging lateral valleys with regions of strong glaciation. The valley of the Ticino manifests these peculiarities very distinctly, as described in some detail in a paper in Appalachia (Davis).

Sub-aërial Erosion during the Glacial Period. It should not be imagined that the glacial erosion of troughs in valley floors was necessarily so rapid that no significant sub-aërial erosion was accomplished during its progress. Ordinary weathering and down-hill transportation of rock waste must have been in active operation on the valley sides above the border of the ice-filled channels; and the very fact that on the upper slopes of the mountains pre-glacial, glacial, and post-glacial erosion was similarly conditioned, makes it difficult to distinguish the work done there in each of these three chapters of time. In the diagrams accompanying this essay no indication of change from pre-glacial to post-glacial outline on the upper mountain slopes is indicated, because no satisfactory measure can be given to it.

Lake Lugano. In the presence of a variety of evidence collected for some years previous to my recent European trip, it had been my feeling that the best explanation offered for the large lakes that occupy certain valleys on the Italian slope of the Alps was that they had resulted from what has been called valley-warping, as set forth by Lyell, Heim, and others. It was my desire to look especially at lakes Maggiore, Lugano, and Como with this hypothesis in mind, and to subject it to a careful test by means of certain associated changes that should expectedly occur on the slopes of the neighboring mountains, as may be explained as follows:

On the supposition of moderate or small glacial erosion, a well-matured stage of dissection must have been attained in the district of the Italian lakes in pre-glacial time; for the main valleys are widely opened, and even the lateral valleys have flaring slopes. In a mature stage of dissection mountains should exhibit a well-advanced grading of their slopes; that is, their sides should be worn back to a comparatively even declivity with little regard to diversity of structure; the descending streams of waste being thus seen to correspond to the flood plains of graded rivers. The agencies of weathering and transportation are delicately balanced wherever graded slopes prevail; and a slight tilting of the mountain mass might suffice to disturb the adjustment between the supply and the removal of waste; then all the steepened slopes would soon be more or less completely stripped of their waste cover; their rock ledges would be laid bare, although still preserving the comparatively even declivity that had been gained under the slowly moving waste.

If the lakes had been formed by warping, it is possible to deduce with considerable accuracy the localities where the mountain slopes would be steepened and stripped; namely, the northern slopes about the southern end of the lakes, and the southern slopes about the northern end; but as far as I was able to examine the district about lake Lugano, no effects of such a warping and tilting were to be detected. The submergence of lateral valleys about the middle of the lakes is also, as has been well pointed out by Wallace, a necessary consequence of the theory of warping; but although the main-valley floor is now deep under water, the side valleys are not submerged. Failing to find evidence of warping, and being much impressed with the evidence of deep glacial erosion as indicated by the hanging lateral valleys of the over-deepened Ticino, I examined the irregular troughs of lake Lugano for similar features and found them in abundance.

One of the reasons why lake Lugano had been selected for special study was that it did not lie on the line of any master valley leading from the central Alps to the piedmont plains; hence, if influenced by ice action at all, its basin must have been less eroded than those of Como and Maggiore on the east and west. But in spite of this peculiarity of position, Lugano received strong ice streams from the great glaciers of the Como and Maggiore troughs (see Glacial Distributaries below), and its inclosing slopes possess every sign of having been strongly scoured by ice action. The sides of the lake trough are often steep and cliff-like for hundreds of feet above present water level, thus simulating the basal cliffs of the Ticino valley; while at greater heights the valley sides lean back in relatively well-graded slopes. The angle at the change of slope is often well defined, but it is independent of rock structure. Narrow ravines are frequently incised in the basal cliffs, and alluvial fans of greater or less size are built into the lake waters from the base of the ravines.

The northeastern arm of the lake, extending from the town of Lugano to Porlezza, receives several cascading streams from hanging valleys on its southern side. The side slopes of the hanging valleys are for the most part flaring open and well graded, from which it must be concluded that their streams had, under some condition no longer existing, ceased to deepen their valleys for a time long enough to allow the valley sides to assume a mature expression; and that since then the bottom trough of the main arm of the lake has been eroded deep and wide, with a very small accompanying change in the lateral valleys. In other words, the side valleys were, in pre-glacial time, eroded to a depth accordant with the floor of the master valley that they joined, and since then the bottom trough has been eroded in the floor of the master valley by a branch of the Como glacier. In post-glacial time the side streams have begun to trench their valley floors, eroding little cañons; but much of this sort of work must be done before the side valleys are graded down even as far as the surface of the lake.

The two southern arms of the lake lead to troughs whose floors ascend southward to the moraines of the foothills, beyond which stretch forward the abundant overwashed gravels of the great plain of the Po.

I do not mean to imply that every detail of form about lake Lugano can find ready explanation by the mature glacial modification of a mature pre-glacial valley system, but a great number of forms may be thus explained, and a belief in strong glacial erosion was forced upon me here as well as in the valley of the Ticino. A detailed study of the Italian lakes with the intention of carefully sorting out all the glacial modifications of pre-glacial forms would be most profitable.

Various Examples of Glaciated Valleys. During my excursions I have observed a number of over-deepened main valleys and hanging lateral valleys in the Alps ; for example, those of the Inn and of the Aar. Lakes Thun and Brienz receive numerous cascades from hanging valleys that stand high above the water surface. The valley of Lauterbrunnen also affords a conspicuous illustration of a deep bottom trough inclosed by high basal cliffs that rise to the edge of more open upper slopes ; the celebrated Staubbach fall is the descent of a small lateral stream from its lofty hanging valley (see extract from an article by Wallace, cited below), and the picturesque village of Mürren, *M* (Fig. 104), stands on the flaring slope, or *Thalstufe*, of the pre-glacial valley, just above the great basal cliff of glacial origin. A mile or so

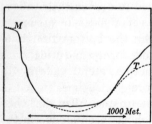

FIG. 104. TRUE-SCALE CROSS SECTION OF THE LAUTER-BRUNNEN VALLEY

south of the village of Lauterbrunnen, the Trummelbach, *T* (Fig. 104), descends the precipitous eastern wall from a hanging valley whose floor is hundreds of feet above that of the Lütschine ; it is roughly sketched in Fig. 105. Although the lateral Trummelbach brings a large volume of water to the main valley, it descends by a very narrow cleft in the rock face, a trifling incision in the valley wall ; while the main valley, whose trunk stream did not seem to be more than five times the volume of its branch, is half a mile or more broad, wide open, and flat-floored. The cross section of the main valley is over a thousand times as large as that of the lateral cleft. Such a disproportion of main valley and lateral cleft is entirely beyond explanation by the inequality of their streams; and for those who feel that they must reject glacial erosion as the cause of the disproportion, there seems to be no refuge but in ascribing the main valley to recent downfaulting, — a process that can hardly be called on to follow systematically along the floors of the larger glaciated valleys of the Alps, and to avoid the non-glaciated valleys and the mountain ridges.

FIG. 105. DIAGRAM OF THE GORGE OF THE TRUMMEL-BACH, LAUTERBRUN-NEN VALLEY.

Certain well-known Alpine glaciers may be instanced as reaching just beyond the end of a hanging lateral valley and thence cascading into the deeper main valley. One is the Mer de Glace by Chamonix; its cascading end is known as the Glacier des Bois. Another is the neighboring Glacier des Bossons, from whose upper amphitheater a steep tongue descends far below; like the waterfalls of Norway, the tongue may be seen lying on the side slope from a considerable distance up or down the main valley. A third example is the Glacier of the Rhone, whose splendid terminal cascade is so conspicuous from the road to the Furka pass. Possibly the Vernagt glacier is another of the same kind; its catastrophic overflows into the lower Rofen valley have often been described. Doubtless many other examples of this class might be named.

While engaged upon these observations in the Alps in the spring of 1899, I sent a brief note about them to my esteemed friend, G. K. Gilbert of Washington, telling him that all the lateral valleys seemed to be "hung up" above the floors of the trunk valleys. His reply was long in coming to Europe, and, on arriving at last, it was dated Sitka, Alaska, where Mr. Gilbert had gone as a member of the Harriman Alaskan Expedition, and where my note had been forwarded. He wrote that, for the fortnight previous to hearing from me, he and his companions had been much impressed with the discordant relations of lateral valleys over the waters of the Alaskan fiords, and he suggested that such laterals should be called "hanging valleys," — a term which I have since then adopted. He fully agreed that hanging valleys presented unanswerable testimony for strong glacial erosion, as will be stated in his forthcoming report on the geology of the Expedition.

After leaving Switzerland I had a brief view of the lake district in northwest England before crossing to Norway. The amount of glacial erosion in the radiating valleys of the English lakes has been much discussed, and, as usual, directly opposite views have been expressed. Rugged rocky knobs were seen in abundance about Ambleside and along the ridge separating the valley of Thirlmere from St. John's Vale ; and the latter receives a hanging valley from the east near Dalehead post office. The famous falls of Lodore seemed to descend from the mouth of a hanging valley into Derwentwater. A model of the lake district, on exhibition at Keswick, showed some other examples of lateral valleys that seemed to stand above the floors of their main valleys, notably one coming from the south near the northeast end of Ulleswater. Since coming home I read the following in Marr's "Scientific Study of Scenery" :

> We find in the Lake District a number of tributary valleys occurring in the hearts of the ridges, and opening out far above the bottoms of the main valleys, discharging their waters down the slopes in cascades. They are specially well marked on the east side of Helvellyn, and a number of them also open into the upper branches of Borrowdale.

The explanation is that of Rütimeyer and Heim :

> For a considerable period after the deepening of the main valley, the minor valleys will end as definite gorges some height above the floor of the main valley, and discharge their waters in a series of cascades or falls down the side of the main valley (136).

One of my former students, Mr. W. B. Lloyd, has recently shown me a number of photographs of the fiords of southern New Zealand, which he brought back from a visit to that distant country. High cascades, plunging from hanging lateral valleys into the broad waters of the fiords, are repeatedly shown.

Fiords and Hanging Valleys in Norway. In Norway I had the pleasure of making a ten days' cross-country excursion in company with Dr. Reusch, director of the Norwegian Geological Survey. We entered from Bergen through Hardanger fiord, and crossed the highlands by the Haukelisaetr road to Skien on the southeastern lowlands, thus making a general cross section on which many characteristic features were seen. Norway has long been known as a land of waterfalls, but it is not generally stated with sufficient clearness or emphasis that many or most of the falls are formed by the descent of streams from maturely opened trough-like hanging valleys which are abruptly cut off by the walls of the fiords. The discordance between main and side streams is simply amazing. The fiord valleys are frequently one or two miles wide ;. the waters of the fiords are of great depths, reaching three thousand feet in some cases. Even when a side valley stands but little above sea-level, its floor may be half a mile above the floor of the fiord. On passing inland beyond the head of the fiord water, where the whole depth of the fiord valley is visible, the side valleys may open more than a thousand feet above the main-valley floor. In many cases where the fiords are inclosed by smooth walls, the cascading side streams have not yet incised a cleft in the bare rock surface, so that their foaming waters are visible for many miles up and down the fiord. Streams of considerable size somtimes plunge down from the rolling uplands in whose edge they seem to have just begun to cut a cleft. Abnormal discordance of trunk and branch stream is, therefore, a strongly marked characteristic of the Norwegian drainage. The necessity for appealing to strong glacial erosion in explanation of this prevailing discordance may be set forth as follows:

Measure of Glacial Erosion in Norwegian Fiords. The deep valleys of Norway, partly occupied by sea water, are incised beneath an uneven highland which bears so many hills and mountains that it makes little approach to a peneplain, yet which here and there shows so many broadly opened uplands between the hills and mountains that it may be taken to represent the well-advanced work of a former cycle of denudation when the region stood much lower than it stands now. As a whole a mature or late-mature stage seems to have been reached before a movement of uplift introduced the present cycle. Let us now make two suppositions regarding the work of normal river erosion in the pre-glacial part of the present cycle, in order to determine, if possible, how much additional erosion must be attributed to ice in the production of existing forms.

First, let it be supposed that the revived main rivers had incised their valleys to the depth of the present fiords in pre-glacial time, and that the discordance of main and side valleys now visible is the appropriate result of the youth of the present cycle. If we recall only the steepness of the fiord walls, this supposition might be justified, and thus the amount of glacial erosion needed to develop existing forms would be small. But it must not be forgotten that the fiords, although often steep-walled, are always broad, much broader than a young pre-glacial valley could have been at that stage of early youth when its side streams had not cut down to its own depth. Hence glacial erosion must, under this supposition, be appealed to for the widening of pre-glacial cañons, steep-walled and narrow, into the existing fiord troughs, steep-walled and broad. At the middle of the fiord troughs the lateral erosion thus demanded would often measure thousands of feet, and that in the most massive and resistant crystalline rocks.

A second supposition leads to no greater economy of glacial action. Let it be supposed that the revived streams of pre-glacial time had reached maturity before the advent of the glacial period. In that case the side streams must have entered the main streams at accordant grade, and hence the main valleys could not then have been cut much deeper than the side valleys are now cut; not so deep, indeed, for the side valleys have been somewhat deepened by glacial action, if one may judge by their trough-like form as well as by the evidence of intense glacial action all over the uplands, even over most of the surmounting hills and mountains. Hence, to develop the existing discordant valley system from a mature pre-glacial valley system of normal river erosion requires a great deepening of the fiords by ice action, again to' be measured in thousands of feet. Thus there seems to be no escape from the conclusion that glacial erosion has profoundly modified Norwegian topography. As far as I could judge from my brief excursion over the highlands, either one of the two suppositions above considered is permissible, provided only that strong glacial erosion comes after the river work of the current cycle.

If the Hardanger fiord may be taken as the type of its many fellows, one may say that hanging lateral valleys are the rule, not the exception, in Norway. Furthermore, the smoothed, spurless walls of the larger fiords, composed of firm, bare rock from the upland to water edge, do not resemble the ravined and buttressed sides of normal valleys. The marks of downward water erosion are replaced by what seem to be marks of nearly horizontal plucking and scouring. Blunt-headed valleys and corries (*botner*) both seem beyond production by normal weathering and washing. Yet, striking as these features are, they do not seem to me so compulsory of a belief in strong glacial erosion as the hanging valleys that have so little relation to the fiords beneath them, and the flaunting waterfalls that descend so visibly from the hanging valleys, instead of retiring, as is the habit of falls all over the unglaciated parts of the world, into ravines where they are hid to sight from most points of view.

The rocky islands that rise from the shallower parts of the fiords should not be taken as signs of feeble glacial erosion, but rather as remnants surviving from the destruction of larger masses in virtue of some slight excess of resistance. A well-known example of this kind is near Odde at the head of the large southern arm (Sörfjord) of the upper Hardanger fiord; but in the same neighborhood are several fine hanging valleys, one of which has its open floor high above the fiord level; its cascading stream, the Strandfos, descends into Sandven lake, just south of the side valley occupied by the well-known Buer glacier.

Correlation of River Valleys and Glacier Valleys. Thus far the consequences of glacial erosion have been described as if they were unlike those of river erosion, especially in respect to the production of hanging valleys. A just comparison of the two agencies will show that their resemblances are more marked than their differences, when due allowance is made for their individual peculiarities.

The likeness of glaciers and rivers has been frequently considered. The motion of water streams and ice streams is retarded by bottom and banks, and is fastest in mid-channel where farthest removed from all hindrances. The motion is faster on strong than on gentle slopes, and in large than in small streams; the line of fastest motion departs from the medial axis towards the concave bank. Forel (204) and Gannett (422) have justly compared ordinary valley glaciers, not to rivers that mouth in the sea, but to rivers that descend from mountains to wither away on piedmont deserts. The terminal moraine of the glacier corresponds to the terminal delta-like fan of withering rivers. The fluctuation of a withering river following changes of weather or season corresponds to the secular fluctuations of glaciers, as during the period of about thirty-five years in the Alps. The advance and retreat at the end of large glaciers does not occur synchronously with the advance and retreat of small glaciers, although both large and small glaciers accomplish their periodic variations of length in the same interval; and it is probable that the same contrast obtains in withering rivers of different length, although I cannot find any direct statements to this effect. Meunier (1043) has suggested that certain peculiar successions of drift deposits in Switzerland may be the result of the enlargement of the drift-bringing glacier by the capture of the head reservoirs of another glacier, after the analogy of rivers. Gannett and Penck (see abstracts below) have gone further still and have shown that the hanging valleys, so characteristic of strongly glaciated drainage systems, have a perfect analogy in the valley systems of ordinary rivers in non-glaciated areas. This comparison is so instructive that it deserves full statement here.

The "nice adjustment of declivities" that characterizes the main and the side valleys of a river system is found only in maturely developed valleys. The adjustment or accordance between main trunk and lateral branch obtains only with respect to the surface of the streams or to the floor of their valleys. The *beds* of the trunk and the branch channels may be discordant at their junction, and this discordance will increase with the difference in volume of trunk and branch stream. Truly, the discordance of stream beds is seldom noted, because the beds are hidden by the streams; but if a river system were laid dry, we may be assured that the beds of the smaller tributaries would open in the banks of the main river a number of feet from its bottom. In the case of the Mississippi, the discordance might easily measure fifty or more feet.

All this applies equally to glacial streams. The surface of a tributary glacier is adjusted to the surface of the trunk glacier that it joins; but the depth of the beds may be very different. As long as the glaciers occupy their channels, the discordance of their beds may not be often considered, but when a climatic change causes the glaciers to melt away, their channels are called valleys, and the discordance of main and lateral glaciated valley floors is taken as an abnormal feature. In reality the discordance is perfectly normal to the peculiar system of ice drainage by which it was produced, however discordant it may be to the system of water drainage now in possession of the valleys. Let us compare the maturely developed channels of rivers and glaciers.

Channels of Mature Rivers and Glaciers. A river flows rapidly, and the cross section of its channel is but a small fraction of the cross section of its valley. The river channel is U-shaped, very broad compared to its depth, while the valley sides flare open, V-like, above the river banks. The water surface slopes steadily downstream, but the channel bed has many small inequalities in the form of bars and basins, and the water in the bottom of the basins must ascend a little to get out of them. If the river should dry away, the deeper parts of the bed would be occupied by pools of standing water, while the bars would show lines suggestive of flowing water. The banks of the river channel are smoothly worn in nearly horizontal lines, parallel to the flow of the river current, while the sloping sides of a river valley are buttressed with spurs and scored by the downhill ravines of descending streams. At the junction of trunk and branch streams a moderate discordance in the level of the channel beds is to be expected, but this is seldom considered because the channels are usually occupied by water and the beds are hidden.

A glacier moves slowly, and the cross section of its channel may be a considerable part of the cross section of the valley that it drains. Forel estimates that the glacier of the Rhone, even where descending its steep cascade, has only $1 : 12,000,000$ of the velocity of a large river on a similar slope (203). The glacial channel is U-shaped, broad and deep, while the valley flares open, V-like, above the ice surface. The ice surface slopes steadily downstream, but the bed of its channel is unevenly scoured, here rising in knobs, there sinking in hollows or basins from which the bottom ice must ascend a little as it moves forward. When the ice melts away, lakes occupy the rock basins; the rocky knobs are seen to be rounded and plucked in a manner suggestive of heavily moving ice. The banks of the channel are scoured and fluted parallel to the ice motion, but above the ice-worn channel the flaring valley sides are ravined by descending water streams. At the junction of trunk and branch glaciers a strong discordance in the level of the channel beds may be expected; and the discordance becomes conspicuous when the glaciers melt away and leave their "channels" to be called "valleys." Hanging side valleys are therefore appropriate as well as characteristic features of glaciated main valleys. They must come to be considered even more significant of glacial erosion than lake basins.

The Cycle of Glacial Denudation. The points of resemblance between rivers and glaciers, streams of water and streams of ice, are so numerous that they may be reasonably extended all through a cycle of denudation. Let us then inquire if glaciers may not, during their ideal life history, develop as orderly a succession of features as that which so well characterizes the normal development of rivers. The "life history of a glacier" need not be taken only in the sense so well illustrated in the last chapter of Russell's "Glaciers of North America," where the glacier is called young when it is small at the beginning of a glacial climatic epoch, mature when it is largest during the full establishment of the glacial climate, and old when it is vanishing under the reëstablishment of a milder climate. Let us here consider the life history of a glacier under a constant glacial climate, from the beginning to the end of a cycle of denudation, just as Russell has considered the "life history of a river" under a constant pluvial climate, in his "Rivers of North America." Thus young glaciers will be those which have been just established in courses that are consequent upon the slopes of a newly uplifted land surface; mature glaciers will be those which have eroded their valleys to grade and thus dissected the uplifted surface; and old glaciers will be those which cloak the whole lowland to which the upland has been reduced, or which are slowly fading in the milder climate of the low levels appropriate to the close of the cycle of denudation.

Imagine an initial land surface raised to a height of several thousand feet, with a moderate variety of relief due to deformation. Let the snow line stand at a height of two hundred feet. As elevation progresses, snow accumulates on all the upland and highland surfaces. Glaciers are developed in every basin and trough; they creep slowly forward to lower ground, where they enter a milder climate (or the sea) and gradually melt away. At some point between its upper heads and its lower end, each glacier will have a maximum volume. Downstream from this point the glacier will diminish in size, partly by evaporation but more by melting, and the ice water thus provided will flow away from the end of the glacier in the form of an ordinary stream, carving its valley in normal fashion. Some erosion may be accomplished under the upper fields of snow and névé, but it is believed that more destructive work is done beneath the ice. The erosion is accomplished by weathering, scouring, plucking, and corrading. Weathering occurs where variations of external temperature penetrate to the bed rock, as is particularly the case between the séracs of glacial cascades, and again along the line of deep crevasses, or *bergschrunds*, that are usually formed around the base of reservoir walls, which are thus transformed into corries (*cirques, karen, botner*), as has been suggested by several observers; scouring is the work of rock waste dragged along beneath the glacier, by which the bed rock is ground down, striated, and smoothed; plucking results from friction under long-lasting heavy pressure, by which blocks of

rock are removed bodily from the glacier bed and banks; corrading is the work of sub-glacial streams, which must be well
charged with tools, large and small, and which must often flow
under heavy pressure and with great energy. All these processes are here taken together as "glacial erosion.'

Let it be assumed that at first the slope of a glacier's path
was steep enough to cause it to erode for the greater part or for
the whole of its length. It is to be understood that a valley includes the channel that is eroded along its floor. The channel,
with its beds and banks, is therefore that part of a valley which
is occupied by the stream. Each young glacier will then proceed to cut down its consequent valley at a rate dependent on
various factors, such as depth and velocity of ice stream, character of rock bed, quantity of ice-dragged waste, and so on; and
the eroded channel in the bottom of the valley will in time be
given a depth and width that will better suit the needs of ice
discharge than did the initial basin or trough of the uplifted surface. The upper slopes of the glacial stream will thus be steepened, while its lower course will be given a gentler descent.
Owing to the diminution of the glacier toward its lower end,
the channel occupied by it will diminish in depth and breadth
downwards from the point of maximum volume, this being
analogous to the decrease in the size of the channel of a withering river below the point of its maximum volume. A time will
come when all the energy of the glacier on its gentler slope will
be fully taxed in moving forward the waste that has been
brought down from the steeper slopes; then the glacier becomes only a transporting agent, not an eroding agent, in its
lower course. This condition will be first reached near the lower
end, and slowly propagated headwards. Every part of the glacier
in which the balance between ability to do work and work to be
done is thus struck may be said to be "graded"; and in all such
parts the surface of the glacier will have a smoothly descending
slope. Maturity will be reached when, as in the analogous case
of a river, the nice adjustment between ability and work is
extended to all parts of a glacial system. In the process of
developing this adjustment a large trunk glacier might entrench the main valley more rapidly than one of the smaller

branches could entrench its side valley; then for a time the branch would join the trunk in an ice rapid of many séracs. But when the trunk glacier had deepened its valley so far that further deepening became slow, the branch glacier would have opportunity to erode its side valley to an appropriate depth, and thus to develop an accordant junction of trunk and branch ice *surfaces*, although the *channels* of the larger and the smaller streams might still be of very unequal depth, and the channel *beds* might stand at discordant levels. If the glaciers should disappear at this stage of the cycle, their channels would be called valleys, and the discordance of the channel beds might naturally excite surprise. The few observers who, previous to 1898, commented upon a discordance of this kind explained it as a result of excessive erosion of the main valley by the trunk glacier, while the hanging lateral valleys were implicitly, if not explicitly, regarded as hardly changed from their pre-glacial form.

When the trunk and branch glaciers have developed well-defined, maturely graded valleys, the continuous snow mantle that covered the initial uplands of early youth is exchanged for a discontinuous cover, rent on the steep valley sides where weathering comes to have a greatly increased value, and thickened where the ice streams have established their courses. This change corresponds to that between the ill-defined initial drainage in the early youth and the well-defined drainage in the maturity, of the river cycle.

It is probable that variations in rock structure will have permitted a more rapid development of the graded condition in one part of the glacial valley than in another, as is the case with rivers of water. Steady-flowing reaches and broken rapids will thus be produced in the ice stream during its youth; and the glacial channel may then be described as "broken-bedded." But all the rapids must be worn down and all the reaches must become confluent in maturity. It is eminently possible that the reaches on the weaker or more jointed rocks may be eroded during youth to a somewhat greater depth than the sill of more resistant or less jointed rock next downstream; and if the glacier should vanish by climatic change while in this condition, a lake would occupy the deepened reach, while the lake outlet would flow forward over rocky ledges to the next lower reach or lake. Many Norwegian valleys to-day seem to be in this condition. Indeed, some observers have described broken-bedded valleys as the normal product of glacial erosion, without reference to the early stage in the glacial cycle of which broken-bedded glacial channels seem to be characteristic. Truly, it is not always explicitly stated that the resistance of the rock bed varies appropriately to the change of form in a broken-bedded channel, but the variations of structural resistance or firmness that the searching pressure and friction of a heavy glacier could detect might be hardly recognizable to our superficial observations; and, on the other hand, the analogy of young ungraded glaciers with young ungraded rivers seems so natural and reasonable that broken-bedded glacial channels ought to be regarded only as features of young glacial action, not as persistent features always to be associated with glacial erosion. If the glaciers had endured longer in channels of this kind, the "rapids" and other inequalities by which the bed may be interrupted must have been worn back and lowered, and in time destroyed.

If a young glacier erodes its valley across rocks of distinctly different resistances, a strong inequality of channel bed may be developed. Basins of a considerable depth may be excavated in the weaker strata, while the harder rocks are less eroded and cross the valleys in rugged sills. Forms of this kind are known in Alpine valleys; for example, in the valley of the Aar above Meiringen (Wallace, b, 176) and in the lower Gasternthal near its junction with the Kanderthal; in both these cases the basins have been aggraded and the sills have been trenched by the post-glacial streams. In the lower Gasternthal the height and steepness of the rocky sill, when approached from upstream, is astonishing; its contrast to the basin that it incloses is difficult enough to explain even for those who are willing to accept strong glacial erosion. It should, however, be noted that river channels also are deeper in the weaker rocks upstream from a hard rock sill; if the river volume should greatly decrease, a small lake would remain above the sill, drained by a slender stream cutting a gorge through the sill.

If an initial depression occurred on the path of the glacier, so deep that the motion of the ice through it was much retarded, an ice lake would gather in it. Then the waste dragged into the basin from upstream might accumulate upon its floor until the depth of the basin was sufficiently decreased and the velocity of the ice through it sufficiently increased to bring about a balance between ability to do work and work to be done. Here the maturely graded condition of the ice stream would have been attained by aggrading its bed instead of degrading it; this being again closely analogous to the case of a river which aggrades initial depressions and degrades initial elevations in producing its maturely graded course.

Water streams subdivide toward the headwaters into a great number of very fine rills, each of which may retrogressively cut its own ravine in a steep surface, not cloaked by waste. But the branches of a glacial drainage system are much more clumsy, and the channels that they cut back into the upland or mountain mass are round-headed or amphitheater-like; but the beds of the branching glaciers cannot be cut as deep as the bed of the large glacial channel into which they flow; thus corries, perched on the side walls of large valleys, may be produced in increasing number and strength as glacial maturity approaches, and in decreasing strength and number as maturity passes into old age. As maturity approaches, the glacial system will include not only those branches that are consequent upon the initial form, but certain others which have come into existence by the headward erosion of their névé reservoirs following the guidance of weak structures; thus a maturely developed glacial drainage system may have its subsequent as well as its consequent branches. It is entirely conceivable, as has been suggested by Meunier, that one ice stream may capture the upper part of another. The conditions most favorable for such a process resemble those under which river diversions and adjustments take place, namely, a considerable initial altitude of the region, allowing a deep dissection; a significant difference of drainage areas or of slopes, whereby certain glaciers incise deeper valleys than others; a considerable diversity of mountain structure, permitting such growth and arrangement of subsequent glaciers as shall bring the head reservoir of a subsequent ice stream alongside of and somewhat beneath the banks of a consequent ice stream. Thus glacial systems may come to adjust their streams to the structures upon which they work, just as happens in river systems.

The load transported by a glacial system may at first be supplied largely by waste plucked and scoured from the beds of the glacial channels as well as by waste detached from the inclosing slopes; but in time, when the graded condition of the chief channels is reached and their further deepening almost ceases, by far the largest share of load will be supplied from the subaërial valley sides, where weathering of the ordinary kind will ravine the slopes, thus producing a topography that is strongly contrasted with the smooth walls of the glacial channels. If the initial glacial system should incise its channels so deeply beneath a lofty highland that the supply of waste from the valley sides continued to increase after the development of graded glacial channels, it is conceivable that the channel beds might have to be aggraded for a time, as is believed to be the case with river channels under similar conditions; but owing to the receipt on the glacial surface of waste from the valley sides, it is also conceivable that this analogy may not closely obtain. Toward the end of the ice stream it may well happen that the diminution of its volume and the consequent diminution of its capacity to do work will result in the aggradation of its bed by waste that cannot be carried farther forward. At the same time, the outflowing river may be unable to wash away all the waste that is delivered to it, and so, for a time through later youth and early maturity, the river may act as an aggrading agent and build up a broad, flat alluvial fan, such as fronts the terminal moraines of the Alpine glaciers that once descended to the plain of Lombardy. Some response to the change thus produced in the altitude of the end of the glacier may be expected far up its channel, whose bed would thus come to be aggraded with till. Similarly, the ice sheets that spread from the Scandinavian and Laurentian highlands over the lowlands on the south changed their behavior from degrading agents in the central area to aggrading agents on the peripheral area. Hence, a belief in effective erosion is not antagonistic to a belief in effective deposition in the case of glaciers any more than in the case of rivers. In each case the action varies appropriately to its place in the drainage system and to its stage in the cycle. But there will be a later stage, when the wasting of the superglacial slopes reduces them to moderate declivity, so that the waste delivered from them decreases in quantity; then the outflowing water stream at the end of the glacier may become a degrading agent; the altitude of the end of the glacier may be slowly lessened; and a very slow and long-continued deepening of the whole glacial channel will take place, without requiring a departure from an essentially graded condition.

As the general denudation of the region progresses, the snow fall must be decreased and the glacial system must shrink somewhat, leaving a greater area of lowland surface to ordinary river drainage. When the upland surface is so far destroyed that even the hill-tops stand below the 200-foot contour, the snow fields will be represented only by the winter snow sheet, and the glaciers will have disappeared, leaving normal agencies to complete the work of denudation that they have so well begun.

If a snow line at sea-level be assumed, glaciation would persist even after the land had been worn to a submarine plain of denudation at an undetermined depth beneath sea-level. The South Polar regions offer a suitable field for the occurrence of such a surface.

Whether glaciers of the Norwegian or of the Alpine type shall occur is dependent partly on initial conditions, partly on the stage of advance through the cycle of denudation. If the initial form offer broad uplands, separated by deep valleys, snow fields of the Norwegian type may have possession of the uplands during the youth of the glacial cycle; but when maturity is reached, the uplands will be dissected, and the original confluent snow field will be resolved into a number of head reservoirs, separated by ridges. On the other hand, as the later stages of the cycle are approached, the barriers between adjacent reservoirs will be worn away, and they will tend to become confluent, here and there broken only by Nunatuker. If the snow line lay low enough, a completely confluent ice and snow shield would cover the lowland of glacial denudation when old age had been reached.

If the glacial conditions of Greenland preceded as long as they have followed the glacial period over the rest of the North Atlantic region, who can say how far the ice of the Greenland shield has modified the forms on which its work began!

Glacial Distributaries. If a maturely dissected mountain range were occupied by snow fields and glaciers of large size, certain peculiar results might be expected near the mountain base. Under normal pre-glacial conditions a small, low ridge suffices for the complete separation of two river systems, because the channels of rivers are so small in comparison to their valleys. But glacial channels are a large part of their valleys, and when great glaciers from the lofty mountain centers descend by the master valleys to the mountain flanks or even to the piedmont plains, distributary ice streams or outflowing branches may naturally enough be given off wherever the ice surface rises high enough to overtop the ridges by which the master valleys are separated from adjacent minor valleys. If a distributary branch has sufficient strength and endurance, it may wear down the ridge that it crosses and thus increase and perpetuate its lateral discharge; but it cannot usually be expected to erode a channel as deep as that of the main glacier from which it departs. On the disappearance of the ice, a hanging valley will be left above the floor of the master valley; but in this case the drainage of the hanging valley will be away from, not toward, the master. Here we probably have the explanation of those broad hanging valleys which lead from the valley of lake Maggiore on the west and, less distinctly, from that of lake Como on the east to the compound basin of the intermediate lake Lugano. On going southward by rail from Bellinzona to Lugano, along a stretch of the St. Gotthard route between the great tunnel and Milan, the railway obliquely ascends Monte Ceneri, the southeastern wall of the trough-like valley of the Ticino just above the head of lake Maggiore; and at a height of several hundred feet over the delta flood plain the line turns off southward into the bleak dale of the Leguana, a well-marked hanging valley in which the stream runs away from the Ticino to lake Lugano. The notch made by this supposed glacial distributary is a conspicuous feature in the view from Bellinzona and thereabouts.

The anomalous forking of lake Como and the open branch from the main valley of the Rhine at Sargans through the trough of Wallen See to lake Zurich appear to be the paths of large glacial distributaries which eroded their channels deeply across divides that presumably existed in pre-glacial time. The west wall of the main valley of the Isère in the Alps of Dauphiny, southeastern France, is deeply breached by passes that lead northwest to the troughs of lakes Annecy and Bourget, through which the distributaries of the Isère glacial system must have flowed. Lugéon (62–70) has explained the breaches as marking the former northwest paths of transverse members of the Isère system, from which they have been diverted by the subsequent growth of the main longitudinal valley — that northeast-southwest part known as the Grésivaudan — above Grenoble. His discussion of the problem takes, however, no account of the modification of valley depth by glacial erosion ; and as this modification must have been considerable (for the valleys hereabouts have superb basal cliffs, as appears in the valley of the Romanche by Bourg d'Oisans), it may well be that the rearrangement of river courses in this interesting region is not altogether the work of river action. Similarly, the various modifications of the Rhine drainage system in eastern Switzerland, explained by Heim as the work of streams alone, may come to be, at least in part, referred to ice erosion.

It may be further supposed that if the pre-glacial valleys were so arranged that a glacial distributary found a shorter and steeper course to the piedmont plain or to the sea than that followed by the master glacier, the distributary might under a long-enduring glaciation become the main line of glacial discharge ; and if so, it could be eroded to a greater depth than the former master valley at the point of divergence. In such a case the post-glacial river drainage would differ significantly from the pre-glacial. There is reason for believing that examples of this kind are to be found in Norway, the evidence of which will soon be published in an essay by Barrett. The diversion of the head of a stream in the Sierra Costa of northwestern California to a deeper-lying valley through a gorge cut by a glacial distributary has lately been described by Hershey (47).

The Depth of Mature Glacial Channels. The depth with respect to sea-level to which the channels of a glacial system may be eroded when the graded condition is reached is a subject of special interest. For many miles along the lower course of a branchless trunk glacier its volume is lessened by melting and evaporation, and at its end the ice volume is reduced to zero; slow ice motion being progressively replaced by rapid water motion. In such a case the law of continuity does not demand that the ice velocity shall be inversely proportional to the area of the cross section, as is the case in the normal river (where it is assumed that there is no loss by evaporation). Indeed, in the lower trunk of a mature glacier it may well be that the velocity of ice movement is in a rough way directly proportional to cross-section area. This appears to be verified by measurements of the Rhone glacier, where the mean annual movement is 110 meters in the heavy trunk above the cascade, 27 meters just below the cascade, and only 5 meters close to the melting front (Forel, 203). Evidently, then, the erosion of the glacial bed, in so far as it is determined by the pressure and motion of the ice stream, will have its maximum some distance upstream from the end of the glacier (J. Geikie, *b*, 236). The glacial channel must therefore become narrower and shallower as its end is neared, as has already been stated. If the glacier ends some distance inland from the sea, its action will be conditioned by the grade and length of the river that carries away the water and waste from its lower end. The deepening of the distal part of the channel accomplished in youth might be followed by a shallowing for a time during maturity, when the accumulation of morainal and washed materials in front of the glacier compelled its end to rise. Now it may well be conceived that the surface slope of such a glacier near its end is less than the angle between the surface and the bottom of the glacier; and in this case the glacial floor must become lower and lower for a certain distance upstream. If such a glacier should melt away, the distal part of its channel would be occupied by a lake, although even the head of the lake may not reach to the locus of maximum glacial erosion. Lakes Maggiore, Como, and Garda seem to occupy basins whose distal inclosure by heavy moraines and sheets of overwashed gravels has added to the depth produced by erosion farther upstream. It would seem, however, that a lake basin thus situated must be only a subordinate incident in the general erosion of the whole length of the glacial ·channel. Too much attention has, as a rule, been given to lakes of this kind, and not enough to the other effects of glacial action; it seems especially out of proportion to suppose that the maximum erosion by a glacier takes place near its end, as has been done by some authors, on account of the prevalent occurrence of lakes in this situation.

If a glacier advances into the sea and ends in an ice cliff, from which ice blocks break off and float away, something of a basin-like form of its lower channel may be produced; but the dimensions of this basin will be determined by the climate at the termination of the glacier. If the climate is such as to allow the glacier to enter the sea in maximum volume, then a basin is not to be expected. The more the glacier diminishes towards its end, the less erosion and the more deposition may occur beneath it, and the more of a basin may be developed inland from its end.

The depth to which a glacier may cut its channel when it enters the sea is of particular importance. If the glacier is 1000 feet thick at its end, it must continue to press upon and scour its bed until only about 140 feet of ice remain above sea-level; its channel will thus be worn more than 800 feet beneath sea-level. Truly, the latter part of this work will be performed with increasing slowness; but if time enough be allowed, the work must be accomplished, just as is the case with rivers. If a glacier should melt away from its deep intrenchment, its channel would be occupied by an arm of the sea, or fiord, reaching many miles into the land. The fiord might be shallower at its mouth than farther inland, if differential erosion and deposition had occurred along its channel. Yet even this result is analogous to the case of a river; for if the Mississippi were to disappear in a prolonged drought, a slender arm of the sea would invade the river channel many miles upstream from the delta front. Indeed, the Mississippi offers an excellent example of a channel that is basined inward from the river mouth; for while it is only a score of feet deep at the passes where most of its sediment is deposited, it is several score of feet in depth farther upstream ; and the slender arm of the sea that would occupy its channel if it should disappear by climatic change would be truly fiord-like in having a less depth at its mouth than farther inland.

An important corollary from this conclusion — perhaps not so much of a novelty to glacial erosionists as to their confrères of the opposite opinion — is that the depth of water in the fiords of a strongly glaciated coast is not a safe guide to the movement of the land since pre-glacial time. If there had been a stillstand of the earth's crust through the whole glacial period, the pre-glacial river channels that were graded down a little below sea-level at their mouths would be replaced by glacial channels that might be eroded hundreds of feet below sea-level. The depth of fiords thus seems to depend on the size of their ancient glaciers, on the height of the mountain background, and on the duration of the glacial period, as well as on movements of the land. If liberal measures of glacial erosion and glacial time are allowed, no depression of glaciated coasts since pre-glacial time is needed to account for their peculiar features. The glacial channels may have been simply invaded by the sea, as the ice melted away, without any true submergence.

Even the advocates of strong glacial erosion do not seem to have explicitly recognized the full importance of this possibility. James Geikie, for example, writes : "The fiords of high latitudes and the narrow inlets of non-glaciated lands are simply submerged land-valleys ; the intricate coast-lines of such regions have been determined by preceding sub-aerial denudation." Again : "In a word, fiords are merely the drowned valleys of severely glaciated mountain-tracts" (b, 263, 250). The deep waters in the valley of the Hudson through the Highlands of southeastern New York are the most fiord-like in the eastern United States, and they are universally explained as the result of submergence of a normal river valley; but the constricted ice current that must have flowed through the Highland gorge may have been energetic enough to deepen its bed beneath sea-level, and since the ice melted away, who can say how much submergence beneath pre-glacial levels has taken place ! I do not know how far this view of the matter has been taken by earlier advocates of strong glacial erosion, but, for my own part, the acceptance of such a possibility means a complete reversal of the belief that I held two years ago. The reversal is, however, accompanied by the memory that it was always difficult to understand why submergence and glaciation were so closely associated; even if glaciation had caused depression, it was difficult to understand why the relief from ice pressure in post-glacial time had not now been followed by a rise of the land much nearer to its former altitude than would be the case if the greater part of the depth of fiords is explained by submergence.

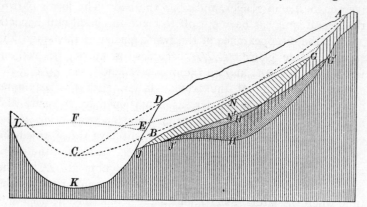

FIG. 106. DIAGRAM SECTION OF A LATERAL VALLEY WITH A
CORRIE BASIN

The Origin of Corrie Basins. On pursuing the above line of consideration a little further, it may give some light on the occurrence of the small rock basins that are so often found in the floor of cliff-walled corries. Imagine that a large glacial system has become maturely established, and that it "rises" in many blunt head-branches that have excavated corries in a pre-glacial mountain mass, and have cut down channels, at their junction with the larger branches or trunk glacier, to a depth appropriate to their volume. Unless the erosion of the corries has been guided by differences of rock structure, there does not seem to be reason for their possessing a basined floor at this stage of development; but if a change of climate should now cause the trunk glacier to disappear, while many of the blunt head-branches remain in their corries, each little glacier thus isolated will repeat the conditions of erosion above inferred for the trunk glacier; and if this style of glaciation linger long enough, rock basins may very generally characterize the floors of the corries when the ice finally melts away. Fig. 106 may make this clearer. Let the broken line ABC be the slope of a pre-glacial lateral ravine which reaches a trunk stream at C, while ADC is the profile of an adjoining lateral spur. After vigorous and mature glaciation the dotted line GE may represent the surface slope of a lateral glacier, and GHJ that of the lateral glacier bed; while EFL is the surface of the trunk glacier, and EKL the bed. The lower part of the lateral spur has been cut off to make the basal cliff beneath D. On the disappearance of the trunk glacier at this stage, the shrunken side glacier $GNJH$ occupies its corrie, or hanging valley, which opens at J on the over-steepened wall DJK of the evacuated channel of the trunk glacier. Let the maximum erosion of the corric glacier, as conditioned by pressure and motion, be at H. Then after some time the weathering of the cliff walls and the erosion of the floor will have transformed the corrie and its glacier to a form $G'N'J'H'$, such that the deepening of the glacial bed should be a maximum at HH'. The continuous slope of the glacial bed GHJ, appropriate to the time when the lateral glacier joined the trunk glacier, may thus be transformed into a basined curve, $G'H'J'$, appropriate to a small glacier terminating at J'; and on the disappearance of the small glacier, a tarn or rock-basin lake may occupy the depression at H'. It is on the basis of a supposition like this that a determination has been attempted of the altitude at which the shrinking remnants of an extensive glacial system endured for a time before their entire disappearance (J. Geikie, b, 233). Richter's supposition that the uplands of Norway result from the consumption of preëxistent mountains by the great extension of corrie-glacier floors, each similar to $J'H'$, thus seems mechanically possible; but it is nevertheless climatically very improbable, and it seems to me deficient in not attributing a greater amount of work to normal stream erosion in preglacial time.

Over-deepened Valleys and Over-steepened Walls. As in the case of the normal cycle of denudation in which the life history of river systems is involved, so in the glacial cycle, all manner of complications may arise, causing great departures from the ideal case. The assumed initial land form may be a surface previously more or less dissected by river erosion, on which glaciers must then proceed to develop a drainage system appropriate to their own peculiar needs, as has been partly considered above in connection with glacial distributaries. It will be instructive to make out a good series of examples illustrating different combinations of river and glacial action, and including young, mature, and old river valleys, modified by young or mature glaciation. For example, the existing valley of the Rhue in the Central Plateau of France shows a sub-mature river valley with incised meanders, moderately affected by young and relatively light glaciation; the valley of the Ticino in the southern Alps is a well-matured pre-glacial river-valley system, modified by strong sub-mature glaciation. The fiords of Norway result from the sub-mature and intense glaciation of a river-valley system whose stage of pre-glacial development is not yet well determined.

Interruptions of regular progress in the glacial cycle must, as in the river cycle, be occasioned by elevation, depression, or deformation of the land mass; but no examples of complications of this kind can be adduced. Variations of climate may replace creeping glaciers in young, mature, or old stages of development by flowing rivers; and the early stages of such rivers are of much importance among existing geographical forms. Lakes, delaying the river flow, occupy the depressions of the glaciated surface, as has been known since Ramsay first pointed out the correlation of lacustrine and glaciated regions in 1861; but the analogy between lakes in the beds of melted glaciers and pools in the beds of dried-up rivers has perhaps not been sufficiently insisted upon. Waterfalls connect the streams that occupy the discordant beds of glacial channels, as has lately been clearly set forth. Landslides frequently occur after the supporting glacier withdraws from the over-steepened banks of its huge channel; fallen masses of this origin have been repeatedly mistaken for moraines in Alpine valleys, as has been lately shown by Brückner. Every lake or fiord is an effective lowering of base-level for the stream above it; for the level of a body of standing water is essentially the same at both ends. As fast as the inflowing river builds its delta forward at the head of the lake or fiord, its flood plain must rise upstream and aggrade the valley floor. This process is very pronounced in many Alpine valleys, where the aggraded valley floor has a relatively rapid descent on account of the plentiful and coarse detritus furnished by the active side streams. Indeed, every ravine furnishes a great quantity of rock waste, whose descent is analogous to repeated landslides of small dimensions. The valley floor beneath the ravines is invaded by great alluvial fans, and the main stream is driven away toward the farther valley wall by their rapid advance. At every flood the waste supplied from the fans is swept abundantly into the main stream, whose flood plain grows rapidly as a delta in the upper end of each lake that it enters. The delta of the Ticino seems to have advanced so far into what was originally the basin of lake Maggiore that the apparent height of the hanging lateral valleys steadily decreases toward the lake; and for several miles above the head of the lake the lateral valleys seem to enter the main valley almost at grade, although there can be little doubt that if all the delta alluvium were removed, the lateral valleys would be found to stand high above the rock floor of the main valley. The standing lakes, the aggrading flood plains, and the growing fans all show that the bed of the glacial channel has been worn too deep to serve as a valley floor for the existing river; the river must aggrade, with water or with waste, the bed of the channel that the glacier degraded; hence Penck has suggested that glaciated valleys of the Alpine kind should be called "over-deepened." In the same way, the waterfalls from the hanging valleys, the showering waste that forms the fans, and the landslides from the basal cliffs, all show that the banks of the glacial channel — the lower walls of the existing valleys — are too steep; and they may be therefore called "over-steepened." Much glacial work had to be done upon the mature pre-glacial valleys of river erosion to bring them into mature adjustment with the needs of glaciers; much river work must likewise now be done upon the over-deepened glaciated valleys, and upon their over-steepened walls and their hanging branches, before they can be maturely adjusted again to the needs of rivers.

Practical Utility of the Ideal Glacial Cycle. In every case the full understanding of the conditions developed by any system of glaciers, existing or extinct, can be reached only by a complete analysis of the conditions under which they began to work, of the energy with which they worked, of the part of a cycle during which they worked, and of the complications of climatic change or of crustal movements by which their work was modified in this way or in that. A partial analysis may suffice for a particular instance ; but the explorer will be better equipped for the explanation of all the instances that he discovers if he sets out with a well-elaborated conception of the ideal glacial cycle of denudation, and of the complications it is likely to suffer. However extensive and definite this conception may be, exploration will probably require its further extension and definition ; however brief exploration may be, it will probably be aided by an orderly examination of all pertinent knowledge previously accumulated.

As a practical instance of the value of the glacial cycle, we may consider the aid given toward the solution of certain problems by the careful reconstruction — or at least the conscious attempt at reconstruction — of the form of the land surface on which the Pleistocene glaciers began their work, and by the legitimate deduction of the characteristics of maturity in the cycle of glacial erosion. Beyond the mature stage we may seldom have occasion to go, as there do not seem to be actual examples of more advanced glacial work. The initial form on which Pleistocene glacial action began is in no case known to be that implied in the opening paragraphs of the section on the Glacial Cycle ; namely, a land mass freshly uplifted from beneath the sea and not previously carved by the streams of an ordinary or normal cycle of erosion. In central France, for example, the initial form was an uplifted and sub-maturely dissected peneplain, in which valleys with incised meanders had been habitually developed. It was there of the greatest assistance to carry into the glaciated area a clear picture of its pre-glacial form, as determined by generalizing the adjacent non-glaciated area. At the same time, the ideal picture of a maturely developed glacial drainage system, with smooth-sided troughs, was seen to represent a much more advanced condition than was attained in the rugged valley of the Rhue; and thus a tolerably definite idea was gained of the youthful stage of glacial development, somewhere between its beginning and its maturity, and of the amount of destructive work needed to reach this youthful stage. This elementary example illustrates a method embodying the cycle of glacial denudation that ought to be applied whenever possible.

The larger Norwegian fiords may be instanced as glacial channels that present every appearance of having advanced far toward the mature stage of a cycle of glacial denudation from an initial or pre-glacial form not yet well understood. The variation of form between the main fiords and their branches gives some indication that the glacial work was accomplished in several successive epochs, with the interglacial epochs of normal river work between; but this is only a suggestion, needing much more field work before it can be assured. Not only the deep fiords, but the hanging valleys and the uplands, also, have been ice-scoured; for hanging valleys frequently have a well-defined U-section, and sometimes receive secondary hanging valleys from the inclosing uplands; and the streams of the uplands exhibit repeated departures from the forms of normal erosion. Although possessing little drift, the uplands frequently bear lakes of moderate depth and irregular outline; in spite of the breadth to which the upland valleys are opened between the surmounting hills and mountains, their streams frequently change from wandering at leisure in split or braided channels along broad floors, to dashing down in haste over rocky rapids: a behavior that is manifestly inconsistent with that of the mature drainage of a normally denuded region. Even the surmounting hills exhibit strong scouring on their up-ice-stream side. It does not therefore seem permissible to conclude that the hanging valleys which open on the walls of the greater fiords have not been deepened by ice erosion because they escaped the more severe glaciation that scoured out the fiords themselves. All the valleys have been glaciated, and all have been significantly modified from their pre-glacial form. The discordance of over-deepened main fiord and hanging lateral valley seems to me best explained as the result of the mature development of glacial drainage, in which the chief trunks and the larger branches of the glacial systems had for the most part reached a graded condition. Trunk and branch glaciers would then have united at even grade as to their upper surface, and the trunk and branch channels would have had dimensions satisfactory to the ice currents which flowed through them, but the channel beds would have been discordant, as they are found to be.

REVIEW OF PREVIOUS WRITINGS ON HANGING VALLEYS

It has already been stated that hanging side valleys and over-deepened main valleys have not yet been generally given the importance that they deserve as witnesses to strong glacial erosion. Russell, in his " Glaciers of North America " (1897), makes no mention of discordant lateral and main valleys when discussing glacial erosion. James Geikie, in his " Earth Sculpture " (1898), allows to discordance of glaciated valleys hardly more than a secondary importance in abstracts and quotations from Wallace's accounts of Alpine lakes and from Richter's essay on Norway (see below), while the glacial erosion of lake basins is much more fully treated. Yet of all the facts that point to strong glacial erosion, none seem to give testimony so unanswerable as do hanging valleys. The following extracts will serve to illustrate the gradually increasing recognition of their importance.

Forbes on the Waterfalls of Norway. Thinking that some interesting early observations on the hanging valleys of Norway might be recorded in Forbes' book of travels in that country, I looked up waterfalls in his index and there found a reference to the cause of their profusion, which was stated as follows :

The source of this astonishing profusion of waters is to be found in the peculiar disposition of the surface of the country so often referred to. The mountains are wide and flat, the valleys are deep and far apart. . . . As the valleys ramify little . . . and are wholly disconnected from the *fjelds* [up-lands] by precipitous slopes, it follows that the single rivers which water those valleys . . . are supplied principally by streamlets which, having run long courses over the *fjelds*, are at last precipitated into the ravines in the form of cascades (251).

Forbes was an excellent observer, yet this quotation is about equivalent to saying that there are many waterfalls in Norway because there are steep slopes over which the streams of the uplands must descend. The quotation deserves a place here if for nothing more than to show the advance of a half century in regard to what constitutes the cause of a geographical feature.

McGee on Glacial Cañons, 1883. The earliest article that I have found touching on this subject is the brief abstract of a paper read by McGee before the American Association in 1883, entitled "Glacial Cañons." Observations in the Sierra Nevada led this keen observer to state that

the effect of the *temporary* occupancy of a typical water-cut cañon by glacier ice will be to (1) increase its width, (2) change the original V to a U cross profile, (3) cut off the terminal portions of tributary cañons and thus relatively elevate their embouchures, (4) intensify certain irregularities of gradient in the cañon bottom, (5) excavate rock basins, (6) develop cirques, and, in general, transform such cañon into an equally typical glacial cañon (*a*, 238).

A later paper by the same author is referred to below.

Hanging Valleys in the Alps. Valleys that are here called "hanging" have frequently been described by observers in the Alps, but either without particular reference to their discordant relation to the main valleys, or with acceptance of normal erosion in the main valley as the cause of their discordance. Rütimeyer's and Heim's views on discordant lateral valleys have been already referred to.

An account of the Salzachthal in the Tyrol, by Brückner, describes it as one valley in the bottom of another; the deeper one being relatively narrow and steep-sided, while the sides of the higher valley flare wide open; the side streams are described as falling into the deeper main valley; but this significant feature is not mentioned as if it were of general occurrence, nor is it explained by glacial erosion (95).

Lubbock, in his "Scenery of Switzerland," follows Rütimeyer and Heim. After stating that the side valleys of the Reuss have a moderate grade which brings them out at the level of one of the terraces, or *Thalstufen*, of the main valley, from which their streams cascade down into the main stream, Lubbock writes :

It is obvious that this terrace represents a former *Thalweg* of the Reuss with much less fall than it has now, and that the river has deepened its valley more rapidly than the lateral streams, so that these glens open at some distance up the side of the valley, and their waters join the Reuss by rapids or waterfalls. . . . The valley shows clear evidence of glacial action. The hard rocks are in places quite polished. This is especially the case with the buttresses which stand like doorposts where the lateral glens open into the main valley, and particularly on the right side of the eastern glens, the left of the western, where of course the pressure of the ice was greatest (332, 334).

Russell on Hanging Valleys, 1887. Russell gave a detailed account of what may be called hanging valleys in his report on the "Quaternary History of Mono Valley, California." In a section on " high lateral cañons," he says :

In a number of instances in the Mono basin the low-grade glaciated cañons receive branching cañons at a considerable elevation above their bottoms, the branches also having a low grade. This is illustrated where lake Cañon opens into Lundy Cañon. Each of these gorges has an approximately horizontal bottom near the place of union, but the former is a thousand feet higher than the latter. The stream flowing through lake Cañon descends precipitously over a rocky face in order to join Lundy Creek. The bottom of the higher cañon is about on a level with the main lateral moraine in the lower cañon. The same series of phenomena is repeated where Silver Creek descends over a rocky face to join Rush Creek. . . . It might be assumed that the main cañons had been excavated by glacial action more deeply than the lateral branches, owing to the greater eroding power of the glaciers which occupied them. This is a simple and natural explanation of the conditions observed, and if we admit the great amount of erosion usually assumed for ancient glaciers, it must be accepted as an adequate cause for the great strength of the main channels of ice discharge. To the writer . . . it appears that the main work of sculpture in the Sierra Nevada . . . is to be attributed to water erosion, while only minor features . . . are to be referred to glacial action. With this conclusion in mind, the great inequality in the depth of the main glacial troughs and of their lateral branches is too great a work to be ascribed to the erosive power of ice (351–352).

The hanging valleys are therefore left without explicit explanation, but it appears from other pages of the report that several of the deeper cañons, such as Lundy, now head to the west of the general line of mountain crest, and it is therefore possible that they are examples of retrogressive erosion, both by water and by ice, since the elevation of the Sierra Nevada. If this be the case, the hanging valleys may be remnants of an ancient west-flowing drainage system, now diverted to a more rapid eastward descent. Some such meaning may be behind Russell's words : " Many of the valleys of the Sierra Nevada ... are in fact relics of a drainage system which antedates the existence of the Sierra as a prominent mountain range" (348, 350).

Wallace on Glaciated Valleys, 1893. One of the most appreciative statements that I have found concerning hanging valleys is an article by Wallace on "The Ice Age and its Work," which presents many arguments in favor of the strong erosive power of glaciers. Wallace says :

It is evident that ice erosion to some extent must have taken place along the whole length of the glacier's course, and that in many cases the result might be simply to deepen the valley all along, not quite equally, perhaps, but with no such extreme differences as to produce a lake basin.

Then after giving much emphasis to the excavation of lake basins near the lower end of a large glacier, where the erosive power is deductively argued to be at its maximum, Wallace examines several lakes to discover if those of glacial origin have not some distinctive feature by which they can be recognized. He points out that greater length than breadth, and simplicity of outline, are highly significant of glacial erosion, and that the absence of lateral bays and branches is strongly against the theory of warping or submergence. In this connection it is recognized that

the lake *surface*, not the lake *bottom*, represents approximately the level of the pre-glacial valley, and that the lateral streams and torrents enter the lake in the way they do because they could only erode their channels down to the level of the old valley before the ice overwhelmed it.... In connection with this subject may be noticed the many cases in which Alpine valleys present indications of having been greatly deepened by glacial erosion, although, owing either to the slope of the ground or to the uniformity of the ice-action, no lake has been produced. In some valleys, as in that of Lauterbrunnen, the trough between the vertical rock-walls was probably partly formed before the ice age, but was greatly deepened by glacial erosion, the result being that the tributary streams have not since had time to excavate ravines of equal depth with the main valley, and therefore form a series of cascades over the lateral precipices, of which the Staubbach is the finest example. In many other cases, however, the side streams have cut wonderfully narrow gorges by which they enter the main valley (*a*, 754, 768).

McGee's Second Paper on Glacial Cañons, 1894. McGee has given a fuller statement of the action of glacial erosion in producing discordance between lateral and main valleys in a second essay, again entitled "Glacial Cañons," published eleven years after his first essay on this subject. After a discussion of glacial erosion in general, it is stated that

glacial cañons are characterized by several peculiar features: (1) they are U-shaped rather than V-shaped in cross-profile; (2) small tributary gorges usually enter at levels considerably above the cañon-bottoms; (3) in longitudinal profile the cañon-bottoms are irregularly terraced, — i.e. made up of a series of rude steps of variable form and dimensions, — and some of the terraces are so deeply excavated as to form rock-basins occupied by lakelets. . . . In a region of rapid corrasion then, the main [water] stream must . . . more rapidly corrade its channel than does its minor tributary; and the tributary cañon must accordingly enter its principal over a rapid or at least a convex curve in longitudinal profile. If now the main cañon become filled with ice and be transformed from the V to the U type by its action, the distal extremity of the tributary will be cut off and the original stream-formed declivity replaced by the precipitous side-wall of the normal glacier valley (*b*, 351, 359).

It is explicitly stated by McGee that this explanation does not demand great glacial erosion, because the U-cañon of glacial origin need not be much deeper, although significantly wider, than the pre-glacial V-cañon of river origin. But the last of the above quotations postulates a special condition, — a region of rapid pre-glacial corrasion by streams, and in so far does not seem applicable to the case of the Ticino or of the many other Alpine valleys; for the well-opened slopes of the lateral valleys and the still wider flare on the upper slopes of the main valleys in the Alps prove that during their formation the main stream must have attained a graded slope which the lateral streams must have joined in accordant fashion; and there is nothing to show that the open and graded floor of the main valley was significantly trenched by river action in pre-glacial time. On the contrary, the shallowness of the trenches now found in the lateral hanging valleys proves that even if the main valley had been trenched, it could not have been cut down very deep.

Tarr on Cayuga Lake, 1894. A significant instance of discordance has been pointed out by Tarr and taken by him as direct evidence of the glacial erosion of a lake basin. He shows that the north and south trough of Cayuga lake, New York, lying in the line of ice motion, is about three hundred feet deeper than the floor of Salmon Creek, a tributary whose course is oblique to the ice motion; and he ascribes the break of grade between the two valleys to greater erosion in the deeper one. He generalizes so far as to refer to lake Ontario as probably exhibiting further instances of discordant valleys.

De Lapparent on Hanging Valleys, 1896. A clear and brief statement is made by De Lapparent in his " Leçons de Géographie Physique," as if the matter were well known and undisputed. Under the heading "Caractères des vallées glaciaires," he writes in effect as follows:

When a glacier disappears, the lateral valleys, which had been eroded before the glacial period with relation to the local base-level determined by the river that the glacier afterwards replaced, may, on the disappearance of the ice, no longer present accordant junctions with the main valley. Cascades and rapids will therefore occur at their mouths in greater number than in a district of the same strength of relief which has not been glaciated. All these features are clearly seen in Norway (*a*, 210; *b*, 219).

Richter on Norway, 1896. The essay by Richter, already referred to, contains a large number of excellent observations. Regarding our special subject, he states that many side valleys in Norway open high on the fiord walls, as if cut off in the deeper erosion of the main valleys; a similar relation being known in the Alps, but of less distinctness. The discordance of valley depth in Norway is thought to depend on the faster erosion of the main valleys by water or ice or both, when the side valleys and the uplands were occupied by slow-moving névé. The side streams descending from the floors of their hanging valleys have not yet cut even narrow clefts in the rock walls of the main valleys (177–179).

J. Geikie on Glacial Erosion, 1898. The recent volume on "Earth Sculpture" by James Geikie gives a generally available access to the results of Richter's observations on Norway. The following quotation comes after a description of the rock walls of the fiords:

Numerous tributary waters, some of which are hardly less important than the head-stream, do indeed pour into the fiord, but they have not yet eroded for themselves deep trenches. After winding through the plateau-land in broad and shallow valleys their relatively gentle course is suddenly interrupted, and they at once cascade down the precipitous rock-walls to the sea. The side-valleys that open upon a fiord are thus truncated by the steep mountain-wall as abruptly, Dr. Richter remarks, as if they had been cut across with a knife. . . .

If we admit that a fiord is simply a partially drowned land-valley, and that the profound hollow in which it lies has been eroded by river action, how is it that the side streams have succeeded in doing so little work? Why should the erosion of the main or fiord-valleys be so immeasurably in advance of that of the lateral valleys? Obviously there must have been a time when the process of valley-formation proceeded more rapidly along the lines of the present fiords and their head-valleys than in the side-valleys which open upon these from the fjelds. At that time the work of rain and running water could not have been carried on equally over the whole land, otherwise we should find now a completely developed hydrographic system — not a plateau intersected by profound chasms, but an undulating mountain-land with its regular valleys. . . . According to Dr. Richter, the remarkable contrast between the deep valleys of the fiords and the shallow side-valleys that open upon them from the fjelds — the profound erosion in the former, and the arrest of erosion on the plateau — admits of only one explanation. While rivers and rapid ice-streams, flowing in previously excavated valleys, were actively engaged in deepening these, the adjacent fjelds were buried under sheets of névé. . . . In short, while rivers and glaciers were deepening the great valleys and making their walls steeper, the intervening mountain-heights were gradually being reduced and levelled by denudation. . . . It was somewhat otherwise in the Alps, where the hydrographic system, perfectly regular in preglacial times, was only slightly modified by subsequent glacial action. Yet even there erosion proceeded most rapidly along the chief lines of ice-flow. Were the great rock-basins of the principal Alpine valleys pumped dry, we should find the mouths or openings of the side valleys abruptly truncated, and their waters cascading suddenly into the ice-deepened main-valleys. For, as Dr. Wallace has shown, it is the present lake-*surface*, not the lake-*bottom*, that represents approximately the level of the preglacial valley. In a word, erosion proceeded most actively in the main-valleys, the bottoms of which have been lowered for several hundred feet below the bottoms of the side-valleys. Precisely the same phenomena are repeated in Scotland. Were all the water to disappear from the Highland lakes and sea-lochs, we should find waterfalls and cascades at the mouth of every lateral stream and torrent (*b*, 246–249).

It is evident from these extracts that the deepening of valleys is regarded as greatest where lake basins have been eroded beneath the pre-glacial valley floors; and this belief is explicitly expressed in the following extract from the latest edition of the same author's "Great Ice Age," the standard work on that subject:

Take the case of a glacier creeping down an Alpine valley and spreading itself out upon the low ground at the foot of the mountains. Let us suppose that, in the upper part of its course, the incline down which it moves is greater than the slope of the lower reaches of the valley. When the glacier attains the more gently inclined part of its course, it is evident that its flow must be retarded, and there will therefore be a tendency in the ice to accumulate or heap up. Now we know that the pressure of a body in motion upon any given surface varies with the degree at which that surface is inclined; as the inclination decreases the pressure increases. It follows from this that when the glacier leaves the steeper part of its course, and begins to creep down the gentler slope beyond, it will press with greater force upon its rocky bed, and this increased pressure will be further intensified by the greater thickness of the accumulated ice. . . . The result of all this is the formation of a rock-basin, the deeper portion of which lies towards the upper end, just where the grinding force of the glacier is greatest (*a*, 228, 229).

It seems to me that too great emphasis is here placed on the erosion accomplished near the end of a glacier, as indicated by lakes, and not enough upon the deepening of the valleys upstream from terminal lakes, as indicated by hanging valleys. It is also to be noted that De Lapparent, Richter, and J. Geikie all describe the hanging valleys of Norway as if their pre-glacial form had not been significantly changed, thus failing to bring clearly forward the fact that the valleys of to-day are the ice channels of the past, and that the larger and smaller channels must have normally discordant floors in a system of glacial drainage, just as they have in a system of river drainage, although to a much greater degree. The full analogy between ice and water channels, which throws so much light on the whole question of glacial erosion, was first clearly set forth by the two following observers.

Gannett on Lake Chelan, 1898. The most complete statement of the general principles involved in the production of hanging valleys that I have found in print is in an article on Lake Chelan, in the Cascade Mountains of Washington, by Henry Gannett. Chelan is a long narrow lake occupying the distal two thirds of the deep U-shaped valley of the Stehekin river on the eastern slope of the mountains. It was occupied in the glacial period by a heavy ice stream, fifty or sixty miles long, and half a mile to a mile broad. The rock walls which inclose the valley are strikingly parallel to one another, without buttressing spurs; they rise from 4000 to 5000 feet above the lake waters. Nearly all the streams which flow into the valley tumble over its walls in a series of cascades. "From all indications it appears that the ice must have been at least 3000 feet deep in this gorge of the Stehekin, since several of the smaller branches join the main glacier at that height above its bed."

Speaking of these features in a more general way, Gannett says:

A glacier is a river of ice, and it behaves almost precisely as a river of water does. Its effects upon its channel are almost precisely similar to those of a river upon its channel, excepting in the fact that all its operations are on a vastly greater scale. . . . A word of caution must here be interpolated. The channel of a river, in which its water flows, must not be confused with its valley, which it drains. The above comparison refers to the *channel* of a river [or of a glacier], not to its valley. . . . The glacier moves down the gorge, scouring and cutting the bottom and sides as it travels. The ends of the mountain spurs are planed off instead of being trimmed to sharp, angular points, as is done by streams in gorges cut by them. . . . Where the main glacier is joined by a branch, the bed of the branch is commonly found to be at a higher level than the bed of the main glacier, because being larger and heavier the main glacier has greater cutting power; indeed, in many cases the beds of small branches are hundreds, or even thousands, of feet higher than that of the main glacier to which they are tributary. The parallelism between the glacier and the river in their channels is further illustrated by this fact. The surface of the ice in the main glacier and in the branch must have been at the same level, although the bottoms, as stated above, differ greatly in elevation. So it is with a river at the point of junction of branches. The surface of the water must be practically at the same level in all cases, but the bottoms of the channels differ by the difference in depth of the streams at their point of junction. This fact affords us a measure of the minimum thickness of the ice at any place. It cannot have been less than the vertical distance between the bed of the main glacier and that of the tributary, and, indeed, must in all cases have been greater, owing to the thickness of the tributary (417–428, especially 418–420).

Penck on Alpine Valleys, 1899. A no less explicit and detailed statement of the peculiar features of glacial channels and their relations to river channels was made by Penck at the meeting of the International Geographical Congress in Berlin, September, 1899. The discordance of lateral and main valley floors was described as a general feature of all the larger Alpine valleys within their glaciated areas. The possibility of explaining the discordance by faulting, as suggested by Rothpletz for the Linththal, was considered, but rejected. The contrasts of the glaciated and non-glaciated Alpine valleys were strongly emphasized. The excess of the depth in the main valley beneath the floor of the hanging laterals was taken as a minimum measure for glacial erosion, and the term "over-deepened," already adopted on earlier pages of this essay, was applied to valleys thus worn to a greater depth than would have been possible to normal rivers. The publication of Penck's address is awaited with interest.

Harker on Glacial Valleys in Skye, 1899. A brief article by Harker on glaciation in Skye describes the valleys as eroded in massives gabbros, with U-shaped cross section, especially in the upper stretches, and frequently heading in a corrie whose floor may hold a small rock-basin tarn. In longitudinal profile the floor of a valley often consists of two or three stretches of relatively gentle slopes, or sometimes of basin form and then holding lakes, separated by relatively sudden descents. Tributary valleys mouth at a considerably higher level than the floor of the main valley (196–199).

Gilbert on Alaskan Valleys, 1899. A valuable contribution to the origin of hanging valleys will be found in a report on the Harriman Alaskan Expedition of 1899. A general statement of results was made by Gilbert during the session of the Geological Society of America in Washington, December, 1899, when the importance of the hanging lateral valleys in the Alaskan fiords, and their bearing on the problem of glacial erosion, was clearly set forth.

Blanford on Scotch Glens, 1900. The only article that I have found on hanging valleys in Scotland is by Blanford, "On a

Particular Form of Surface, apparently the Result of Glacial Erosion, seen on Loch Lochy and elsewhere." The "particular form" here referred to is the smoothness of the sides of the Great Glen of Scotland, a feature that may be held analogous to the smooth rock walls of the Norwegian fiords and to the spurless basal cliffs of the glaciated Alpine valleys. It is inferred that in pre-glacial time the streams of the lateral glens were separated by advancing spurs which buttressed the sides of the Great Glen. Now the spurs seem to have been truncated, producing the smooth and even sides of the glen, to which attention is especially directed. The lateral glens are described as at present opening a thousand feet above the floor of the Great Glen, whose smoothed sides are very little eroded by the descending tributary streams. The change from the inferred pre-glacial form is conservatively taken to indicate a glacial erosion of "at least 250 or 300 feet of rock" (198–204).

Hershey on Sierra Costa, California, 1900. An article by Hershey, already referred to above, is the latest contribution to the subject in hand. In following up a valley in the Sierra Costa in northwest California, it is at first V-shaped, with jagged ledges between sharp-cut ravines on the sides, and hardly wider at the bottom than the stream that drains it. On reaching the stretch once occupied by a local glacier, the valley becomes an open U-shaped trough, with smooth slopes free from ravines and spurs. Above the limit of glacial smoothing, the mountain sides are still deeply scored with ravines and jagged with outcropping ledges. The descent of a glaciated valley floor is effected by a series of steps; the stretches of more gentle fall alternate with almost precipitous falls where the floor is let down several hundred feet. Corries with tarns in their floors are well developed (42–57).

Several essays by Norwegian authors remain to be considered. It has not been possible to make reference to them without postponing the appearance of this paper, and consideration of them is therefore deferred to another occasion.

With all these new contributions to the subject, it may be expected that hanging lateral valleys and over-deepened main valleys will soon gain the importance that they deserve in geographical literature.

REFERENCES

Barrett, R. L. "The Sundal Drainage System in Central Norway." *Bull. Am. Geog. Soc.*, XXXII (1900).

Blanford, W. T. "On a Particular Form of Surface, apparently the Result of Glacial Erosion, seen on Loch Lochy and elsewhere." *Quart. Jour. Geol. Soc.*, LVI (1900), 198–204.

Boule, M. "La Topographie Glaciaire en Auvergne." *Ann. de Géog.*, V (1896), 277–296.

Brückner, E. "Die Vergletscherung des Salzachgebietes." *Geog. Abhandlungen*, I (Vienna, 1885), 1–183.

Davis, W. M. "Glacial Erosion in the Valley of the Ticino." *Appalachia*, IX (1900), 136–156.

Forbes, J. D. Norway and its Glaciers. Edinburgh, 1853.

Forel, F. A. "Fleuves et Glaciers." *Bull. Soc. Vaud. Sci. Nat.*, XXXIII (1897), 202–204.

Gannett, H. "Lake Chelan." *Nat. Geog. Mag.*, IX (1898), 417–428.

Geikie, J. (*a*) The Great Ice Age. New York, 3d ed., 1895.
  (*b*) Earth Sculpture. London, 1898.

Hall, J. Geology of New York. Part IV, comprising the geology of the fourth district. 1843.

Harker, A. "Glaciated Valleys in the Cuillins, Skye." *Geol. Mag.*, VI (1899), 196–199.

Heim, A. (*a*) Mechanismus der Gebirgsbildung. Basel, 1878.
  (*b*) "Ueber die Erosion im Gebiete der Reuss." *Jahrb. Schw. Alpenclub*, XIV (1879), 371–405.

Hershey, O. H. "Ancient Alpine Glaciers of the Sierra Costa Mountains in California." *Jour. Geol.*, VIII (1900), 42–57.

Lapparent, A. de. (*a*) Leçons de Géographie Physique. Paris, 1st ed., 1896.
  (*b*) Leçons de Géographie Physique. Paris, 2d ed., 1898.

Lubbock, J. The Scenery of Switzerland. New York, 1896.

Lugeon, M. "Leçon d'Ouverture du Cours de Géographie Physique professé à l'Université de Lausanne." *Bull. Soc. Vaud. Sci. Nat.*, XXXIII (1897), 49–78.

Marr, J. E. The Scientific Study of Scenery. London, 1900.

McGee, W. J. (*a*) "Glacial Cañons." *Proc. Am. Assoc.* (1883), 238.
  (*b*) "Glacial Cañons." *Jour. Geol.*, II (1894), 350–364.

Meunier, S. "Sur l'Allure Générale de la Dénudation Glaciaire." *Comptes Rendus*, CXXIV (1897), 1043.

Playfair, J. Illustrations of the Huttonian Theory of the Earth. Edinburgh, 1802.

Richter, E. "Geomorphologische Beobachtungen aus Norwegen." *Sitzungsber. k. k. Akad. Wien, Math. Naturw. Classe*, CV, Abth. I (1896), 147–189.

Rothpletz, A. Das geotektonische Problem der Glarner Alpen. Jena, 1898.

Russell, I. C. " Quaternary History of Mono Valley, California." *U.S.Geol. Surv.*, *VIII Ann. Rep.* (1889), 261–394.

Rütimeyer, L. Ueber Thal- und See-Bildung. Basel, 1869.

Tarr, R. S. " Lake Cayuga a Rock Basin." *Bull. Geol. Soc. Am.*, V (1894), 339–356.

Wallace, A. R. (*a*) " The Ice Age and its Work." *Fortnightly Review*, LX (1893), 616–633, 750–774.

    (*b*) " The Gorge of the Aar and its Teachings." *Fortnightly Review*, LXVI (1896), 175–182.

XXV

THE OUTLINE OF CAPE COD

NOTE. This essay attempts to restore the original outline of Cape Cod by reversing the processes at work on the present outline. In order to gain good understanding of these processes, a review of previous accounts of the Cape is introduced, a general consideration of the development of sea-shores is outlined, and the conclusions reached are applied to the problem in hand. It is thus estimated that the land here once extended at most two or more miles into the sea on the east, and that perhaps three or four thousand years have been required for the retreat of the shore-line to its present position. This period cannot, however, be taken as a full measure of the time since the glacial deposits of the Cape were formed, for there is reason to believe that the land stood higher than now for an unknown interval between the building of the Cape and the assumption of the present attitude with respect to sea-level.

The chief interest in the problem here discussed turns on the growth of the great sand spit of the "Provincelands" northwestward from the "mainland" of the Cape, and on the protection thus afforded to the old cliffs of High head. Brief account is given of the growth and waste of the Provincelands, and of the changes of the western shore-line. The essay closes with some practical suggestions regarding the protection of Provincetown harbor, and some speculations concerning the future change of the Cape. The consumption of the north arm — from the elbow to the hand — will probably require about eight or ten thousand years.

INTRODUCTION

An excursion to Provincetown and the "mainland" of Truro on Cape Cod with the students of the Harvard summer course in physical geography, in July, 1895, brought to my attention a number of problems concerning the changes of outline suffered by the Cape. These problems had taken rough shape on the occasion of a visit to the peninsula several years ago. Supplementing the observations made on the ground by a study of the Coast Survey charts and by a review of what has been written on the subject, this essay has gradually grown up. Its substance was presented before the Geological Society of America at the winter meeting in Philadelphia, December, 1895, and again before the Harvard Geological Conference in April, 1896.

The end of the Cape is pleasantly reached by a four-hour run in a steamboat from Boston across Massachusetts bay to Provincetown, in whose neighborhood the most significant of the features here described are to be found. By driving to High head, the northernmost point of the "mainland," a general view of the peninsula of Provinceland may be gained; thence driving or walking to Highland light, one may see a portion of the long harborless cliff that forms the "back," or eastern side, of the Cape. Walking northwestward along the beach to Peaked hill life-saving station, the action of the surf can be observed at leisure; and thence crossing the sandy belt to Provincetown, the varied forms of the dunes can be studied in detail. A second day may well include a visit to Race point, the northwestern extremity of the Cape, and a return southward along the wasting shore to Wood end, or Long point, whence the town can be regained by boat, previously arranged for.

Cape Cod is an excellent region for the study of shore-forms in the light of their development from some antecedent outline, and their continued change towards some future state. Although the mainland of the Cape rises about two hundred feet above sea-level, it is built of uncompacted clays and sands, with occasional bowlders, and is therefore easily consumed by the waves. Standing far out beyond the general shore of New England, it receives a violent attack from storm waves, which alter the shore-line so rapidly that the changes are measurable even in the short time covered by our records.

Extracts from Previous Writings

The following extracts summarize a number of previous references to the Cape:

In the "Geology of Massachusetts" (1841), E. Hitchcock makes brief mention of the erosion on the eastern coast and the growth of the Cape into Massachusetts bay (323), the southward growth of Nauset beach, a mile in fifty years (324), the dunes of Provincetown (325), and the "diluvial elevations and depressions" of Truro (367); Provinceland is "alluvial; that is, washed up by the ocean" (371).

Lieutenant (afterwards Admiral) C. H. Davis wrote a " Memoir upon the Geological Action of the Tidal and Other Currents of the Ocean," in which he called attention to the repeated occurrence along our coast of bars built northward from coastal bluffs, such as Sandy Hook, New Jersey, and Cape Cod, and suggested that "a generic term" should be applied to these forms. He mentioned a place of division of the tidal currents on the east side of Cape Cod, near Nauset inlet, from which the flood tide flows north and south.

Thoreau's narrative of his excursions on the Cape in 1849, 1850, and 1855 tells of various changes in the coast line known to the people there. A log canoe, buried long before on the inner side of the bar that forms the eastern wall of the marshy East harbor at the north end of the mainland, was found many years afterwards on the Atlantic side of the bar; that is, the bar had been pushed westward over the buried canoe as the sea cut away the outer beach. Swamp peat was sometimes found on the exposed beach, although it was originally formed undoubtedly on the inside of the bar. Stumps had been seen off Billingsgate point; the implication being, not that the land had been depressed, but that it had been washed away, leaving the stumps mired in their native soil. I have found this explanation of the occurrence of tree stumps on the shoals of Chatham current among the fishermen of the Cape. A writer in the *Massachusetts Magazine* of the previous century is quoted to the effect that an island, called Webbs island, formerly existed three leagues off Chatham, containing twenty acres of land; the people of Nantucket carried wood from it; but in the writer's day a large rock alone marked the spot, and the water thereabouts was six fathoms deep (182, 183).

Freeman's " History of Cape Cod " (1860) attributes much wasting of land to reckless cutting of the trees, — a doubtful conclusion as far as it refers to shore work, although probably applicable to the interior district of the dunes. He says:

The work of devastation was too extensively accomplished; as is seen on the shores of the Cape since washed away by tides aided by the force of the winds, so that vast flats of sand extend in some places a mile from the shore, now, at low water, dry, or nearly so, and in some instances these flats disclose large stumps of ancient trees embedded in their native peat (752).

H. L. Whiting prepared a "Report on the Special Study of Provincetown Harbor, Massachusetts." He distinguishes Truro-land, the mainland of the Cape, " by the existence of clay and of bowlders, and by the peculiar form of the 'bowl and dome' drift"; and Provinceland, "of sand only, — so free from all earthy matter that it will not even discolor water, — while the forms which the dunes and ridges here assume are mainly characteristic of wind drift" (155). He concludes that

the outer ridges of the peninsula of Provincetown were the earliest in date, and that the flats, marshes, and ponds now existing are subsequent accumulations and accidents, which have taken place under the shelter and eddy influences of the outer hooked bar or beach (155).

The narrow outer bar that connects the cliffs of Highland light with the Provincetown peninsula is described as wasting back with the cliffs, and is said to be in danger of breaking through at two points.

H. Mitchell wrote a "Report . . . concerning Nausett Beach and the Peninsula of Monomoy." Monomoy is described as built of sands derived from the bluff of Cape Cod during northeast storms; it grew southward into Nantucket sound at the rate of one hundred and fifty-seven feet a year from 1856 to 1868. The changes in the beach near Chatham are particularly described. The same author submitted an "Additional Report on the Changes in the Neighborhood of Chatham and Monomoy."

W. Upham published some notes on Cape Cod in the "Geology of New Hampshire" (1878), and a more extended essay on "The Formation of Cape Cod" a year later. He described the moraine extending eastward from Sandwich and entering the sea at Orleans (494); north of this point the Cape consists chiefly of modified drift, rarely containing bowlders (537). When the drift plains were deposited, the land stood somewhat higher than at present (561). Provinceland consists of sea sand, supplied by erosion on the east side of the Cape (564).

Chamberlin makes a brief reference to Cape Cod in his essay on the "Terminal Moraine of the Second Glacial Epoch."

The great northward hook of Cape Cod is composed of plains and rolling hills of sand and gravel, which resemble accumulations that often accompany the morainic belt on its interior side, and suggest the thought that the hook may be the modified inner border of the moraine which enters the sea near Orleans, and may be presumed to curve northward concentric with the hook, forming thus a loop inclosing the basin of Cape Cod (379).

H. L. Marindin studied the "Encroachment of the Sea upon the Coast of Cape Cod, Massachusetts" (a). From Highland light to Nauset lights the average recession from 1848 to 1888 was 128 feet, or 3.2 feet per annum. The face of the cliff, whose average height is 50 or 100 feet, has thus lost a total of 30,231,038 cubic yards, or 755,776 cubic yards per annum. The bar south of Nauset, inclosing the north side of Pleasant harbor, extended its length southward some distance in the same period. The same author has made a detailed report on the changes in shore-line and anchorage areas of Provincetown harbor (b).

K. Weule has, in his "Beiträge zur Morphologie der Flachküsten," discussed Cape Cod at some length (232–238). The tidal currents are regarded as the most important factors in its shaping. A misunderstanding of local conditions is implied when the author asks how "the narrow mainland of uncompacted materials can remain intact in an exposed situation, when even so resistant landmasses as rocky Nantucket and Martha's Vineyard suffer great loss" (232). The present preservation of the Cape is ascribed to the beach sand, brought from the shoals on the southeast by the flood tide. Weule follows Whiting in attributing a greater age to the outer than to the inner side of Provincetown peninsula (234). The existing mainland is regarded as only a remnant of a great extent of drift land (233); this opinion being taken from a report by A. Agassiz.

A brief article of my own, describing "Facetted Pebbles on Cape Cod," argued from these evidences of æolian action that the plains of gravel and sand were deposited under the air rather than under the sea.

A "Report of the Trustees of Public Reservations on the Subject of the Province Lands" (6) states that "there is evidence that the tides and waves have built one beach after another, each farther north than the last, and that the so-called Peaked hill bar is a new beach now in process of formation." The report contains an elaborate map of the sandy peninsula by J. N. McClintock, on a scale of about five inches to a mile, with ten-foot contours. The manner in which the outer beaches overlap the inner ones is very clearly shown. Five photographic illustrations present characteristic views of the dunes.

A general work on coastal forms — "La Géographie Littorale" — by J. Girard, briefly compares Sandy Hook and the end of Cape Cod, classifying them with spits formed by littoral currents, but giving no specific description.

The structures of the mainland of Truro and of the peninsula of Provinceland are so unlike that their different origins have long been recognized; the former being attributed chiefly to diluvial or glacial and aqueo-glacial agencies, the latter to marine agencies acting on the former. The general character of existing processes by which the shores are undergoing change and the present rate of action of these processes have been carefully examined by various observers; but no systematic attempt has been made to trace the processes and the changes that they have produced backward to their beginning. This task is therefore attempted here.

Reconstruction of the Original Outline of the Cape

The development of the existing outline of Cape Cod must be traced backward to the original outline. The initial form that it had before the present cycle of cutting and filling began along its shores may be roughly reconstructed by reversing the marine processes now at work and following them until they lead back through earlier and earlier conditions. The restoration may be regarded as complete, when the reconstructed forms are everywhere of non-marine origin. Then, reversing the order of study, the normal operation of cutting and filling processes should lead forward again to the existing outline of the Cape, and should even allow a reasonable prediction of future changes for some time to come.

Provinceland, the Chatham bars, Monomoy, and a few small bars near Wellfleet must first be removed, as they consist wholly of sea-carried materials, their arrangement being closely accordant with action at present sea-level. The tidal marshes north of Wellfleet, along Pamet river, and elsewhere, should be excavated. The mainland, chiefly of glacial and aqueo-glacial

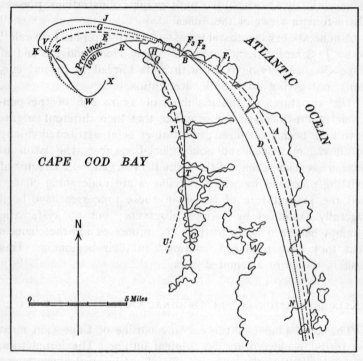

FIG. 107

deposits, will then stand out alone, as indicated by the outline *NBHQPTC* (Fig. 107). It descends to the shore on nearly all sides in steep cliffs of moderate height; long, straight, or gently curving beaches running along the base of the cliffs. Exceptions to this rule are found almost exclusively on the shores of protected bays, such as those north of Chatham and about Wellfleet. The cliffed descent of the mainland to the smooth beaches is manifestly an indication of destructional retreat from a formerly greater extension seaward, just as the gentle slope of the land to the irregular shore-line of the bays is an indication of small change from constructional form.

Although no close accuracy is to be expected in restoring the seaward extension of the cliffed mainland, there are nevertheless some simple principles that will at least serve to guide us towards a not altogether imaginary reconstruction. First, it must be remembered that general sub-aërial denudation has not effected significant changes in glacial topography during post-glacial time; second, the restored outline should possess irregularities of pattern comparable to those in the protected bays of to-day, advancing from the headlands and retreating towards the troughs or "valleys" in the high ground; third, the amount of land restored should be much less on protected shores than on exposed shores; fourth, cliffs that are now protected by forelands of marsh and bar must not be built out so far that their recession could not have been accomplished before the bars began to grow in front of them.

POSSIBLE CHANGES OF LEVEL

These four guiding principles do not include reference to the effects of change of level, because, if any change has occurred since the time of accumulative construction of the mainland, it has been of small amount, and it has, to my mind, acted on the whole in favor of decreasing the land area by submergence, thus coöperating with the destructive action of the sea. This view is in accord with that expressed by Upham, who thinks that, when the drift was deposited hereabouts, the land stood somewhat higher than at present, and that the numerous small indentations or reëntrants of the shore-line, such as occur along the south side of the Cape, are results of a slight submergence of trough-like depressions or valleys. The digitate bays of Marthas Vineyard would seem to lend support to this view; but they were otherwise interpreted by Professor Shaler, who regarded them as having been formed by sub-glacial streams acting on sea-floor deposits that had been strewn in front of the ice margin when the sea stood higher than now, although he suspected, also, that "at the close of the glacial period this region was considerably higher than at present " (318, 319, 350). The latter view is further supported by the small amount of erosion — about three miles — suffered by the low, sandy, southern shore of Marthas Vineyard (349) since the present level of the land was assumed.

Without undertaking to determine precisely the original level of the Cape mainland, the most plausible explanation of the facts seems to me that the washed gravels and sands correspond to the supermarine *sandr* of Greenland and Alaska ; that the troughs, by which the plains of washed sands are trenched, result from the channeling by streams when they carried less waste than while they were previously aggrading the plains ; and that the indentations of the shore-line are the result of slight depression, whereby the troughs were partly drowned. The reconstruction of what I have above called the " original outline" will therefore not necessarily lead us to the shore-line that obtained at the close of the time of accumulative construction, if the land then stood higher than now ; but only to a contour line drawn on the original constructional mainland at present sea-level. However, between the actual original shore-line and the reconstructed contour line there must have been a difference of degree rather than of kind ; the latter embracing a smaller land area than the former, but the general outline and disposition of the land areas probably being of much the same style in both cases, except for the indentations of drowned valleys after submergence. For this reason no further especial attention will be given to depression in its effect in altering the outline of the Cape.

A proposed reconstruction of the outline of the Cape has been drawn, with the four guiding principles, above stated, in mind. Trifling additions are made in the bays ; none more than two thousand feet. Significant additions are made on the west side of the Cape ; some of these measure four thousand or five thousand feet. Two miles or more of land are added on the east side, or " back," facing the broad Atlantic. The margin of the restored outline is indented toward the various troughs and valleys that break the general surface of the mainland. About High head, the northern point of the cliffed mainland, the fourth of the guiding principles comes into play ; and hereabouts the most interesting problem of the Cape is found. The view of the peninsula of Provinceland from this commanding point is therefore particularly instructive.

THE PROBLEM OF HIGH HEAD

The cliffed margin of the mainland at High head, H (Fig. 107), is notably even both on the northern and western sides. At present the head is protected both on the west and north by forelands of marsh and bar, the bars springing tangent from cliff fronts farther south or southeast. The bar, QR, on the west is part of a long, concave shore-line, $TPQR$, — the "west concave" shore, — whose excavated curve is manifestly dependent on the existence of the peninsula of Provinceland to the northwest. Before this concave curve was cut, a nearly straight shore-line, $CTYQH$, — the "west straight" shore, — had been made, as indicated by its remnants now seen on the west marginal cliff, QH, of High head, and again about six miles to the south, TC, on Boundbrook, Griffins, and other islands. The cutting of the west straight cliff, QH, must have continued until the peninsula of Provinceland began to project northwest to High head. Then, as the movement of the shore currents was somewhat changed by the interference of the peninsula, the middle of the straight cliff was excavated more rapidly, forming the west concave shore, TPQ, and the northern part of the straight cliff on High head at the same time came to be protected by the outspringing concave bar, QR, that now incloses East harbor and its marshes on the southwest side.

The bar, BJ, on the north of High head is part of the long eastern convex shore-line, $NBJK$, whose form is determined by the masterly Atlantic currents. It is along the outer beach of this bar — or of its representative in former days — that the sands of the peninsula have been transported from the southeast; this being the conclusion of all observers, unless perhaps of Hitchcock. Now it follows from the relation of this northeast bar to the peninsula of Provinceland, and from the relation of the peninsula to the western bar, that a somewhat shorter time was allowed for cutting the north cliff of High head than for cutting its west cliff ; but inasmuch as wave energy was greater on the north than on the west, time and energy varied inversely, and hence about the same amount of lost land may be added to each cliff. The amount of reduction suffered on either side of High head is therefore roughly proportional to the time before the bar was built in front of the north cliff.

The north bar, *BJ*, which for this reason takes our attention, is one of the class built by marine action, as recognized by Admiral Davis. It springs tangent to the curve of the long convex cliff and beach, *NB*, on the east side, or " back," of the Cape. As the retreat of the margin of High head is measured by the time before the north bar was built, the question arises whether bars of this kind are built in front of straight cliffs early or late in the attack made by the sea on the land. This question may be divided into two : the first considering the development of the cliff ; the second considering the stage in the development of the cliff when the protecting bar would be likely to grow out in front of it.

DEVELOPMENT OF SHORE PROFILES

Let the activities of the sea be resolved into two components: one acting on and off shore, the other along shore ; and let the effects of the first of these components be now examined alone, postponing consideration of the effects of the second component to the next section.

On some young coasts the on-and-off-shore movements of the sea carry out to deep water all of the waste that is abraded from the land and its submarine slope, leaving the shore-line bare. The rocky floor seen at low tide on the coast of Brittany illustrates this condition. Here the sea is able to do more work than it has to do. Its action is like that of a young river, whose ability to carry load is greater than the resistance of the load that it has to carry, and whose valley floor is therefore attacked and deepened. But as the valley is deepened, the slope, velocity, and carrying power of the river are all decreased ; at the same time, the load, derived chiefly from the valley slopes, is increased ; thus ability to do work gradually falls into equality with the work to be done. When this happy condition is reached, the river may be said to have graded its channel. Youth then passes into adolescence.

A comparable series of changes may be detected in studying the profile of a seacoast at right angles to the general shore-line. As the sea can at first usually dispose of more waste than it gathers, the coast is energetically attacked and forced to retreat, and sea cliffs are thus produced. But in virtue of the changes thus brought about, the energy of on-and-off-shore attack decreases, while the waste coming from the growing cliffs increases; thus ability to do work approaches equality with work to be done, and the sea-floor profile, like that of the valley floor, may be said to be graded. When a graded profile is attained, the adolescent stage of shore development is reached.

The amount of retreat necessary before a graded profile is attained, varies with the texture of the coast, and with its exposure to the sea. A coast of unconsolidated deposits will soon supply a large amount of waste from its cliffed margin, while the cliffs of a rock-bound coast will shed waste slowly; hence, on coasts of given exposure, grade will be assumed with a less amount of cliff-cutting where the rocks are weak than where they are strong. This recalls the behavior of rivers in regions of weak and resistant rocks; in the latter they may assume gentle slopes; but in the former rather steep slopes are necessary to carry off the freely offered waste; and gentler slopes can be assumed only as the whole surface is worn down; this general relation having been pointed out some years ago by Major Powell ("Uinta Mountains," 194). Moreover, inasmuch as a greater amount of waste can be handled on exposed coasts than on protected coasts, a considerable retreat may develop high cliffs on the former before enough waste is shed from the cliff face to give the shore-waves all the work they can do; while on protected coasts a moderate retreat, producing low cliffs, will supply as much waste as can be handled by the sea.

The under-water form of a graded profile, when first developed, also depends largely on the violence of the on-and-off-shore movements of the sea. On a protected coast the bottom will be degraded so as to descend from the shore-line by a gentle slope to

an eroded platform of moderate depth ; but on an exposed coast
the bottom will be degraded so as to descend from the shore-line
by steeper slope to a platform of greater depth.

TYPICAL SHORE PROFILES

A graded profile being once attained, its graded condition will
be preserved through all the rest of an undisturbed or normal
cycle of shore development ; shore profiles and river profiles
being alike in this as in so many other respects. Before grade
is assumed, the ability of the sea may be so far in excess of its
load that it under-cuts the shore and forms sea caves at tide level,
as in profile 1 (Fig. 108). When grade is first assumed, the coast
is usually cut back to a steep cliff, like profile 2. Much later,

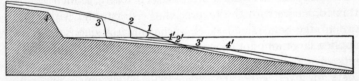

FIG. 108

when the sea has cut back the shore so that the waves must
traverse a submarine platform before attacking the land, their
strength is thereby so much lessened that the cliff leans back to
a moderate slope, as in profiles 3 and 4, and even then supplies
enough waste to keep the waves at its foot fully occupied.

There is something more than analogy in the comparison that
may be drawn between the longitudinal profile of a stream and
the transverse profile of a shore. In youth each usually has its
torrent or upper portion, where ability to carry load is greater
than load to be carried ; but as development progresses, the
graded condition of midstream extends headward, and after a
time reaches all the way to the headwaters. At the same time,
the lower or flood-plain-delta portion extends seaward, its grade
being rather steeper in adolescence, when much material is
brought from the headwaters, than later, in maturity and old
age, when the supply of waste is very slow. The critical point,
where marine action changes from degrading the near-shore

bottom to aggrading the off-shore bottom, migrates seaward, as 1', 2', 3', 4', in Fig. 108. At the same time, the seaward extension of the bottom deposits increases. Furthermore, the comparison between stream and sea suggests the need of examining that process on the sea floor, which corresponds to corrasion in the stream bed. Sea-shore profiles make it clear that a considerable deepening is accomplished on the floor of the platform, landward from the critical points 1', 2', etc. Off the eastern cliff of Cape Cod this deepening can hardly have been less than fifteen or twenty fathoms; off the Chalk cliffs of Normandy a similar scouring and deepening of the bottom may be inferred. We are accustomed to study transportation and deposition as submarine processes, but little attention has been given to decomposition, disintegration, corrasion, or any other process by which the sea floor is degraded. The subject deserves careful investigation.

It is manifest from the preceding paragraphs that a graded profile may be attained much earlier on one part of a shore-line than on another; for the texture, the original profile, and the exposure of a coast all vary from place to place. But in a region like Cape Cod, where the original shore-line consisted wholly of uncompacted materials, this aspect of the problem need not be considered further.

DEVELOPMENT OF SHORE OUTLINES

It is not, however, only in on-and-off-shore action that a close comparison may be drawn between the operations of marine and fluviatile agencies. The longshore action of the sea also is in many respects comparable to the downstream action of rivers. Beginning on an unevenly deformed land surface in a region of moderate rainfall, where there are many heights and hollows, the drainage will at first consist of many small independent systems, each one transporting waste from the initial divides down the initial slopes into the initial hollows. Every stream proceeds, by degrading and aggrading its course, to develop a line of slope on which its ability to do work shall everywhere equal the work that it has to do. As the eminences are worn down and the hollows are filled up, local systems that were at first independent become confluent, and the drainage of the higher ones is discharged to the lower ones. Every change of this kind will call for rearrangement of the degraded and aggraded slopes in the confluent basins. Ultimately, all the separate systems will, in one combination or another, find outlet to the sea, and the waste will be carried a long distance from the main divides to the main river deltas.

It is much the same with the action of the sea. Leaving the on-and-off-shore action out of consideration for the moment, let

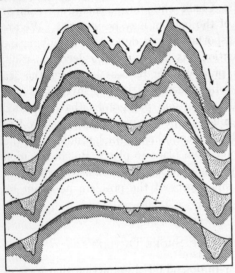

FIG. 109

us view only the longshore action, as determined by the dominant rather than by the prevailing movements of the littoral waters. The projections, or headlands, of the constructional shore-line act as so many divides, on either side of which the longshore currents flow away from the apex, as in the uppermost outline in Fig. 109. The reëntrants, or bays, are so many basins into which the longshore currents converge from the adjacent headlands. The headlands are slowly worn back, and the waste is carried along their sides into the bays, where it forms aggrading pocket beaches or bridging bars, as in the second and later outlines of Fig. 109. The initial irregularity of shore outline is thus replaced by a graded outline, grade being first attained in the bays, and last on the headlands, much as was the case with stream action. As the headlands are cut farther back and beaches are formed at the base of their cliffs, then the longshore action is more and more thrown into one direction or the other from the chief headlands, transportation is carried on past many of the subordinate headlands, and much of the waste finds its way into the chief reëntrants of the shore-line, as in the lowermost outline of Fig. 109. We should expect to find inside the long-sweeping curve of the aggrading shore-line of the chief bays more or less distinct record of the sharp-curved pocket beaches of an earlier stage.

However irregular the initial shore-line was originally, and however many divisions were then made in the direction of the longshore currents, the time will come when only a few of the most prominent and resistant headlands survive, as in the later outlines of Fig. 109; elsewhere the longshore action is developed into a continuous movement. Truly, the direction of transportation along the graded shore-line is sometimes one way, sometimes the other, according to the sweep of storm winds; but if the dominant currents alone are considered, the movement is essentially constant. The graded condition, first reached on the pocket beaches, comes to prevail all along the shore; ability to do the work of transportation is everywhere equal to the work of transportation to be done.

In the river problem the number of independent river systems that occupy the originally deformed surface varies with the strength of the initial relief and with the rainfall. A light rainfall and a strong, rapid-growing initial relief of resistant rocks produce many independent river systems, and a long time must elapse before a general grade is attained. The early stage of this condition is illustrated in the lava-block mountains of southern Oregon, so well described by Russell (435). But a heavy rainfall and a faint, slow-growing initial relief of weak materials may allow the immediate development of a single river system, soon attaining grade over the whole area concerned. So with the sea. Moderate longshore action and strong initial irregularity of resistant rocks break up the longshore currents into many systems at first; the grading of the shore-line and the union of the many currents can be accomplished only after a long time of endeavor. But strong longshore action and moderate initial irregularity of weak materials may permit continuous longshore movements for a long distance on well-graded beaches almost from the very first.

Both in valleys and on coasts — in rivers and on shores — the graded condition will be reached sooner on certain stretches than on others; and just as an alternation of rough rapids and smooth-flowing reaches indicates a youthful stage of river life, so an alternation of ragged headlands and smooth-beached bars indicates a youthful stage of shore-line development. But in time even the more resistant parts will be trimmed off so as to accord with the less resistant, and then downstream transportation — or longshore movement — is well developed; the adolescent stage is reached. From this time forward, on a shore as in a river, the grade is normally changed only where and when a change of load calls for readjustment; the readjustment necessitating an aggradation or degradation of the valley floor, or an advance or retreat of the shore-line, as the load may increase or decrease.

It should of course be understood that comparisons of this kind are not formal comparisons in which the condition of one member may be inferred immediately from those of its analogue. The purpose of the comparison is not to compel explanation, but chiefly to borrow illustration of the systematic processes of land sculpture from the better known examples of river action, and apply them to the less studied examples of shore action; less studied certainly in this country, where our great interior areas have for some decades past absorbed the attention of geologists; more studied than river action in Great Britain, but not from the point of view here taken.

Under favorable conditions irregular shore-lines may be smoothly graded early in their cycle of development. This is well illustrated in the case of Marthas Vineyard. Here an extremely irregular constructional shore has been reduced to a remarkably even and well-graded outline in a relatively early stage of the attack of the sea on the land; for although a matter of two or three miles of the southern headlands of the island have probably been cut away by the sea (Shaler, 349), a good part of the original shore-line still remains in the branching bays behind the bridging bars. The straight-cliffed headlands stand perfectly in line with the bars across the bays. The later stages of outline on graded shores are considered in the third section below.

APPLICATION OF THE FOREGOING TO CAPE COD

The foregoing account of the development of shore-lines is perhaps an overlong preparation for the application of the simple principles that govern shore changes to the case of Cape Cod; but the excuse for the details into which I have entered is the desire to show good ground for the conclusion which they support; namely, that on a coast as weak as the mainland of Cape Cod, any originally irregular shore-line would soon be reduced to grade by the action of a sea so energetic as the Atlantic, with its frequent southeast and northeast storms. Only a moderate time and a moderate recession is therefore necessary for the production of the even northeast cliff of High head. It does not, however, follow from this that only a short time actually elapsed in this work, for as far as has yet been stated, the High head cliff that we see may have been cut far back from the first position of an even cliff on this part of the coast line. Whether the time was long or short can be best determined by examining into the conditions which determine the development of the bar by which the cliff is now protected, this being the second problem announced above.

It should be noted that when the northeast cliff of High head formed the open shore-line of this part of the Cape, the outline must have extended in a sympathetic curve, HBF_1A, for some distance southeast of its present limit; and from this early form there must have been a gradual change to the shore-line of to-day. At some time during this change the protecting bar, BJ, must have been built out to the northwest. The problem is to determine at what stage in the history of a cliffed shore-line such a bar or spit might grow out from one part of its face and protect another part.

OFF-SHORE BARS

In order to avoid misapprehension, it is advisable to make careful distinction between those bars or spits which spring as tangent attachments to a cliffed shore, often extending into comparatively deep water, and those off-shore bars which are built up from the bottom in shallow water, not immediately connected with the mainland. Examples of the latter class are common along a great extent of our southern coast, especially where the tides are weak. Briefly stated, their history seems to be as follows: When waves roll in upon a shelving shore, as in Fig. 110, much of their energy is expended on the bottom. Between the line of their first action far off shore and their final exhaustion on the coast, *C*, there must be somewhere a zone of maximum action. This zone must lie farther seaward when large storm waves roll in than when the sea is slightly ruffled in fair weather.

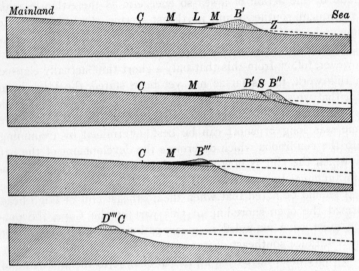

FIG. 110

Let the zone of maximum action for storm waves be shown by *Z* in profile. Here the bottom is deepened; the coarser particles are moved landward, forming a shoal and in time a bar, *B'*, inclosing a lagoon, *L*; while the finer particles are moved seaward, beyond the limits of Fig. 109, where they are distributed in moderate thickness over a considerable area. During this process we may imagine the storm waves to say: "We cannot to advantage attack a coast where the off-shore water shoals so gradually; let us therefore first deepen the off-shore bottom, so that we may afterwards make better attack on the coast." So saying, a preliminary off-shore bar is built up by the storm waves in position B'; and afterwards, at times of exceptional storms, successive additions may be made on its outer side, as B''. Wind action builds the bar up with dunes, and carries much sand over into the lagoon. But a time will come when the bottom farther to seaward has been deepened enough to enable even the greatest waves to act severely on the outer slope of the bar, taking from it more than they bring to it; then the outward advance of the bar is changed to a landward retreat, and it is pushed back to such a position as B'''. This change in behavior may be taken to separate the stages of youth and adolescence in the development of a shore-line of this kind.

Young bars that are advancing or that have advanced seaward may often be recognized by belts of dunes, B', B'', roughly parallel to the shore, inclosing lines of marsh, or "slashes" (S), as they are called on the coast of New Jersey. Adolescent bars, retreating landward like B''', may be distinguished by the exposure of the dark mud of the lagoon marsh, M, on their outer slope, as is sufficiently explained by the diagrams. Many examples of this kind might be cited. In time the retreat of the bar will carry it back to the mainland; then, as long as the marginal cliff is not too high, the "dunes," D'''', will be heaped directly on the land slope, and the mature stage of shore development is reached. In this stage the depth of water near the shore is much greater than it was originally; degradation of the sea floor reaching to depths much below low tide.

An interesting variation on this type of coastal forms is found on coasts whose submarine slope varies, so that off-shore bars are formed in one district, but an immediate attack is made on the land in a neighboring district. The coast of New Jersey gives a standard example of this kind. About Atlantic City the bars are built off shore; about Long Branch the land is cut back in a retreating cliff of moderate height. Although now generally retreating and exposing marsh mud on their ocean side (*Geol. Surv. New Jersey, Ann. Rep.* (1885), 80 et seq.), the bars frequently possess dune ridges and slashes, as if they had once advanced seaward. Somewhere in the earlier history of this coast there must have been a point or fulcrum of no advance or retreat between the advancing bars and the retreating cliff. It should not be overlooked that longshore action has a share, often a large share, in the development or compound forms of this kind; but it is quite conceivable that they might be developed essentially under the control of on-and-off-shore action alone. A second example of this kind is perhaps to be found in the combination of the bars from Chatham to Nauset with the cliffed margin of the Cape mainland farther north ; but into this problem it is not desirable to enter further at present. The origin of tangent bars or spits, built out into comparatively deep water, may now be taken up.

Tangent Bars or Spits

In order to understand more clearly the conditions under which tangent bars would form, it is necessary to return for a few moments to the problem of the varying outline of a graded shore as dependent on an increase of load. It is advisable to enter this phase of the problem through comparison again with the development of rivers and valleys.

In the case of adolescent rivers, the increasing dissection of the drainage basin by growing headwater branches may frequently cause the load to continue to increase after the first attainment of a graded slope along the trunk river. As a consequence, the trunk river must aggrade the valley floor, forming a flood plain, until the load begins to decrease later on in maturity. Much in the same way longshore action of the sea on a coast of graded outline may gather an increasing load as the cliffs retreat and become longer and higher ; and with this increase of load, certain parts of an early-graded outline may have to be built forward into the sea. But on pursuing this comparison a step further we find here, as in some earlier cases, a contrast replacing the agreement thus far traced between the river and the longshore action. Not only the load, but also the volume of a river increases from youth to maturity by reason of the better development of stream lines all over the drainage basin ; and this increase of volume tends to prevent the aggradation asked for by the increase of load. Similarly, the volume of water involved in the longshore movements becomes greater as the inequalities of a young shore-line are reduced to the smooth curves of adolescence and maturity ; but here the increase of volume causes the shore waters to move in curves of larger radius than before, and this change may require the beaches to grow forward on certain concave or incurved parts of the shore-line. In such case increase in the volume of long-shore water movements may coöperate with the increase of load in tending to build the land out into the sea. Here rivers and longshore currents have unlike behavior.

One of the best examples of this kind that has come to my notice is found on the coast of Georgia and Florida, where the better adjustment of coastal bars to shore currents and the consequent increase in volume and strength of the latter seems to have led to the out-building of the several bars that are involved in the southward migration of cape Canaveral. The accompanying diagram (Fig. 111) illustrates the essential features of the changes here inferred. The general attack that is at first made nearly all along the ragged coast soon comes to be resolved into two diverse actions: a persistent attack on the chief medial headlands, while the subordinate headlands are protected by the growth of off-shore bars. Let the ragged outline of Fig. 111 represent the original shore-line of an uncompacted land mass. The general attack by the sea first cuts

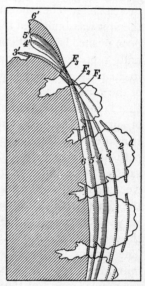

FIG. 111

off all the headlands, forming cliffs 2, 3, more or less connected by bars. When longer and higher cliffs, 4, are developed, they supply so large an amount of waste and allow the movement of so large a volume of water along shore that the less exposed cliff of earlier intention in the upper part of the figure is no longer attacked, but is protected by a spit, 4′, that springs out from the main cliff, prolonging its curve in one direction or the other, — here, upward, — according as the tides and the on-shore winds determine the direction of the longshore movement. In this case on-and-off-shore action and depth of water have little to say. Wherever the dominant longshore movement advances, there the tangent bar must grow, whether the water is shallow or deep.

ILLUSTRATION FROM THE COAST OF NEW JERSEY

An example suitable for illustration of this case is found in the relation of Sandy Hook to the Long Branch cliffs on the New Jersey coast, as exhibited on the excellent topographical maps of that state. Although now protected by the spit of Sandy Hook, both Rumsor neck and the highlands of Navesink are truncated by sea cliffs. The truncation must have been accomplished before the spit was built, and therefore before the Long Branch cliff had been pushed back to its present position. Stage 3 (Fig. 111) essentially represents this relation. In the change from earlier stages to the present, the longshore action has increased in consequence of the general smoothing of the outline, and the direction of longshore movement has been somewhat changed, so that now instead of carrying the waste from the Long Branch cliff directly to the truncated headlands next north, it is carried along an independent path forming the spit of Sandy Hook outside of the line of truncation. It is interesting to notice that the Long Branch cliffs were evenly graded, and that the spit was formed rather early in the general attack of the sea on the land hereabouts, and that a very slight change in the outline of the chief cliff sufficed to cause the growth of the spit outside of the subordinate cliffs farther north. The various fluctuations in the growth of the spit and the intermittent destruction of its slender bar are described on page 78 of the annual report of the New Jersey Geological Survey for 1885.

The Long Branch cliff has for some time been retreating under the blows of the Atlantic breakers. The farther it retreats the longer the stretch of cliff becomes ; it is undoubtedly much longer now than formerly. It may be fairly inferred that the two great spits, to the south as well as to the north of the cliff, have always been, as now, essentially tangent to the cliff front. It follows necessarily that the point of the attachment of the spits to the mainland has shifted, and that the spits have also been pushed backward at equal pace with the retreat of the cliff. With these conclusions in mind, the problem of High head and the northeast bar may at last be taken up.

GROWTH OF THE PROVINCELANDS

There is good reason to think that the analogy between Sandy Hook and the Provincelands pointed out by Admiral Davis may be carried much further than he suspected. The great convex cliff line on the back of the Cape corresponds to the slightly convex line of the Long Branch cliff; the northeast cliff of High head is the counterpart of the protected cliff of the Navesink highlands; the slender bar that springs tangent to the curve of the back of the Cape and runs to the broad peninsula of the Provincelands is essentially a repetition of the slender bar that springs north from the Long Branch cliff and runs to the broadened peninsula of Sandy Hook. The point where the bar now springs northwestward from the long convex back of the Cape is not the point where the bar first began to grow. Its original point of attachment must have been southeast of the present point; and in the change from the original to the present arrangement, both the cliff and the slender bar must have been forced back, in the very manner already described for the example in New Jersey. Marindin's report gives precise data for the retreat of the cliff; and the story of the buried canoe, recorded by Thoreau, gives support to the retreat of the bar near its point of attachment. In both examples the further part of the great spit has grown by addition to its seaward side in order to keep the outline in a curve sympathetic with the retreating cliff; the outward or eastward growth of Sandy Hook being described on page 77 of the annual report of the New Jersey Geological Survey for 1885; the similar growth of the Provincelands is more fully stated below. As a result of the outward growth of the spit while the cliff is retreating, there must be a neutral point or fulcrum of no change somewhere on the connecting bar; and with the further straightening of the cliff front, the position of this fulcrum must generally shift toward the spit, as shown by F_1, F_2, F_3 (Fig. 111).

The original point of attachment of the connecting bar on Cape Cod must have been at the intersection of two converging lines determined by the northeast cliff of High head and the innermost or oldest of the bars in the Provinceland peninsula. The first of these lines is well defined, HB (Fig. 112); the second is less distinct, but appears to be recorded in a sand bar on the line EF_2. The form of this bar has probably been somewhat changed by wind action, yet the trend of its inner margin along the shore of East harbor is comparatively straight, as if it had not been much altered from the form given when it was built. Its trend departs slightly from the direction of the adjacent Atlantic shore, as if it had been determined by conditions now vanished.

The intersection of the two guide lines HB and EF_2, when prolonged to the east-southeast, is found at a point F_1, about four

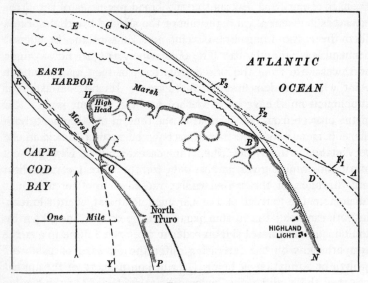

FIG. 112

thousand feet off the present shore, and about a mile and two thirds east-southeast from the present point of attachment of the springing bar. Judging by the present rate of retreat of the cliff line, this outer position must have been occupied about twelve hundred years ago. These figures are of necessity only approximate, but they are believed to give a fair indication of the order of magnitudes involved, both in space and time. We may then infer that when the general outline of the back of the Cape had assumed the position of the line AF_1BH, the shore was well enough graded to supply material for the building of a spit ; and that the curvature of the shore at the point F_1, assigned for the beginning of the spit, was such that the dominant long-shore currents, moving from south to north in flood tide or under southeast storms, could no longer follow the shore, but departed from it outwardly by a small angle. Thus the protecting bar F_1E began to grow in front of the High head cliff.

At an earlier stage the longshore currents must have been much interrupted by the irregularities of the original shore-line. No large and well-developed current could at that time follow these irregularities. But as the headlands were cut back and the bays bridged across, and the shore assumed the outline ABH, then the resistance to the development of the current became less and less ; thereby the current became stronger and stronger, and desired a straighter and straighter path for its movement. At the same time, a greater and greater volume of waste was supplied from the growing cliffs. As long as the back of the Cape projected farther into the sea than now, the northward shore current may have swung pretty well around the mainland, as sketched in line ABH. But as the east side of the Cape was cut away and straightened, and as the shore current grew stronger and stronger, it became increasingly difficult for the waters to turn the curve that led to High head; and at last, when the turning was impossible, the spit began to form on the line F_1E. As the change progresses the current swings on a fulcrum, F_2 ; the spit broadens by the external addition of new bars, F_2G, as well as by the formation of sand dunes inside of the curve ; and the fulcrum shifts along the shore to the northwest, as indicated by the points F_2, F_3 (Fig. 112), in the manner already explained for Fig. 111.

The important point to note is that here, just as on the New Jersey coast, the grading of the initial irregular shore-line into a curved cliff shore, and the straightening of the curved cliff shore enough to require the growth of the tangent bar, must have been accomplished early in the development of so weak a land mass as Cape Cod in face of waves so strong as those of the Atlantic.

DIMENSIONS OF THE ORIGINAL CAPE

Now inasmuch as no very long time can have been required for the Atlantic waves to wear back the original shore-line of the Cape to a graded outline, *ABH*, of which the High head cliff is a part, and inasmuch as the growth of the springing spit must have been begun soon after the grading of the shore, it follows that the original constructional outline of the land in front of the High head cliff cannot have extended far into the sea. I have given it an extension of three thousand feet in Fig. 107. A similar original extension of all the mainland of the Cape may be assumed outside of the graded shore-line, *ABH*, that existed before the springing spit was formed; and thus the original outline of the eastern side of the mainland has been roughly sketched in. As drawn in Fig. 107, the greatest retreat from the original shore to the present shore is nearly two and a half miles, and at the present strength of wave action, three thousand or four thousand years may be roughly taken to have sufficed for the accomplishment of this change. This time is probably too long rather than too short, for the retreat now must be slower than when the cliff was lower.

It should be carefully understood that the period here computed does not measure post-glacial time; for, as already stated, it is believed that the land hereabouts stood somewhat higher than now during the accumulation of the stratified sands, and that only after the time of accumulation were the valleys and low grounds slightly submerged by a moderate depression of the land, and the work whose duration is here computed begun. The time that passed while the sea was at work on some lower shore is not measured. There is no indication of a recent elevation of the land hereabouts, as far as the shore features testify; even the protected cliffs of High head are cut down to present sea-level.

The Nauset bar extends southward from the cliff at the point *N*. The earlier positions were prolongations of the lines *A*, *D*. The point of attachment must therefore have migrated to the southwest; the retreat of the cliff front determining the retreat of the bar that stands in line with it. How the problematic islands off Chatham affected the behavior of the bar is not here inquired into.

Inasmuch as the recession of the eastern shore is believed to have been of moderate measure, the loss on the western shore must have been still less. This is considered in a later section.

The Origin of Race Point

Two important consequences follow from the swinging of the shore current on its movable fulcrum. The first gives explanation of the overlapping of the newer shore-lines outside of the older body of the peninsula. This is only a repetition of the process by which the spit first departed from the beach on the back of the Cape itself. The outer margin of the Provinceland peninsula is therefore its very youngest part, and not its oldest, as supposed by Whiting. The long bar, F_3JK, ending in Race point, is a distinct external addition to the older body of the Provincelands, and a long, narrow "slash" is included behind it. It has grown out into comparatively deep water, for the twenty-fathom line lies only seventeen hundred feet off shore to the northwest. Peaked hill bar may be, as the commissioners have plausibly suggested, the embryo of still another external bar.

It may be noted that small spits departing tangentially from curved beaches are not uncommon. The map accompanying Whiting's report shows two of them near Wood end, one pointing east, the other north, from the sharp curve of the bar, as if determined by a strong southwest storm, whose waves worked eastward and northward from the apex of the curve at Wood end. A minute spit of this kind is shown on the chart of Cape Cod bay (Coast chart 110, printed 1890), a little northeast of Race point; but a later edition of the chart (1892) carries a smooth curve around the point. Small examples of these forms, trending eastward, were seen on the south shore near Long point light, at the time of my last visit to the Cape.

The Wasting Shore from Race Point to Wood End

The second consequence of the outward deflection of the current around the peninsula is the rapid consumption of the bar, VW, that extends south from Race point inlet to Wood end, the long "finger" at the end of the Cape. This suggests a preliminary digression. Wonder is often expressed at the ability of sand bars to withstand the violence of the surf that breaks unceasingly upon them. The sands are entirely unconsolidated, and their surface layers are moved by every surge of the waters. Yet the form of the bar changes very slowly. The reason for this must be found in the continual feeding, from the cliffs and from the bottom off shore, by which the volume of the bars is sustained. The bars of our southern Atlantic coast presumably receive much of their sand from the bottom. Sandy Hook receives much of its supply from the retreating cliffs at Long Branch. If the supply be withheld, the bar will be rapidly swept away. It may not be that the grains of sand are actually ground to dust, but that they are brushed along, and when no followers come to take their place, it is left vacant, and the face of the bar retreats ; its dunes are cut back, and a low cliff shore is formed.

As long as the outside of the peninsula formed a continuous curve, sand was carried along it in plenty from the cliff and the sea floor on the back of the Cape, and probably also from the shoals where Webbs island and its vanished mates once stood off Chatham. This condition is represented in line *DGVW*. But as the cliff from Nauset to Highland was cut farther back, and the shore current became unable to follow its earlier path along the margin of the peninsula, the additional bar, ending in Race point, was laid out, and the long, marshy "slash" was inclosed behind it. From the beginning of this additional bar until the present time, the supply of sand carried around the western curve of the peninsula was greatly reduced ; at times it may have ceased entirely. The supply being thus reduced or cut off, the bar southward from Race point inlet nearly to Wood end rapidly wasted ; and the sand taken from it by northwest gales went to supply the correspondingly rapid growth of Long point, *WX*, into Provincetown harbor, which Whiting shows to have extended many feet eastward in the fifty years past. Like Race point, Long point has advanced into comparatively deep water ; the twenty-fathom curve lies only six hundred feet off shore : the same depth is not found for almost three miles off the cliffed shore of the back of the Cape.

THE WESTERN SIDE OF THE CAPE

The western side of the Cape offers simpler problems than those of the eastern side. The first task here attempted by the waves was the development of the long west straight shore-line, $HQTC$, of which only the extremities now remain. This does not seem to have required anywhere a greater recession than three thousand feet. It must have been accomplished chiefly by northwest gales and north-to-south shore currents, by which the waste gathered from the more continuously cliffed shore was carried southward to tie together the several islands below South Truro. If southwest gales and south-to-north shore currents had been dominant, an acuminate spit should have been formed in prolongation of High head, where the waste would have been supplied from both sides of the Cape; but of this there is no sign.

The modification of the west straight shore-line by the excavation of the present concave shore-line, QPT, undoubtedly results, as has already been stated, from the disturbance of antecedent conditions that was caused by the growth of the Provincelands to the northwest. The northwest gales gradually came to have less and less influence; for some time past they must have ceased to be dominant; the chief control of shore movements now seems to be in the hand of the weaker southwest gales; for both the offsetting spit at the mouth of Pamet river, P, and the outspringing bar, QR, that protects High head on the west imply a northward transportation of sands. Some southward movement, however, still occurs, as might be expected; for at the faint angle, T, where the older straight shore-line, $HQTC$, is now cut by the concave shore-line, QPT, a spit projecting to the southwest seems to have been begun, and its continuation under water is indicated by a shoal of sympathetic curvature, TU, some five and a half miles in length. How far this shoal may be a new feature, originating with the excavation of the concave shore-line, or how far it may be of much greater age, dependent on the extensive Billingsgate shoals, where outlying islands are thought to have originally stood, is for the present an undecided question.

Protection of Provincetown Harbor

A matter of considerable economic importance turns on the changes experienced by the "wrist" of the Cape, the narrowest part of the bar that connects the mainland, or "forearm," of the Cape with the peninsula, or "hand." The people of Provincetown feel anxiety lest the sea should breach the bar and wash a great amount of sand westward past High head into their excellent harbor. The records of changes in the bar that connects Sandy Hook with the Long Branch cliffs give ground for this anxiety. The point that I wish here to call attention to is that the only part of the northeast shore that is liable to be broken through lies on the stretch, BF_3, between the point where the connecting bar springs northwest from the great cliff and the point where the "fulcrum" is at present located. Within this stretch the bar is generally retreating, being cut on the outer side and reconstructed on the inner side.

Two safeguards may be suggested. One would cause the fulcrum to migrate southeastward, thus diminishing the length of the narrow and breakable bar, and at the same time increasing its breadth and strength. This would be accomplished by the construction of bulkheads along the outside of the narrow bar, or "wrist," so as to catch the drifting sand instead of allowing it to pass by; thus the bar might be broadened and strengthened. Judging by the rapidity with which the body of a wrecked vessel causes an accumulation of sand on its southeastern side, a significant addition to the narrow bar might soon be made in this manner. Manifestly, the greatest economy in the use of the drifting sand requires that the bulkheads should be continually built out so as always to project a little beyond the aggrading shore-line. There are indications that this very result is at present being accomplished by natural process, for the beach in the narrow stretch, BF_3, is now notably broadened in front of its former line at the base of the surmounting dunes.

A more economical and enduring protection of Provincetown harbor than the above plan suggests has been already secured by completing the extremity of the bar, QR, that some years ago almost inclosed East harbor ; so that if storm waves should temporarily breach the narrow connecting bar on the ocean side, — the "wrist" of the "hand" of Provincetown at the end of the "bended arm of Massachusetts," — all the sand that was carried through the breach would settle in East harbor, and thereby strengthen the embankment against further encroachments. A second protecting dike has been built across the marsh northeastward from near High head. The fear that in case the narrow connecting bar, or "wrist," should be breached, the whole action of the Atlantic longshore currents would thereafter be directed through the breach into Provincetown harbor, is groundless. The whole history of the growth of the peninsula demonstrates that the longshore currents must continue to swing in long curves of large radius in the future as in the past.

The danger of silting up the Provincetown harbor by drift coming from the west concave shore-line along the west protecting bar of High head does not appear to be imminent, for the processes of transportation are comparatively slow on the inner side of the Cape ; but the danger is nevertheless real, and nothing but an extensive and expensive system of bulkheads from North Truro northward, on the stretch PQ, appears to be sufficient to avert it.

The destruction of the narrow strip of sand-bar shore, VW, between Race point and Wood end seems to me to threaten Provincetown harbor with a greater danger than any that it is exposed to from the east. This shore is now wasting rapidly. Once broken through, the currents driven by northwest gales, as well as by the rising tide, would no longer have to swing around Wood end, W, and deliver their load of drifting sand to Long point, X; they would in all probability invade the harbor directly, cutting away the low-tide flats that now expand south of the village, and throwing the detritus thus gained into the harbor. Attention has been called to this danger by Marindin in the *United States Coast Survey Report* for 1891, Appendix 8. While bulkheads may delay the destruction of the narrow bar, they can hardly preserve it even through a brief historical period. It has been proposed to abandon the wasting bar to its fate, and to protect the harbor by building a dike from the west end of the village across the flats to Wood end. A partial protection might be gained by building bulkheads on the northern shore of the peninsula, two or three miles east of Race point, K. Drifting sand from the east would then be stopped there. Race point, no longer so well supplied with sand as now, would be wasted by the northwest storms, and the sands carried from it would go southward to repair the shore towards Wood end. The protection of the bar northeast of High head near F_3 would, to a certain extent, work in the same direction by diminishing the supply of sand for the Race point bar; but a considerable time might elapse before any advantageous effect from this cause would be felt.

The Future of the Cape

The encroachment of the sea on the back of the Cape is undoubtedly destined to continue until the Truro mainland is all consumed north of Orleans, the "elbow" of the bended arm. At the present rate of recession — 3.2 feet a year — eight or ten thousand years will be required for this task; and this without considering the aid given by the waves of Cape Cod bay, whose concave sweep along the Truro shore shows their competence to do no insignificant share of the work.

It does not seem at all likely that while the rest of the Truro mainland is wearing away, the spit at Race point will of itself curve around to the south, and thus save from destruction the narrowing bar which incloses Provincetown harbor on the west. A great volume of transported sand would be needed to continue the bar in the deep water through which its present curve would lead. Moreover, the shoal known as Peaked hill bar may, as has been suggested, mark the beginning of a shore-line exterior to that of the present Race point curve. It is possible that as additional tangent spits are lapped on the outside of the curve, Race point will be cut back by a current from the northwest, working opposite to the great current that rounds the peninsula from the east; a cuspate or acuminate spit being then formed in the angle between the two, such as now exists at Great point, Nantucket. There the transportation of shore waste is northward on the east shore and southward on the west shore, according to the memoir by Admiral Davis; this being proved by the drift of coal and bricks from vessels wrecked on the east shore (139). The occurrence of these "cuspate forelands," as Gulliver has called them, is not so much of a rarity in nature as might be imagined from the little that appears about them in books; their growth being sometimes attributable to accordant currents that flow towards the point on either side; sometimes to opposing currents, one flowing inwards, the other outwards. Good reasons have been given by Abbe for believing that cape Hatteras and the other cuspate capes of the Carolina coast have been built between opposing currents (489).

The Provincetown peninsula may be expected to outlast the Truro mainland; for as long as the latter exists, the former must receive contributions from it. But when the mainland is washed away, — ten thousand years hence, at the present rate of wearing, — then Provinceland must rapidly disappear. Sable island, a long sand bar off Nova Scotia, is perhaps to be regarded as the vanishing remnant of a destroyed drift island [see *Trans. Roy. Soc. Canada*, XII (1894), Pt. II, 3–48; also, note in *Science*, II (1895), 886]. It may in this sense be taken to represent a future stage in the destruction of Cape Cod. All these changes are rapid, as changes go on the earth's surface. The Truro mainland will soon be destroyed, and the sands of Provinceland will be swept away as the oceanic curtain falls on this little one-act geographical drama.

REFERENCES

Abbe, C. *Proc. Boston Soc. Nat. Hist.*, XXVI (1895).

Chamberlin, T. C. "Terminal Moraine of the Second Glacial Epoch." *U. S. Geol. Surv., III Ann. Rep.* (1883).

Davis, C. H. "Memoir upon the Geological Action of the Tidal and Other Currents of the Ocean." *Mem. Am. Acad.* (Boston, 1849), IV, 117–156.

Davis, W. M. "Facetted Pebbles on Cape Cod." *Proc. Boston Soc. Nat. Hist.*, XXVI (1893), 166–175.

Freeman, F. History of Cape Cod. 1860.

Girard, J. La Géographie Littorale. Paris, 1895.

Gulliver, F. P. *Bull. Geol. Soc. Am.*, VII (1896).

Hitchcock, E. Geology of Massachusetts, I. 1841.

Marindin, H. L. (*a*) "Encroachment of the Sea upon the Coast of Cape Cod, Massachusetts." *U. S. Coast Surv. Rep.* (1889), 403–407; chart 28.

(*b*) *U. S. Coast Surv. Rep.* (1891), Appendix 8, with chart.

Mitchell, H. (*a*) "Report . . . concerning Nausett Beach and the Peninsula of Monomoy." *U. S. Coast Surv. Rep.* (1871), 134–143.

(*b*) "Additional Report on the Changes in the Neighborhood of Chatham and Monomoy." Ibid. (1873), 103–107.

" Report of the Trustees of Public Reservations on the Subject of the Province Lands." *Mass. Legislature, House, Pub. Doc. 339* (February, 1893), 6.

Russell, I. C. *U. S. Geol. Surv., IV Ann. Rep.*, 435.

Shaler, N. S. "Geology of Marthas Vineyard." *U. S. Geol. Surv., VII Ann. Rep.* (1888).

Thoreau, H. D. Narrative of his Excursions on Cape Cod in 1849, 1850, 1855. See "Cape Cod," in new Riverside edition of Thoreau's Works, 1894.

Upham, W. (*a*) Geology of New Hampshire, III, 300–305. 1878.

(*b*) "The Formation of Cape Cod." *Am. Nat.* (1879), 489–502, 552–565.

Weule, K. "Beiträge zur Morphologie der Flachküsten," *Kettler's Zeitschr. wiss. Geogr.*, VIII (1891), 211–256.

Whiting, H. L. " Report on the Special Study of Provincetown Harbor, Massachusetts." *U. S. Coast Surv. Rep.* (1867), 149–157.

XXVI

THE MOUNTAIN RANGES OF THE GREAT BASIN

Historical Statement. The larger mountain ranges of the Great Basin offer problems of especial interest, inasmuch as the faulting by which their present relief is believed to have been produced is not proved by stratigraphic evidence of the kind familiar to geologists, but by physiographic evidence of a kind to which little attention is usually given. These ranges were described by King in 1870 as "ordinarily the tops of folds whose deep synclinal valleys are filled with Tertiary and Quaternary detritus" (*a*, 451). Soon afterwards Gilbert concluded that the individual ranges were the carved upper parts of tilted or lifted blocks, resulting from "the displacement of comparatively rigid bodies of strata by vertical or nearly vertical faults" (*a*, 50). The same view was elaborated in a later report (*b*, 21–42). Powell, Dutton, and Russell adopted essentially the same explanation. King also seems to have recognized the validity of Gilbert's conclusion, for in 1878 he modified his earlier views by recognizing frequent faulting at a later date than that of the folding by which the great anticlinals and synclinals had been produced (*b*, 735). None of these observers, however, gave explicit consideration to the three elements necessarily involved in the problem of block faulting; namely, the pre-faulting topography, the topographical effect of the faulting, and the work of erosion on the faulted blocks.

One of the latest general discussions of the region is by Spurr, in whose essay a review of earlier writings may be found. This author concludes that "the mountain fronts studied are, in general, not marked by great faults, and, conversely, that the ascertainable faults are very rarely attended by simple fault scarps." He therefore rejects Gilbert's hypothesis and explains the Basin ranges as the "results of compound erosion active since Jurassic times, operating on rocks upheaved by compound earth movements which have been probably also continuous during the same period." It is further suggested that the ranges were probably differentiated during Cretaceous time, when a greater precipitation is assumed to account for their dissection : "subsequently the climate became arid and the water supply was not sufficient to remove the detritus from the valleys, which filled up " (265, 266). I have elsewhere briefly stated the reasons why this explanation seems unsatisfactory (*a*).

The Basin ranges have for some years been of especial interest in systematic physiography, for if Gilbert's explanation of them is correct, they offer unusually simple examples of mountain uplift and sculpture ; examples that may be adduced as relatively elementary illustrations of the difficult group of mountains in general, and that may therefore be with propriety presented to beginners for introductory practice before the description of complicated mountain ranges is undertaken. This opinion was confirmed on the appearance in 1884 of Russell's vivid account of the faulted lava-block ranges of southern Oregon; for these seemed to be even simpler and younger than the ranges farther south. Ranges of this kind are of a further interest in that they support in a certain measure the more primitive theory of mountain-making ; namely, that mountains are the immediate results of uplift, comparatively little modified by erosion, while the intermediate troughs are the effects of depression ; in a word, that dislocations of the earth's crust are here chiefly responsible for the observed relief of the region, and that the part played by erosion is subordinate. It is now generally agreed that this primitive theory finds little support in such ranges as the Alps, where the existing forms of peak and pass, spur and valley, are the product of extensive erosion in a deformed and broadly uplifted mass. A recurrence to the older theory in explanation of the ranges of the Great Basin is therefore a wholesome discipline.

It has for some time seemed to me that there was good evidence for regarding the Oregon lava-block ranges as types of the youngest, most elementary mountain forms known to geographers, and for placing the ranges of the Great Basin in Utah and Nevada as types of larger and more maturely sculptured ranges, appropriately following the introductory examples of southern Oregon. In view of this relation of the Basin ranges to the problems of systematic physiography, the opportunity of seeing some of them last summer was especially welcome, even though the time that could be given to them was brief. The conclusion reached was that faulting has recently exercised and, indeed, still exercises a dominant control over the uplift of all the larger mountain ranges observed, but that erosion has greatly modified the form which would be produced by faulting alone, and that the pre-faulting form is for this reason generally not recognizable.

Theoretical Considerations. It seems desirable to present the observations that have led to this conclusion in an order that is suggested by a deductive consideration of the problem, such as is necessarily entertained in the establishment of ideal physiographic types of mountain forms. In this way the complete ideal types of carved block mountains may be first carefully conceived and visualized in the imagination, all their essential features being systematically developed. The observed elements of form may then be described in their proper relation to the whole of which they are believed to be but parts.

The various types thus conceived in the imagination must represent all the hypotheses by which the facts in hand may be explained, the advantages that follow from a due consideration of "multiple-working hypotheses" having been convincingly set forth by Chamberlin. In publication, however, it is permissible to give relatively little space to those hypotheses which have been proved incompetent during the progress of an investigation, and to set forth in detail only the one which has gained — in the author's opinion at least — the rank of a successful theory. For this reason the following pages are chiefly devoted to a consideration of the Basin ranges as dissected fault-block mountains.

The author feels that some apology is needed for his writing on a field where his own observations are very limited in comparison to those of others who have a much wider experience in the Cordilleran region. His reason for adding yet another essay to the already abundant literature on the mountain ranges of the Great Basin is chiefly that the articles thus far published have not included a detailed analysis of the problem in hand, and in particular that the effects of erosion upon the faulted mountain blocks have received but little consideration. Gilbert's brief statement, written thirty years ago as the result of his first west-ern expeditions in 1871, 1872, and 1873 (*b*, 40, 41), is hardly more than a summary of conclusions. Russell explains the Basin ranges as having been "formed by the orographic tilting of blocks that are separated by profound faults" (*a*, 8), and leaves the erosion that they have suffered to be inferred. Elsewhere, when describing the West Humboldt range, he says: "The precipitous mountain face . . . is in reality an ancient fault scarp of grand proportions, which was somewhat eroded before the existence of Lake Lahontan" (*a*, 277); but "somewhat eroded" does scanty justice to the fine sculpturing of this range as shown in the accompanying Plate XLV. Spurr distinguishes between scarps directly due to faulting, and scarps due to the erosion of a long-ago faulted mass; but he gives no explicit discussion of the forms assumed by a simple fault scarp as it undergoes dissection; and his attention to the physiographic features of the Basin ranges in general is so brief that he implies that they possess an intimate correlation of structure and form by saying that the Appalachians "likewise consist of parallel ridges eroded along lines of folding" (255).

In spite, therefore, of the many descriptions of the Basin ranges that have been published, there has not yet appeared any detailed statement of the theory by which they are explained; the essential consequences of the theory have not been explicitly formulated; the criteria by which a fault-block mountain may be recognized in early or later stages of dissection have not been defined; and it is to supply these deficiencies that the preparation of this essay was undertaken.

When the essay had reached an almost completed form, the writer had the advantage of hearing the Basin-range problem discussed by Mr. Gilbert at the Washington meeting of the Geological Society of America, in January, 1903. It was a gratification to find that the plan of presentation here adopted very closely resembled in various ways the treatment offered by the originator of the Basin-range theory; it was at the same time an embarrassment to see that many of these pages would be hardly more than repetitions of Mr. Gilbert's report. They may, however, have a certain value in so far as they show that independent study leads to accordant results.

Ideal Types of Fault-Block Mountains. There are two chief types of fault-block mountains as illustrated in Figs. 113 and 114: one shows what may be called a tilted block, the other a lifted block. In order to economize space, only the tilted-block type will be here considered in detail.

The most char-
acteristic features
of a typical tilted-
block mountain in
its youth or early
maturity may be
summarized in

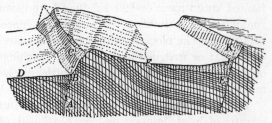

FIG. 113. A TILTED BLOCK, YOUTHFUL STAGE

Fig. 113 in which the block, *ACE*, has been raised and more or less inclined. The upper part, *BC*, of the faulted face, *AC*, rises above a piedmont plain of waste, *BD*, by which the backward slope of an adjoining block is buried; while the backward slope of the block, *CE*, is also partly buried in a plain of waste, *FJ*, which meets another waste plain from a third faulted block, *EK*.

Certain features shown in the figure are essential to the type in the stage of erosion here considered. The fault-bounded block, *ACE*, must present a back-sloping surface, *CFE*, whose form before the faulting occurred is now more or less modified by erosion
in its exposed
part, *CF*, and
buried under
waste in its de-
pressed part,
FE. The lower
part, *AB*, of the
faulted face,
ABC, is buried
under the waste

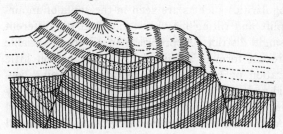

FIG. 114. A LIFTED BLOCK, YOUTHFUL STAGE

derived from the exposed and more or less dissected part, *BC*. Blocks which stand so high that the trough between them is now dissected instead of aggraded are not here considered. Examples of this kind are described in the northern Sierra Nevada by Diller (12–16).

Other features of the type are extremely variable. The size, structure, and form of the block are entirely undefined. Its upper surface may have been in the pre-faulting period, a peneplain worn down on ancient schists; a mountain area of folded or faulted strata more or less subdued by erosion; a series of horizontal and slightly dissected aqueous or igneous strata; or anything else. The block faulting may be on a large or small pattern; of regular or irregular arrangement; reaching over an extensive or a restricted area; of great or little displacement; and with much or little tilting.

The displacement may be slow or rapid, uniform or variable in rate, of brief duration or long continued, of remote or recent beginning and ending; it may vary greatly in amount along the fault line, diminishing to its end; as faulting continues, the length of the block may increase, and its end will thus vary in position. The faults may be simple or complex; the faulted front of a block may be clean cut, stepped, or shattered; the fault line along the mountain base may be essentially indifferent to the structure of the block, for the fault may be of deep-seated origin and not necessarily guided by the preëxistent foliation, stratification, folding, or faulting that is seen in the upper part of the block. The fault surface may be nearly a plane or a conspicuously curved surface, but from all that is known of faults it cannot possess sharp or exaggerated irregularities such as are seen in the septa of an ammonite. The uplift and tilting may vary widely in the different examples of a single district. Appropriate to all these variable elements, the present form of a faulted block may exhibit little or much modification by erosion; little modification being consistent with rapid and recent faulting of a resistant block in very arid climate; much modification being consistent with slow and ancient faulting of a weak block in a climate of sufficient rainfall to produce active erosion. In a block whose length has been increasing during a long time of increasing displacement, it would be reasonable to expect a mature dissection near the middle of the block to give way to young dissection near the ends of the block; for the middle part will have been long exposed to erosion, while the ends will have been but lately uplifted. The pre-faulting form of the block surface will usually be longest preserved near the base of its exposed back slope, *CF*, and the form due immediately to faulting will be best seen near the base of the front, *CB*.

As long as the faulting and tilting continue, strong relief may be maintained; but after displacement ceases, erosion will advance without more hindrance than is offered by the resistance of the rocks; it will slowly subdue the earlier relief to rounded forms, and still more slowly widen the valleys and consume the intervening hills as the forms of old age (Fig. 115) are realized. In a late stage of degradation the mountain mass will be invaded by numerous flat-floored, branching valleys between low, rounded forking spurs. The valleys will then be largely adjusted to the weaker rock structures, while the fading ridges will stand longest where upheld by the resistant structures. The mountain base, an irregular line, will have no close relation to the path of the fault, and the slope between the

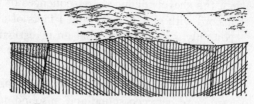

FIG. 115. A TILTED BLOCK, OLD STAGE

mountain base and the fault line will carry a thin and discontinuous veneer of waste on a planed rock floor. It would probably be impossible to distinguish the residuals of tilted and lifted blocks in a late stage of erosion.

Place and Value of Deduction. It is important here to emphasize two general considerations. First, the details of form appropriate to any desired special case under the ideal type should be deduced with as much completeness and definiteness as possible. As long as the details of a theoretical form are vaguely conceived, the observer will be unable to give his theory a rigorous test; its consequences will be so indefinite that he can hardly say whether they are confirmed or contradicted when he confronts them with the appropriate facts of observation. It is particularly important that deduction should not be postponed till after the field work is "completed" and after the field is left. The two processes of observation and deduction should go on together in the field, each aiding the other, if the investigator would avoid as far as possible the disappointment of finding afterwards that the field records are deficient in some particular point where fuller record would have been of critical value in testing a deduction. Memory may sometimes supplement written record, but it is notoriously dangerous to trust to unwritten notes. In my own experience, however, careful deduction is more difficult than observation in the field, but it is greatly aided by deliberate thinking and writing while the facts are before the eyes.

Second, it must not be assumed that a theory gains support because its consequences can be definitely deduced. However accurately one may argue out the details of form appropriate to a certain stage in the dissection of a faulted mountain block, the theory of block faulting becomes a demonstrated occurrence only when the sharply deduced consequences of the theory are shown to accord with closely determined facts of observation.

Not only is it important that an investigation should give equal attention to deduction and induction : it is essential to clear presentation that both phases of inquiry should be sufficiently published. It is otherwise almost impossible for the reader to discriminate between sound and unsound conclusions. It is conceivable that an able observer should patiently collect and record a multitude of facts, and that he should very imperfectly set forth the reasons that lead him to the announced explanation of the facts. The hurried reader may in such a case quote the announced explanation and accept it, if he wishes, on the authority of the writer ; but the more critical reader will wish to make his own measure of the validity of the announced conclusion, and this he will find difficult in the absence of explicit announcement of the method of reaching it. It is particularly important to consider the deductive side of any problem in which there is substantial agreement among different observers as to the facts directly observable, but in which there is difference of opinion as to the explanation of the facts ; for in such a case the correct solution of the problem turns essentially on the validity of the deductions by which the unobservable facts of the past are brought into mental vision.

It may not be amiss to point out that the investigator's effort in all such problems as the one here in hand is simply to supplement the directly observable present facts by the discovery of the unobservable past facts, so that the entire phenomenon shall become known. If observers of sufficient penetration had been present in the Great Basin during all the formative period of each mountain range now seen, their records of unobserved fact might give a complete account of all the processes involved; and it would then be perfectly clear whether the mountain ranges were carved fault blocks or not. In the necessary absence of such observers we try to replace their records by our discoveries, and although our method of discovery necessarily has recourse to the imagination, the phenomena that we successfully discover are facts of only a slightly different order from those of direct observation. We see certain forms imprinted in stratified rocks, and by reasonable mental process arrive at the conclusion that these are the remains of once living organisms. We see two groups of similar strata in similar sequence, and by reasonable mental process reach the belief that their present discontinuity is the result of what is called faulting. In both these cases the inferred explanation is accepted by most geologists as of essentially the same order of verity as the observed fact, because it has now stood the test of repeated and minute scrutiny. In the case of the Basin ranges, interpreted as carved fault blocks, many geologists are at present by no means disposed to attach equal value to the existing facts of structure and form reached by direct observation and the supposed past facts of dislocation reached by mental inference. It is therefore appropriate that special attention should be here given to the method of inference by which the past facts are resurrected.

It is the application of the combined inductive and deductive method here sketched, although always applied less consciously and completely in the field than could be wished, that has satisfied me of the essential correctness of the theory which explains the larger ranges of the Great Basin as well-dissected blocks of long-maintained faulting, continued into recent time.

Evidence of Faulting along the Mountain Base. The first elements for consideration in this problem are those which should, in a type example of a long-faulted, well-dissected mountain block, be expectably associated with the occurrence of a fault along the mountain base.

The simplest and most manifest element of this kind is a nearly straight or but moderately curved base-line (Fig. 113) passing indifferently across or obliquely along the structure of the mountain mass which rises rather abruptly and continuously on one side, while a sloping plain of waste is spread out on the other. The simple continuity of the base-line and the complete absence of rock outcrops on one side of it are essential consequences of long-continued block faulting, and are at the same time not characteristic of any other available geological process. As Emmons wrote nearly thirty years ago, one cannot "imagine an erosion which would leave an abrupt wall of 7500 feet in height on one side of a valley nearly twenty miles wide" (345). Hence, wherever these theoretical consequences are borne out by facts of direct observation, block faulting is thereby given so high a degree of probability while other processes are rendered so highly improbable that the theory of block faulting may be looked upon as well introduced, at least.

The best examples that came under my observation of actual forms which match these preliminary members of the whole series of deduced type forms were not among the Basin ranges proper, but along the bordering Wahsatch mountain front, by which the Great Basin is limited on the east. The mountain base near Provo and near Ogden deserves careful study in this respect.

The Wahsatch range is divided into several local mountain groups by the cañons of streams that rise a number of miles east of the line of higher summits and flow westward to Salt Lake Basin. In the neighborhood of Provo the cañons are those of Spanish fork, Hobble creek, and Provo river, between which the mountain groups may be called the Spanish peaks Wahsatch, and the Provo peaks Wahsatch, or, more briefly, the Spanish and the Provo Wahsatch (Emmons, 340, 344).

Close by Provo, where my party had the most leisure for attention to this problem and where we had the advantage of guidance by Professor E. H. Hinckley of the academy in that city, the expectations of theory are extraordinarily well supported by the facts. The mountains spring boldly from the plain; their base-line breaks obliquely across the tilted and folded rocks of the mountain mass; the occurrence of a base-line fault is explicitly stated by Emmons (345). We made an excursion up Rock cañon to a mid-monoclinal ridge back of the frontal summits, and returned by Slate cañon. There are some indications of faults in the longitudinal valleys between the monoclinal ridges (Emmons, 345, 348), but nothing at present known serves to give date to these faults, should they be proved to occur. Fig. 116 shows the generalized structure thus determined: an anticlinal axis lies near the western base of the mountains opposite Provo, while a great monocline, the eastern half of the incomplete anticline, constitutes the rest of the range. Farther south the anticline is not seen at the mountain base. The rocks in the anticlinal axis are said to be mid-Paleozoic; those of the crests are Carboniferous (Emmons, 345, 346); farther east the maps of the 40th parallel

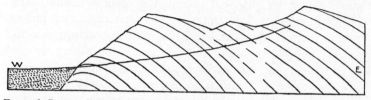

FIG. 116. ROUGH CROSS SECTION OF THE PROVO WAHSATCH, LOOKING NORTH

survey indicate Mesozoic strata. West of the mountain base no rocks are seen in place; the gravel beaches and deltas of lake Bonneville descend to the alluvial plain that slopes under the shallow waters of Utah lake.

About twelve miles southeast of Provo, the Spanish Wahsatch, lying next north of Spanish fork cañon, is even more emphatic in its testimony for block faulting. Its rock layers are nearly horizontal, or dip gently eastward. Some significant details of its form will be considered later.

The Wahsatch near and northwest of Ogden presents several significant features, even when seen only from a railroad train. Its base-line is here of moderate curvature, and manifestly traverses various structures, as indicated both by form and by color. The mountain front rises abruptly and continuously from the base-line, except for brief interruptions in narrow-mouthed cañons.

The features of this range and of several others farther west, as seen from the passing train, were so accordant with the features more deliberately observed near Provo that it seemed to me one could hardly regard them as other than carved fault blocks ; but while observations from a train may have a high value to the observer, I am well aware that they will not be regarded as convincing by others, especially not by those whose habitual work in paleontology, petrography, or minute stratigraphy has given them no acquaintance with the value of large elements of form in physiographic problems, even though these elements be only hastily observed from a car window.

During a stage ride northward from Winnemucca, Nevada, into southern Oregon, I passed the Santa Rosa and Pine Forest ranges, both of which exhibited very clearly the gently curving base-line, regardless of rock structure, and the bold mountain front, continuous except for sharp-cut cañons, that are essentially characteristic of carved-block mountains. The western face of Jackson range near its northern end had the same appearance, but this was very imperfectly seen. Further details concerning the first two of these ranges are given in a later section.

The Base-Line of Residual Mountains. It may be worth while to state at this stage of the discussion the reasons for rejecting the theory that the mountain ranges just described are the residuals of much larger masses, of which the vanished parts have been removed by erosion. These reasons are found, not at all in the incompetence of erosion to wear away mountains, but in the impossibility of explaining the forms of the mountain ranges above-named as the residuals of much larger masses. There are numerous examples in which general sub-aërial erosion has sufficed to remove mountains more or less completely, but no examples in which the residuals of half-consumed mountains exhibit the features above described as characteristic of certain Basin ranges. Several special cases may be considered.

The only residual mountains known to physiographers as having a relatively continuous mass and rectilinear base are those in which structure controls form, as in the stratified Appalachians of Pennsylvania and Virginia. There the ridges of resistant sandstone rise between rolling lowlands of weaker strata ; the ridges are occasionally cut through in water gaps, but between the gaps they frequently present a continuous mass sloping evenly to a nearly rectilinear base. When the strata bend, the ridges turn ; when the strata are cut off by a fault, the ridges end. Structure is perfectly expressed in form. The same rule applies to the trap ridges of the Triassic areas of Connecticut, New Jersey, and Pennsylvania, but the rule clearly enough does not apply to the Wahsatch mountains and the other Basin ranges above named.

Residual mountains whose survival is not dependent on contrasts of rock resistance so striking as those of the Appalachians, and whose structure is relatively massive, are well illustrated in the crystalline Appalachians of North Carolina and Georgia. In mountains so old as these, it is to be presumed that the valleys have generally come, by a process of long-sought adjustment, to follow the somewhat weaker rocks, while the mountains represent the more resistant masses. None of these mountains, however, have a bold descent to a nearly rectilinear base ; all of them give forth spurs which, as a rule, slope more and more gradually as they fade away on the valley low-

FIG. 117. THE BLUE RIDGE ESCARPMENT, NORTH CAROLINA, LOOKING NORTH

lands, while branch valleys enter between the spurs far into mountains. The mountain base-line is sinuous and ill-defined.

One of the most remarkable of these many residuals is a group of radiating spurs that culminate in Big Bald mountain in the older Appalachians of northern Georgia (Ellijay map sheet). The spurs have a notably stellate arrangement between open centrifugal valleys, showing that the mountain is to-day the mere skeleton of a once much larger body ; its emaciated form is highly suggestive of the gnawing erosion which it has so long suffered.

A good example for contrast with the Basin ranges is found in the strong, east-facing escarpment known in northern North Carolina and southern Virginia as the "Blue Ridge." The escarpment, *AB* (Fig. 117), is evidently retreating westward, for it is simply the headwater slope of the short-course Atlantic rivers, which are actively capturing drainage area from the higher-lying headwaters, *AD*, of the much longer rivers of the Mississippi system. Viewed in a very general way, as on a small scale map, the base of the scarp is of moderate curvature, and its slope is essentially independent of structure; hence in both these general features it might be said to resemble the face of a Basin range. But when viewed in detail, the base of the escarpment is sinuous in a high degree, with numerous branching spurs that advance between well-carved amphitheaters; the spurs gradually fade out forward instead of being abruptly terminated at a well-defined base-line, as is so persistently the case with the above-described ranges of Utah and Nevada. In some cases the spurs run far forward, forming ridges of undulating outline, by which embayments of the piedmont lowland are divided. The contrast of the Blue Ridge escarpment and the Basin ranges is therefore extremely instructive. The topographical maps of the North Carolina mountains are worth examining in this connection: Wilkesboro, Cranberry, Mt. Mitchell, and Pisgah (North Carolina), and Hillsville (Virginia) sheets afford the best illustrations.

The only conditions under which residual mountains have a well-defined, moderately curved base-line is where they are cut across by a master river, or laterally attacked by the waves of a vigorous sea; but these conditions are so manifestly inapplicable to the region of the Basin ranges that they need no consideration here, except in so far as they suggest that a trenchant cause is needed to explain the well-defined base-line to which the ranges descend.

Residual Mountains in the Great Basin. There are, however, some excellent examples of residual mountains among the Basin ranges. Those that I saw are of much less height than the ranges thus far described. Their forms are thoroughly subdued. They have no well-defined and moderately curved base-line, but descend in branching, sprawling, fading spurs, which interlock with broad, flat-floored, branching valleys. The contrast of these nearly worn-out mountains with the more vigorous forms previously considered is most striking, yet it is entirely conceivable that the contrast may be due simply to stage of development and not to difference of origin. It has already been shown that the late stage of dissection of a fault-block mountain would, long after faulting had ceased, present essentially such worn-out forms as are here described, for the sharp definition of the base-line would be lost after faulting had weakened and stopped. On the other hand, the old residuals of massive mountains of any other kind would also present these worn-out, sprawling forms. There are, indeed, no tests by which the two kinds of old mountains can be easily distinguished.

Several examples of residual ranges in the Great Basin were noted as follows: North of Tecoma, Central Pacific Railroad, there are mountains of moderate relief, whose rounded, branching spurs descend gradually to low, sprawling, dwindling terminals between wide-open, waste-floored valleys. The fading spurs and open valleys interlock on a very sinuous line. These well-defined features gain an added value by their contrast with the Ombe and Ute ranges, south and west of Tecoma: both of these are of strong relief, with relatively rectilinear base-lines on the sides toward the railroad. Their valleys are steep-sided and narrow-floored, causing but little interruption in the otherwise continuous mountain front. Nevertheless, these higher ranges have been abundantly carved, so that their peaks and spurs preserve no indication of an original block form; and no signs of modern faulting, elsewhere so easily recognizable from the train, were here visible.

North of Omar there is a typical subdued mountain mass, whose dwindling spurs interlock with open valleys. This example was strongly contrasted with the lofty Humboldt range, south of Wells; here the snow-patched peaks descended by strong slopes to a relatively rectilinear base-line on the northwest.

Northeast of Golconda, Nevada, a low range descends to a very ragged base, one of the best examples of the kind that my trip discovered. Its description would involve a repetition of what has just been said for other similar ranges, though the description here might be somewhat more emphatic than before.

Another example of this class is a small, unnamed range, about forty miles north of St. George, Utah. Its spurs are long drawn out, with concave profiles toward their base; its valley mouths are wide open, holding broad, waste-covered slopes. Its base-line is sinuous and indefinite, in the strongest contrast to the simple and definite base-line of the Spanish Wahsatch.

The Cañons and Ravines of Block Mountains. If we now return to the consideration of the higher Basin ranges, it seems undeniable that faulting gives a much better explanation of their base-line than can possibly be given by erosion. Indeed, erosion can be appealed to for the removal of the missing mountain masses only so long as the processes and results of erosion are looked upon as arbitrary and beyond reduction to those generalizations known as natural laws. The day has passed when this is permissible. Erosion, whether sub-aërial or littoral, fluvial, glacial, or æolian, proceeds systematically through a series of stages; and while there is still more to be learned than is now known regarding the progress of mountain sculpture, enough is already safely understood to exclude the resort to erosion in general as a ready means of accounting for any desired result. It remains, however, to be seen whether not only the base but the face of the Basin ranges is consistent with the theory of block faulting. The form of the valleys that are carved in the monntain face will be first considered, and after this the form of the spurs between the valleys.

It follows from the scheme graphically represented in Fig. 113 that a very rapid and modern faulting of a very resistant rock mass in a very conservative climate would produce a mountain block having a notably smooth fault-face or escarpment along its front. On the other hand, the gradual and long-continued faulting of a weak rock mass in a destructive climate would produce a mountain block having well-developed ravines and cañons whose erosion had been accomplished during the progress of the faulting. The essential characteristic of such ravines would be a V-like cross section even down to the ravine mouths; and as long as the uplifting of the mountain block actively continues, the streams that are dissecting it cannot widen their valley floors. Indeed, many of the smaller streams might be unable under such conditions to attain a graded slope even in weak rocks, and their channels would be marked by rapids near the base-line of the mountain, where the V-ravine would suddenly open upon an alluvial fan, sloping gently forward to the waste-covered piedmont plain. It is only after faulting has ceased that the streams can advance in an uninterrupted progress toward mature development and widen their valley floors toward the mountain front; and only after faulting has long ceased can the valley floors be so far developed as to leave nothing but residual skeletons of the original mountain block between them. Variations in rate of faulting and in resistance of rock masses would produce many corresponding variations in ravine forms, many of which may be easily deduced, but none of which demand immediate consideration.

The points that need special emphasis in this connection are that the characteristic form of ravines and cañons, carved in a faulted mountain block during the progress of a long-continued and still active faulting, can be reasonably determined by deduction; that these forms are well specialized; and that their most notable peculiarity is the persistence of a V-section down to the mountain base, where the steep-walled ravine or cañon suddenly opens upon a gravel fan that slopes forward to the wide piedmont plain. It goes without saying that this peculiarity of cañon form is impossible in a residual mountain, carved by the extensive erosion of a once much larger mass, unless the most special conditions conspire to produce it. Such conspiracy is found, as has been said, in the stratified Appalachians, where the belts of resistant sandstone, interstratified with much weaker shales and limestones, now stand in relief as residual mountains in which the streams and rivers have cut sharp V-section ravines and notches. The resistance of the sandstones, on which the survival of the sharply limited mountain ridge depends, is, therefore, also the cause of the narrowness of the ravines and notches cut in it by the streams; and it may be added that the sharpness of these forms is in part due to the relatively recent uplift that the middle Appalachian belt has suffered.

All the higher Basin ranges that I saw in the summer of 1902 are characterized by sharp-cut V-section ravines and cañons, narrow-floored and steep-walled down to their very mouths. All these cañoned ranges are so unlike in structure to the ridges of the stratified Appalachians that it is utterly out of the question to explain the former by the theory that is appropriate for the latter.

Rock cañon in the Wahsatch, near Provo, has a narrow gravel plain near its mouth, probably the result of delta building in front of the mountain base during the presence of lake Bonneville; but after going up the cañon a few hundred feet, its stream is found cascading on the more resistant strata, whose rising outcrops form prominent ribs on the steep cañon wall. The same features are observable in Slate cañon, three miles farther south, except that the stream here being smaller, its descent is steeper, and it has accumulated hardly any gravels upstream from its Bonneville delta on the mountain front. The beds of both these streams have a rapid descent, and are not cut down as low at the cañon mouth as might be expected in view of the much lower level of the broad piedmont plain a little way forward from the mountain base. Some detention of their down-cutting must be ascribed to the temporary rises of the local base-level during Bonneville time, and to the work of removing high-level delta gravels in post-Bonneville time; but this cause of detention does not seem nearly sufficient to account for the height of the stream beds over the plain. Hence, not only the steepness of the cañon walls, the narrowness of their floors, and the rapid descent of their stream, but also the relatively high level of their mouths suggest recent uplift of the mountain block.

The general form of these two steep-walled cañons suggests not only that the up-faulting of the mountain block has been continued into relatively recent time, but that the uplift of the block by an amount equal to the height of the summits over the base (in the Provo Wahsatch) has been accomplished since the latter part of Tertiary time. The cañons have a much younger expression than that of the narrow valleys in the uplands of southeastern Pennsylvania, for there the streams have formed narrow flood plains and the valley sides are for the most part smoothly graded even in crystalline rocks; yet the elevation of these uplands is not of remote date. If it is thought unsafe to make a comparison between cañons in the arid interior basin of Utah and young valleys in our better-watered Atlantic slope, the Wahsatch cañons with their perennial streams may be compared with the dry side cañons of the Colorado cañon in Arizona. The expression of the two is much the same, allowance being made for the unlike attitude of the rocks. The chief difference between these two groups of cañons is this: those of the Arizona plateaus were cut down in a rising plateau mass by intermittent wet-weather streams working with respect to the sinking local base-level, the intrenching Colorado; those of the Wahsatch were cut down in a rising mountain mass by more persistent streams working with respect to a relatively fixed local base-level. The erosion of the Arizona cañons, trunk and branch, cannot have been begun earlier than the latter part of Tertiary time; the erosion of the Wahsatch cañons may well have had an even later beginning. The date assigned to the Wahsatch fault by King, on incomplete geological evidence, is the close of the Eocene; but this seems inadmissibly early in view of the sharpness of the Wahsatch peaks and spurs and of the enormous amount of erosion accomplished in the plateau province in post-Eocene time.

It should be noted, however, that certain transverse streams in the Provo district have valleys that are more maturely opened than the cañons just considered. The so-called cañons of Provo river, Hobble creek, and Spanish fork are all relatively open, with moderately steep and frequently graded side slopes. This seemed to me in part due to the occurrence of weaker rocks where the transverse streams have cut down their valleys, but I am not sure that this explanation applies in all cases. It may be that in some examples the more open valleys are connected with differences in the date, amount, and rate of faulting. Some of the transverse valleys are nevertheless of true cañon-like form; such is Weber cañon, which is followed from the east by the Union Pacific Railroad into the Great Basin at Ogden; and also Ogden cañon, a few miles farther north, if the maps may be trusted.

The part of the Wahsatch range next north of Spanish fork cañon, here called the Spanish Wahsatch, is beautifully carved with sharp ravines which preserve their narrow floor and steep walls directly to the mountain base. Two of these ravines were visited. The beds of their wet-weather streams pitch forward at an angle of from 22° to 34°, steepening near their mouth; the slope of the side walls is 30°. All the ravines open close to the level of the Bonneville beach instead of being cut down nearer to the level of the piedmont plain; as in the Provo

Wahsatch, this peculiar relation should be here also, at least in part, ascribed to the recent up-faulting of the mountain block.

The Wahsatch range has many other cañons and ravines of similar form, so far as observation from the plain in front of the mountains can determine, and so far as description by local observers testifies.

The southwestern slope of the Santa Rosa range north of Cane spring deserves further statement. I had time to examine its general features from a spur next south of Cane spring. The strike of various ledges outcropping on the bare mountain flanks was in general northeastward; that is, about at right angles to the trend of this part of the mountain base. The dip of the ledges was steep southeast, or nearly vertical. Rock structure was, however, very faintly exhibited as a rule; the mountain mass is for the most part worn to the stage of smoothly graded summits and spurs, whose graceful forms were beautifully brought out in late afternoon light. The spurs terminate in strong slopes, sometimes maintaining convex longitudinal profiles almost to their base. The valleys and ravines are steep-walled and narrow-floored to their very mouths. The mountain base is of long and gentle curvature, here convex to the southwest. Faint scarps in the washed gravels close to the mountain base were seen at several points, and were noted as indicating modern faulting. The gravel wash extends far forward on an even slope, thus suggesting a vigorous discharge of waste from the mountain valleys. For several miles east of Cane spring the strong wash from the mountains on the north meets a much weaker wash from a series of low spurs on the south; these spurs descend gently, some reaching farther forward than others, and all blending by gradual concave slopes with the inclined gravel plain before them. So distinct a contrast between the forms of the mountains on the north and those of the spurs on the south must have a meaning. No meaning seems so probable as that which associates the mountain with strong block faulting and active carving, both continued into recent time, and the spurs with a long period of undisturbed erosion.

As a characteristic of this arid and thinly settled region, note may be made of the fruit ranch of a Basque settler at the mouth of one of the valleys in the Santa Rosa mountains. The small stream from the valleys supplies water enough to irrigate an orchard of a thousand apple trees and some alfalfa fields ; the alfalfa serves for local needs ; the fruit is sold to neighboring ranches and villages. Another valley supplies water for some alfalfa fields belonging to the ranch at Cane spring. This spring itself seems to rise where the long wash slope from the mountains on the north comes against the rock that descends from the spurs on the south. Every drop of water available in the growing season is used. Storage reservoirs in the mountains would increase the summer supply, but such reservoirs would be so soon filled with waste — should they indeed escape destruction by a cloud-burst torrent — that the cost of their construction would, it is to be feared, never be repaid.

The Mountain Face. The study of mountain morphology is so little advanced that one encounters difficulty both as to method and terms in attempting to present a definite account of mountain forms. It is evident, however, that the face of a range, carved on the fault scarp of its tilted or lifted block, should present certain features characteristic of such an origin, and that these features should be deduced as carefully as any others in the mental construction of the type example, so that their occurrence or absence in actual ranges may be determined. In no other way can it be ascertained whether the face of the range as well as its base and its cañons testify in favor of block faulting. The following paragraphs therefore attempt to discover the forms that should characterize the ideal case of a faulted block of homogeneous structure whose faulting has progressed at a slow and relatively uniform rate, so that the sides of the ravines that are eroded in it shall be weathered back to graded slopes about as fast as the fault block is raised. Three

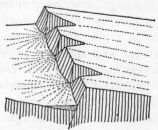

FIG. 118. NOTCHES IN THE FRONT OF A YOUNG TILTED BLOCK

Some of the front edge of the block still remains

significant stages of faulting and erosion may be considered. In an early stage (Fig. 118) the low fault scarp is notched by ravines whose location and length are determined by the site of pre-faulting inequalities in the upper surface of the block. Adjacent

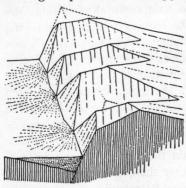

FIG. 119. NOTCHES IN THE FRONT OF A YOUNG TILTED BLOCK, MORE UP-LIFTED THAN IN FIG. 118

Nothing of front edge remains

ravines have not yet widened sufficiently to consume the edge at the top of the block between them. In a later stage (Fig. 119) the block is raised higher, the ravines are worn deeper and farther back, some of them being larger than others. Nothing of the upper front edge of the block now remains, for the flaring walls of the ravines now meet in a sharp ridge crest that rises backward from the vertex of a triangular facet on the block front, toward the top of the block. In the third stage (Fig. 120) the block is raised still higher, and the ravines have become still longer and deeper; at this stage the mountain crest might become serrate,

and its back slope would be well dissected. The long, sharp-crested ridges between the larger front ravines are still terminated by triangular facets, very systematic in form and position, with their bases aligned along the mountain front. The spur sides and the facets themselves will have suffered some carving, as is shown in Fig. 121, where some of the terminal facets are enlarged. The moderate dissection of the large facet by small ravines results in the development of several little basal facets along the fault line,

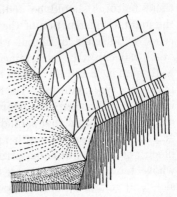

FIG. 120. SPURS AND DEEP RAVINES IN THE FRONT OF A TILTED BLOCK, MUCH UPLIFTED

Upper surface not shown

where they form the truncating terminals of several little spurs. These basal facets are of importance in this stage of dissection, for they have suffered the least change of any part of the mountain front.

We are thus led to conclude that the features of special significance as the necessary result of long-continued faulting, persistent into the recent period, are, first, the sharp-cut, narrow-floored valleys which have already been considered; and secondly, the large and small terminal facets of the spurs, whose bases show a notable alignment all along the mountain front.

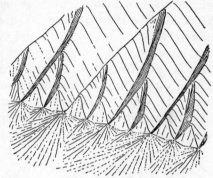

FIG. 121. DISSECTED TERMINAL FACETS OF MAIN SPURS

Showing small basal facets between short ravines; drawn on a larger scale than Figs. 118–120

If faulting be supposed to cease after the stage of Fig. 120 is reached, the valleys will widen without much deepening at their mouths, the spurs will be narrowed, and the truncating terminal facets will in time be so far consumed that the spurs will become pointed, as

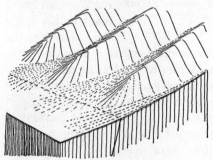

FIG. 122. TAPERING SPURS BETWEEN OPEN VALLEYS

Late-mature stage of a tilted block; same scale as Figs. 118–120

in Fig. 122. The further erosion progresses into maturity, the farther will the points of the wasting spurs withdraw from the fault line, and the more perfect will be the relation of structure and form; but as old age is reached this relation is more and more suppressed. It is evident that late maturity or early old age will introduce the system of interlocking valleys and spurs already described as characteristic of subdued residual mountains.

Spurs and Terminal Facets of the Wahsatch Range. The Spanish Wahsatch, opposite the villages of Springville and Mapleton, presents a group of forms that resembles to a singular degree those represented in Figs. 120 and 121. The mountain base is characterized by a series of basal spur facets, sloping at an angle of 38° or 40°, and possessing remarkably systematic forms which correspond closely to those deduced for the ideal type in its maturely dissected stage. The ridge or crest line of the spurs slopes at angles that do not vary greatly from 25°. Fig. 123, enlarged from photograph and sketch, presents a detailed view of this part of the Wahsatch, in which the sharp-crested ridges, with their peculiarly systematic terminal facets, rise between the sharp-cut ravines of the mountain front. The difference between these beautifully sculptured forms and the more rigid diagrammatic features of Figs. 118–122, is not a difference of kind, for every element in the ideal view is matchable with a corresponding element in the actual view; it is rather a difference due to the occurrence in nature of innumerable little irregularities, the

FIG. 123. RAVINES, SPURS, AND TERMINAL FACETS
OF THE SPANISH WAHSATCH
Looking east; drawn from sketch and photograph

result of slight variations of rock mass and of sculpturing process, whereby actual mountains depart in so pleasing and graceful a manner from the hard and conventional lines of diagrams. In spite of these differences, the notable characteristic of this part of the Wahsatch front is its model-like form, every element of which is so systematically arranged that it can be understood; and thereon depends much of its attractiveness. The expression of its features is open and frank, without that complication of unresolvable elements which makes the meaning of larger mountain forms so difficult of full understanding. One reason for the simplicity of form here exhibited is the simplicity of rock structure in the mountain block. The strata of which it is built lie nearly horizontal in the district that we examined, and none of them are sufficiently unlike their neighbors in strength or weakness to determine the occurrence of strong cliffs or benches. There are indeed several delicately embossed contouring lines on the spur slopes by which the structure of the mass is indicated in the distant view; and on climbing the slopes there are abundant small outcrops by which the inference from the distant view is confirmed; but as a whole the slopes are graded and cloaked with a thin cover of creeping waste, so that the observer's attention is not too soon diverted from the study of mountain sculpture by an emphatic exhibition of mountain structure.

I first saw the spurs, facets, and ravines of this mountain front from the passing excursion train of the International Geological Congress in 1891, but they were then only regarded as "peculiar." They were seen a second time on returning from a Colorado cañon excursion in 1900, and on that occasion, although they were then again observed only from passing trains northward on one road in the morning, and southward on another in the afternoon, the possibility and necessity of explaining them as a result of erosion on a faulted block was recognized. During the summer of 1902 my party made a special visit to these significant spurs, walked along their base for a short distance, ascended the slope of one of the facets, and came down again by the ravine alongside of it. There seemed to be no escape from the conclusion that extensive and recent faulting of the mountain block is here indicated, not only by the complete absence of the mountain rocks west of the almost rectilinear base-line, as already set forth, but also by the detail of form on the mountain face, and particularly by the well-defined facets in which the spurs terminate.

The late afternoon view of the Wahsatch range from the shore of Utah lake brings the mountain forms clearly forth. The eye, after wandering along other less intelligible parts of the range, turns repeatedly to the block north of Spanish fork cañon with enjoyment of the fuller meaning found there. Elsewhere one's curiosity is excited; there it is satisfied. After the sharply defined terminal facets of the mountain spurs are found to be systematic elements of form in the Spanish Wahsatch, they may be recognized in many other parts of the range, but nowhere, so far as I have seen, with the model-like distinctness of development that is exhibited in the example just described.

When the Wahsatch, near Provo, is seen from a point not too near its base, several spur facets may be distinguished between the cañons and ravines by which the mountain front is scored; but the edges of the facets are dull, like the edges of a crystal of apatite. In the Spanish block the sharp-edged facets tempt one to sketch in outline; in the Provo block it is by no means so easy to do justice to the mountain form in an unshaded drawing. One reason for this is that the ravines here are not very deeply carved — except the larger ones, called cañons, whose streams head in subsequent valleys back of the frontal ridge — and hence the spurs do not stand forth between the ravines in strong relief. Moreover, accompanying and perhaps causing this loss of definition in the spurs and facets, there is an increased variety of texture in the rock mass, whereby certain resistant strata stand forth bare and prominent between weaker neighbors; the attention is thus involuntarily somewhat distracted from sculpture and turned toward structure. The facets are nevertheless undeniably present, and in essentially the same relation to spur and base-line as is shown in the type diagram (Fig. 120). The southern end of the Provo block possesses the most distinct examples, some of which will be described in the following section.

The Wahsatch spurs that descend near Little Cottonwood cañon, between Provo and Salt Lake, are systematically terminated by clearly recognizable facets.

The Ogden Wahsatch also offers illustrations of the systematic faceting of its spurs, those adjoining Weber cañon being the most distinct. Farther north, back of the city of Ogden, the facets are round-edged, yet distinctly recognizable as systematic elements of form, like those of the Provo Wahsatch.

The spurs of several other ranges, seen from train and stage in Utah and Nevada, were terminated by facets of more or less distinct form. The spurs of the Santa Rosa range were more rounded than many of the others, and the terminal facets were indistinct. The eastern face of Pine Forest mountains in northern Nevada is notably steep and scarp-like, descending to a relatively rectilinear base. The scarp is sharply cut by narrow valleys which remain narrow to their very mouths. Some of the spurs end in rounded facets. Signs of recent faults in the gravels at the mountain base were noted, but at too great a distance for me to feel certain of their meaning. The height of the range gradually decreases to its trailing southern end. In this range more clearly than elsewhere the narrow valleys seemed to be cut beneath a rolling upland of earlier origin.

The Spur Facets are not Wave-Cut. The terminal facets of the Wahsatch front rise over the Bonneville beaches in such a way as to suggest a possible origin as wave-cut cliffs. It is not to be doubted that waves could, if time be allowed, cut off the points of spurs so as to truncate them in triangular facets, but in that case the facets should be associated with certain other features which are significantly absent from the Wahsatch range.

This may, as usual, be best demonstrated by consideration of the progress of wave work in an ideal case.

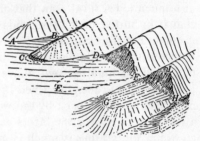

FIG. 124. SPURS CUT BY WAVES

ABCD, initial shore-line at time of submergence; *DKF*, cliff facet cut back in spur *DEF*; *FGH*, spur platform fronting its cliff facet *FLH*, after withdrawal of lake waters

If the surface of a sea or lake should rise on a ravined mountain front, so as to gain an irregular shore-line, *ABCD* (Fig. 124), the promontories might in time be cut back to the straight shore-line, *DFH*, over which the spurs would then terminate in triangular cliff facets, *DKF, FLH.* But in such a case the valleys should not remain narrow-mouthed during the progress of the wave work, but should widen somewhat and allow the streams to develop flood plains on which they could wander a little; and after the lake waters had disappeared, the facets should look out upon triangular rock platforms, *FGH*, systematically related in form and area to the facets. As a matter of fact, the triangular rock platforms and the widened valley mouths are wanting in every case that came under my notice. It cannot be supposed that the mountain front was cut back by waves at so low a level that the wave-cut platform is now concealed by mountain waste; for in that case the narrow ravines should also have been cut down to the same low level, instead of opening, as they so often do, rock-floored on the mountain flank, and allowing the streams to continue their descent on gravel fans that rise at the apex distinctly above the intermont plain. One of the best localities for the illustration of these features is at the southern end of the Provo Wahsatch, northeast of Springville, where the baseline curves from south to southeast. Several ravines furrow the mountain face, dividing it into a number of sub-parallel spurs, all of which are cut off by rather well-defined triangular facets. If these facets are explained as shore-line cliffs, rock platforms should stretch from a quarter to a half mile forward from the cliff base into the plain; but no such platforms are to be seen. If any rock platform exists, it must be supposed that it was cut at a much lower level than that of the Bonneville shore-line, and that it is buried under the sands and clays that cover the low ground; but the existence of a wave-cut platform at such a depth is inconsistent with the opening of the ravines in the mountain flank several hundred feet above the plain; the ravines would necessarily have been deepened by their streams as the cliffs and platforms were cut back by the waves; hence the supposition of a wave-cut origin for the facets cannot be favorably entertained; an origin by faulting is much more reasonable. It is noticeable that the stream lines in this part of the Wahsatch pitch with increasing steepness in the narrow, gorge-like mouths of the ravines, thus hurrying between a gentler but still steep descent down the ravines in the mountain flank above, and a gentler descent through the Bonneville gravels on the way to the plain below. Indeed, the gorge-like mouths of the ravines seems to be incised somewhat below the base of a series of simply triangular facets, so as to give the spur sections the beginning of a house-end pattern, as if the faulting of the mountain block had been locally accelerated not long ago. The features of this interesting locality would well repay a detailed study.

True wave-cut cliffs and their correlated rock platforms may, as is well known, be seen at various points on the Bonneville shore-line, but the cliffs are usually of much less height than that of the spur facets in the Wahsatch front; and in no case had the rock platforms that I saw nearly so great a breadth as would be demanded by the forward prolongation of the faceted

Wahsatch spurs, so that the slope of the spur crest line should descend to the platform level. The facets of the Spanish Wahsatch front the basin of Utah lake, not over twenty-five miles broad from east to west : the Bonneville waters here must have been much less powerful than in their more open areas farther north ; yet these facets are much larger than the true wave-cut cliffs that are seen on more exposed parts of the old shore-line. The best facets of the Ogden Wahsatch, above mentioned as lying close to Weber cañon, cannot have been much affected by the Bonneville waves, for during much of Bonneville time this part of the mountain base was well protected by the growing delta of Weber river.

The Erosion of the Spur Facets. It is evident from what has been said in the section on the mountain face that the retreat of a mountain front from its initial fault scarp will be greater on the stream lines than on the interstream surfaces, and again greater at the apex of a facet than at its base. The concentration of drainage — even if it be only wet-weather drainage — along the stream line of the ravines, and the increase in the volume of the streams from head to mouth has given them strength enough to remove the waste that weathers and creeps down from the ravine walls. There is, however, at present no such concentration of removing agencies along the foot of the mountains ; and as the duration of the Bonneville waters at their various levels has been but a small fraction of the whole life of the mountains, it may be said that there has prevailingly been no active agent available for the removal of waste from the mountain base between the mouths of the streams.

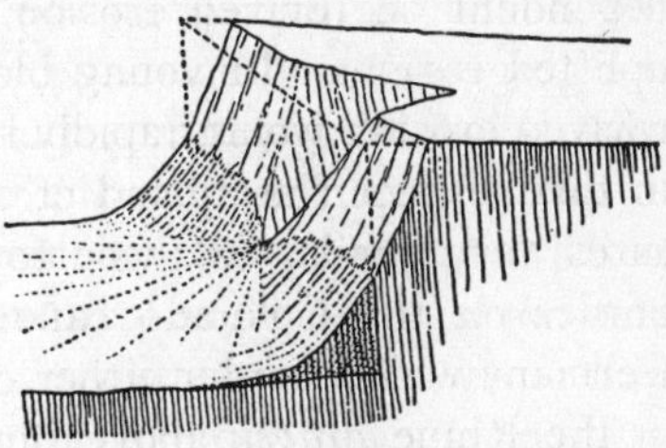

If the fault plane were vertical, a large amount of rock waste would have fallen from it, and in the absence of any effective removing agency along the moun-

FIG. 125. TALUS AT BASE OF A VERTICAL BLOCK FRONT

tain base, some of the waste should accumulate there as a talus (Fig. 125), whose foot should advance in front of the fault line. The conspicuous absence of such talus makes it probable that the fault plane was by no means vertical, and suggests that the slope of the spur facets may not be greatly unlike the slope of the faults. In the Spanish Wahsatch the small facets slope at an angle of 38° or 40°; in the Provo Wahsatch the slope is from 32° to 38°. Certain ranges in northern Nevada had similarly steep basal slopes.

Other Parts of Block Mountains. In the early stages of faulting the back slope of a tilted mountain block should exhibit its pre-faulting form little changed, except that all the slopes and streams which had been steepened by the tilting would show signs of more active erosion than the other parts. The lower part of the back slope would be buried under accumulating waste.

In a later stage of faulting it might be impossible to recognize any survivors of the pre-faulting forms, unless near the back base where the small depth to which erosion could penetrate would delay change. The back base-line would expectably be much more sinuous than the front base-line, for at the back of the range the gravels and sands of the intermont depression would mount obliquely upon a surface in which the inequalities of pre-faulting time had been somewhat exaggerated by the revived erosion of the early stages of tilting.

In the early and later stages of faulting both faces of a lifted mountain block would present features similar to those already described as occurring on the faulted face of a tilted block, while the upper surface of the lifted block would exhibit features dependent on revived erosion, such as are commonly found in uplifted regions. In young blocks of this kind the intensity of revived erosion would rapidly increase toward the block border; in this respect the upland of a young block would present features very similar to those found in the Arizona plateaus that border on the Colorado cañon, or in the plateaus of western Germany which border either on the Rhine gorge below Bingen or the Rhine *graben* above Bingen; for so far as the dissection of an upland is concerned, it matters little whether its streams descend by a fault scarp to a lowland or by a cañon wall to a river.

In older uplifted blocks of longer continued faulting, the contrast of scarp and upland would be weakened; and after the faulting was far advanced, the contrast would disappear entirely. The battered retreat of both scarps, gnawed by retrogressive ravines, would result in transforming the upland into a more or less serrated ridge.

Many special conditions might be imposed upon these general deductions by assuming particular features of pre-faulting relief and drainage. These conditions need not be entered upon here, because my observations did not go far enough to provide a large variety of facts with which deductions of specialized types could be confronted. It may be noted, however, that the deduced features of the back slope of a tilted block are not so much unlike the forms of residual mountains as are those of the front of such a block. It is, therefore, not to be expected that tilted-block ranges can be recognized so well when their back is seen as when one looks at their expressive face. But when the features characteristic of the back slope of a tilted block occur on one side of a range, while those appropriate to the faulted face occur on the other side, it is reasonable to look upon such a range as the result of block faulting.

The eastern side of the Santa Rosa mountains north of Winnemucca, Nevada, for example, does not imitate the well-defined base-line of the western side, so far as I saw this range. The eastern valleys are open and well graded between spaced spurs. The same is true of the eastern base of Jackson range, whose western base has already been mentioned as suggestive of faulting. Moreover, in profile this range resembles a tilted block when seen from the north in such a way that its ravines are hidden behind its spurs. The crest line is near the western side where the slopes are precipitous, while the eastern slopes are much more gradual.

If any ranges have been carved from uplifted blocks, bounded by faults on both sides, they have — so far as the examples that I saw are concerned — reached the advanced stage of dissection in which the initial upland is carved into a serrate ridge. My line of travel seldom made it possible to see both sides of a single range, and hence my notes leave it uncertain in most cases whether or not a range with a well-defined base-line on one side is similarly formed on the other side.

Modern Faulting. It is certainly very significant that indisput-
able evidence of modern displacement should be found close along
certain mountain base-lines where abundant evidence of long-
continued earlier faulting is provided by the mountain form. This
has been so clearly pointed out by Gilbert and Russell that little
space need be given to it here. Suffice it to say, that repeated
instances of scarps in gravel deltas and fans were noted last
summer along the Wahsatch base, as well as along the border
of certain other ranges to be described below. A distinct scarp
in the gravels of the Bonneville beach is traceable all along
the front of the Spanish Wahsatch, a little forward from the
base of the facets. The breaks in the delta of Rock cañon
creek and in various other gravel deposits near Provo were
easily recognized.

It is sometimes suggested that the displacements in the
Bonneville gravels are more of the nature of superficial landslides than of deep-seated faults. Taken alone they might perhaps be so considered, but taken in connection with all the
associated features, they cannot be regarded as independent
of displacement in the underlying rock mass.

There is, however, one aspect of the modern faulting that deserves consideration. In all cases that I have seen, the modern
movements are so placed that they must be taken as the continuation of long-maintained displacements whose total measure
must, as a rule, amount to many hundreds or some thousands
of feet. No other explanation has been found for the presence
of such mountain masses as have been described above, standing
in strong relief on one side of the base-line, while there are only
gravels and sands to be seen on the other side. It is, of course,
conceivable that modern faulting may have been here and there
begun on new lines, essentially independent of the older fault
lines, but such cases must be rare; for it is to be expected that
if a modern fault occurs on a new line, it should run across
country indifferent to preëxistent structures. Such a fault
might run obliquely across an intermont plain, then traverse a
mountain range, and continue into another plain beyond the
range, the whole length of the fault being marked by a scarp of
more or less distinct form. The Great Basin has not yet been

carefully enough explored to prove that no such faults occur; but the region is well enough known to warrant the provisional statement that new faults of a date as recent as the scarps of the Bonneville deposits are rare, except in connection with old faults.

On the other hand, there seem to be many ancient faults in the Basin ranges on which movement ceased long ago. This is shown by the obliteration through erosion of the relief due to faulting; or sometimes by so great an excess of erosion in the uplifted block over that in the thrown block that the thrown block now stands above the lifted block, the fault scarp being thus topographically reversed by erosion. Many examples of these kinds are given by Spurr. It does not, however, seem admissible to argue from the absence of modern movement on these faults, or from the apparent absence of modern faults within the ranges, that no long-maintained faulting can have taken place along the range borders. That must be determined by evidence furnished by the borders of the ranges themselves.

The Measure and Distribution of Faulting. It may be noted that only an incomplete measure of the total movement in block faulting is determined by the difference of altitude between the mountain base and the reconstructed crest in a lifted or tilted block; for in addition to this measure there must be a certain supplement by which the inequalities of the pre-faulting surface have been depressed out of sight in the thrown block. Advanced old age in the pre-faulting cycle, and youth or early maturity in the present cycle, are the conditions demanding the least measure of block faulting; for the small relief of advanced old age in the preceding cycle would be consistent with the easy burial of all rock surfaces near the fault line in the thrown block; and youth or early maturity in the present cycle would call for the least addition to the existing height in reconstructing the crest of the mountain block near the fault-line.

It is worth while to call attention at this point to a corollary that follows from the provisional conclusion above stated regarding the prevailing absence of modern faults except along the base-lines of certain ranges where independent lines of evidence lead to the belief that the modern movements are but the latest displacements on faults of much greater age. The corollary is this : the total displacement on these long-lived faults must be usually greater than the ordinary measure of pre-faulting relief in the Great Basin region. For the fault lines must have originally run indifferently to the structure of the region, and therefore indifferently also to whatever relief the region had assumed when the faulting began; and yet the thrown block is now as a rule completely covered with gravels and sands washed from the heaved block. Exceptions to this rule are found at certain points, but they are rare. If further exploration confirm the provisional conclusion above referred to, this corollary may have some value.

In this connection it may be noted that the great measure of displacement inferred by King for the Wahsatch fault (*b*, 745) seems unnecessary. If the folded strata of the range had been reduced to moderate relief by pre-faulting erosion, — and this seems not improbable if one may judge by the enormous volume of the Eocene (Vermilion creek) Tertiary to the east (King, *b*, 745), — the measure of the fault need not be more than enough to raise the crest of the range above the rock floor that is buried under the sediments of the Salt Lake basin; that is, from six thousand to ten thousand feet instead of forty thousand.

It was suggested by Van Hise in the discussion of this subject at the recent Washington meeting of the Geological Society of America that the displacement in faults of large throw, such as those by which the Basin ranges have been formed are believed to be, is usually distributed on grouped fractures instead of taking place on a single plane of displacement. All the ranges that came under my observation last summer are non-committal on this point, except in so far as the absence of discoverable fractures in the front part of the mountains requires that any additional fractures besides the one which determines the mountain base should be forward from it, and concealed under the gravels of the piedmont plain. Certainly, if there are distributed faults in the Spanish Wahsatch block, the displacements on the minor faults within the block must have ceased long enough ago to have been obliterated, so far as surface form is concerned, in the smoothly graded slopes of the spurs; while the movement on the main fault along the front margin of the block has continued to so modern a date as still to have distinct control over the form of the terminal facets.

An article of interest in this connection has been published by D. W. Johnson on block mountains in New Mexico, from which it appears that Sandia mountain, near Albuquerque, is a large block with its chief displacement along the strong escarpment that it presents to the west, but with many smaller displacements within its mass, thus confirming the suggestion of distributive faulting as made by Van Hise. The dynamics of faulting are, however, not yet so well understood that it is safe to assert the occurrence of distributive faulting in all block mountains. Surely no one could have hesitated to believe that the Sandia block was faulted, even if minor faults had not been found on its back slope. In the plateau province of Utah and Arizona several of the greater faults are demonstrably on relatively simple fractures; for the strata of the adjoining blocks come close to the fault line without noticeable disturbance; there is room for fault breccias fifty or one hundred feet wide, but apart from that the faults seem to be for the most part simple and clean cut.

It is evident that the examples of Basin ranges here described are alone too few in number to support any safe conclusion as to the origin of the Basin ranges in general. The Wahsatch range forms the eastern border of the Great Basin province, and although it seems to be of fault-block origin, it cannot be taken as a typical example of one of the isolated ranges within the Great Basin. The chief profit that comes from the study of the Wahsatch range is the definition of certain criteria by which fault-bordered ranges may be determined elsewhere; and this profit will be increased when the back or eastern slope of the Wahsatch shall have been studied in the same relation. The other ranges above mentioned have, however, a certain value in that they were chance samples, not selected beforehand because they were believed to be faulted blocks, but observed as they happened to be passed while the observer was on his way to other points. They thus serve to indicate at least a probability that other ranges in the same region have a similar structure.

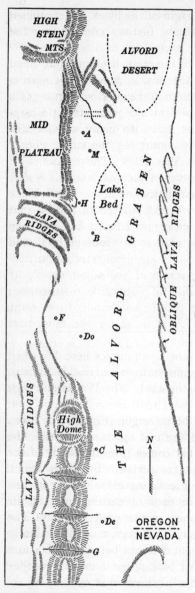

The Pueblo-Stein Mountains. By taking a three-day dusty stage ride northward from Winnemucca, Nevada, I was enabled to give a week to the study of the Pueblo and Stein mountains that cross the Nevada-Oregon boundary a little west of the north and south line marked by the post offices of Denio and Andrews. The stage road carried me past the Santa Rosa, Jackson, and Pine Forest ranges, of which some mention has already been made. The route for part of the distance lay on the dead-level gray silt plain of the extinct lake Lahontan, whose successive shore-lines were traceable at various heights on the inclosing slopes. A long gravel spit, hooked to the east at various levels, stretched northward from the Jackson range to Mason's crossing of Quinn river.

The general result of this week's work gave me the impression that the Pueblo-Stein mountain range is more eroded than would be inferred from Russell's description of it (*b*, 439, 444); but there can be no reasonable doubt that it represents a long fault block. The following pages contain a direct statement of the evidence to this conclusion, without analysis of the method by which the conclusion is reached. The analysis has been sufficiently stated in the preceding pages ; its results may now be employed without restatement of the method of reaching them. This is the historical order in the development of methods of investigation, with the time element condensed. When a geologist nowadays describes vertical strata of conglomerate as of sedimentary origin, he does not again go over De Saussure's argument concerning the conglomerate of Valorsine ; when a physiographer now asserts the occurrence of a subsequent valley on the evidence of stream course and rock structure, he need not repeat the argument by which subsequent valleys were first explained by Jukes in the basin of the Blackwater. These are settled questions and may therefore be treated by the short and direct method that steps at once from observation to con-

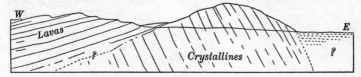

FIG. 127. CROSS SECTION OF PUEBLO MOUNTAINS, LOOKING NORTH

clusion. So may the question of block mountains be treated by the short method, provided the complete method has been tried and found valid.

The Pueblo mountains of southern Oregon (Fig. 126) overstep the state boundary at Denio and extend about ten miles southward into Nevada. They trend northward to a high dome fifteen miles north of Denio, and then fall off in a broad, westward reëntrant back of Doane's and Field's ranches. The high serrated range north of the reëntrant is the beginning of the Stein (or Steen) mountains. The Pueblo mountains consist of two ranges for most of their length. The eastern or front range (Fig. 127) is made of ancient crystalline rocks, such as diabases and mica schists. The western or back range is made of bedded lavas, basaltic so far as I saw them, whose westward dip of 15° or 20° is well expressed in a series of east-facing escarpments. Paired wet-weather subsequent streams drain the longitudinal

depression between the two ranges, and their gathered waters
escape eastward by deep-cut, narrow-floored, steep-walled gorges
through the front range to the broad plain known as Alvord
valley. Russell marks a fault along the intermediate depression
(*b*, 444, Plate LXXXIV); but the relation of the western lavas
to the older rocks of the eastern range, as seen from the Stein
mountains (Fig. 128) from Doane's ranch near the north end of
the range, and again in the depression between the ranges back
of Deegan's, seemed to be best explained by normal superposition of the lavas on the crystallines, followed by tilting and
erosion without faulting. The depression between the front and
back ranges is thus to be interpreted as a series of normal subsequent valleys, eroded along the weaker basal members of the

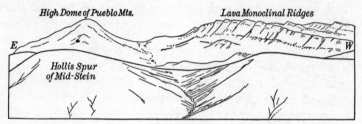

FIG. 128. THE NORTH END OF THE PUEBLO MOUNTAINS

Looking south over the Hollis Spur of the Mid-Stein mountains

lava beds by branches of streams that transect the eastern range
and that are probably persistent from an earlier pre-faulting
cycle of erosion.

The eastern base of the mountains is, however, unquestionably
determined by a fault on which a total movement of several thousand feet has probably taken place, the latest displacements being
of recent date, as Russell has shown. The base-line of the range
is of gentle curvature, indifferent to the structure of the mass.
An excellent illustration of this is seen a mile or more south of
Catlow's ranch, where a boldly outcropping rib of strong rock,
standing oblique to the trend of the range, terminates evenly
with the adjoining weaker rocks at the mountain base, and the
face of the rib seems much sheared and broken. The ravines
and gorges through which the range is drained are steep-walled
and narrow to their mouths. The spurs between the ravines are

abruptly cut off by the base-line, and show no tendency whatever to trail forward into the plain.

Recent faulting along the mountain base is shown by several topographical features. At a number of points near the northern end of the range, between Catlow's and Doane's, open, graded valley floors now stand a hundred feet or more above the mountain base, and are sharply trenched by the streams that formerly graded them. Uplifted and dissected fragments of broken fans are often seen one hundred feet or more above the mouth of a gorge, an excellent example of this kind being found back of Denio, while others occur near Catlow's. In general, the summits and higher slopes are of moderate declivity, frequently well covered with waste and exposing few ledges ; while the walls of the cross-cut gorges are steep, with abundant ledges, and in some cases the gorge walls steepen as they descend to the stream line. The slopes of the spur profiles commonly steepen toward the front base-line ; their general descent is at angles of from 10° to 25° ; but they often steepen downwards to 30° or 35°. The spur terminals are, however, well rounded, and but faintly recall the sharp-edged facets of the Spanish Wahsatch.

The southern part of the Pueblo range offered the best illustrations that I found of the trailing end of a faulted block, less dissected than the middle part and therefore probably representing a sub-recent increase in the length of the block by a southward extension of its marginal fault. The front base of the range is here, as elsewhere, oblique to the structure ; the crystalline rocks disappear first, and the lava monocline continues several miles farther south before dying out. The frontal escarpment of the monocline is very straight and but little dissected ; the fans at its base are low, and a very gentle slope of alluvium leads from the base-line to a dead level playa, half a mile to the east. The lava monocline is somewhat complicated by a transverse fault and a transverse monoclinal fold ; but the frontal escarpment pays no attention to these disturbances.

The Stein mountains (Fig. 126) continue the general line of the Pueblo mountains, although separated from them by the westward reëntrant already mentioned. The structure of this range is, however, unlike that of the other in consisting almost wholly of lavas for at least as far as some distance north of Andrews. The lavas resemble basalts and andesites, commonly porphyritic. The range may be conveniently described in three parts. The southern part is a warped monocline, dipping south and southwest, and obliquely cut off on the east by the north and south mountain base; the crest of this part of the range is serrated. The middle part is a plateau-like mass, with gentle western dip. The northern part is much higher than the rest; it was generally hidden in clouds or haze during my visit, and its structure was not determined.

I had an excellent view over most of the southern part of the range from the southeast corner of the middle plateau section, whence a great extent of country is disclosed. Alvord valley has every appearance of being a *graben*, limited by a fault on the east as well as the west; many low ranges trending to the south-southeast are obliquely cut off in a notably even line along the eastern valley margin. To the northeast an escarpment bordering the valley is banked up with sands blown from the extensive playa of Alvord desert, which occupies that part of the depression. Not only is the Alvord depression seemingly a trough, or *graben*, but the southern and middle parts of the Stein mountains are carved in what seems to be a lifted block, with a fault along the western as well as along the eastern border. The reason for this opinion cannot be presented as conclusive, for it is based only on what was seen from the point of view above named, yet there is little doubt in my own mind of its being correct. The southern and middle division of the range appeared to be evenly cut off along their western border, and this appearance was especially distinct for the southern division where the western border trends nearly square across a series of monoclinal ridges and valleys. The mountain block is ten or twelve miles wide, and is succeeded on the west by a brown-gray plain, at one thousand or fifteen hundred feet lower than the ridges, and two thousand or twenty-five hundred feet lower than the middle plateau division.

The monoclinal structure of the southern division has a strike in its western part to the west-northwest, with a southerly dip of 15° or 20°. Erosion has developed a number of well-defined ridges and valleys, and the generally accordant heights of the

Alvord trough, by a lower escarpment which overlooks the mono-clinal ridges and valleys on the south, and by a strong escarp-ment again on the west. I believe all these escarpments have been worn back from fault lines, and there is some reason for thinking that the fault between the two divisions of the range, trending west-northwest, is older than the meridional faults on the east and west; but I will leave the discussion of this point to some one who can treat it in greater detail. As in the south-ern block, the crest line of the eastern block is now worn back two or three miles from base, indicating a long period since the block was first uplifted.

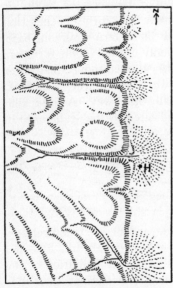

FIG. 130. ROUGH MAP AROUND HOLLIS'S RANCH

Side of map is five or six miles, north and south

The face of the eastern es-carpment presents many graded slopes between the ledges of more resistant lavas. The spurs be-tween the obsequent ravines by which the escarpment is dis-sected usually descend with con-cave slopes toward the plain; but a short convex profile is often seen as the spur reaches the base-line. The lower parts of many spurs exhibit well-defined graded slopes on the interstream surfaces, but the spurs are now rather sharply separated by the ravines, and thus indicate a prolonged pause followed by a sub-recent uplift.

For the greater part of the range front the fans that spread forward from the ravines are not faulted, but near the junction of the southern and middle blocks sub-recent and recent fault-ing is conspicuous. The most interesting locality is near Hollis's ranch (Fig. 130). Here several strong bluffs rise rather boldly from the plain, forming terminal escarpments to spurs whose interstream surface, six hundred or eight hundred feet over the ridges as they rise gradually eastward suggests that the monoclinal mass had been much eroded previous to the uplift whereby the present dissection was initiated. As the ridges approach the crest of the range, which lies about three miles from its eastern base, the strike of the monocline turns to the southeast or south-southeast; the harder beds in the monoclinal ridges rise eastward to form the peaks, while the valleys of the monocline may be traced upward to the notches in the serrated mountain crest. On the eastern slope the harder beds form benches that descend obliquely southward toward the eastern mountain base, where they are successively and evenly cut off. This form can be easily explained as a block of a base-leveled monoclinal mass, lifted and somewhat tilted to the west, and maturely eroded; but I find it difficult to explain it in any other way. A sub-recent pause in the uplift of the block is indicated by the occurrence of

FIG. 129. CROSS SECTION OF MID-STEIN MOUNTAINS, LOOKING NORTH

well-defined graded basal slopes, independent of structure, now raised several hundred feet above the Alvord plain and dissected by numerous streams. During this pause the definition of the mountain base would have been much less distinct than it is to-day; indeed, the base-line would have been obliterated along a considerable fraction of the mountain front. Renewal of uplift has made the base-line well-defined to-day in the southern division of the range, but the streams on the aggraded floor of Alvord valley do not share in the revival by which the same streams on the mountain flanks have trenched the old graded slopes. A considerable period of time must have elapsed since the original uplift of the block began, for the crest of the range is now worn two or three miles back from the eastern base.

The middle division of the Stein mountains (Fig. 129) is a monocline of so gentle a westward dip that it possesses a broadly rolling upland surface, limited on the east by the strong escarpment which falls twenty-five hundred or three thousand feet to the mountain base, seems to have been well graded and reduced to small relief before it was cut by the streams that are now eroding sharp ravines in it; but the same streams run forward on aggraded gravel fans east of the mountain base-line. The bluffs between the streams occasionally show outcropping ledges, but most of the bluff face is an even slope of slide-rock at an angle near 35°. Just north of Hollis's ranch the bluff must be nearly one thousand feet high, but it rapidly diminishes in strength north and south; and a mile and a half or two miles from the highest part of the bluff the mountain base is of the usual gentle expression. The largest stream that cuts the bluff has a sharp-cut gorge next north of Hollis's ranch, whose irrigated fields lie on the fan that the stream has built. Very recent faulting is indicated by fragments of an older fan, now standing about one hundred and fifty or two hundred feet above the present fan on either side of the cañon mouth. Next north and south there are two "hanging valleys," five hundred or six hundred feet over the plain, the like of which was not noted elsewhere along the Stein mountain front.

Some of these local features might be explained, independently of faulting, by the occurrence of a mass of unusually resistant rock at this part of the mountain base; but in that case it might be expected that a greater number of outcrops would be seen on the bluff faces and in the ravine walls. As far as the rock was examined, it seemed to be a porphyritic andesite, similar to other lavas of the mountain block. Moreover, a mass of resistant rock could hardly be expected to be limited, except by a long block fault, so close to the line of the general mountain front; and it can hardly be a matter of chance that just where the general form of the mountain base suggests the most extensive sub-recent faulting, there should occur the strongest recent fault as indicated by a broken gravel fan. Accepting then the conclusion that faulting is responsible for these basal bluffs, it may be noted that they are roughly in the stage of dissection indicated in Fig. 118, except that all the edges are rounded off; but the initial upland of Fig. 118 is here represented by the graded interstream surfaces that had been worn down to gentle slopes before the sub-recent faulting began. There is some reason for associating this renewed uplift with the fault that has been above suggested to separate the southern and middle division of the range; but more detailed field work is necessary on this point.

The northern part of the middle Stein escarpment is breached by a large valley that comes southeast from the high Steins, and a small plateau-like block is thus cut off from the main mass as shown in Fig. 126. Several low lava-bed monoclines, of gentle dip to the southwest, extend southeast from the detached block; they gradually dip underground near the southern end of the Alvord desert (playa) and their trend very strongly suggests a connection with the monoclinal ridges of similar strike on the eastern side of the Alvord trough. It is certainly reasonable to infer a fault with downthrow on the southeast between these low lava monoclines and the high detached block that over-looks them.

The Quaternary lake that Russell has described as occupying the Alvord trough left shore-lines of moderate strength at vari-ous levels up to a few hundred feet over the present lake bed plain. The best examples noted are seen on the low lava mono-clines, just mentioned, where faint benches are developed; in the embayment of the main depression that heads between the low monoclines and the main escarpment of the middle Stein plateau, where two cross-bay bars were built to a height of ten or twenty feet, about a mile north of Andrews; beneath the strong bluffs just north of Hollis's ranch, where shore-lines are associated with the chief fan delta of that district; and near the north end of the Pueblo range, between Doane's and Catlow's, where what seems to be a long spit was built out into the lake from the bend in the mountain front near the beginning of the reëntrant between the Pueblo and the Stein ranges.

To any one who wishes to give a month to the study of a well-defined *graben*, bordered east and west by uplifted and well-dissected mountain blocks, Alvord valley may be highly commended.

The Shoshone Range. On returning from Oregon I passed by the northern end of the Shoshone range in north central Nevada in an eastbound afternoon express train on the Central Pacific Railroad between Argenta and Shoshone. My notes, rather hurriedly written at the time, are as follows : " A very fine fault block, with manifest recent and sub-recent faulting. Broken fans ; light-colored basal slopes, ripped with gullies ; uplifted grades, truncated spurs, revived streams in full-bodied spurs ; spur tops dark gray, sides lighter ; tops graded, sides ripped. Even fronted base, facing west and north ; all excellent examples for study. At some points on west base, very short fans, as if plain had been depressed."

This specimen of a block mountain interested me greatly. It served as an example for rapid review of many features that I had studied at more leisure in other ranges. It sufficed to show that physiographic evidence of block faulting may be easily and quickly recognized when it is looked for. It confirmed my opinion that such evidence compares well in logical and compulsory value with the stratigraphic evidence on which the demonstration of faulting is usually dependent. It strengthened my belief in the importance and the possibility of describing all land forms rationally and systematically in view of their evolution.

The description of the Shoshone range in the reports of the 40th Parallel Survey is so closely limited to matters of geological structure — as was natural enough at the time the survey was made, and the reports were written — that no consideration is given to the physiographic features here discussed. The range is not mentioned in Gilbert's or Russell's reports, or in Spurr's essay. The fuller meaning of my notes, supplemented by the maps and reports of the 40th Parallel Survey, and by the thoughts that accompanied the observations, is as follows :

The northern ten miles of the Shoshone range in north central Nevada is an east-dipping monocline of Weber quartzite overlaid by basalt (40th Par. Surv., Map 4, west half). It is bordered on the north and west by the open alluvial plain through which Humboldt river wanders. From five to ten miles north of the range lies Shoshone mesa, composed of rhyolite covered by basalt, fronting southward in a strong escarpment, and dipping gently northward. The Central Pacific Railroad skirts the base of the range for twelve miles along its northern end, giving a good view of part of its western outcropping face and its northern cross section. The range has every appearance of being a dissected monoclinal fault block, owing its relief to gradual and long-continued displacement, whose later movements are clearly recorded in the form of its base. Although the observations on which this statement is made were made only from a passing train, they are believed to be fully deserving of credit. It should be understood, however, that they apply only to the northern part of the range. The passage from observation to explanation may be stated as follows :

The first feature to be noted is the block-like appearance of the mass, especially as indicated by its basal outline. The base-line is relatively well defined, of very small irregularity and of moderate curvature ; the basal mass is continuous but for the narrow ravines that divide it into full-bodied spurs.

In the second place, attention should be given to the contrast of the heavy mountain mass and the broad piedmont plain. The lower slopes of the mountain are strong ; they change rather abruptly into the broad alluvial plain that stretches away un-broken for several miles. The depression, floored by the pied-mont plain and drained by Humboldt river, is five or ten miles wide between Shoshone range on the south and Shoshone mesa on the north, and does not give the impression of being a normal trunk valley, eroded in a once continuous rock mass ; for if it were of such origin, the branch valleys by which the mountain is drained ought to be of correspondingly advanced development with broad-open floors ; while as a matter of fact the branch valleys are narrow to their mouths at the mountain base. More-over, in the neighborhood of Palisade, twenty-five or thirty miles farther east, the Humboldt river has what appears to be a per-fectly normal valley, a narrow cañon cut in lavas. The broad plain and the narrow cañon cannot both be parts of an undis-turbed, normally eroded valley ; and as the narrow cañon is manifestly of river origin, the broad depression must be other-wise explained.

The depression might at first sight be regarded as a down-warped part of a normal valley, heavily aggraded with alluvium ; but this supposition is untenable because the alluvium does not invade the ravines on the mountain flank as it certainly should if the ravines had been carved with respect to a now-buried trunk valley. Some other origin than erosion must therefore be discovered for the depression alongside of the mountain.

Differential movement or faulting, the only other conceivable origin of the depression, — the supposition that the mountain rocks were originally deposited only on their present limited area need not be considered, — is not only permissible by its appropriateness to the outline of the mountain base, but it receives strong support from the abundant evidence of the recently continued movement on the fracture by which the depression and the mountain block were originally outlined. The evidence to this end is interesting from its variety and its accordance.

Graded valley floors of moderate width dissect the mountain side, but their floors lie one hundred or two hundred feet above the plain; the valley streams have now entrenched narrow ravines in the valley floors, and thus flow out upon alluvial fans at the mountain base. The spurs between the ravines are of rounded, full-bodied form; they do not taper away on the plain, but are rather sharply cut off by the basal slope of the mountain. The upper surface of the spurs is maturely graded, but their lower slopes are often gashed or "ripped" by little gullies, suggestive of active erosion; the color of the spur slopes is therefore prevailingly lighter than that of the spur tops. Many of the fans are broken by low scarps closely in line with the mountain base; this indicates a continuation of faulting into a very recent period. Some of the fans at the northern end of the western base of the range seem unusually low, as if the plain there had been depressed while the mountain was rising. Taken all together, one can hardly imagine more satisfactory evidence of block faulting.

It should be noted, however, that the higher parts of the mountain seem to have been abundantly dissected since the faulting began. The west-facing scarp of the basalt sheet is now a mile or more back from the west-facing scarp of the underlying strata, but the accordant outlines of the two scarps strongly suggest the original definition of both by the same surface of fracture. Deliberate and detailed study of this range would well repay the observer who could undertake it.

REFERENCES

Davis, W. M. (*a*) "The Ranges of the Great Basin: Physiographic Evidence of Faulting." *Science*, XIV (1901), 457–459.

(*b*) "The Stream Contest along the Blue Ridge." *Bull. Geog. Soc. Philadelphia* (1903).

Diller, J. S. "Notes on the Geology of Northern California." *U. S. Geol. Surv., Bull. No. 33* (1886).

Emmons, S. F. Report of the Geological Survey of the Fortieth Parallel. Vol. II, Descriptive Geology. Washington, 1877.

Gilbert, G. K. Geographical and Geological Explorations and Surveys West of the One Hundredth Meridian. (*a*) Progress Report, 48–52, Washington, 1874; (*b*) Vol. III, Geology, 17–187, Washington, 1875.

Johnson, D. W. "Block Mountains in New Mexico." *Am. Geol.* XXXI, (1903), 135–139.

King, C. Report of the Geological Survey of the Fortieth Parallel. (*a*) Vol. III, Mining Industry, Washington, 1870; (*b*) Vol. I, Systematic Geology, Washington, 1878.

Russell, I. C. (*a*) "Geological History of Lake Lahontan, a Quaternary Lake of Northwestern Nevada." *U. S. Geol. Surv., Mon. XI* (Washington, 1885).

(*b*) "Geological Reconnaissance in Southern Oregon." *U. S. Geol. Surv. IV Ann. Rep.* (Washington, 1884), 431–464.

Spurr, J. E. "Origin and Structure of the Basin Ranges." *Bull. Geol. Soc. Am.*, XII (1901), 217–270.

INDEX

Accidents in the cycle, 180, 274; climatic, 180, 289; volcanic, 180, 290
Activities of the lands, 139
Adjustment, stream, 262, 343, 434, 488; examples of, 439; process of, 435; terminology, 438; Tertiary, of the Juniata, 476; with revival, 442
Adolescence of cycle, 176, 430
Aggraded streams, 259, 392
Aire river, 609
Alaska, hanging valleys of, 652, 686
Alaskan boundary, 25
Almanac, Nautical, 232
Alpine valleys, 80, 640, 651, 686
Alvord valley, 764
American school of physiographers, 144, 339
Anaclinal streams, 510
Angle of repose, 267
Animals and plants in geography, 134, 144
Antecedent stream, 81, 274, 444, 447, 486
Anthracite basins, drainage of, 465
Appalachian drainage, studies of, 417
Ardennes, 615
Argentine-Chilian boundary, 25
Arid climate, geographical cycle in, 296
Aristotle, 219
Astronomical geography, 100, 219
Atmosphere, 49, 136, 213, 228
Austria, topographical maps of, 191
Autumn field studies, 240
Axis of the earth, 221; relation to orbit, 232

Bar river, 609
Bars, off-shore, 707
Base-level, 84, 111, 171, 175, 275, 381, 390, 397; kinds of, 400; local, 244
Base-leveling, leveling without, 306
Basin range province, 298, 725
Beheaded streams, 438, 500, 600, 605, 609
Betrunked streams, 181
Blanford, W. T., 686
Block mountains, 725
Blue Ridge, 737
Bohemia, 373

Boundaries, political, 25, 39, 59
Branch valleys, development of, 260; relation to trunk, 645

Campbell, M. R., 82
Cantal, 639
Capture, river, 82, 438, 461, 477, 480, 500, 587, 737; elbow of, 602
Cartographer, 156
Cataclinal streams, 510
Catastrophism, 71, 72
Cayuga lake, 682
Chamberlin, T. C., 694
Channels of rivers and glaciers, 657
Charts, 188
Chelan, lake, 685
Classification, of land forms, 77, 107, 249, 252; of geography, 212
Climate, normal, 296
Climatic changes, 289; control, 134, 143
Coast Survey charts, 188, 228
Coastal plain, 198
Cod, Cape, 690
Colleges, geography in, 28, 146, 165
Colorado cañon, 80, 91, 202
Colorado plateaus, 203, 304
Como, lake, 667
Complexity of geography, 5, 37
Composite topography, 181, 273
Connecticut river, 89, 113, 529, 578
Consequent streams, 81, 172, 174, 256, 447
Continental shelf, 133
Control, climatic, 134, 143
Corrie basins, 671
Cut-offs, 536; of the Connecticut, 581; of the Meuse, 592; of the Mississippi, 582
Cycle, 170, 249, 408; agencies of, 288; complications of, 279; deductive nature of, 281; in an arid climate, 296; ideal, 254, 279; of glacial erosion, 288, 658; interruptions of, 180, 203, 272, 285, 315; stages in, 176; of the shore-line, 290

Davis, C. H., 692
Deductive method, 58, 165, 170, 179, 731

Degradation, 408, 559
Denudation, 79, 111, 323, 343, 344, 408, 421, 425
Desert drainage, diversion of, 317
Desert leveling, 310
Deserts, kinds of, 311
Disciplinary value of geography, 63
Distributaries, glacial, 666
Distribution, geography as the study of, 8
Divides, 174, 261; migration of, 434, 442, 477, 488, 500, 596, 737
Drowned valleys, 274, 441, 697
Dryer, C. R., 406
Dutton, C. E., 81, 332, 369

Earth, as a globe, 100, 213, 218; axis of, 221, 233; orbit of, 233, 234; revolution of, 229; rotation of, 104, 220; shape of, 219; size of, 224
Earthquakes, 141
Elementary schools, geography in, 105
Engineering schools, geography in, 154
English school of physiographers, 339
Entrenched or incised meanders, 588, 590, 594, 636
Episode, 181
Equator, 222
Equinox, 232, 234
Equipment, geographical, 216
Eratosthanes, 224
Eudoxus, 219, 222
Europe, geography in, 72, 134
Evans, Lewis, 414
Evolution, geographical, 131; inorganic, 86
Exercises, laboratory, 62, 210
Experimental geography, 211
Explorers, 157
Extended streams, 181

Faceted spurs, 746
Fault-block mountains, 725
Features of the lands, 140
Field work, 236
Fiords, 653, 669, 682, 683
Flood plain, 95, 259, 261, 264, 433
Forbes, J. D., 677
Forms assumed by land waste, 276
France, Army Staff map, 190
France, central plateau of, 371; glacial erosion in, 636; rivers of, 587
Freeman, F., 692

Gannett, H., 685
Geikie, A., 80, 325
Geikie, J., 670, 677, 683

Genetic classification of land forms, 107, 249, 252
Geographical equipment, 152, 188, 216
Geographical errors, 102
Geographical evolution, 131
Geographical excursions, 116, 236
Geographical journals, 154
Geographical laboratory, 57, 216
Geographical observations, 215
Geographical studies, sequence of, 151
Geographical teaching, 193
Geographical terminology, 26
Geography, astronomical, 100, 218; classification of, 18, 212; in the colleges, 28, 146, 165; commercial, 18, 67; complexity of, 5, 37, 38; content of, 3; descriptive, 66, 87, 105; distribution of the divisions of, 66; educational value of, 68; exercises in, 210; expansion of, 16; field work in, 236; in the elementary schools, 105; in the engineering schools, 154; in the grammar schools, 115, 151; in the high school, 67, 129, 152, 215, 237; in scientific schools, 149; in the university, 28, 146, 165; mathematical, 100, 218; modern 33, 279; political, 14; practical side of, 68; progress of, 23; rational element, 63; regional, 10, 41, 55, 144; relation to geology, 196, 214, 293; sequence of parts of, 64; subdivisions of, 18, 66, 212; systematic, 10, 41, 43, 55; teaching of, 87; theoretical, 251; time needed for a course in, 99; unity of, 36
Geological structure as a basis of classification, 107
Geological Survey of the United States, 188
Geologist, 39, 77
Geology, 18, 71, 73, 147, 196, 214, 293
Geometry, 213
Geomorphogeny, 254
Geomorphology, 83
German Empire, map, 191
Germany, geography in, 72, 587
Gilbert, G. K., 351, 686, 726
Glacial cañons, 635, 678, 681
Glacial distributaries, 666
Glacial erosion, 617, 635; argument against, 627; cycle of, 288, 658, 673; measure of, 653
Glacial sculpture, 617
Glaciers, channels of, 657, 668; load of, 664
Globe, earth as a, 100, 213, 218
Gobi, desert of, 318
Grade, 381, 390, 393, 397, 400

Graded shore-line, 702
Graded slope, 175
Graded stream, 175, 243, 258, 260, 389, 390, 533
Graded valley floors, 257
Graded valley sides, 266
Grammar schools, geography in, 115, 151
Great Britain, Ordnance Survey map, 190
Green river, 444, 504
Greenwood, G., 78
Gulliver, F. P., 79
Guyot, A., 73, 76, 133

Hanging valleys, 563, 645, 677
Harker, A., 686
Hayes, C. W., 82, 406
Heim, A., 80
Hershey, O. H., 687
High school, geography in, 67, 129, 152, 215, 237
History of a river, 430
History, teaching of, 39, 159
Hitchcock, E., 691
Humboldt, F. H. A. von, 73
Huxley, T. H., 75, 134

Incised meanders, 588, 590, 594
Inductive study, 169
Infancy of cycle, 176
Ingressin river, 607
Initial drainage, 172
Inorganic evolution, 86
Insequent stream, 174
Interruptions of the cycle, 180, 203, 272; in an arid climate, 315; of the shore-line, 290; due to tilting, 285
Italy, geography in, 72

Johnson, W. D., 399
Journals, geographical, 154
Juniata river, 454, 467, 476
Jura mountains, 453

Kentucky, 200
Kittatinny mountain and valley, 489
Knobs in glaciated areas, 638

Laboratory exercises, 62, 186
Laboratory, geographical, 57, 168, 216
Lands, physical geography of, 70; activities of, 139; features of, 140; waste of, 142
Language, geographical elements in, 20, 54
Lapparent, A. de, 682
Lateral cutting of rivers, 533

Latitude, 132, 222
Lauterbrunnen valley, 650
Lava caps, 201
Lesley, J. P., 78
Leveling without base-leveling, 306
Load, relation to river ability, 260; of glaciers, 664
Location, geography as the study of, 8
Longitude, 132, 226
Lubbock, J., 678
Lugano, lake, 647

McGee, W. J., 77, 333, 396, 487, 678, 681
Maggiore, lake, 648
Magnetism, terrestrial, 228
Man in geography, 35, 133, 144
Map projection, 227
Map scales, 122
Maps, 193, 214; drawing of, 122; foreign, 189; making of, 122; topographical, 166, 188; United States government, 188; weather, 63, 229
Marindin, H. L., 694
Marine erosion, 79, 323, 700, 703
Marne river, 599
Mathematical geography, 100, 218
Maturity, stage of the cycle, 177, 200
Meanders, compressed, 550; development of, 264, 532; incised, 588, 590, 594, 636; slipping of, 549; sweeping and swinging, 559
Meridians, 221
Merrimac river, 89, 585
Mesas, 201
Methods and models, 193
Meuse river, 587
Migration of divides, 434, 442, 477, 488, 500, 596, 737
Mississippi River Commission, maps, 188, 535
Mitchell, H., 693
Models, 193, 214
Monadnock, 362, 591
Moselle river, 587
Mountains, 77, 80, 109, 617, 725; fault-block, 725; glacial sculpture of, 617; of the Great Basin, 725

National Education Association, 25, 57, 64, 76, 129, 136, 144, 237
Nautical Almanac, 232
New England, uplands of, 91, 111; terraces of, 514
New Jersey, coast of, 712; rivers of, 485; topography of northern, 489
Newberry, J. S., 80
Niagara falls, 88

Nile cataract, 88
Norway, glacial erosion in, 635; maps of, 191

Obsequent streams, 264
Ocean, treatment of the, 138
Off-shore bars, 707
Old age, stage of cycle, 177
Old plain, example of, 201
Ontography, 10, 11, 14, 17, 34, 51; regional, 55; systematic, 50, 55
Orbit of the earth, 233
Outdoor observations, 61
Over-deepened valleys, 646, 673

Pagny river, 607
Pedagogical principles, 119
Penck, A., 271, 338, 373, 686
Peneplain, 112, 323, 350, 352, 381, 405
Pennsylvania, 111, 413; events of the Quaternary cycle in, 480; events of the Tertiary cycle in, 473; geological history of, 418; migration of the Atlantic-Ohio divide, 477; Permian topography and drainage of, 451; reversal of rivers in, 459; rivers and valleys of, 413; topography of, 427
Percival, J. G., 353
Philology, 20, 54
Physical geography, 15, 34, 70; abroad, 134; defined, 105, 129; exercises in, 210; field work in, 236; in the grammar schools, 115, 151; in the high school, 129, 215, 236; in the university, 165; treatises on, 74. See also Geography
Physiographic controls, 17, 76, 144
Physiography, 10, 15, 34, 51, and Part Two; regional, 47, 48, 67; subdivisions of, 44; systematic, 43, 48, 67. See also Physical geography and Geography
Plains, examples of, 197 et seq.; of marine denudation, 323; and peneplains, 405
Plants and animals in geography, 134, 144
Playfair, J., 72, 80, 563, 618
Polar flattening, 227
Poles, 222
Political geography, 14, 87
Powell, J. W., 81, 84, 331, 350, 381, 404, 405, 486, 504
Preparation of teachers, 56
Prestwich, J., 80
Primary schools, geography in, 115
Profile of equilibrium, 175; stream, 174
Progress of geography, 23

Provincetown harbor, 720
Pueblo mountains, 760

Race Point, Mass., 717
Rainfall, explanation of, 103
Ramsay, A. C., 79, 323
Rational treatment of geography, 63, 65, 72, 131
Ratzel, F., 13, 18, 51
Red River of the North, 197
Regional geography, 10, 41, 55, 144
Regional ontography, 55
Regional physiography, 47
Relation, of river ability to load, 260; of trunk and branch valleys, 645
Residual mountains, 736; of the Great Basin, 738
Reversal of rivers, 459, 510
Revived streams, 181, 441, 442, 494
Rhue river, 636, 673
Richter, E., 682
Richthofen, F. von, 79
Ritter, K., 33, 34, 71, 72, 129
Rivers, adjusted, 262, 343, 434, 439, 476, 488; anaclinal, 510; antecedent, 81, 274, 444, 447, 486; behavior of a wandering, 532; branches, 260, 645; capture, 82, 596; characteristics of, 242; complete cycle of, 430; complex, 446; composite, 446, 502; compound, 446, 502; consequent, 81, 447; graded, 175, 243, 258, 260, 389, 390, 533; history of, 430; inverted, 603; lateral cutting of, 533; meandering, 264, 532, 549, 559; profile of, 174; reversed, 459, 510; revived, 494; simple, 446; subsequent, 82, 172, 177, 487; superimposed, 444, 469, 487, 494; and valleys, 141
River terraces, 514; theory of, 531
Rotation of the earth, 220; influence of, 104
Russell, I. C., 78, 658, 677, 679, 728
Russia, maps, 191

Ste. Austreberte river, 588
Schooley peneplain, 489
Schools, progress of geography in, 23. See High, Grammar, and Primary schools
Scientific schools, physical geography in, 149
Scotland, glacial valleys in, 686
Scrope, G. P., 78
Sculpture of mountains, 617, 625
Seasons, 229
Seine river, 588
Sequence of the parts of geography, 64

Sequential drainage, 257
Shape of the earth, 219
Shore-lines, 143, 178, 690; cycle of, 290; graded, 702; topography of, 79
Shore profiles, 700
Shoshone falls, 88
Shoshone range, 768
Size of the earth, 224
Slope, graded, 175
Sonoran district, Mexico, 318
Spits, 710
Spurr, J. E., 725
Spurs of the Wahsatch range, 747
Spurs, wave-cut, 751
Stein mountains, 760
Streams. See Rivers
Subsequent streams, 82, 172, 177, 262, 487, 497
Superimposed rivers, 444, 469, 487, 494
Superimposition of the Susquehanna, 469
Susquehanna river, 461, 466, 467, 469
Sutlej river, 508
Systematic geography, 10, 41, 43, 55
Systematic ontography, 50, 55
Systematic physiography, 43, 48, 67

Tarr, R. S., 350, 682
Teachers' meetings, 118, 217
Teachers, preparation of, 56, 158
Teaching of geography, 87; what to avoid in, 95
Teleology, 72, 131
Terminology, of the cycle, 292; geographical, 26, 271; of rivers changed by adjustment, 438; time element in, 251; of wandering rivers, 537
Terrace patterns, 558.
Terraces, 514; defended, 547; effect of rock barriers on, 556; ideal, 538; kinds of, 516; theory of, 531
Terrestrial magnetism, 228
Text-books, geographical, 117, 159
Theoretical geography, 251
Thoreau, H. D., 692
Tibet, 318
Ticino valley, 640, 674
Tilting, effect on streams, 82; as an interruption of the cycle, 285
Time element in geographical terminology, 251

Time needed for a geographical course, 99
Topographer, 150
Topographical maps, 166, 188
Topography, composite, 181, 273
Trunk valleys, 645

Uniformitarianism, 71, 78
United States Coast Survey, maps, 188, 228
United States Geological Survey, maps, 188
United States government bureaus, maps, 188
Unity of geography, 36
Upham, W., 693
Utah, 202, 725

Valley floors, graded, 257
Valley sides, graded, 266
Valley walls, over-steepened, 673
Valleys, 77, 80, 141; antecedent, 81, 274, 444, 447, 486; broken-bedded, 661; consequent, 81, 172, 174, 256, 447; hanging, 645, 653, 677; over-deepened, 646, 673; relation of trunk to branch, 645
Van Hise, C. R., 362
Varigradation, 396
Volcanic accidents, 180, 290

Wahsatch mountains, 734, 742, 747
Wallace, A. R., 680
Waste, forms assumed by, 276
Water gaps, 454
Water partings, 261
Waterfalls, 88, 677
Wave action, 323, 700, 701, 703
Wave-cut spurs, 751
Weather, 212
Weather maps, 63, 229
Weathering, 214; field lesson on, 240
West Virginia, 199
Weule, K., 694
Whiting, H. L., 693
Winds, 103; erosion by, 299

Year, determination of length of, 232
Yosemite falls, 88
Young plain, examples of, 197
Youth, stage of the cycle, 176

CATALOG OF DOVER BOOKS

BOOKS EXPLAINING SCIENCE AND MATHEMATICS

THE COMMON SENSE OF THE EXACT SCIENCES, W. K. Clifford. Introduction by James Newman, edited by Karl Pearson. For 70 years this has been a guide to classical scientific and mathematical thought. Explains with unusual clarity basic concepts, such as extension of meaning of symbols, characteristics of surface boundaries, properties of plane figures, vectors, Cartesian method of determining position, etc. Long preface by Bertrand Russell. Bibliography of Clifford. Corrected, 130 diagrams redrawn. 249pp. 5⅜ x 8.
T61 Paperbound **$1.60**

SCIENCE THEORY AND MAN, Erwin Schrödinger. This is a complete and unabridged reissue of SCIENCE AND THE HUMAN TEMPERAMENT plus an additional essay: "What is an Elementary Particle?" Nobel Laureate Schrödinger discusses such topics as nature of scientific method, the nature of science, chance and determinism, science and society, conceptual models for physical entities, elementary particles and wave mechanics. Presentation is popular and may be followed by most people with little or no scientific training. "Fine practical preparation for a time when laws of nature, human institutions . . . are undergoing a critical examination without parallel," Waldemar Kaempffert, N. Y. TIMES. 192pp. 5⅜ x 8.
T428 Paperbound **$1.35**

PIONEERS OF SCIENCE, O. Lodge. Eminent scientist-expositor's authoritative, yet elementary survey of great scientific theories. Concentrating on individuals—Copernicus, Brahe, Kepler, Galileo, Descartes, Newton, Laplace, Herschel, Lord Kelvin, and other scientists—the author presents their discoveries in historical order adding biographical material on each man and full, specific explanations of their achievements. The clear and complete treatment of the post-Newtonian astronomers is a feature seldom found in other books on the subject. Index. 120 illustrations. xv + 404pp. 5⅜ x 8.
T716 Paperbound **$1.50**

THE EVOLUTION OF SCIENTIFIC THOUGHT FROM NEWTON TO EINSTEIN, A. d'Abro. Einstein's special and general theories of relativity, with their historical implications, are analyzed in non-technical terms. Excellent accounts of the contributions of Newton, Riemann, Weyl, Planck, Eddington, Maxwell, Lorentz and others are treated in terms of space and time, equations of electromagnetics, finiteness of the universe, methodology of science. 21 diagrams. 482pp. 5⅜ x 8.
T2 Paperound **$2.00**

THE RISE OF THE NEW PHYSICS, A. d'Abro. A half-million word exposition, formerly titled THE DECLINE OF MECHANISM, for readers not versed in higher mathematics. The only thorough explanation, in everyday language, of the central core of modern mathematical physical theory, treating both classical and modern theoretical physics, and presenting in terms almost anyone can understand the equivalent of 5 years of study of mathematical physics. Scientifically impeccable coverage of mathematical-physical thought from the Newtonian system up through the electronic theories of Dirac and Heisenberg and Fermi's statistics. Combines both history and exposition; provides a broad yet unified and detailed view, with constant comparison of classical and modern views on phenomena and theories. "A must for anyone doing serious study in the physical sciences," JOURNAL OF THE FRANKLIN INSTITUTE. "Extraordinary faculty . . . to explain ideas and theories of theoretical physics in the language of daily life," ISIS. First part of set covers philosophy of science, drawing upon the practice of Newton, Maxwell, Poincaré, Einstein, others, discussing modes of thought, experiment, interpretations of causality, etc. In the second part, 100 pages explain grammar and vocabulary of mathematics, with discussions of functions, groups, series, Fourier series, etc. The remainder is devoted to concrete, detailed coverage of both classical and quantum physics, explaining such topics as analytic mechanics, Hamilton's principle, wave theory of light, electromagnetic waves, groups of transformations, thermodynamics, phase rule, Brownian movement, kinetics, special relativity, Planck's original quantum theory, Bohr's atom, Zeeman effect, Broglie's wave mechanics, Heisenberg's uncertainty, Eigen-values, matrices, scores of other important topics. Discoveries and theories are covered for such men as Alembert, Born, Cantor, Debye, Euler, Foucault, Galois, Gauss, Hadamard, Kelvin, Kepler, Laplace, Maxwell, Pauli, Rayleigh, Volterra, Weyl, Young, more than 180 others. Indexed. 97 illustrations. ix + 982pp. 5⅜ x 8.
T3 Volume 1, Paperbound **$2.00**
T4 Volume 2, Paperbound **$2.00**

CONCERNING THE NATURE OF THINGS, Sir William Bragg. Christmas lectures delivered at the Royal Society by Nobel laureate. Why a spinning ball travels in a curved track; how uranium is transmuted to lead, etc. Partial contents: atoms, gases, liquids, crystals, metals, etc. No scientific background needed; wonderful for intelligent child. 32pp. of photos, 57 figures. xii + 232pp. 5⅜ x 8.
T31 Paperbound **$1.35**

THE UNIVERSE OF LIGHT, Sir William Bragg. No scientific training needed to read Nobel Prize winner's expansion of his Royal Institute Christmas Lectures. Insight into nature of light, methods and philosophy of science. Explains lenses, reflection, color, resonance, polarization, x-rays, the spectrum, Newton's work with prisms, Huygens' work with polarization, Crookes' with cathode ray, etc. Leads into clear statement of 2 major historical theories of light, corpuscle and wave. Dozens of experiments you can do. 199 illus., including 2 full-page color plates. 293pp. 5⅜ x 8.
S538 Paperbound **$1.85**

PHYSICS, THE PIONEER SCIENCE, L. W. Taylor. First thorough text to place all important physical phenomena in cultural-historical framework; remains best work of its kind. Exposition of physical laws, theories developed chronologically, with great historical, illustrative experiments diagrammed, described, worked out mathematically. Excellent physics text for self-study as well as class work. Vol. 1: Heat, Sound: motion, acceleration, gravitation, conservation of energy, heat engines, rotation, heat, mechanical energy, etc. 211 illus. 407pp. 5⅜ x 8. Vol. 2: Light, Electricity: images, lenses, prisms, magnetism, Ohm's law, dynamos, telegraph, quantum theory, decline of mechanical view of nature, etc. Bibliography. 13 table appendix. Index. 551 illus. 2 color plates. 508pp. 5⅜ x 8.

Vol. 1 S565 Paperbound **$2.00**
Vol. 2 S566 Paperbound **$2.00**
The set **$4.00**

FROM EUCLID TO EDDINGTON: A STUDY OF THE CONCEPTIONS OF THE EXTERNAL WORLD, Sir Edmund Whittaker. A foremost British scientist traces the development of theories of natural philosophy from the western rediscovery of Euclid to Eddington, Einstein, Dirac, etc. The inadequacy of classical physics is contrasted with present day attempts to understand the physical world through relativity, non-Euclidean geometry, space curvature, wave mechanics, etc. 5 major divisions of examination: Space; Time and Movement; the Concepts of Classical Physics; the Concepts of Quantum Mechanics; the Eddington Universe. 212pp. 5⅜ x 8.
T491 Paperbound **$1.35**

THE STORY OF ATOMIC THEORY AND ATOMIC ENERGY, J. G. Feinberg. Wider range of facts on physical theory, cultural implications, than any other similar source. Completely non-technical. Begins with first atomic theory, 600 B.C., goes through A-bomb, developments to 1959. Avogadro, Rutherford, Bohr, Einstein, radioactive decay, binding energy, radiation danger, future benefits of nuclear power, dozens of other topics, told in lively, related, informal manner. Particular stress on European atomic research. "Deserves special mention . . . authoritative," Saturday Review. Formerly "The Atom Story." New chapter to 1959. Index. 34 illustrations. 251pp. 5⅜ x 8.
T625 Paperbound **$1.45**

THE STRANGE STORY OF THE QUANTUM, AN ACCOUNT FOR THE GENERAL READER OF THE GROWTH OF IDEAS UNDERLYING OUR PRESENT ATOMIC KNOWLEDGE, B. Hoffmann. Presents lucidly and expertly, with barest amount of mathematics, the problems and theories which led to modern quantum physics. Dr. Hoffmann begins with the closing years of the 19th century, when certain trifling discrepancies were noticed, and with illuminating analogies and examples takes you through the brilliant concepts of Planck, Einstein, Pauli, de Broglie, Bohr, Schroedinger, Heisenberg, Dirac, Sommerfeld, Feynman, etc. This edition includes a new, long postscript carrying the story through 1958. "Of the books attempting an account of the history and contents of our modern atomic physics which have come to my attention, this is the best," H. Margenau, Yale University, in "American Journal of Physics." 32 tables and line illustrations. Index. 275pp. 5⅜ x 8.
T518 Paperbound **$1.45**

SPACE AND TIME, Emile Borel. An entirely non-technical introduction to relativity, by world-renowned mathematician, Sorbonne Professor. (Notes on basic mathematics are included separately.) This book has never been surpassed for insight, and extraordinary clarity of thought, as it presents scores of examples, analogies, arguments, illustrations, which explain such topics as: difficulties due to motion; gravitation a force of inertia; geodesic lines; wave-length and difference of phase; x-rays and crystal structure; the special theory of relativity; and much more. Indexes. 4 appendixes. 15 figures. xvi + 243pp. 5⅜ x 8.
T592 Paperbound **$1.45**

THE RESTLESS UNIVERSE, Max Born. New enlarged version of this remarkably readable account by a Nobel laureate. Moving from sub-atomic particles to universe, the author explains in very simple terms the latest theories of wave mechanics. Partial contents: air and its relatives, electrons & ions, waves & particles, electronic structure of the atom, nuclear physics. Nearly 1000 illustrations, including 7 animated sequences. 325pp. 6 x 9.
T412 Paperbound **$2.00**

SOAP SUBBLES, THEIR COLOURS AND THE FORCES WHICH MOULD THEM, C. V. Boys. Only complete edition, half again as much material as any other. Includes Boys' hints on performing his experiments, sources of supply. Dozens of lucid experiments show complexities of liquid films, surface tension, etc. Best treatment ever written. Introduction. 83 illustrations. Color plate. 202pp. 5⅜ x 8.
T542 Paperbound **95¢**

SPINNING TOPS AND GYROSCOPIC MOTION, John Perry. Well-known classic of science still unsurpassed for lucid, accurate, delightful exposition. How quasi-rigidity is induced in flexible and fluid bodies by rapid motions; why gyrostat falls, top rises; nature and effect on climatic conditions of earth's precessional movement; effect of internal fluidity on rotating bodies, etc. Appendixes describe practical uses to which gyroscopes have been put in ships, compasses, monorail transportation. 62 figures. 128pp. 5⅜ x 8.
T416 Paperbound **$1.00**

MATTER & LIGHT, THE NEW PHYSICS, L. de Broglie. Non-technical papers by a Nobel laureate explain electromagnetic theory, relativity, matter, light and radiation, wave mechanics, quantum physics, philosophy of science. Einstein, Planck, Bohr, others explained so easily that no mathematical training is needed for all but 2 of the 21 chapters. Unabridged. Index. 300pp. 5⅜ x 8.
T35 Paperbound **$1.60**

A SURVEY OF PHYSICAL THEORY, Max Planck. One of the greatest scientists of all time, creator of the quantum revolution in physics, writes in non-technical terms of his own discoveries and those of other outstanding creators of modern physics. Planck wrote this book when science had just crossed the threshold of the new physics, and he communicates the excitement felt then as he discusses electromagnetic theories, statistical methods, evolution of the concept of light, a step-by-step description of how he developed his own momentous theory, and many more of the basic ideas behind modern physics. Formerly "A" Survey of Physics." Bibliography. Index. 128pp. 5⅜ x 8.   S650 Paperbound $1.15

THE NATURE OF LIGHT AND COLOUR IN THE OPEN AIR, M. Minnaert. Why is falling snow sometimes black? What causes mirages, the fata morgana, multiple suns and moons in the sky? How are shadows formed? Prof. Minnaert of the University of Utrecht answers these and similar questions in optics, light, colour, for non-specialists. Particularly valuable to nature, science students, painters, photographers. Translated by H. M. Kremer-Priest, K. Jay. 202 illustrations, including 42 photos. xvi + 362pp. 5⅜ x 8.   T196 Paperbound $1.95

THE STORY OF X-RAYS FROM RONTGEN TO ISOTOPES, A. R. Bleich. Non-technical history of x-rays, their scientific explanation, their applications in medicine, industry, research, and art, and their effect on the individual and his descendants. Includes amusing early reactions to Röntgen's discovery, cancer therapy, detections of art and stamp forgeries, potential risks to patient and operator, etc. Illustrations show x-rays of flower structure, the gall bladder, gears with hidden defects, etc. Original Dover publication. Glossary. Bibliography. Index. 55 photos and figures. xiv + 186pp. 5⅜ x 8.   T662 Paperbound $1.35

TEACH YOURSELF ELECTRICITY, C. W. Wilman. Electrical resistance, inductance, capacitance, magnets, chemical effects of current, alternating currents, generators and motors, transformers, rectifiers, much more. 230 questions, answers, worked examples. List of units. 115 illus. 194pp. 6⅞ x 4¼.   Clothbound $2.00

TEACH YOURSELF HEAT ENGINES, E. De Ville. Measurement of heat, development of steam and internal combustion engines, efficiency of an engine, compression-ignition engines, production of steam, the ideal engine, much more. 318 exercises, answers, worked examples. Tables. 76 illus. 220pp. 6⅞ x 4¼.   Clothbound $2.00

TEACH YOURSELF MECHANICS, P. Abbott. The lever, centre of gravity, parallelogram of force, friction, acceleration, Newton's laws of motion, machines, specific gravity, gas, liquid pressure, much more. 280 problems, solutions. Tables. 163 illus. 271pp. 6⅞ x 4¼.   Clothbound $2.00

GREAT IDEAS OF MODERN MATHEMATICS: THEIR NATURE AND USE, Jagjit Singh. Reader with only high school math will understand main mathematical ideas of modern physics, astronomy, genetics, psychology, evolution, etc., better than many who use them as tools, but comprehend little of their basic structure. Author uses his wide knowledge of non-mathematical fields in brilliant exposition of differential equations, matrices, group theory, logic, statistics, problems ot mathematical foundations, imaginary numbers, vectors, etc. Original publication. 2 appendixes. 2 indexes. 65 illustr. 322pp. 5⅜ x 8.   S587 Paperbound $1.55

MATHEMATICS IN ACTION, O. G. Sutton. Everyone with a command of high school algebra will find this book one of the finest possible introductions to the application of mathematics to physical theory. Ballistics, numerical analysis, waves and wavelike phenomena, Fourier series, group concepts, fluid flow and aerodynamics, statistical measures, and meteorology are discussed with unusual clarity. Some calculus and differential equations theory is developed by the author for the reader's help in the more difficult sections. 88 figures. Index. viii + 236pp. 5⅜ x 8.   T440 Clothbound $3.50

FREE! All you do is ask for it!

THE FOURTH DIMENSION SIMPLY EXPLAINED, edited by H. P. Manning. 22 essays, originally Scientific American contest entries, that use a minimum of mathematics to explain aspects of 4-dimensional geometry: analogues to 3-dimensional space, 4-dimensional absurdities and curiosities (such as removing the contents of an egg without puncturing its shell), possible measurements and forms, etc. Introduction by the editor. Only book of its sort on a truly elementary level, excellent introduction to advanced works. 82 figures. 251pp. 5⅜ x 8.   T711 Paperbound $1.35

FAMOUS BRIDGES OF THE WORLD, D. B. Steinman. An up-to-the-minute revised edition of a book that explains the fascinating drama of how the world's great bridges came to be built. The author, designer of the famed Mackinac bridge, discusses bridges from all periods and all parts of the world, explaining their various types of construction, and describing the problems their builders faced. Although primarily for youngsters, this cannot fail to interest readers of all ages. 48 illustrations in the text. 23 photographs. 99pp. 6⅛ x 9¼.   T161 Paperbound $1.00

BRIDGES AND THEIR BUILDERS, David Steinman and Sara Ruth Watson. Engineers, historians, everyone who has ever been fascinated by great spans will find this book an endless source of information and interest. Dr. Steinman, recipient of the Louis Levy medal, was one of the great bridge architects and engineers of all time, and his analysis of the great bridges of history is both authoritative and easily followed. Greek and Roman bridges, medieval bridges, Oriental bridges, modern works such as the Brooklyn Bridge and the Golden Gate Bridge, and many others are described in terms of history, constructional principles, artistry, and function. All in all this book is the most comprehensive and accurate semipopular history of bridges in print in English. New, greatly revised, enlarged edition. 23 photographs, 26 line drawings. Index. xvii + 401pp. 5⅜ x 8.   T431 Paperbound **$2.00**

FADS AND FALLACIES IN THE NAME OF SCIENCE, Martin Gardner. Examines various cults, quack systems, frauds, delusions which at various times have masqueraded as science. Accounts of hollow-earth fanatics like Symmes; Velikovsky and wandering planets; Hoerbiger; Bellamy and the theory of multiple moons; Charles Fort; dowsing, pseudoscientific methods for finding water, ores, oil. Sections on naturopathy, iridiagnosis, zone therapy, food fads, etc. Analytical accounts of Wilhelm Reich and orgone sex energy; L. Ron Hubbard and Dianetics; A. Korzybski and General Semantics; many others. Brought up to date to include Bridey Murphy, others. Not just a collection of anecdotes, but a fair, reasoned appraisal of eccentric theory. Formerly titled IN THE NAME OF SCIENCE. Preface. Index. x + 384pp. 5⅜ x 8.   T394 Paperbound **$1.50**

See also: A PHILOSOPHICAL ESSAY ON PROBABILITIES, P. de Laplace; ON MATHEMATICS AND MATHEMATICIANS, R. E. Moritz; AN ELEMENTARY SURVEY OF CELESTIAL MECHANICS, Y. Ryabov; THE SKY AND ITS MYSTERIES, E. A. Beet; THE REALM OF THE NEBULAE, E. Hubble; OUT OF THE SKY, H. H. Nininger; SATELLITES AND SCIENTIFIC RESEARCH, D. King-Hele; HEREDITY AND YOUR LIFE, A. M. Winchester; INSECTS AND INSECT LIFE, S. W. Frost; PRINCIPLES OF STRATIGRAPHY, A. W. Grabau; TEACH YOURSELF SERIES.

HISTORY OF SCIENCE AND MATHEMATICS

DIALOGUES CONCERNING TWO NEW SCIENCES, Galileo Galilei. This classic of experimental science, mechanics, engineering, is as enjoyable as it is important. A great historical document giving insights into one of the world's most original thinkers, it is based on 30 years' experimentation. It offers a lively exposition of dynamics, elasticity, sound, ballistics, strength of materials, the scientific method. "Superior to everything else of mine," Galileo. Trans. by H. Crew, A. Salvio. 126 diagrams. Index. xxi + 288pp. 5⅜ x 8.
S99 Paperbound **$1.65**

A DIDEROT PICTORIAL ENCYCLOPEDIA OF TRADES AND INDUSTRY, Manufacturing and the Technical Arts in Plates Selected from "L'Encyclopédie ou Dictionnaire Raisonné des Sciences, des Arts, et des Métiers" of Denis Diderot. Edited with text by C. Gillispie. This first modern selection of plates from the high point of 18th century French engraving is a storehouse of valuable technological information to the historian of arts and science. Over 2000 illustrations on 485 full page plates, most of them original size, show the trades and industries of a fascinating era in such great detail that the processes and shops might very well be reconstructed from them. The plates teem with life, with men, women, and children performing all of the thousands of operations necessary to the trades before and during the early stages of the industrial revolution. Plates are in sequence, and show general operations, closeups of difficult operations, and details of complex machinery. Such important and interesting trades and industries are illustrated as sowing, harvesting, beekeeping, cheesemaking, operating windmills, milling flour, charcoal burning, tobacco processing, indigo, fishing, arts of war, salt extraction, mining, smelting, casting iron, steel, extracting mercury, zinc, sulphur, copper, etc., slating, tinning, silverplating, gilding, making gunpowder, cannons, bells, shoeing horses, tanning, papermaking, printing, dyeing, and more than 40 other categories. Professor Gillispie, of Princeton, supplies a full commentary on all the plates, identifying operations, tools, processes, etc. This material, presented in a lively and lucid fashion, is of great interest to the reader interested in history of science and technology. Heavy library cloth. 920pp. 9 x 12.   T421 Two volume set **$18.50**

DE MAGNETE, William Gilbert. This classic work on magnetism founded a new science. Gilbert was the first to use the word "electricity", to recognize mass as distinct from weight, to discover the effect of heat on magnetic bodies; invent an electroscope, differentiate between static electricity and magnetism, conceive of the earth as a magnet. Written by the first great experimental scientist, this lively work is valuable not only as an historical landmark, but as the delightfully easy to follow record of a perpetually searching, ingenious mind. Translated by P. F. Mottelay. 25 page biographical memoir. 90 figures. lix + 368pp. 5⅜ x 8.   S470 Paperbound **$2.00**

CHARLES BABBAGE AND HIS CALCULATING ENGINES, edited by P. Morrison and E. Morrison. Babbage, leading 19th century pioneer in mathematical machines and herald of modern operational research, was the true father of Harvard's relay computer Mark I. His Difference Engine and Analytical Engine were the first machines in the field. This volume contains a valuable introduction on his life and work; major excerpts from his autobiography, revealing his eccentric and unusual personality; and extensive selections from "Babbage's Calculating Engines," a compilation of hard-to-find journal articles by Babbage, the Countess of Lovelace, L. F. Menabrea; and Dionysius Lardner. 8 illustrations, Appendix of miscellaneous papers. Index. Bibliography. xxxviii + 400pp. 5⅜ x 8.　　　　　　　　　　　　**T12 Paperbound $2.00**

A HISTORY OF ASTRONOMY FROM THALES TO KEPLER, J. L. E. Dreyer. (Formerly A HISTORY OF PLANETARY SYSTEMS FROM THALES TO KEPLER.) This is the only work in English to give the complete history of man's cosmological views from prehistoric times to Kepler and Newton. Partial contents: Near Eastern astronomical systems, Early Greeks, Homocentric Spheres of Eudoxus, Epicycles, Ptolemaic system, medieval cosmology, Copernicus, Kepler, etc. Revised, foreword by W. H. Stahl. New bibliography. xvii + 430pp. 5⅜ x 8.
S79 Paperbound $1.98

A SHORT HISTORY OF ANATOMY AND PHYSIOLOGY FROM THE GREEKS TO HARVEY, Charles Singer. Corrected edition of THE EVOLUTION OF ANATOMY, classic work tracing evolution of anatomy and physiology from prescientific times through Greek & Roman periods, Dark Ages, Renaissance, to age of Harvey and beginning of modern concepts. Centered on individuals, movements, periods that definitely advanced anatomical knowledge: Plato, Diocles, Aristotle, Theophrastus, Herophilus, Erasistratus, the Alexandrians, Galen, Mondino, da Vinci, Linacre, Sylvius, others. Special section on Vesalius; Vesalian atlas of nudes, skeletons, muscle tabulae. Index of names, 20 plates. 270 extremely interesting illustrations of ancient, medieval, Renaissance, Oriental origin. xii + 209pp. 5⅜ x 8.　　　　　**T389 Paperbound $1.75**

FROM MAGIC TO SCIENCE, Charles Singer. A great historian examines aspects of medical science from the Roman Empire through the Renaissance. Includes perhaps the best discussion of early herbals, and a penetrating physiological interpretation of "The Visions of Hildegarde of Bingen." Also examined are Arabian and Galenic influences; the Sphere of Pythagoras; Paracelsus; the reawakening of science under Leonardo da Vinci, Vesalius; the Lorica of Gildas the Briton; etc. Frequent quotations with translations. New Introduction by the author. New unabridged, corrected edition. 158 unusual illustrations from classical and medieval sources. Index. xxvii + 365pp. 5⅜ x 8.　　　　　　　**T390 Paperbound $2.00**

HISTORY OF MATHEMATICS, D. E. Smith. Most comprehensive non-technical history of math in English. Discusses lives and works of over a thousand major and minor figures, with footnotes supplying technical information outside the book's scheme, and indicating disputed matters. Vol I: A chronological examination, from primitive concepts through Egypt, Babylonia, Greece, the Orient, Rome, the Middle Ages, the Renaissance, and up to 1900. Vol 2: The development of ideas in specific fields and problems, up through elementary calculus. Two volumes, total of 510 illustrations, 1355pp. 5⅜ x 8. Set boxed in attractive container.　　　　　　　　　　　　　**T429, 430 Paperbound, the set $5.00**

A SHORT ACCOUNT OF THE HISTORY OF MATHEMATICS, W. W. R. Ball. Most readable non-technical history of mathematics treats lives, discoveries of every important figure from Egyptian, Phoenician mathematicians to late 19th century. Discusses schools of Ionia, Pythagoras, Athens, Cyzicus, Alexandria, Byzantium, systems of numeration; primitive arithmetic; Middle Ages, Renaissance, including Arabs, Bacon, Regiomontanus, Tartaglia, Cardan, Stevinus, Galileo, Kepler; modern mathematics of Descartes, Pascal, Wallis, Huygens, Newton, Leibnitz, d'Alembert, Euler, Lambert, Laplace, Legendre, Gauss, Hermite, Weierstrass, scores more. Index. 25 figures. 546pp. 5⅜ x 8.　　　　　　　**S630 Paperbound $2.00**

A SOURCE BOOK IN MATHEMATICS, D. E. Smith. Great discoveries in math, from Renaissance to end of 19th century, in English translation. Read announcements by Dedekind, Gauss, Delamain, Pascal, Fermat, Newton, Abel, Lobachevsky, Bolyai, Riemann, De Moivre, Legendre, Laplace, others of discoveries about imaginary numbers, number congruence, slide rule, equations, symbolism, cubic algebraic equations, non-Euclidean forms of geometry, calculus, function theory, quaternions, etc. Succinct selections from 125 different treatises, articles, most unavailable elsewhere in English. Each article preceded by biographical, historical introduction. Vol. I: Fields of Number, Algebra. Index. 32 illus. 338pp. 5⅜ x 8. Vol. II: Fields of Geometry, Probability, Calculus, Functions, Quaternions. 83 illus. 432pp. 5⅜ x 8.
Vol. 1: **S552 Paperbound $1.85**
Vol. 2: **S553 Paperbound $1.85**
2 vol. set, boxed **$3.50**

A HISTORY OF THE CALCULUS, AND ITS CONCEPTUAL DEVELOPMENT, Carl B. Boyer. Provides laymen and mathematicians a detailed history of the development of the calculus, from early beginning in antiquity to final elaboration as mathematical abstractions. Gives a sense of mathematics not as a technique, but as a habit of mind, in the progression of ideas of Zeno, Plato, Pythagoras, Eudoxus, Arabic and Scholastic mathematicians, Newton, Leibnitz, Taylor, Descartes, Euler, Lagrange, Cantor, Weierstrass, and others. This first comprehensive critical history of the calculus was originally titled "The Concepts of the Calculus." Foreword by R. Courant. Preface. 22 figures. 25-page bibliography. Index. v + 364pp. 5⅜ x 8.　　　　　　　　　　　　　　　**S509 Paperbound $2.00**

A CONCISE HISTORY OF MATHEMATICS, D. Struik. Lucid study of development of mathematical ideas, techniques from Ancient Near East, Greece, Islamic science, Middle Ages, Renaissance, modern times. Important mathematicians are described in detail. Treatment is not anecdotal, but analytical development of ideas. "Rich in content, thoughtful in interpretation," U.S. QUARTERLY BOOKLIST. Non-technical; no mathematical training needed. Index. 60 illustrations, including Egyptian papyri, Greek mss., portraits of 31 eminent mathematicians. Bibliography. 2nd edition. xix + 299pp. 5⅜ x 8. T255 Paperbound **$1.75**

See also: **NON-EUCLIDEAN GEOMETRY, R. Bonola; THEORY OF DETERMINANTS IN HISTORICAL ORDER OF DEVELOPMENT, T. Muir; HISTORY OF THE THEORY OF ELASTICITY AND STRENGTH OF MATERIALS, I. Todhunter and K. Pearson; A SHORT HISTORY OF ASTRONOMY, A. Berry; CLASSICS OF SCIENCE.**

PHILOSOPHY OF SCIENCE AND MATHEMATICS

FOUNDATIONS OF SCIENCE: THE PHILOSOPHY OF THEORY AND EXPERIMENT, N. R. Campbell. A critique of the most fundamental concepts of science in general and physics in particular. Examines why certain propositions are accepted without question, demarcates science from philosophy, clarifies the understanding of the tools of science. Part One analyzes the presuppositions of scientific thought: existence of the material world, nature of scientific laws, multiplication of probabilities, etc.: Part Two covers the nature of experiment and the application of mathematics: conditions for measurement, relations between numerical laws and theories, laws of error, etc. An appendix covers problems arising from relativity, force, motion, space, and time. A classic in its field. Index. xiii + 565pp. 5⅝ x 8⅜. S372 Paperbound **$2.95**

WHAT IS SCIENCE?, Norman Campbell. This excellent introduction explains scientific method, role of mathematics, types of scientific laws. Contents: 2 aspects of science, science & nature, laws of science, discovery of laws, explanation of laws, measurement & numerical laws, applications of science. 192pp. 5⅜ x 8. S43 Paperbound **$1.25**

THE VALUE OF SCIENCE, Henri Poincaré. Many of the most mature ideas of the "last scientific universalist" covered with charm and vigor for both the beginning student and the advanced worker. Discusses the nature of scientific truth, whether order is innate in the universe or imposed upon it by man, logical thought versus intuition (relating to math, through the works of Weierstrass, Lie, Klein, Riemann), time and space (relativity, psychological time, simultaneity), Hertz's concept of force, interrelationship of mathematical physics to pure math, values within disciplines of Maxwell, Carnot, Mayer, Newton, Lorentz, etc. Index. iii + 147pp. 5⅜ x 8. S469 Paperbound **$1.35**

SCIENCE AND METHOD, Henri Poincaré. Procedure of scientific discovery, methodology, experiment, idea-germination—the intellectual processes by which discoveries come into being. Most significant and most interesting aspects of development, application of ideas. Chapters cover selection of facts, chance, mathematical reasoning, mathematics, and logic; Whitehead, Russell, Cantor; the new mechanics, etc. 288pp. 5⅜ x 8. S222 Paperbound **$1.35**

SCIENCE AND HYPOTHESIS, Henri Poincaré. Creative psychology in science. How such concepts as number, magnitude, space, force, classical mechanics were developed, and how the modern scientist uses them in his thought. Hypothesis in physics, theories of modern physics. Introduction by Sir James Larmor. "Few mathematicians have had the breadth of vision of Poincaré, and none is his superior in the gift of clear exposition," E. T. Bell. Index. 272pp. 5⅜ x 8. S221 Paperbound **$1.35**

PHILOSOPHY AND THE PHYSICISTS, L. S. Stebbing. The philosophical aspects of modern science examined in terms of a lively critical attack on the ideas of Jeans and Eddington. Discusses the task of science, causality, determinism, probability, consciousness, the relation of the world of physics to that of everyday experience. Probes the philosophical significance of the Planck-Bohr concept of discontinuous energy levels, the inferences to be drawn from Heisenberg's Uncertainty Principle, the implications of "becoming" involved in the 2nd law of thermodynamics, and other problems posed by the discarding of Laplacean determinism. 285pp. 5⅜ x 8. T480 Paperbound **$1.65**

EXPERIMENT AND THEORY IN PHYSICS, Max Born. A Nobel laureate examines the nature and value of the counterclaims of experiment and theory in physics. Synthetic versus analytical scientific advances are analyzed in the work of Einstein, Bohr, Heisenberg, Planck, Eddington, Milne, and others by a fellow participant. 44pp. 5⅜ x 8. S308 Paperbound **60¢**

THE NATURE OF PHYSICAL THEORY, P. W. Bridgman. Here is how modern physics looks to a highly unorthodox physicist—a Nobel laureate. Pointing out many absurdities of science, and demonstrating the inadequacies of various physical theories, Dr. Bridgman weighs and analyzes the contributions of Einstein, Bohr, Newton, Heisenberg, and many others. This is a non-technical consideration of the correlation of science and reality. Index. xi + 138pp. 5⅜ x 8. S33 Paperbound **$1.25**

THE PHILOSOPHY OF SPACE AND TIME, H. Reichenbach. An important landmark in the development of the empiricist conception of geometry, covering the problem of the foundations of geometry, the theory of time, the consequences of Einstein's relativity, including: relations between theory and observations; coordinate and metrical properties of space; the psychological problem of visual intuition of non-Euclidean structures; and many other important topics in modern science and philosophy. The majority of ideas require only a knowledge of intermediate math. Introduction by R. Carnap. 49 figures. Index. xviii + 296pp. 5⅜ x 8. S443 Paperbound **$2.00**

MATTER & MOTION, James Clerk Maxwell, This excellent exposition begins with simple particles and proceeds gradually to physical systems beyond complete analysis: motion, force, properties of centre of mass of material system, work, energy, gravitation, etc. Written with all Maxwell's original insights and clarity. Notes by E. Larmor. 17 diagrams. 178pp. 5⅜ x 8. S188 Paperbound **$1.35**

THE ANALYSIS OF MATTER, Bertrand Russell. How do our senses concord with the new physics? This volume covers such topics as logical analysis of physics, prerelativity physics, causality, scientific inference, physics and perception, special and general relativity, Weyl's theory, tensors, invariants and their physical interpretation, periodicity and qualitative series. "The most thorough treatment of the subject that has yet been published," THE NATION. Introduction by L. E. Denonn. 422pp. 5⅜ x 8. T231 Paperbound **$1.95**

SUBSTANCE AND FUNCTION, & EINSTEIN'S THEORY OF RELATIVITY, Ernst Cassirer. Two books bound as one. Cassirer establishes a philosophy of the exact sciences that takes into consideration newer developments in mathematics, and also shows historical connections. Partial contents: Aristotelian logic, Mill's analysis, Helmholtz & Kronecker, Russell & cardinal numbers, Euclidean vs. non-Euclidean geometry, Einstein's relativity. Bibliography. Index. xxi + 465pp. 5⅜ x 8. T50 Paperbound **$2.00**

PRINCIPLES OF MECHANICS, Heinrich Hertz. This last work by the great 19th century physicist is not only a classic, but of great interest in the logic of science. Creating a new system of mechanics based upon space, time, and mass, it returns to axiomatic analysis, to understanding of the formal or structural aspects of science, taking into account logic, observation, and a priori elements. Of great historical importance to Poincaré, Carnap, Einstein, Milne. A 20-page introduction by R. S. Cohen, Wesleyan University, analyzes the implications of Hertz's thought and the logic of science. Bibliography. 13-page introduction by Helmholtz. xlii + 274pp. 5⅜ x 8. S316 Clothbound **$3.50** S317 Paperbound **$1.85**

THE PHILOSOPHICAL WRITINGS OF PEIRCE, edited by Justus Buchler. (Formerly published as THE PHILOSOPHY OF PEIRCE.) This is a carefully balanced exposition of Peirce's complete system, written by Peirce himself. It covers such matters as scientific method, pure chance vs. law, symbolic logic, theory of signs, pragmatism, experiment, and other topics. Introduction by Justus Buchler, Columbia University. xvi + 368pp. 5⅜ x 8. T217 Paperbound **$1.95**

ESSAYS IN EXPERIMENTAL LOGIC, John Dewey. This stimulating series of essays touches upon the relationship between inquiry and experience, dependence of knowledge upon thought, character of logic; judgments of practice, data and meanings, stimuli of thought, etc. Index. viii + 444pp. 5⅜ x 8. T73 Paperbound **$1.95**

LANGUAGE, TRUTH AND LOGIC, A. Ayer. A clear introduction to the Vienna and Cambridge schools of Logical Positivism. It sets up specific tests by which you can evaluate validity of ideas, etc. Contents: Function of philosophy, elimination of metaphysics, nature of analysis, a priori, truth and probability, etc. 10th printing. "I should like to have written it myself," Bertrand Russell. Index. 160pp. 5⅜ x 8. T10 Paperbound **$1.25**

THE PSYCHOLOGY OF INVENTION IN THE MATHEMATICAL FIELD, J. Hadamard. Where do ideas come from? What role does the unconscious play? Are ideas best developed by mathematical reasoning, word reasoning, visualization? What are the methods used by Einstein, Poincaré, Galton, Riemann? How can these techniques be applied by others? Hadamard, one of the world's leading mathematicians, discusses these and other questions. xiii + 145pp. 5⅜ x 8. T107 Paperbound **$1.25**

FOUNDATIONS OF GEOMETRY, Bertrand Russell. Analyzing basic problems in the overlap area between mathematics and philosophy, Nobel laureate Russell examines the nature of geometrical knowledge, the nature of geometry, and the application of geometry to space. It covers the history of non-Euclidean geometry, philosophic interpretations of geometry—especially Kant—projective and metrical geometry. This is most interesting as the solution offered in 1897 by a great mind to a problem still current. New introduction by Prof. Morris Kline of N. Y. University. xii + 201pp. 5⅜ x 8. S232 Clothbound **$3.25** S233 Paperbound **$1.60**

BIBLIOGRAPHIES

GUIDE TO THE LITERATURE OF MATHEMATICS AND PHYSICS, N. G. Parke III. Over 5000 entries included under approximately 120 major subject headings, of selected most important books, monographs, periodicals, articles in English, plus important works in German, French, Italian, Spanish, Russian (many recently available works). Covers every branch of physics, math, related engineering. Includes author, title, edition, publisher, place, date, number of volumes, number of pages. A 40-page introduction on the basic problems of research and study provides useful information on the organization and use of libraries, the psychology of learning, etc. This reference work will save you hours of time. 2nd revised edition. Indices of authors, subjects. 464pp. 5⅜ x 8. S447 Paperbound **$2.49**

THE STUDY OF THE HISTORY OF MATHEMATICS & THE STUDY OF THE HISTORY OF SCIENCE, George Sarton. Scientific method & philosophy in 2 scholarly fields. Defines duty of historian of math., provides especially useful bibliography with best available biographies of modern mathematicians, editions of their collected works, correspondence. Observes combination of history & science, will aid scholar in understanding science today. Bibliography includes best known treatises on historical methods. 200-item critically evaluated bibliography. Index. 10 illustrations. 2 volumes bound as one. 113pp. + 75pp. 5⅜ x 8. T240 Paperbound **$1.25**

MATHEMATICAL PUZZLES

AMUSEMENTS IN MATHEMATICS, Henry Ernest Dudeney. The foremost British originator of mathematical puzzles is always intriguing, witty, and paradoxical in this classic, one of the largest collections of mathematical amusements. More than 430 puzzles, problems, and paradoxes. Mazes and games, problems on number manipulation, unicursal and other route problems, puzzles on measuring, weighing, packing, age, kinship, chessboards, joiners', crossing river, plane figure dissection, and many others. Solutions. More than 450 illustrations. vii + 258pp. 5⅜ x 8. T473 Paperbound **$1.25**

THE CANTERBURY PUZZLES, Henry Ernest Dudeney. Chaucer's pilgrims set one another problems in story form. Also Adventures of the Puzzle Club, the Strange Escape of the King's Jester, the Monks of Riddlewell, the Squire's Christmas Puzzle Party, and others. All puzzles are original, based on dissecting plane figures, arithmetic, algebra, elementary calculus, and other branches of mathematics, and purely logical ingenuity. "The limit of ingenuity and intricacy . . ." The Observer. Over 110 puzzles. Full solutions. 150 illustrations. viii + 225pp. 5⅜ x 8. T474 Paperbound **$1.25**

SYMBOLIC LOGIC and THE GAME OF LOGIC, Lewis Carroll. "Symbolic Logic" is not concerned with modern symbolic logic, but is instead a collection of over 380 problems posed with charm and imagination, using the syllogism, and a fascinating diagrammatic method of drawing conclusions. In "The Game of Logic," Carroll's whimsical imagination devises a logical game played with 2 diagrams and counters (included) to manipulate hundreds of tricky syllogisms. The final section, "Hit or Miss" is a lagniappe of 101 additional puzzles in the delightful Carroll manner. Until this reprint edition, both of these books were rarities costing up to $15 each. Symbolic Logic: Index, xxxi + 199pp. The Game of Logic: 96pp. Two vols. bound as one. 5⅜ x 8. T492 Paperbound **$1.50**

PILLOW PROBLEMS and A TANGLED TALE, Lewis Carroll. One of the rarest of all Carroll's works, "Pillow Problems" contains 72 original math puzzles, all typically ingenious. Particularly fascinating are Carroll's answers which remain exactly as he thought them out, reflecting his actual mental processes. The problems in "A Tangled Tale" are in story form, originally appearing as a monthly magazine serial. Carroll not only gives the solutions, but uses answers sent in by readers to discuss wrong approaches and misleading paths, and grades them for insight. Both of these books were rarities until this edition, "Pillow Problems" costing up to $25, and "A Tangled Tale" $15. Pillow Problems: Preface and introduction by Lewis Carroll. xx + 109pp. A Tangled Tale: 6 illustrations. 152pp. Two vols. bound as one. 5⅜ x 8. T493 Paperbound **$1.50**

DIVERSIONS AND DIGRESSIONS OF LEWIS CARROLL. A major new treasure for Carroll fans! Rare privately published puzzles, mathematical amusements and recreations, games. Includes the fragmentary Part III of "Curiosa Mathematica." Also contains humorous and satirical pieces: "The New Belfry," "The Vision of the Three T's," and much more. New 32-page supplement of rare photographs taken by Carroll. Formerly titled "The Lewis Carroll Picture Book." Edited by S. Collingwood. x + 375pp. 5⅜ x 8. T732 Paperbound **$1.50**

MATHEMATICAL PUZZLES OF SAM LOYD, Vol. I, selected and edited by M. Gardner. Puzzles by the greatest puzzle creator and innovator. Selected from his famous "Cyclopedia of Puzzles," they retain the unique style and historical flavor of the originals. There are posers based on arithmetic, algebra, probability, game theory, route tracing, topology, counter, sliding block, operations research, geometrical dissection. Includes his famous "14-15" puzzle which was a national craze, and his "Horse of a Different Color" which sold millions of copies. 117 of his most ingenious puzzles in all, 120 line drawings and diagrams. Solutions. Selected references. xx + 167pp. 5⅜ x 8. **T498 Paperbound $1.00**

MATHEMATICAL PUZZLES OF SAM LOYD, Vol. II, selected and edited by Martin Gardner. The outstanding second selection from the great American innovator's "Cyclopedia of Puzzles": speed and distance problems, clock problems, plane and solid geometry, calculus problems, etc. Analytical table of contents that groups the puzzles according to the type of mathematics necessary to solve them. 166 puzzles, 150 original line drawings and diagrams. Selected references. xiv + 177pp. 5⅜ x 8. **T709 Paperbound $1.00**

CALIBAN'S PROBLEM BOOK: MATHEMATICAL, INFERENTIAL, AND CRYPTOGRAPHIC PUZZLES, H. Phillips ("Caliban"), S. T. Shovelton, G. S. Marshall. 105 ingenious problems by the greatest living creator of puzzles based on logic and inference. Rigorous, modern, piquant, and reflecting their author's unusual personality, these intermediate and advanced puzzles all involve the ability to reason clearly through complex situations; some call for mathematical knowledge, ranging from algebra to number theory. Solutions. xi + 180pp. 5⅜ x 8.
T736 Paperbound $1.25

MATHEMATICAL PUZZLES FOR BEGINNERS AND ENTHUSIASTS, G. Mott-Smith. 188 mathematical puzzles to test mental agility. Inference, interpretation, algebra, dissection of plane figures, geometry, properties of numbers, decimation, permutations, probability, all enter these delightful problems. Puzzles like the Odic Force, How to Draw an Ellipse, Spider's Cousin, more than 180 others. Detailed solutions. Appendix with square roots, triangular numbers, primes, etc. 135 illustrations. 2nd revised edition. 248pp. 5⅜ x 8. **T198 Paperbound $1.00**

INGENIOUS MATHEMATICAL PROBLEMS AND METHODS, L. A. Graham. 100 best problems from Graham "Dial," at least ¾ absolutely original in book form, submitted by applied mathematicians and math puzzle fans. Posed in practical terms, utilize number theory, statistics, compass geometry, networks, inversion, in proofs. Accent on heuristics (problem-solving technique) with various methods of solution discussed, compared, for each problem. First publication. Full solutions. 254pp. 5⅜ x 8. **T545 Paperbound $1.45**

101 PUZZLES IN THOUGHT AND LOGIC, C. R. Wylie, Jr. Designed for readers who enjoy the challenge and stimulation of logical puzzles without specialized mathematical or scientific knowledge. These problems are entirely new, and range from relatively easy to brain-teasers that will afford hours of subtle entertainment. It contains detective puzzles, how to find the lying fisherman, how a blind man can identify color by logic, and many more. Easy-to-understand introduction to the logic of puzzle solving and general scientific method. 128pp. 5⅜ x 8. **T367 Paperbound $1.00**

MAZES AND LABYRINTHS: A BOOK OF PUZZLES, W. Shepherd. Mazes, formerly associated with mystery and ritual, are still among the most intriguing of intellectual puzzles. This is a novel and different collection of 50 amusements that embody the principle of the maze: mazes in the classical tradition; 3-dimensional, ribbon, and Möbius-strip mazes; hidden messages; spatial arrangements; etc.—almost all built on amusing story situations. 84 illustrations. Essay on maze psychology. Solutions. xv + 122pp. 5⅜ x 8. **T731 Paperbound $1.00**

MATHEMAGIC, MAGIC PUZZLES, AND GAMES WITH NUMBERS, Royal V. Heath. Over 60 new puzzles and stunts based on properties of numbers. Demonstrates easy techniques for multiplying large numbers mentally, identifying unknown numbers, determining date of any day in any year, dozens of similar useful, entertaining applications of mathematics. Entertainments like The Lost Digit, 3 Acrobats, Psychic Bridge, magic squares, triangles, cubes, circles, other material not easily found elsewhere. Edited by J. S. Meyer. 76 illustrations. 128pp. 5⅜ x 8 **T110 Paperbound $1.00**

MATHEMATICAL RECREATIONS, M. Kraitchik. Some 250 puzzles, problems, demonstrations of recreational mathematics for beginners & advanced mathematicians. Unusual historical problems from Greek, Medieval, Arabic, Hindu sources: modern problems based on "mathematics without numbers," geometry, topology, arithmetic, etc. Pastimes derived from figurative numbers, Mersenne numbers, Fermat numbers; fairy chess, latruncles, reversi, many topics. Full solutions. Excellent for insights into special fields of math. 181 illustrations. 330pp. 5⅜ x 8. **T163 Paperbound $1.75**

PUZZLE QUIZ AND STUNT FUN, Jerome Meyer. 238 high-priority puzzles, stunts, and tricks—mathematical puzzles like The Clever Carpenter, Atom Bomb, Please Help Alice; mysteries and deductions like The Bridge of Sighs, Dog Logic, Secret Code; observation puzzlers like The American Flag, Playing Cards, Telephone Dial; more than 200 others involving magic squares, tongue twisters, puns, anagrams, word design. Answers included. Revised, enlarged edition of FUN-TO-DO. Over 100 illustrations. 238 puzzles, stunts, tricks. 256pp. 5⅜ x 8. **T337 Paperbound $1.00**

THE BOOK OF MODERN PUZZLES, G. L. Kaufman. More than 150 word puzzles, logic puzzles. No warmed-over fare but all new material based on same appeals that make crosswords and deduction puzzles popular, but with different principles, techniques. Two-minute teasers, involved word-labyrinths, design and pattern puzzles, puzzles calling for logic and observation, puzzles testing ability to apply general knowledge to peculiar situations, many others. Answers to all problems. 116 illustrations. 192pp. 5⅜ x 8.   T143 Paperbound **$1.00**

NEW WORD PUZZLES, Gerald L. Kaufman. Contains 100 brand new challenging puzzles based on words and their combinations, never published before in any form. Most are new types invented by the author—for beginners or experts. Chess word puzzles, addle letter anagrams, double word squares, double horizontals, alphagram puzzles, dual acrostigrams, linkogram lapwords—plus 8 other brand new types, all with solutions included. 196 figures. 100 brand new puzzles. vi + 122pp. 5⅜ x 8.   T344 Paperbound **$1.00**

MATHEMATICAL RECREATIONS

MATHEMATICS, MAGIC AND MYSTERY, Martin Gardner. Card tricks, feats of mental mathematics, stage mind-reading, other "magic" explained as applications of probability, sets, theory of numbers, topology, various branches of mathematics. Creative examination of laws and their applications with scores of new tricks and insights. 115 sections discuss tricks wtih cards, dice, coins; geometrical vanishing tricks, dozens of others. No sleight of hand needed; mathematics guarantees success. 115 illustrations. xii + 174pp. 5⅜ x 8.
T335 Paperbound **$1.00**

MATHEMATICAL EXCURSIONS, Helen A. Merrill. Fun, recreation, insights into elementary problem-solving. A mathematical expert guides you along by-paths not generally travelled in elementary math courses—how to divide by inspection, Russian peasant system of multiplication; memory systems for pi; building odd and even magic squares; dyadic systems; facts about 37; square roots by geometry; Tchebichev's machine; drawing five-sided figures; dozens more. Solutions to more difficult ones. 50 illustrations. 145pp. 5⅜ x 8.
T350 Paperbound **$1.00**

CRYPTOGRAPHY, L. D. Smith. Excellent elementary introduction to enciphering, deciphering secret writing. Explains transposition, substitution ciphers; codes; solutions. Geometrical patterns, route transcription, columnar transposition, other methods. Mixed cipher systems; single-alphabet, polyalphabetical substitution; mechanical devices; Vigenere system, etc. Enciphering Japanese; explanation of Baconian Biliteral cipher; frequency tables. More than 150 problems provide practical application. Bibliography. Index. 164pp. 5⅜ x 8.
T247 Paperbound **$1.00**

CRYPTANALYSIS, Helen F. Gaines. (Formerly ELEMENTARY CRYPTANALYSIS.) A standard elementary and intermediate text for serious students. It does not confine itself to old material, but contains much that is not generally known, except to experts. Concealment, Transposition, Substitution ciphers; Vigenere, Kasiski, Playfair, multafid, dozens of other techniques. Appendix with sequence charts, letter frequencies in English, 5 other languages, English word frequencies. Bibliography. 167 codes. New to this edition: solution to codes. vi + 230pp. 5⅜ x 8.   T97 Paperbound **$1.95**

MAGIC SQUARES AND CUBES, W. S. Andrews. Only book-length treatment in English, a thorough non-technical description and analysis. Here are nasik, overlapping, pandiagonal, serrated squares; magic circles, cubes, spheres, rhombuses. Try your hand at 4-dimensional magical figures! Much unusual folklore and tradition included. High school algebra is sufficient. 754 diagrams and illustrations. viii + 419pp. 5⅜ x 8.   T658 Paperbound **$1.85**

PAPER FOLDING FOR BEGINNERS, W. D. Murray and F. J. Rigney. A delightful introduction to the varied and entertaining Japanese art of origami (paper folding), with a full crystal-clear text that anticipates every difficulty; over 275 clearly labeled diagrams of all important stages in creation. You get results at each stage, since complex figures are logically developed from simpler ones. 43 different pieces are explained: place mats, drinking cups, bonbon boxes, sailboats, frogs, roosters, etc. 6 photographic plates. 279 diagrams. 95pp. 5⅝ x 8⅜.
T713 Paperbound **$1.00**

CHESS, CHECKERS, GAMES, GO

A TREASURY OF CHESS LORE, edited by Fred Reinfeld. A delightful collection of anecdotes, short stories, aphorisms by and about the masters, poems, accounts of games and tournaments, photographs. Hundreds of humorous, pithy, satirical, wise, and historical episodes, comments, and word portraits. A fascinating "must" for chess players; revealing and perhaps seductive to those who wonder what their friends see in the game. 49 photographs (14 full page plates). 12 diagrams. xi + 306pp. 5⅜ x 8.   T458 Paperbound **$1.75**

THE ADVENTURE OF CHESS, Edward Lasker. A lively story of the history of chess, from its ancient beginnings in the Indian four-handed game of Chaturanga, through to the great players of our own day, as told by one of America's finest chess masters. He introduces such unusual sidelights and amusing oddities as Maelzel's chess playing automaton that beat Napoleon three times. One of the most valuable features of this work is the author's personal recollections of men he has played against and known—Nimzovich, Emanuel Lasker, Capablanca, Alekhine, etc. Lasker's discussion of chess-playing machines (revised for this edition) is particularly knowledgeable, since he is an electrical engineer by profession. 5 page chess primer. 11 illustrations; 53 diagrams. 296pp. 5⅜ x 8.

T510 Paperbound **$1.45**

FREE! All you do is ask for it!

HOW DO YOU PLAY CHESS?, Fred Reinfeld. A 40-page book of 86 lively questions and answers explaining all aspects of chess to beginners, by a noted writer on chess. Copies limited, no more than 1 to a customer.

THE PLEASURES OF CHESS, Assiac. Internationally-known British writer, influential chess columnist, writes wittily about wide variety of chess subjects: Anderssen's "Immortal Game;" only game in which both opponents resigned at once; psychological tactics of Reshevsky, Lasker; varieties played by masters for relaxation, such as "losing chess;" sacrificial orgies; etc. These anecdotes, witty observations will give you fresh appreciation of game. 43 problems. 150 diagrams. 139pp. 5⅜ x 8. T597 Paperbound **$1.25**

WIN AT CHESS, Fred Reinfeld. 300 practical chess situations enable you to sharpen your chess eye and test your skill against the masters. You start with simple examples and progress at your own pace to complex positions. This selected series of crucial moments in chess will stimulate your imagination and enable you to develop a stronger more versatile game. A simple grading system enables you to judge your progress through the course of the book. 300 diagrams. Notes and solutions to every situation. Formerly entitled CHESS QUIZ. vi + 120pp. 5⅜ x 8. T438 Paperbound **$1.00**

THE ART OF CHESS, James Mason. An unabridged reprinting of the latest revised edition of the most famous general study of chess ever written. Also included, a complete supplement by Fred Reinfeld, "How Do You Play Chess?", invaluable to beginners for its lively question and answer method. Mason, an early 20th century master, teaches the beginning and intermediate player more than 90 openings, middle game, end game, how to see more moves ahead, to plan purposefully, attack, sacrifice, defend, exchange, and govern general strategy. Supplement. 448 diagrams. 1947 Reinfeld-Bernstein text. Bibliography. xvi + 340pp. 5⅜ x 8. T463 Paperbound **$1.85**

THE PRINCIPLES OF CHESS, James Mason. This "great chess classic" (N. Y. Times) is a general study covering all aspects of the game: basic forces, resistance, obstruction, opposition, relative values, mating, typical end game situations, combinations, much more. The last section discusses openings, with 50 games illustrating modern master play of Rubinstein, Spielmann, Lasker, Capablanca, etc., selected and annotated by Fred Reinfeld. Will improve the game of any intermediate-skilled player. 1946 Reinfeld edition. 166 diagrams. 378pp. 5⅜ x 8. T646 Paperbound **$1.85**

LASKER'S MANUAL OF CHESS, Dr. Emanuel Lasker. World Champion 28 years, perhaps greatest modern player, writes one of most thorough studies on all facets of chess. How to gain advantage, value of pieces, combinations, etc. Dozens of openings analyzed. Valuable illumination, elaboration of theories of Steinitz. For intermediate-skilled player, but may be read by beginner. Introduction. Indexes. 308 illus. 397pp. 5⅜ x 8. T533 Paperbound **$1.00**

THE ART OF CHESS COMBINATION, E. Znosko-Borovsky. Proves that combinations, perhaps the most aesthetically satisfying, successful technique in chess, can be an integral part of your game, instead of a haphazard occurrence. Games of Capablanca, Rubinstein, Nimzovich, Bird, etc. grouped according to common features, perceptively analyzed to show that every combination begins in certain simple ideas. Will help you to plan many moves ahead. Technical terms almost completely avoided. "In the teaching of chess he may claim to have no superior," P. W. Sergeant. Introduction. Exercises. Solutions. Index. 223pp. 5⅜ x 8.

T583 Paperbound **$1.45**

CHESS STRATEGY, Edward Lasker. Classic study has taught 2 generations of players, including Grandmasters Fine, Keres. Emphasis is on general strategy, not memorization. How to formulate general strategy in terms of opponent's weaknesses, how to form "pawn skeleton," objects of attack, backward pawns, etc. 48 major tournament games analyzed. "The finest book I know of in the English language," J. R. Capablanca. Introduction. Index. 167 illus. 5⅜ x 8. T528 Paperbound **$1.50**

REINFELD ON THE END GAME IN CHESS, Fred Reinfeld. Analyzes 62 end games by Alekhine, Flohr, Tarrasch, Morphy, Bogolyubov, Capablanca, Vidmar, Rubinstein, Lasker, Reshevsky, other masters. Only first-rate book with extensive coverage of error; of immense aid in pointing out errors you might have made. Centers around transitions from middle play to various types of end play. King & pawn endings, minor piece endings, queen endings, bad bishops, blockage, weak pawns, passed pawns, etc. Formerly titled PRACTICAL END-GAME PLAY. 62 figures. vi + 177pp. 5⅜ x 8. **T417 Paperbound $1.25**

HOW TO FORCE CHECKMATE, Fred Reinfeld. If you have trouble finishing off your opponent, this book is for you. It is a collection of lightning strokes and combinations from actual tournament play. Starting with one-move checkmates and working up to three-move mates, you develop the ability to look ahead, and gain new insights into combinations, complex or deceptive positions, and ways of estimating both your own and your opponent's strengths and weaknesses. 300 diagrams. Solutions to all positions. Formerly entitled CHALLENGE TO CHESS PLAYERS. 111pp. 5⅜ x 8. **T439 Paperbound $1.25**

CHESSBOARD MAGIC! A COLLECTION OF 160 BRILLIANT ENDINGS, compiled, annotated by Irving Chernev. Illustrate not only ingenuity of composition, method of solution, but inherent beauty of solution. Many, by foremost Russian chess authorities, have won first prize in Russian chess magazines; are unavailable in this country. "Marvelous . . . sheer magic," Emanuel Lasker. "An endless feast of delight," Reuben Fine. Introduction. 160 diagrams. Index. 184pp. 5⅜ x 8. **T607 Paperbound $1.00**

LEARN CHESS FROM THE MASTERS, Fred Reinfeld. Improve your chess, rate your improvement, by playing against Marshall, Znosko-Borovsky, Bronstein, Najdorf, others. Formerly titled CHESS BY YOURSELF, this book contains 10 games in which you move against masters, and grade your moves by an easy system. Games selected for interest, clarity, easy principles; illustrate common openings, both classical and modern. Ratings for 114 extra playing situations that might have arisen. Full annotations. 91 diagrams. viii + 144pp. 5⅜ x 8. **T362 Paperbound $1.00**

MORPHY'S GAMES OF CHESS, edited by Philip W. Sergeant. You can put boldness into your game by following the brilliant, forceful moves of the man who has been called the greatest chess player of all time. Here are 300 of Morphy's best games, carefully annotated to reveal Morphy's principles. 54 classics against masters like Anderssen, Harrwitz, Bird, Paulsen, and others. 52 games at odds; 54 blindfold games; plus over 100 others. Unabridged reissue of the latest revised edition. Bibliography. New introduction by Fred Reinfeld. Annotations and introduction by Sergeant. Index. 235 diagrams. x + 352pp. 5⅜ x 8. **T386 Paperbound $1.75**

MODERN IDEAS IN CHESS, R. Réti. Clearest and most readable explanation of major developments in chess styles. Concentrates on the games of the master most closely associated with each major advance of the last hundred years. Seven world champions (Anderssen, Morphy, Steinitz, Lasker, Capablanca, Alekhine, and Euwe) are analyzed by a modern master. 34 diagrams. 192pp. 5⅜ x 8. **T638 Paperbound $1.25**

THE BOOK OF THE NEW YORK INTERNATIONAL CHESS TOURNAMENT, 1924, annotated by A. Alekhine and edited by H. Helms. Long a rare collector's item, this is the book of one of the most brilliant tournaments of all time, during which Capablanca, Dr. Lasker, Alekhine, Reti, and others immeasurably enriched chess theory in a thrilling contest. All 110 games played, with Alekhine's unusually penetrating notes. 15 photographs. xi + 271pp. 5⅜ x 8. **T752 Paperboard $1.85**

KERES' BEST GAMES OF CHESS, selected, annotated by F. Reinfeld. 90 best games, 1931-1948, by one of boldest, most exciting players of modern chess. Games against Alekhine, Bogolyubov, Capablanca, Euwe, Fine, Reshevsky, other masters, show his treatments of openings such as Giuoco Piano, Alekhine Defense, Queen's Gambit Declined; attacks, sacrifices, alternative methods. Preface by Keres gives personal glimpses, evaluations of rivals. 110 diagrams. 272pp. 5⅜ x 8. **T593 Paperbound $1.35**

THE DEVELOPMENT OF A CHESS GENIUS: 100 INSTRUCTIVE GAMES OF ALEKHINE, by Fred Reinfeld. Games from vital formative years 1905-1914, most of them never before in book form, show a future great master being shaped by experience and challenge in matches against Bernstein, Bogolyubov, Capablanca, Marshall, Rubinstein, Tarrasch, others. Interesting as chess biography, instructive as a master's increasingly adept responses to problems of every player. Annotated by F. Reinfeld. "One of America's most significant contributions," Chess Life. Formerly "The Unknown Alekhine." Introduction. Indexes of players, openings. 204 illustrations. 242pp. 5⅜ x 8. **T551 Paperbound $1.35**

RESHEVSKY'S BEST GAMES OF CHESS, Samuel Reshevsky. One time 4-year old chess genius, 5-time winner U. S. Chess Championship, selects, annotates 110 of his best games, illustrating theories, favorite methods of play against Capablanca, Alekhine, Bogolyubov, Kashdan, Vidmar, Botvinnik, others. Clear, non-technical style. Personal impressions of opponents, autobiographical material, tournament match record. Formerly, "Reshevsky on Chess." 309 diagrams, 2 photos. 288pp. 5⅜ x 8. **T606 Paperbound $1.25**

HYPERMODERN CHESS as developed in the games of its greatest exponent, ARON NIMZOVICH, edited by Fred Reinfeld. An intensely original player and analyst, Nimzovich's extraordinary approaches startled and often angered the chess world. This volume, designed for the average player, shows in his victories over Alekhine, Lasker, Marshall, Rubinstein, Spielmann, and others, how his iconoclastic methods infused new life into the game. Use Nimzovich to invigorate your play and startle opponents. Introduction. Indices of players and openings. 180 diagrams. viii + 220pp. 5⅜ x 8. T448 Paperbound **$1.35**

ONE HUNDRED SELECTED GAMES, Mikhail Botvinnik. Author's own choice of his best games before becoming World Champion in 1948, beginning with first big tournament, the USSR Championship, 1927. Shows his great powers of analysis as he annotates these games, giving strategy, technique against Alekhine, Capablanca, Euwe, Keres, Reshevsky, Smyslov, Vidmar, many others. Discusses his career, methods of play, system of training, 6 studies of endgame positions. 221 diagrams. 272pp. 5⅜ x 8. T620 Paperbound **$1.50**

RUBINSTEIN'S CHESS MASTERPIECES, selected and annotated by H. Kmoch. Thoroughgoing mastery of opening, middle game; faultless technique in endgame, particularly rook and pawn endings; ability to switch from careful positional play to daring combinations; all distinguish the play of Rubinstein. 100 best games, against Janowski, Nimzowitch, Tarrasch, Vidmar, Capablanca, other greats, carefully annotated, will improve your game rapidly. Biographical introduction, B. F. Winkelman, 103 diagrams. 192pp. 5⅜ x 8. T617 Paperbound **$1.25**

TARRASCH'S BEST GAMES OF CHESS, selected & annotated by Fred Reinfeld. First definitive collection of games by Siegbert Tarrasch, winner of 7 international tournaments, and the leading theorist of classical chess. 183 games cover 50 years of play against Mason, Mieses, Paulsen, Teichmann, Pillsbury, Janowski, others. Reinfeld includes Tarrasch's own analyses of many of these games. A careful study and replaying of the games will give you a sound understanding of classical methods, and many hours of enjoyment. Introduction. Indexes. 183 diagrams. xxiv + 386pp. 5⅜ x 8. T644 Paperbound **$2.00**

MARSHALL'S BEST GAMES OF CHESS, F. J. Marshall. Grandmaster, U. S. champion for 27 years, tells story of career; presents magnificent collection of 140 of best games, annotated by himself. Games against Capablanca, Alekhine, Emanuel Lasker, Janowski, Rubinstein, Pillsbury, etc. Special section analyzes openings such as King's Gambit, Ruy Lopez, Alekhine's Défence, Giuoco Piano, others. A study of Marshall's brilliant "swindles," slashing attacks, extraordinary sacrifices, will rapidly improve your game. Formerly "My Fifty Years of Chess." Introduction. 19 diagrams. 13 photos. 250pp. 5⅜ x 8. T604 Paperbound **$1.35**

THE ENJOYMENT OF CHESS PROBLEMS, K. S. Howard. A classic treatise on this minor art by an internationally recognized authority that gives a basic knowledge of terms and themes for the everyday chess player as well as the problem fan: 7 chapters on the two-mover; 7 more on 3- and 4-move problems; a chapter on selfmates; and much more. "The most important one-volume contribution originating solely in the U.S.A.", Alain White. 200 diagrams. Index. Solutions. viii + 212pp. 5⅜ x 8. T742 Paperbound **$1.25**

HOW TO SOLVE CHESS PROBLEMS, K. S. Howard. Full of practical suggestions for the fan or the beginner—who need only know the moves of the chessmen. Contains preliminary section and 58 two-move, 46 three-move, and 8 four-move problems composed by 27 outstanding American problem creators in the last 30 years. Explanation of all terms and exhaustive index. "Just what is wanted for the student," Brian Warley. 112 problems, solutions. vi + 171pp. 5⅜ x 8. T748 Paperbound **$1.00**

CHESS AND CHECKERS: THE WAY TO MASTERSHIP, Edward Lasker. Complete, lucid instructions for the beginner—and valuable suggestions for the advanced player! For both games the great master and teacher presents fundamentals, elementary tactics, and steps toward becoming a superior player. He concentrates on general principles rather than a mass of rules, comprehension rather than brute memory. Historical introduction. 118 diagrams. xiv + 167pp. 5⅜ x 8. T657 Paperbound **$1.15**

WIN AT CHECKERS, M. Hopper. (Formerly CHECKERS). The former World's Unrestricted Checker Champion discusses the principles of the game, expert's shots and traps, problems for the beginner, standard openings, locating your best move, the end game, opening "blitzkrieg" moves, ways to draw when you are behind your opponent, etc. More than 100 detailed questions and answers anticipate your problems. Appendix. 75 problems with solutions and diagrams. Index. 79 figures. xi + 107pp. 5⅜ x 8. T363 Paperbound **$1.00**

GAMES ANCIENT AND ORIENTAL, AND HOW TO PLAY THEM, E. Falkener. A connoisseur's selection of exciting and different games: Oriental varieties of chess, with unusual pieces and moves (including Japanese shogi; the original pachisi; go; reconstructions of lost Roman and Egyptian games; and many more. Full rules and sample games. Now play at home the games that have entertained millions, not on a fad basis, but for millennia. 345 illustrations and figures. iv + 366pp. 5⅜ x 8. T739 Paperbound **$1.85**

GO AND GO-MOKU: THE ORIENTAL BOARD GAMES, Edward Lasker. Best introduction to Go and its easier sister-game, Go-Moku—games new to Western world, but ancient in China, Japan. Extensively revised work by famed chess master Lasker, Go-player for over 50 years, stresses theory rather than brute memory, presents step-by-step explanation of strategy, gives examples of world championship matches, in game which has replaced chess as favorite of many physicists, mathematicians. 72 diagrams. xix + 215 pp. 5⅜ x 8.

T613 Paperbound **$1.45**

FICTION

FLATLAND, E. A. Abbott. A science-fiction classic of life in a 2-dimensional world that is also a first-rate introduction to such aspects of modern science as relativity and hyperspace. Political, moral, satirical, and humorous overtones have made FLATLAND fascinating reading for thousands. 7th edition. New introduction by Banesh Hoffmann. 16 illustrations. 128pp. 5⅜ x 8.

T1 Paperbound **$1.00**

THE WONDERFUL WIZARD OF OZ, L. F. Baum. Only edition in print with all the original W. W. Denslow illustrations in full color—as much a part of "The Wizard" as Tenniel's drawings are of "Alice in Wonderland." "The Wizard" is still America's best-loved fairy tale, in which, as the author expresses it, "The wonderment and joy are retained and the heartaches and nightmares left out." Now today's young readers can enjoy every word and wonderful picture of the original book. New introduction by Martin Gardner. A Baum bibliography. 23 full-page color plates. viii + 268pp. 5⅜ x 8.

T691 Paperbound **$1.45**

THE MARVELOUS LAND OF OZ, L. F. Baum. This is the equally enchanting sequel to the "Wizard," continuing the adventures of the Scarecrow and the Tin Woodman. The hero this time is a little boy named Tip, and all the delightful Oz magic is still present. This is the book with the Animated Saw-horse, the Woggle-Bug, and Jack Pumpkinhead. All the original John R. Neill illustrations, 16 in full color. 287pp. 5⅜ x 8.

T692 Paperbound **$1.45**

FIVE GREAT DOG NOVELS, edited by Blanche Cirker. The complete original texts of five classic dog novels that have delighted and thrilled millions of children and adults throughout the world with stories of loyalty, adventure, and courage. Full texts of Jack London's "The Call of the Wild"; John Brown's "Rab and His Friends"; Alfred Ollivant's "Bob, Son of Battle"; Marshall Saunders' "Beautiful Joe"; and Ouida's "A Dog of Flanders." 21 illustrations from the original editions. 495pp. 5⅜ x 8.

T777 Paperbound **$1.50**

3 ADVENTURE NOVELS by H. Rider Haggard. Complete texts of "She," "King Solomon's Mines," "Allan Quatermain." Qualities of discovery; desire for immortality; search for primitive, for what is unadorned by civilization, have kept these novels of African adventure exciting, alive to readers from R. L. Stevenson to George Orwell. 636pp. 5⅜ x 8.

T584 Paperbound **$2.00**

THE CASTING AWAY OF MRS. LECKS AND MRS. ALESHINE, F. R. Stockton. A charming light novel by Frank Stockton, one of America's finest humorists (and author of "The Lady, or the Tiger?"). This book has made millions of Americans laugh at the reflection of themselves in two middle-aged American women involved in some of the strangest adventures on record. You will laugh, too, as they endure shipwreck, desert island, and blizzard with maddening tranquility. Also contains complete text of "The Dusantes," sequel to "The Casting Away." 49 original illustrations by F. D. Steele. vii + 142pp. 5⅜ x 8.

T743 Paperbound **$1.00**